S Erlich

10 9

Basic

PHYSIOLOGY
and **ANATOMY**

Basic
PHYSIOLOGY
and ANATOMY

Second Edition

ELLEN E. CHAFFEE

R.N., M.N., M.Litt., Science Coordinator and Associate Professor of
Nursing, University of Pittsburgh School of Nursing

ESTHER M. GREISHEIMER

Ph.D., M.D., Professor Emeritus of Physiology, Temple University
Medical Center, Philadelphia; Formerly Professor of Physiology,
Woman's Medical College of Pennsylvania, Philadelphia; Formerly
Associate Professor of Physiology, The University of Minnesota,
Minneapolis

412 Illustrations

J. B. LIPPINCOTT COMPANY
PHILADELPHIA · TORONTO   1969

Distributed in Great Britain by
Blackwell Scientific Publications
Oxford, London, and Edinburgh

ISBN-0-397-47198-X

Library of Congress Catalog Card Number 73—101355

Printed in the United States of America

8   7   6   5   4

To our students—
past, present and future

Preface

Five years ago the first edition of this textbook became a reality. The months of reading, writing and re-writing gradually faded into a blurred memory. However, with the passage of time came the realization that certain content areas very much needed to be expanded, as well as updated. In addition, there was a need for many new illustrations and for the redrawing of others. These were the primary forces that motivated the revision process.

Although these are exciting times for teachers of physiology and anatomy, there are moments of frustration, moments when we despair of ever keeping abreast of the scientific times. Fortunately, such moments are fleeting and we press onward with optimism and enthusiasm. Thus, the second edition of *Basic Physiology and Anatomy* has become a reality. Again the hours of work fade into memory as we look to a future bright with promise for even more exciting advances.

One of the key features of this edition is the appearance of approximately 70 new, or redrawn, illustrations. We were most fortunate in securing the help of Miss Margaret Croup, medical illustrator at the University of Pittsburgh Health Center. In Chapter 2, for example, 12 new illustrations accompany a greatly expanded discussion of the cell and its organelles. The discussion of the muscular system benefits from the addition of 26 new illustrations, plus a comprehensive revision and reorganization of material on the contractile process and excitation of muscle tissue.

In the section on the nervous system, there is a comprehensive revision of the explanation of structure and the properties of nerve tissue. A new illustration accompanies discussion of a change in the approach to intramuscular injections in the gluteal region. Material dealing with the hypothalamus, the reticular formation, the cerebrospinal fluid and chemical mediators has been revised and updated.

The section on the cardiovascular system benefits from the addition of 22 new illustrations. Material dealing with the granular leukocytes and the lymphocytes has been completely revised. More attention is given to the electrical activity of the heart and to the electrocardiogram. There have been many editorial changes and a general updating of material where appropriate.

A major revision and reorganization of the content sequence should improve the unit that deals with the digestion, absorption and utilization of foods. Chapter 16 now includes the digestive processes as well as the digestive machinery. Chapter 17 then deals with absorption, intermediate metabolism, and temperature regulation. Material concerned with the endocrine glands has been rewritten and extensively revised, as has that dealing with human reproduction.

Thus, in this new edition, we endeavor to meet the expressed needs of colleagues in many schools across the country. On behalf of Dr. Greisheimer and myself I wish to state that we are particularly grateful for the various letters of evaluation that have been sent to us; these proved most helpful during the process of revision. Valuable suggestions also were made by friends and associates in the Health Center of the University of Pittsburgh: Marguerite J. Schaefer, D.Sc., Virginia E. Washburn, M.D., M.P.H., Campbell Moses, Jr., M.D. and Shirley Burke, R.N., M.S.N.Ed.

In conclusion, I would like to make the most important acknowledgment of all—to Dr. Esther M. Greisheimer, my friend and co-author. Her help and encouragement, her counseling and guidance, are most deeply appreciated.

Ellen E. Chaffee

Contents

"Another book was opened, which is the book of life."

REV. 20:12

INTRODUCTION to Human Anatomy and Physiology

A very wise man once said that the greatest gift in all of the world is not ours to give but to receive, and that is the gift of life! From the simplest of microscopic creatures to the complex body of man runs a protoplasmic thread that distinguishes living matter from the inanimate stones and clods. Each one of us knows how it feels to be alive, but even our greatest scientists as yet cannot explain the mystery of life itself.

However, centuries of observation and experimentation have led to the establishment of certain facts and theories which help in our general understanding of all living matter, whether it be plant or animal. This highly organized body of knowledge is referred to as the science of *biology*, the study of life and living things. Such a vast subject would be impossible to study were it not broken down into plant and animal divisions, plus an infinite variety of subdivisions, two of which are human anatomy and physiology. These biologic sciences are of basic importance to those who would not only recognize and preserve good health, but give intelligent care to the sick.

ORIENTATION

The significance of anatomy

Human anatomy is primarily concerned with **structure**, with the way in which our bodies are built. The word "anatomy" is of Greek origin; it is derived from the prefix *ana* meaning "apart" and the root *tome* meaning "a cutting," so it literally means "a cutting apart." The Latin word "dissection" is derived from the prefix *dis* meaning "apart" and the root *secare* meaning "to cut," so it likewise means "to cut apart." Although both terms, anatomy and dissection mean cutting apart, the former has acquired a much broader application and now includes many subdivisions. The terms indicate that the anatomy of early days consisted of that learned by dissecting human bodies.

Our study of anatomy will be taken up according to the systems of the body (**systemic anatomy**) and will be devoted primarily to **gross anatomy**, the study of structures which can be seen with the naked eye. The study of **microscopic anatomy** will be limited to relatively brief studies of cells (**cytology**) and tissues (**histology**) as seen with the aid of a microscope. There are many other subdivisions of anatomy, and each year still more branches are developed as scientific investigations become increasingly specialized.

The significance of physiology

Human physiology is concerned with **function,** with the study of all activities which are characteristic of living matter. It is perhaps the most fascinating of all the sciences and is essential for total understanding of the body, but we must not overlook the fact that a knowledge of basic anatomy is prerequisite to the comprehension of physiology. In other words, anatomy and physiology are inseparable companions when one considers the body as an integrated whole. For example, cells are not only the structural units of the body, but they are the functional units as well.

All living organisms are made up of cells, and each cell, in turn, is composed of **protoplasm.** T. H. Huxley described protoplasm as "the physical basis of life," and this semiliquid material is indeed the essential substance in every living cell. Whether an organism exists as a single cell, such as the lowly amoeba, or as the fantastic human complex of trillions of cells, there are certain **basic life processes** which are essential for its survival in a hostile world. These processes are as follows:

Excitability or **irritability** is the capacity to respond to a stimulus (any change in the environment). We constantly use this fundamental characteristic of excitability as a test of "aliveness" or awareness in another person or in an animal. Children pinch each other, call each other names, poke animals and make loud noises to see if they can call forth responses in any living organism in their vicinity.

Conductivity refers to the capacity of a cell to transmit a wave of excitation from the point of stimulation to other parts. In higher animals, irritability and conductivity are developed most highly in nerve cells.

Contractility refers to the ability of a cell to undergo shortening and to change its form. This property is highly developed in muscle cells and makes possible all muscular activity.

Metabolism in its broadest sense includes all physical and chemical processes involved in the activities of life. However, in common use it is limited to those processes by which food substances are converted into energy or into complex substances such as protoplasm; in this respect, there are two phases of metabolism: (1) *anabolism,* or the *building-up* processes which involve the formation of complex substances from simpler ones, and (2) *catabolism,* or the *breaking-down* processes, particularly the break-down of food with a resultant liberation of energy.

The detailed processes of food-getting and utilization, which are such an important part of the metabolic picture, include ingestion, digestion, absorption, assimilation, respiration, secretion, excretion and egestion.

The **ingestion,** or taking in, of food is followed by **digestion,** a process whereby complex foods are broken down to simple substances which can be absorbed, or taken into the protoplasm of a cell. **Assimilation** refers to the processes within cells by which the absorbed material is used to build protoplasm. **Respiration** usually involves the use of oxygen and the production of carbon dioxide (CO_2) with the release of energy.

Excretion refers to the ability of a cell to eliminate waste products which it has produced during its metabolic activities (e.g., water, urea, CO_2, etc.). Specialized cells also can remove raw materials from the blood and build useful substances, such as digestive juices and hormones; the process whereby such substances leave the cell is called **secretion. Egestion** refers to the elimination of indigestible or unusable material which has not taken part in metabolic activities.

Growth is the increase in the amount of protoplasm from sources within an organism. It is due to an increase in the number of cells by cell division, rather than to an increase in the size of cells. It includes the process of repair by which damaged parts are replaced. When one reaches the adult stage the body no longer increases in size,

Crown
parietal

Base of skull
occipital

Neck
cervical

deltoid

scapular

Arm
brachial

Small of back
lumbar

sacral

Buttock
gluteal

Shoulder

Transverse plane

Midsagittal plane

Flank

Hip

Back of knee
popliteal

Calf

Sole of foot
plantar

Fig. 1-2. The anatomic position, posterior view. Common terms used in reference to body parts are shown in light print. Anatomic terms used in reference to various regions are shown in dark print.

find a mountainous task awaiting you. Your attitude toward the course may well determine your level of achievement.

Body parts and regions

Familiarity with terminology used in reference to the surface anatomy of your body should precede any study of underlying structures. Figures 1-1 and 1-2 illustrate the various parts and regions of the body as a whole; common words appear in regular type while the anatomic terms which should be added to your vocabulary appear in boldface type. For example, the forehead is the **frontal** region, the neck is the **cervical** region, etc. If you wish to avoid confusion during the study of bones and muscles, you should no longer refer to your **upper extremities** as "arms" or to your **lower extremities** as "legs"; pay particular attention to these parts and their subdivisions as illustrated in Figure 1-1.

The nine regions of the abdomen are illustrated in Figure 16-24, and the location of underlying organs is listed on page 483.

Terms of location and position

Of fundamental importance are the terms used in describing the location and the position of various body parts. When using these terms we must always consider the body to be in the **anatomic position,** or standing erect, facing forward, with the upper extremities at the sides and palms turned forward (Fig. 1-1).

superior, or *cranial:* above, or toward the head end of the body (e.g., the chest is superior to the abdomen).

inferior, or *caudal:* below, or toward the tail end of the body (e.g., the neck is inferior to the head).

anterior, or *ventral:* nearer the front or belly side of the body (e.g., the breasts are on the anterior, or ventral, aspect of the chest).

posterior, or *dorsal:* nearer the back side of the body (e.g., the shoulder blades are on the posterior, or dorsal, aspect of the chest).

medial: nearer the midline of the body (e.g., the nose is medial to the eyes).

lateral: farther from the midline of the body (e.g., the eyes are lateral to the nose).

internal: deeper within the body (e.g., the internal surface of the nose is lined with mucous membrane).

external: nearer the outer surface of the body (e.g., the external surface of the nose is covered with skin).

NOTE: Internal and external may also be used in reference to nearness to or distance from the midline. For example, the medial rectus muscle of the eye also may be called the internal rectus, and the lateral rectus muscle of the eye may be called the external rectus.

proximal: nearer to the body or to the origin of a part (e.g., with respect to the upper extremity, the arm is proximal to the forearm).

distal: farther from the body or from the origin of a part (e.g., the hand is distal to the elbow).

central: the principal part; situated at, or related to, a center (e.g., the brain and the spinal cord comprise the central nervous system).

peripheral: toward the surface of the body, or extensions from, the principal part or center (e.g., the peripheral nervous system refers to nerves which go out to, or come in from all parts of the body).

parietal: pertaining to the walls of a cavity (e.g., parietal blood vessels are those which supply structures in the walls of a cavity, such as the chest or the abdomen).

visceral: pertaining to the organs within a cavity (e.g., visceral blood vessels supply the viscera or organs within a cavity, such as the chest or the abdomen).

The preceding terms will be used with great frequency during this course, and after a bit of practice they should be an integral part of your anatomic vocabulary.

The fundamental planes of the body

In order to show the various internal structures of the body, sections are cut in different planes as shown in Figure 1-4.

The midsagittal plane passes through the mid-

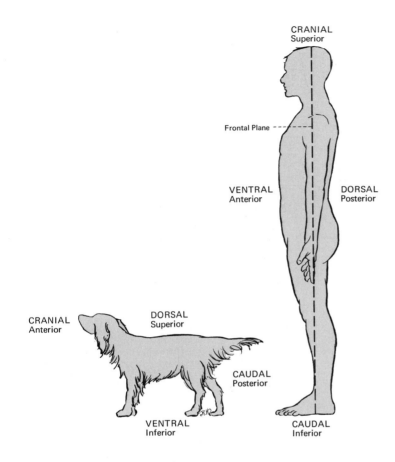

CRANIAL
Superior

Frontal Plane ---

VENTRAL
Anterior

DORSAL
Posterior

CRANIAL
Anterior

DORSAL
Superior

CAUDAL
Posterior

VENTRAL
Inferior

CAUDAL
Inferior

Fig. 1-3. Comparative terminology in quadruped and man, for location or position; frontal plane is indicated by broken line.

line of the body lengthwise, from front to back, and divides it into exactly even right and left halves, excluding such internal organs as the heart and the liver that do not lie exactly in the midline. This plane is so named because it passes through the sagittal suture of the skull (p. 78). Any other plane which divides the body into right and left portions but does not pass through the midline of the body is referred to as a **sagittal** plane.

The **coronal** or **frontal plane** takes its name from the coronal suture of the skull (p. 78). It passes through the body from top to bottom and divides it into front and back portions.

The **transverse** or **horizontal plane** passes through the body dividing it into upper and lower portions.

STRUCTURAL FEATURES OF THE BODY

Just as a city, a factory, a hospital or even your wrist watch has a plan of organization, so does the human body. In each case, a large unit is made up of smaller units, all of which work together in close harmony for the welfare of the unit as a whole. Should one or more of the small units fail to carry out its function, the end-result could be a breakdown of the entire complex; for example, just as a broken mainspring stops the action of your watch, so does a failing heart stop the activity of your body. Throughout your study of anatomy and physiology you must always keep in mind the fact that the human body is an integrated whole.

Fig. 1-4. The Fundamental planes of the body.

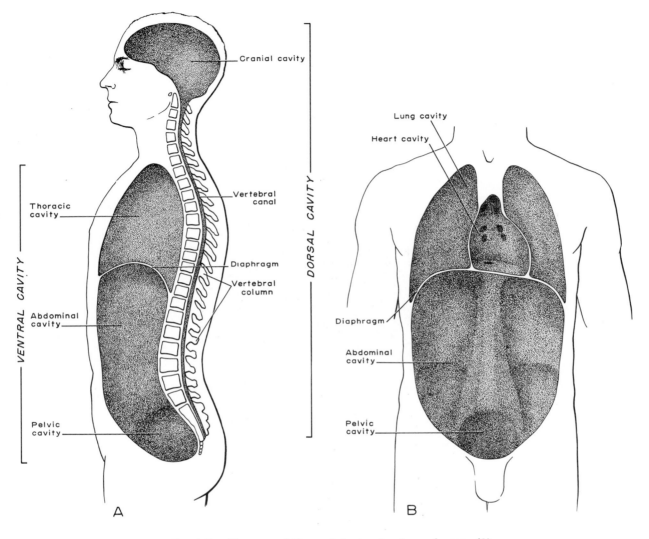

Fig. 1-5. Diagram of the vertebrate structure of man. (A) lateral view showing ventral and dorsal cavities. (B) anterior view showing divisions and subdivisions of the ventral cavity.

The vertebrate structure of man

Man is a member of the vertebrate group of animals. In addition to possessing a vertebral column (backbone), vertebrates are characterized by the presence of dorsal and ventral cavities. Figure 1-5 illustrates the vertebrate structure of man.

The dorsal cavity lies within the skull and the backbone. It consists of two portions: (1) the *cranial portion,* which is occupied by the brain, and (2) the *vertebral portion,* which is occupied by the spinal cord.

The ventral cavity is divided into thoracic and abdominal portions by a muscular partition called the diaphragm. Each of these portions may be subdivided further. The *thoracic cavity* comprises

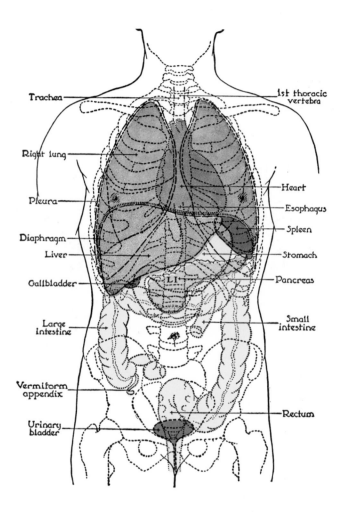

Fig. 1-6. The anterior surface projection of some of the thoracic, abdominal and pelvic viscera.

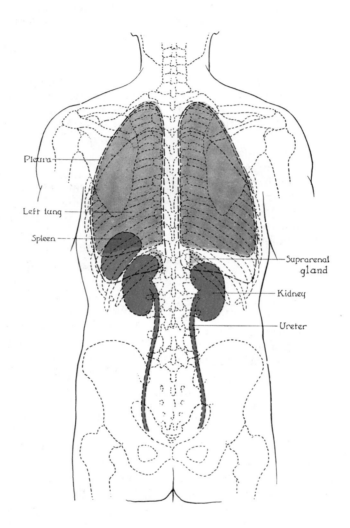

Fig. 1-7. Posterior surface projection
of some of the viscera.

two pleural compartments, each of which is occupied by a lung, and the pericardial compartment, which is occupied by the heart. In addition to the heart, the space between the lungs contains the following: trachea, esophagus, thymus, large blood vessels, lymphatic vessels and nerves.

The *abdominal cavity* lies inferior to the diaphragm. It is occupied by the stomach, the small intestine, most of the large intestine, the liver, the gallbladder, the pancreas, the spleen, the kidneys, the adrenal glands and the ureters. The lowermost portion of the abdominal cavity is called the *pelvic cavity;* it is occupied by the urinary bladder, the end of the large intestine (sigmoid colon and rectum), and certain reproductive organs (uterus, uterine tubes and ovaries in the female; prostate gland and seminal vesicles in the male).

Figures 1-6 and 1-7 illustrate the anterior and the posterior surface projections of the various organs to help with your orientation to their location.

Component units

Detailed information relating to the structural and the functional units of the body will be found in subsequent chapters. However, it usually is helpful if one has a general idea of the total organizational picture before studying the component parts.

Let us compare the organization of the body with that of a large hospital. When you first walk into a hospital corridor you see a large number of persons, each walking briskly about, apparently busy with his own tasks.

Each person may be thought of as a unit and is comparable with a **cell** in the body. There is a great difference in appearance between the persons whom you see and also in the work that each does. There is an even greater difference between the various cells of the body and the functions that they perform.

As you become a little better acquainted with the hospital, you realize that the persons who do a certain type of work, such as surgical nurses, constitute one large group; and each large group carries out certain definite tasks. The nurses give nursing care to patients; the physicians take histories, do physical examinations and prescribe certain tests, medications and treatments for patients. Each of these groups, the nurses and the physicians, is made up of persons who are performing specific functions. Similarly, in the body there are groups of cells which perform specific functions. Such groups of cells are called **tissues.**

In a larger sense, nurses and physicians work together to improve the health of patients; another way of stating this is that two groups with different individual functions work together for one purpose. Likewise, in the body, tissues of various kinds are grouped together to form **organs,** which perform a surprising number of related functions.

No matter how efficient nurses and physicians may be, hospitals would not exist long without supervisors, maintenance men, elevator operators, telephone operators, cooks, maids and a host of other workers to carry out innumerable duties. In the body, groups of organs work together to accomplish a particular function, such as to supply the body with oxygen; these groups of organs are called **systems.** It is as impossible for the body to function properly without the cooperation of each individual cell as it is for a hospital to run efficiently without the cooperation of each person, no matter whether the work is giving nursing care or cooking meals.

Without carrying the analogy further, we shall list the systems of the body. They are: skeletal, muscular, nervous, digestive, respiratory, circulatory, excretory, reproductive and endocrine systems. Our plan is to have you study cells, then tissues and finally systems.

SUMMARY

1. Biology—organized body of knowledge dealing with life and living things
   A. Anatomy concerned with structure of body
      a. Systemic anatomy: studied according to the body systems
      b. Gross anatomy: structures seen with the naked eye
      c. Microscopic anatomy: that seen only with the microscope
   B. Physiology concerned with functions of body
      a. Cells are functional as well as structural units
      b. Basic life processes essential to survival
         (1) Excitability or irritability
         (2) Conductivity
         (3) Contractility
         (4) Metabolism:
            (a) Ingestion and digestion
            (b) Assimilation and respiration
            (c) Excretion, secretion and egestion
         (5) Growth and reproduction
      c. Dependent on other branches of knowledge (e.g., chemistry, physics, pathology, electronics)
2. Descriptive terminology
   A. Body parts and regions (review Figs. 1-1 and 1-2)
   B. Terms of location and position (body always considered to be in anatomic position)
      a. Superior (cranial): above; inferior (caudal): below
      b. Anterior (ventral): in front; posterior (dorsal): in back
      c. Medial: nearer midline; lateral: farther from midline
      d. Internal: deeper within body; external: nearer outer surface of body
      e. Proximal: nearer the origin; distal: farther from origin
      f. Central: principal part; peripheral: toward body surface, extensions from the center
      g. Parietal: pertaining to walls of cavity; visceral: pertaining to organs within a cavity
   C. Fundamental planes
      a. Midsagittal: exactly even right and left halves of body
      b. Sagittal: right and left halves, but not necessarily even
      c. Coronal or frontal: front and back portions
      d. Transverse or horizontal: upper and lower portions
3. Structural features of the human body
   A. Cavities
      a. Dorsal—cranial portion; vertebral portion
      b. Ventral
         (1) Thoracic cavity
         (2) Abdominal and pelvic cavities
   B. Component units: cells, tissues, organs and systems; all functioning as an integrated whole

2

ORGANIZATION OF THE LIVING BODY

Perhaps the most striking property of living matter is its organization. A cell is the smallest unit of life, a microscopic bit of protoplasm, yet each of its parts, as well as the cell as a whole, is so organized that it performs special functions. For example, muscle cells are so constructed that they can shorten and so move part of the body; nerve cells can transmit impulses to and from the brain and the spinal cord; gland cells produce secretions that are essential to the health of the body, etc.

Although cells vary in function, size, shape and composition, they have much in common. In this chapter we shall consider not only the structural and functional similarities between cells but also the way in which they combine to form tissues and membranes.

PROTOPLASM

Protoplasm is the only known form of matter in which life is evident. It is a viscid, translucent, colloidal substance that makes up the essential material of every cell.

Composition

Even though the chemical composition of protoplasm has been determined with accuracy, scientists cannot yet make synthetic protoplasm in the laboratory. It is the *organization* of protoplasm that is unique and apparently cannot be duplicated. None of the chemical elements composing protoplasm are any different from those which are found in nonliving material, but their organization with relation to each other spells the difference between "life" or "death" for any given cell. The following table merely indicates those elements and compounds which are found in protoplasm; the way in which these substances are "put together" to form living protoplasm is not yet known.

While examining the following table one should keep in mind the fact that only the gases (oxygen and nitrogen) are present in the body in their elemental state. The other elements are present in the form of inorganic compounds (those lacking carbon) and organic compounds (those containing carbon). The percentage distributions as shown are for the adult human body as a whole.

Elements	Percentage
Oxygen	65.00
Carbon	18.00
Hydrogen	10.00
Nitrogen	3.00
Calcium	2.00
Phosphorus	1.00
Potassium	0.35
Sulfur	0.25
Chlorine	0.15
Sodium	0.15
Magnesium	0.05
Iron	0.004
Other elements	0.046

Compounds	Percentage
Inorganic Compounds	
Water	65 to 70
Inorganic salts	4.4
Organic Compounds	
Proteins	16.0
Lipids	13.0
Carbohydrates	0.6

Importance of inorganic compounds

Water is by far the most abundant of the compounds in all living tissue, and life can continue for only a few days without it. Some of the functions of water are as follows:

1. Water serves as a solvent. It holds the various components of protoplasm in solution so that they are free to move about within the cell or from one cell to another. Most chemical reactions take place only in solution.

2. The high chemical stability of water makes it possible for chemical reactions to occur in water without involving the water itself.

3. Many substances ionize in water, that is, their molecules separate into ions which bear electrical charges. For example, sodium chloride (NaCl) separates into a positive sodium ion (Na^+) and a negative chloride ion (Cl^-). Such substances in solution are called *electrolytes* (capable of conducting an electric current). The properties and the classes of electrolytes are determined by the kinds of ions they yield when they dissolve in water. These classes are acids, alkalies or bases, and salts. All of these are of great importance in living matter.

Normality		Conc. H ions	Conc. OH ions	pH
Normal HCl		1	10^{-14}	0
0.1 N HCl		10^{-1}	10^{-13}	1
0.01 N HCl		10^{-2}	10^{-12}	2
0.001 N HCl	increasing acidity	10^{-3}	10^{-11}	3
0.0001 N HCl		10^{-4}	10^{-10}	4
0.00001 N HCl		10^{-5}	10^{-9}	5
0.000001 N HCl		10^{-6}	10^{-8}	6
Pure water Neutral		10^{-7}	10^{-7}	7
0.000001 N NaOH		10^{-8}	10^{-6}	8
0.00001 N NaOH		10^{-9}	10^{-5}	9
0.0001 N NaOH	increasing alkalinity	10^{-10}	10^{-4}	10
0.001 N NaOH		10^{-11}	10^{-3}	11
0.01 N NaOH		10^{-12}	10^{-2}	12
0.1 N NaOH		10^{-13}	10^{-1}	13
Normal NaOH		10^{-14}	1	14

By looking at the table it is evident that every rise of 1 in pH means lowering of the concentration of H ions to 1/10 of its previous value.

The maintenance of a proper balance between acid and base in the body is essential to life itself. Hydrogen (H^+) and hydroxyl (OH^-) ions are involved in all chemical processes taking place in living cells, and their concentration determines the degree of acidity or alkalinity of body fluids (i.e., the pH). If there are more hydrogen ions than hydroxyl ions in a fluid, it is acid in reaction. On the other hand, an alkaline fluid would have more hydroxyl ions than hydrogen ions. The preceding table will refresh your memory in regard to the determination of pH.

Acids are formed constantly in the body as a result of metabolic activity. For example, carbonic acid (or its precursor, carbon dioxide) is produced by the oxidation (burning) of all types of food. Substances which produce *bases*, such as sodium, potassium, calcium and magnesium, are taken into the body in our food. Since living cells are very sensitive to changes in reaction, either toward acidity or alkalinity, there are various means of keeping the pH relatively constant in the body. Buffer salts in the blood (p. 298) tend to keep the pH of that fluid within the very narrow range of 7.3 to 7.5. A slight shift in the pH of the blood, which indicates the condition of the entire body, can seriously alter the functions of many cells. Such a change in pH might occur when one loses large amounts of acid during bouts of prolonged vomiting (gastric juice contains HCl); the reaction of the blood becomes more alkaline, and the patient is said to be in a state of *alkalosis*. On the other hand, for example, a patient with lung disease may fail to blow off CO_2 and thus get rid of carbonic acid as rapidly as it is formed; acid accumulates in the blood, the pH begins to fall, and a state of *acidosis* exists. Either case may be fatal in a very short period of time if proper acid-base balance is not restored.

4. Another role played by water is in the regulation of body temperature. Evaporation of the water in perspiration cools the skin and helps to prevent a rise in body temperature. Human cells function most efficiently at optimum body temperature which averages 98.6° F. (37° C.). Elevation of the body temperature (fever) may interfere with the activity of many cells.

Inorganic salts are found in the cells and the fluids (blood, tissue fluid and lymph) of the body. They occur primarily as chlorides, carbonates, sulfates, and phosphates of sodium, potassium, calcium and magnesium. The principal *extracellular ions* (outside of the cell) are sodium and chloride; the principal *intracellular ions* (within the cell) are potassium and phosphate. Inorganic salts are needed for such things as:

1. Maintenance of proper osmotic conditions (p. 34)

2. Maintenance of proper acid-base balance (e.g., the buffer salts in the blood)

3. The clotting of blood (calcium)

4. Development of bones and teeth (calcium and phosphorus)

5. Formation of hemoglobin in red blood cells (iron)

6. Normal functioning of muscle and nerve (sodium, potassium and calcium)

The proper concentration and distribution of various salts is referred to as **electrolyte balance.** Alteration of this balance can lead to serious disturbances. For example, a slight increase in the concentration of sodium chloride increases excitability of muscles, and they undergo convulsive contractions. The contractility and the conductivity of heart muscle are disturbed by either too low or too high a concentration of potassium chloride in the blood. Too low a concentration of calcium in the blood can lead to convulsions. Maintenance of fluid and electrolyte balance is a highly complicated process involving not only the intake of adequate food and water but also activity of various organs such as the kidneys, the heart, the lungs and the glands.

Importance of organic compounds

Proteins form the framework of protoplasm and are the most abundant of the organic constituents. Growth of new tissue and the repair of old tissue depend on the availability of protein. Thus growing children, elderly persons, and those who have undergone surgical operations and the like, need more protein in their diet than do healthy young adults.

Proteins are large molecules consisting of many small structural units called *amino acids*, the "building blocks" of the body. Twenty different amino acids commonly are found in protein molecules, but the number and the arrangement of these building blocks varies with the kind of protein that is being constructed. For example, the amino acid arrangements in a muscle cell are quite different from those found in a nerve cell, inasmuch as each type of tissue is characterized by its own specific kinds of protein. The importance

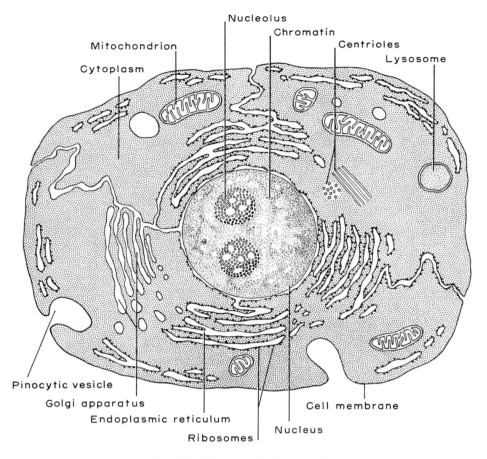

Fig. 2-1. Diagram of a typical cell.

Labels on figure: Mitochondrion, Nucleolus, Chromatin, Centrioles, Lysosome, Cytoplasm, Pinocytic vesicle, Golgi apparatus, Endoplasmic reticulum, Ribosomes, Nucleus, Cell membrane

of the chromosomes and genes in protein synthesis is described on page 29.

In addition to the role they play in building and repairing tissues, proteins also are extremely important in maintaining the colloidal osmotic pressure of the blood (p. 37), and in the formation of enzymes and certain hormones. Under certain conditions protein is oxidized to supply energy for the body.

Carbohydrates include the starches and the sugars. These large units are broken down by digestive processes to simple sugars such as *glucose*, which is the principal sugar present in the blood. Carbohydrates are the most abundant and economical source of energy. However, if one's diet includes more carbohydrate than is required

to meet the immediate energy needs of the body, some of the excess is converted to *glycogen* (animal starch) and some to adipose tissue (fat) for storage purposes. When one goes without food (as in starvation) the glycogen and fat deposits are used up first, then the protein of protoplasm itself is broken down and oxidized, because energy needs take precedence over all others. This gradual destruction of protoplasm accounts for the extreme emaciation and ultimate death of starvation victims.

Lipids include both fats and fat-related substances. They are sources of energy and are stored as reserve food in adipose tissue. These fatty deposits of adipose tissue serve also as "shock absorbers" in the support and the protection of various organs and as an insulator, preventing excessive loss of body heat. Lipids are present in high concentration in cell membranes, and they play an important role in maintaining normal permeability (p. 23).

Therefore, each foodstuff has its own contribution to make to the welfare of the body as a whole, and a balanced diet contributes greatly to the maintenance of good health.

ORGANIZATION OF THE CELL

At one time cells were considered to be merely microscopic droplets of protoplasm, or little bags of water containing assorted chemicals and enzymes. Now the electron microscopes, coupled with sophisticated biochemical research, indicate that each cell is a highly organized "molecular factory." Inasmuch as entire books have been written about the detailed structure and function of these microscopic masterpieces, it is obvious that our discussion must be limited to broad concepts and generalizations regarding the living cell. Figure 2-1 illustrates the structure of a so-called "typical cell," but it must be kept in mind that there are many variations in cell structure and function. For example, a brain cell does not look like nor act like a liver cell, yet both cells have a nucleus, a cytoplasm that contains various organelles ("little organs") and an external cell membrane. Although these parts have specialized functions, they are so highly organized and interrelated that the cell functions as a unified whole.

The Nucleus

The nucleus may quite accurately be termed the control center of the cell. Not only does it exert a controlling influence over the chemical reactions that occur in these little "factories", but it also is of fundamental importance in reproduction of the cell as a whole. These vital functions depend upon the fact that the nucleus is an amazing storehouse of genetic information.

In a resting cell (i.e., one not ready to divide) the nucleus shows darkly staining granules that are referred to as *chromatin material.* Actually, this chromatin material is arranged in loosely coiled strands that are better known as **chromosomes,** but they are not readily visible as such until they become more tightly coiled just prior to division of the cell. Every normal somatic (body) cell has exactly 46 chromosomes in its nucleus, and each chromosome in turn may have thousands of genes distributed along its threadlike structure. The genes are the ultimate units that determine what a cell will be and what activities it will carry out.

Chemically, each chromosome consists of **deoxyribonucleic acid (DNA)** combined with a protein, but it is the DNA that constitutes the primary hereditary material of each cell. For an understanding of how genetic information can be stored in a chemical compound, and how such a compound can be precisely duplicated, it is necessary to know the basic structure of DNA.

In 1953, Dr. James Watson and Dr. Francis Crick first introduced the concept that a DNA molecule resembles a spiral ladder. The sides of the ladder are formed by alternating units of deoxyribose sugar and phosphate, while the rungs are composed of pairs of nitrogenous bases. One end of each nitrogenous base is attached to a sugar-phosphate unit, and the other end is linked to its partner on the opposite side of the ladder to complete the rung. These nitrogen compounds are only four in number: adenine, thymine, guanine and cytosine or, as they are referred to in scientific shorthand: A, T, G, and C. However, the pairing of these bases is highly specific, as A is so constructed that it will fit precisely only with T, and G only with C. Thus the sequence of bases along one side of the ladder must necessarily determine the sequence along the other. This fact is of fundamental importance in understanding the ability of DNA to duplicate itself prior to cell division. Figures 2-2 and 2-3 illustrate the basic structure of DNA.

Although the sides of the ladder are an important part of the DNA molecule, it is the order or sequence of bases in the rungs of the ladder that constitutes the so-called "genetic code." In other words, the order in which A, T, G and C appear

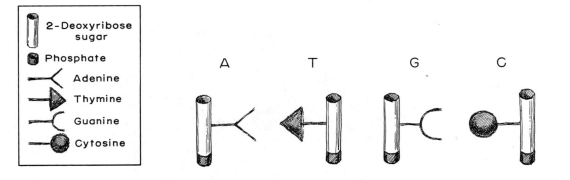

2-Deoxyribose sugar

Phosphate

Adenine

Thymine

Guanine

Cytosine

A T G C

Fig. 2-2. Structural units (nucleotides) of a DNA molecule. Each unit consists of a phosphate group and a sugar group to which is attached a nitrogenous base (adenine or thymine or guanine or cytosine).

apparently "spells out" the genetic instructions that control the activities of the cell in general, and the construction of complex protein molecules in particular. Because most of the molecules in every cell are proteins, their production is the key to life itself. For example, enzymes (the essential organic catalysts of the body) are proteins, and every one of the *thousands* of different chemical reactions that take place in the body is expedited by a specific enzyme. Thus DNA has the monumental task of directing the formation of thousands of different proteins just to meet the enzyme requirements of the body. Added to this task is the formation of many other proteins that serve as the major structural components of skin, muscle, blood vessels, and all internal organs.

How does DNA accomplish this task? First let us think of a protein molecule as resembling a line of alphabet blocks, each lettered block representing one of 20 amino acids; the sequence of these amino acid blocks determines the protein "word" that will be spelled out. Inasmuch as the fact that DNA carries the genetic code letters A, T, G, and C has already been established, it now remains to see how this chemical alphabet of only 4 letters can be used to write "protein words" that may contain anywhere from a mere 50 letters to tens of thousands of letters. The secret lies in the fact that this 4-letter alphabet is used to write only

Fig. 2-3. Schematic representation of the spiral ladder arrangement of repeating nucleotide units found in the DNA molecule. It is thought that anywhere from 500 to 1,000 of these rungs make up a single gene, and that there are over 1,000 genes in a single chromosome.

Fig. 2-4. The endoplasmic reticulum (ER). Diagram of a portion of the ER showing ribosomes that dot the surface.

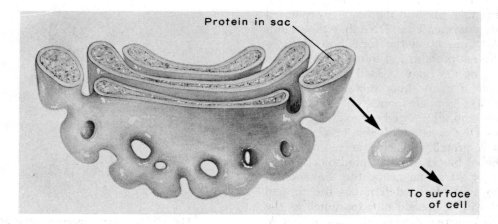

Fig. 2-5. The Golgi apparatus. Protein formed in the endoplasmic reticulum enters the Golgi apparatus, where it is "packaged" in membrane and dispatched toward the surface of the cell for delivery to the extracellular environment.

3-letter code words. Because a total of only 20 code words (one for each of the amino acids) is needed to construct any one of the thousands of body proteins, the 4 letters are more than adequate. For example, when one does not have to worry about pronouncing the words, any 4 letters can be so arranged as to form 64 different 3-letter combinations or code words. Then, if one thinks of the 20 amino acid code words as being analogous to 20 letters of the English alphabet, it does not require too much imagination to visualize the almost infinite number of protein words of varying lengths that could be constructed. As a matter of fact, it has been estimated that if all of the coded DNA instructions found in one single cell were translated into English they would more than fill 1000 volumes of an encyclopedia. Figure 2-3 illustrates the spiral ladder appearance of only a small fraction of a DNA molecule because if all of the DNA in a single human cell nucleus were stretched out in a thin thread it would be about 3 feet long!

In addition to the chromosomes, the nucleus also contains one or more small rounded bodies known as **nucleoli** (sing. nucleolus). The function of a nucleolus is still shrouded in mystery, but it may be the place where another nucleic acid, known as **ribonucleic acid (RNA),** is stored until needed. RNA is formed from DNA and is part of an elaborate "messenger system" that enables DNA to control the manufacture of protein (p. 29). The nucleolus also may be the place where the actual "protein factories" (ribosomes) are assembled, and from whence they migrate into the cytoplasm where the bulk of protein synthesis occurs.

The Cytoplasm

Although the nucleus contains the "board of directors" for each living cell, most of the actual work is done in the surrounding cytoplasm, where we find various organelles that have highly specific functions. These organelles include the ribosomes, endoplasmic reticulum, lysosomes, centrioles, and mitochondria.

Ribosomes are tiny rounded bodies that play an important part in the manufacture of protein molecules. They are rich in RNA and serve as the site where the genetic code is "read" and then acted upon. Some ribosomes float freely in the cytoplasm and are concerned with the production of proteins that are required for the cell's own use. Other ribosomes are attached to the membranes of the endoplasmic reticulum, described below, and are generally concerned with the synthesis of protein that is to be exported from the cell and used elsewhere in the body.

The endoplasmic reticulum (ER) is a system of delicate membranes so interconnected and arranged as to form a network of tiny canals. The most common type of ER has a granular, rough-surfaced appearance, because the outer surface of the membrane is studded with ribosomes (Fig. 2-4). Communicating with the endoplasmic reticulum is the **Golgi apparatus,** an array of parallel membranes arranged as flattened sacs (Fig. 2-5). It is believed that this apparatus is concerned with the export of substances produced by the cell (e.g., protein molecules produced in the ER) and with the production of the cell membrane.

Other membranous structures in the cytoplasm are the **lysosomes.** These organelles are tiny closed sacs containing powerful digestive enzymes that are capable of breaking down worn-out parts of the cell itself, as well as molecules of protein, glycogen and any other substances that may enter the cell by the process of phagocytosis or pinocytosis (p. 26). These enzymes are so potent that, if they are released into the cytoplasm through rupture of their confining membrane, the entire cell (and possibly some of the surrounding cells) will be destroyed; for this reason lysosomes are sometimes called "suicide bags."

Close to the nucleus, in all cells capable of reproducing themselves, lie one or two cylindrical organelles called *centrioles.* During cell division centrioles are involved in the formation of the mitotic spindle, as described on page 26.

Every living cell requires a constant supply of energy to carry on its many activities, and the powerhouse that produces the greatest amount of this vital commodity is the **mitochondrion.** The number of mitochondria found in any given cell

Outer limiting membrane
Inner limiting membrane
Cristae

Fig. 2-6. Diagram of a mitochondrion. The inner limiting membrane is thrown into transverse folds (cristae) that project into the fluid-containing interior of this cellular "powerhouse."

varies from hundreds to thousands, depending upon the amount of energy required by that cell to carry out its assigned functions. The average mitochondrion roughly resembles a bean pod and consists of 2 surrounding membranes, as shown in Figure 2-6. Various enzymes within the fluid interior make possible the complex oxidative reactions whereby the food that we eat is "burned" to release its energy. Other enzymes, located along the folds of the inner membrane, help to "trap" this food energy and to store it temporarily in the chemical bonds of *adenosine triphosphate* (*ATP*). This energy-rich compound then diffuses out of the mitochondrion and is ready to power the various metabolic processes that take place throughout the cell. Although some ATP is produced by anaerobic reactions in the cytoplasm, 90 to 95 per cent of all the ATP produced by a cell is formed by aerobic reactions within the "mighty mitochondria."

Other substances that may be present in the cytoplasm include stored foods, pigments, and the like. These may have resulted from activities carried on by the cell, but they are not part of the "machinery."

The Cell Membrane

The cytoplasm and its contents are separated from the surrounding liquid environment by a thin, elastic membrane that is fairly resistant to damage, minor injuries being rapidly repaired by cytoplasmic constituents. The cell membrane consists of 2 layers of protein molecules enclosing a middle layer of lipid (fat) molecules. Many tiny openings or *pores* pass through these layers from one side of the membrane to the other. Needless to say, this membrane does much more than merely hold the cell together. Its physical and chemical properties enable it to play an important regulatory role in determining just what substances may enter or leave the cell and in what quantity at any given time; thus we can say that the cell membrane is famous for its **selective permeability.** Generally speaking, there are 3 main processes whereby substances may pass through the cell membrane: diffusion, active transport, and ingestion (i.e., pinocytosis or phagocytosis).

Diffusion is a physical process that involves the constant scattering or spreading out of molecules of gases or liquids until they tend to become equally concentrated in all parts of the container. This process occurs because molecules are constantly moving, bumping into one another, and bouncing away. Thus they tend to scatter from areas in which they are more highly concentrated to areas in which they are less concentrated. For example, when one enters a room in which there are flowers, such as lilies of the valley, one immediately notes the odor. Molecules of the perfume diffuse from the flowers to all parts of the room, and within a short time the odor is uniform throughout the area. Diffusion of substances through the cell membrane generally follows this same pattern of movement; that is, from areas of greater concentration to those of lesser concentration. However, certain structural and chemical features of the cell membrane enable it to be highly selective of the substances that may pass through it, regardless of their concentration.

First, let us consider the lipid or fatty layer of the cell membrane and the related factor of *lipid-solubility*. Substances that are lipid-insoluble are prevented from entering or leaving the cell, but molecules such as oxygen (O_2) and carbon dioxide (CO_2) that dissolve easily in fats cross the membrane without difficulty. This exchange of gases (O_2 moving into the cell and CO_2 moving out of the cell) is of fundamental importance. Other lipid-soluble substances such as ether, chloroform, and alcohol also can enter cells, but they may interfere with normal activities. For example, when ether enters nerve cells in the brain their function is so altered that the person becomes temporarily unconscious.

Another factor that influences the permeability of cell membranes is the *size of the pores*. Substances such as water molecules, urea molecules

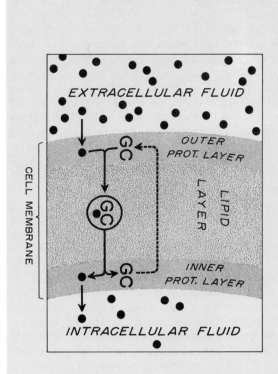

Fig. 2-7. Facilitated diffusion. Glucose molecules, represented by circles, are more concentrated outside of the cell. After passively diffusing into the outer protein layer of the cell membrane, they are picked up by a glucose carrier (GC), which makes them temporarily lipid-soluble, so that they can diffuse through the middle lipid layer to the inner protein layer, where they are released by GC and can enter the cell.

(waste products) and chloride ions are much smaller in size than the pores, thus they pass through with ease. Water is by far the most abundant substance to diffuse through the cell membrane, but ordinarily it diffuses out of the cell in amounts that are exactly equal to those that enter the cell; when this balance exists there has been no *net* diffusion of water. However, this precise balance may be upset if a *concentration gradient for water* should develop (i.e., if there should be more water molecules on one side of the membrane than on the other). When this state of affairs exist, a net diffusion of water occurs, and the cell either shrinks or swells, depending on the direction of the net diffusion (Fig. 2-16). This process of a net diffusion of water due to a concentration gradient is referred to as osmosis; it is discussed further on page 34.

Particles that are too large to squeeze through the tiny pores in a cell membrane must enter by other means. For example, glucose and other simple sugars may enter the cell by a process known as *facilitated diffusion.* In facilitated diffusion a special carrier substance in the cell membrane combines with the sugar, making it temporarily lipid-soluble, so that it can diffuse from an area of greater concentration outside of the cell to an area of lesser concentration within the cell (Fig. 2-7). This process is somewhat similar to that of active transport, which will be described shortly. Other large molecules, such as protein or bacteria, may enter a cell by the process of pinocytosis or phagocytosis (p. 26).

Still another factor that influences permeability is the *electrical charge* on the cell membrane and on the ion which is seeking entrance. For example, if both cell and ion carry a positive charge, the substance is repelled; on the other hand, a negatively charged ion may freely enter or leave a positively charged cell.

Active transport is a physiologic process whereby a cell releases energy for the movement of certain substances through its membrane. In contrast to facilitated diffusion, substances involved in active transport are moved from areas of lower concentration to areas of higher concentration. Thus it is said that they are *moving against a concentration gradient* or being "pumped uphill" rather than "coasting downhill," as is the case in diffusion. As might be expected, this "pumping" action requires the expenditure of a considerable amount of energy, and the mitochondria are kept busy producing the necessary ATP power source.

The basic mechanism of active transport is thought to involve certain *carrier systems* that exist within cell membranes. Such carriers are highly specific in that each one transports only certain substances. This specificity probably is determined by the chemical nature of the carrier or by the nature of the enzymes that catalyze the specific chemical reactions. A few substances, such as sodium ions, potassium ions, and amino acids, are thought to have active transport systems in all cells of the body. On the other hand, glucose and certain other sugars undergo active transport in only a few places, such as the intestine and the kidney. For example, glucose is continually pumped from the intestinal tract into the blood stream, even though its concentration in the intestine may be very low; this prevents fecal loss of a valuable source of energy.

The sodium and potassium transport mechanism plays an important role in maintaining the proper concentration of ions within the cell and in the surrounding extracellular fluid. Proper cell function is related to the existence of a greater concentration of potassium ions (K^+) within the cell than there is in the surrounding tissue fluid, while the opposite is true of sodium ions (Na^+); i. e., Na^+ is the chief extracellular ion, only a relatively small amount being found within the cell. Inasmuch as a certain amount of K^+ tends to diffuse *out* of the cell (where it is more concentrated) and a certain amount of Na^+ tends to diffuse *into* the cell (where it is less concentrated), it is absolutely essential that we have an active transport mechanism to pump these "wandering" ions against their concentration gradients—i.e., into the cell in the case of K^+ and out of the cell in the case of Na^+. Figure 2-8 illustrates the carrier system theory of active transport of sodium and potassium.

Substances also may enter a cell by a process of

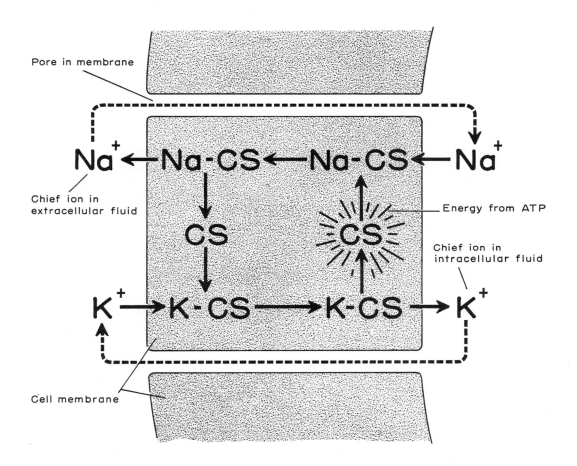

Fig. 2-8.   Active transport. Diagram of carrier system theory for the active transport of sodium and potassium. Sodium (Na^+) that diffused into the cell through a pore in the cell membrane is actively pumped out of the cell by a carrier system (CS); A similar fate awaits the potassium (K^+) that diffuses out of the cell as it is actively pumped back into the cell. The energy for this transport is obtained from ATP.

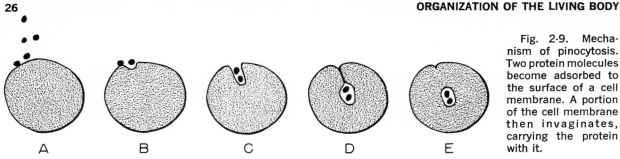

ingestion known as **pinocytosis** or **phagocytosis,** terms derived from Greek roots meaning "drinking by cells" and "eating by cells." Figure 2-9 illustrates the mechanism of pinocytosis as two protein molecules become adsorbed to the outer surface of a cell membrane, then are engulfed by the cell as the membrane invaginates or infolds, carrying with it the protein and a variable amount of fluid from the extracellular environment. The invaginated portion of the membrane then breaks away from the cell surface and forms a little vesicle that moves off into the cytoplasm. It is thought that the lysosomes may play a part in the breakdown of the vesicle and in the digestion of its contents. Phagocytosis occurs in essentially the same way as pinocytosis, but the former term is used when larger particles such as bacteria and cell fragments are ingested.

CELL DIVISION

Growth of the body, replacement of cells that have a short life span, and the repair of various injuries—all depend upon a miraculous process of cell division known as *mitosis.* We do not yet know what starts mitosis, or all of the factors that control it, but we do know that it follows a distinct pattern requiring a variable length of time.

When cells are not undergoing division they are said to be in a resting stage, or **interphase,** during which time they carry on their specialized tasks. Also during interphase, a very important preliminary step must be taken prior to division of the cell as a whole. This preliminary activity involves a duplication of the chromosomes, those

marvelous gene-carrying threads that contain the all-important deoxyribonucleic acid or **DNA** (Fig. 2-3). Because the chromosomes with their genetic material determine what a cell will be and what activities it will carry out, it is essential that they be duplicated before the "mother" cell divides and forms 2 new "daughter" cells.

Duplication of the chromosomes occurs within the nucleus a few hours before mitosis takes place. Each one of the 46 chromosomes splits longitudinally and forms 2 exact replicas of itself; these replicas are called *chromatids.* The net result of this duplication is 92 chromatids, which ultimately will become the 46 chromosomes in each of the 2 daughter cells formed during mitosis. Figure 2-10 illustrates the way in which the DNA component is able to duplicate itself.

Although mitosis is a continuous process requiring a variable amount of time, it usually is divided into 4 stages for convenience of description (Fig. 2-11).

1. **Prophase.** The centrioles separate and begin to move toward opposite sides of the cell. The chromosome threads become more tightly coiled, and each one can be seen to consist of 2 chromatids. The nuclear membrane and the nucleolus disappear.

2. **Metaphase.** By the time that the nuclear membrane has dissolved, fine tubules can be seen radiating from the centrioles through the nuclear region to the mid-line of the cell. The divergence of these tubules gives the appearance of a spindle. The paired chromatids of each chromosome have become aligned in orderly fashion in the middle of the cell and are attached to the tubules at that point.

Fig. 2-10. Schematic representation of the replication of DNA. (A) prior to cell division, the bonds between the nitrogenous bases are broken, the two strands separate, and each strand takes with it the bases attached to its side. (B) The bases attached to each single strand attract free-floating nucleotide units and pair off in the usual way: adenine with thymine, guanine with cystosine. (C) The end result is 2 exact replicas of the original DNA molecule, and the cell is ready to undergo division.

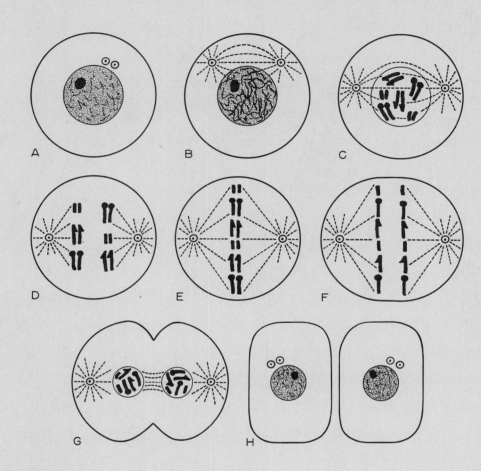

Fig. 2-11. Schematic representation of mitosis. See text for description. (A) interphase (resting); (B), (C) and (D) prophase; (E) metaphase; (F) anaphase; (G) telophase; (H) daughter cells (resting).

3. **Anaphase.** The 2 chromatids of each chromosome become completely separated from each other, and each one is now considered to be a chromosome in its own right. The spindle tubules then pull the separated chromatids to their respective ends of the cell.

4. **Telophase.** The chromosomes uncoil and begin to assume the thread-like form characteristic of interphase. The nuclear membrane and nucleoli of the daughter cells are formed. Each centriole has produced a daughter centriole in preparation for the next division. The cell membrane constricts at the midpoint of the elongated cell, and 2 new cells are formed, each with 46 chromosomes. The miracle of mitosis may then be repeated, the 2 cells becoming 4, and so on.

Some cells in the body undergo mitosis throughout life; for example, cells in the growth layer of the skin are constantly dividing and pushing upward to replace those that are worn away by friction as one works and plays. Still other cells are unable to reproduce themselves after their initial work of organ formation has been completed; for example, cells of the central nervous system can never be replaced if they are destroyed through injury or disease. Normally, cell division proceeds at an orderly pace, just rapidly enough to ensure proper growth or repair of tissues. Occasionally, however, certain cells may begin to divide with abnormal rapidity, with no regard for the needs of the body. These abnormal cells crowd out the surrounding normal cells, robbing them of their nourishment and resulting in a malignant growth which is called **carcinoma** or **cancer.** Despite the tremendous amount of research in this area we do not yet know what starts cells on this mad course of lawless, uncontrolled reproduction.

PROTEIN SYNTHESIS

The synthesis of protein, a vital function of every living cell, takes place along the ribosomes. However, these little "protein factories" must be provided with specific instructions and with the proper raw materials for construction of such complex molecules. As described on page 18, deoxyribonucleic acid (DNA) is the source of genetic information that determines protein structure—thus, it must provide the specific "blueprints." Because DNA is far too busy and too important to leave its "office" in the nucleus, it forms vast numbers of "assistant molecules," called *ribonucleic acid (RNA)*. The RNA molecules then travel to the cytoplasm and see to it that the various construction jobs are completed according to DNA's master plan.

Although RNA is formed from DNA, it differs from DNA in that it contains ribose sugar groups instead of deoxyribose, and uracil instead of thymine. In forming RNA, the DNA strands separate and RNA nucleotides are attracted to the appropriate bases (uracil with adenine, guanine with cytosine); because this happens along only one half of the DNA ladder, RNA molecules occur as single strands.

DNA forms different kinds of RNA, each equipped to carry out specific tasks in the assembly of a protein molecule. One kind is called *messenger RNA (m-RNA)*, and on this molecule DNA "prints" the genetic instructions needed to make one specific kind of protein; thus, there must be as many different m-RNA molecules as there are different proteins. Another kind of RNA, called *transfer RNA (t-RNA)*, is equipped to "recognize" a specific amino acid and then attach itself to that amino acid; thus ,there must be as many different t-RNA molecules as there are amino acids. Prior to their pick-up by t-RNA, the amino acids are activated by being coupled with energy-rich ATP.

As shown in Figure 2-12, m-RNA carries the "blueprint" from DNA to the ribosomes. As soon as m-RNA is attached to the ribosomes it is ready to direct the alignment of amino acids that are carried by t-RNA. In a manner that resembles an automobile assembly line, amino acids are "dropped" into position by t-RNA as dictated by the coded message on m-RNA. The amino acids are bonded together; then, after the chain is completed, the finished protein molecule moves away from the ribosome. This molecule may be used by the cell that produced it, or it may be exported from the cell for use elsewhere in the body.

It is believed that m-RNA carries only one message; thus, it probably is broken down to its basic

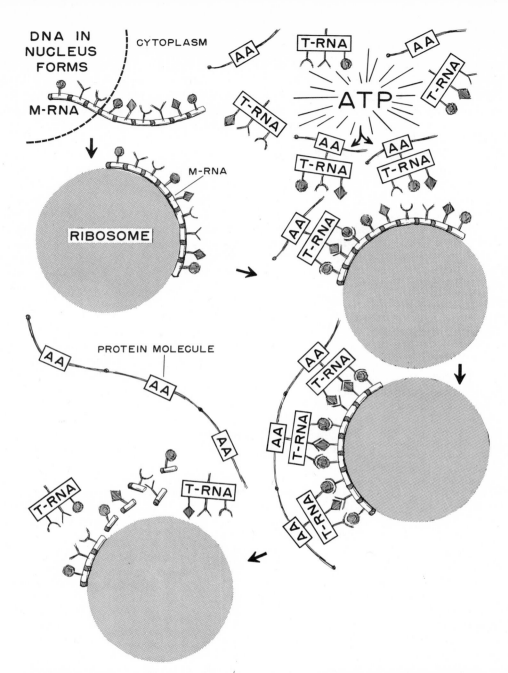

Fig. 2-12. Diagram of protein synthesis. A small section of single strand messenger RNA (m-RNA), seen leaving nucleus at upper left, attaches to surface of ribosome. Amino acids (AA) in cytoplasm are activated by ATP and coupled to transfer-RNA(tRNA). The 3-letter code word of t-RNA then is attracted to the appropriate site on m-RNA, ensuring the proper sequence of amino acids. The amino acids are bonded together, forming protein molecules of varying sizes.

nucleotide units following the synthesis of a protein molecule. On the other hand, it is believed that the ribosomes and the t-RNA molecules are free to work again.

MAINTAINING HOMEOSTASIS IN THE LIQUID CELLULAR ENVIRONMENT

Over a billion years ago life apparently began in the sea. Although this organization of protoplasm was probably in the form of simple, microscopic plants, it was life. The kindly sea water constantly bathed these cells, delivering their food and serving as a receptacle for wastes. Now, one thousand million years later, we find that the same basic pattern prevails in our own bodies. Even though we live on dry land and breathe air, we literally have a "sea within" as water bathes every living cell in a manner quite similar to that of the oceanic waters of long ago. This intercellular water is called **tissue fluid** or *interstitial fluid* (meaning in the spaces between cells); it serves as the "middleman" between the blood stream and the cells, which also are composed primarily of water. In fact, the human body as a whole is approximately 65 to 70 per cent water: about three fourths of this water is found within the cells and the remainder in the tissue spaces and in the blood stream.

Sea water and body fluid are remarkably similar in chemical composition in that both contain *water* and *electrolytes*. The principal ions in both fluids are sodium, potassium, magnesium, calcium, chloride, sulfate and phosphate, but the total concentration is much greater in sea water than in our body fluid. In other words, creatures in the sea live in a saltier environment than do cells in the human body. However, whether we are dealing with sea water or with body fluid, the important thing to keep in mind is the fact that each liquid environment meets the particular needs of those cells which it serves.

Just as the ocean is a dynamic, moving mass of water, so is the human body. From the great spurting of blood in our arteries, to the microscopic seeping of water through a cell membrane, our body fluids are constantly on the move, constantly striving to maintain a fairly uniform environment for the working cells of the body. For example, as a cell uses molecules of food and oxygen, other such molecules must be moving in to take their place; at the same time secretions and excretions resulting from cellular activity must be removed from the immediate vicinity and carried to other cells for use or for elimination from the body. Thus we can see that the internal environment is truly in a state of *dynamic equilibrium* or **homeostasis;** it is constantly changing, yet it remains essentially unchanged insofar as volume, pH and chemical composition are concerned. Every system in the body plays some part in maintaining this constancy of environment, and our very survival depends on their continued ability to do so.

The circulatory "subway" system

Much as a subway train serves a city by picking up passengers at one point and discharging them at another, so the circulatory system serves the human body. Various substances are carried as "passengers" in the blood stream as it is pumped through a series of tubes or blood vessels. Each beat of the heart sends a spurt of blood into thick-walled vessels, called *arteries.* These vessels branch out to all parts of the body, gradually becoming so small that they are no longer visible to the naked eye. With the help of a microscope, however, one can see that these tiny arteries, or arterioles, open into a network of still smaller tubes which are called *capillaries.*

The capillaries are microscopic vessels whose walls are only one cell thick. Between these cells are the tiny openings or intercellular spaces through which the blood picks up and discharges its various "passengers." However, capillary membranes, unlike regular cell membranes, do not exhibit selective permeability, and any particle smaller than the intercellular spaces may pass through. Large particles, such as most of the colloidal blood proteins, are unable to pass through the openings in this microscopic sieve, so they normally remain in the blood stream. On the other hand, water, oxygen, carbon dioxide, crystalloids and other tiny molecules can pass freely through the capillary membrane. For example, as blood passes through the lung capillaries it picks up some oxygen and gets rid of some carbon dioxide; in muscle capillaries it delivers food and oxygen needed by the muscle cells, and, at the same time, it picks up carbon dioxide and other waste products resulting from the metabolic activity of these hard-working cells. Similar patterns of pick-up and delivery may be observed in other tissues of the body.

When blood reaches the end of the microscopic capillary network it flows into a series of slightly larger tubes called venules, then into still larger vessels, the *veins*, and finally back into the heart where it is again pumped out into the arteries.

Thus, we can see that the circulatory system is a completely closed circuit of tubes, all parts being of equal importance in the total functioning of the system. However, we must not lose sight of the fact that *the capillary is the focal point of the entire system,* for only in this thin-walled portion of the circuit can the necessary exchanges be made between the blood and its surrounding environment.

Movement of substances through membranes

Maintenance of homeostasis in our liquid cellular environment depends on the movement of substances through the membranes which separate our fluid compartments. For example, materials needed by the cell must pass from the blood stream through the capillary membrane into the tissue fluid, then through the cell membrane and into the cell; materials produced by the cell must travel in the opposite direction, first passing through the cell membrane into the tissue fluid, then through the capillary membrane and into the blood.

Movement of substances through a cell membrane by the processes of diffusion, active transport, pinocytosis and phagocytosis are described on pages 23–26. We shall now consider the processes of filtration, diffusion and osmosis, with emphasis on capillary membranes in addition to cell membranes.

Funnel

Filter Paper

Water

Dissolved Salt

Sand

Water

Dissolved Salt

Fig. 2-13. Diagram representing filtration.

Fig. 2-14. Diagram representing filtration in the capillaries. A capillary of a glomerulus of the kidney is used as an example.

Filtration

Filtration is the process whereby water and dissolved substances are literally pushed through a permeable membrane from an area of higher pressure to an area of lower pressure. This mechanical force is referred to as **hydrostatic pressure,** or "pushing pressure." Figure 2-13 illustrates a laboratory demonstration of filtration in which water and dissolved substances are pushed through filter paper. Due to the weight of the fluid in the funnel, together with atmospheric pressure, movement of fluid occurs from the area of greater hydrostatic pressure in the funnel to the area of lower hydrostatic pressure in the empty beaker below. Since the filter paper is not permeable to the large sand particles, they are held back.

The formation of tissue fluid is an excellent example of filtration in the human body. Due to the pumping action of the heart, the hydrostatic pressure exerted by the blood against the walls of the capillaries is greater than that of the surrounding tissue fluid; therefore, water and dissolved substances filter through the capillary membrane into the tissue fluid. Large particles such as red blood cells and most of the proteins remain in the blood stream. Small molecules of protein also may be pushed out of the blood, but they are normally so few in number that they have little significance. However, in certain instances, the appearance of extravascular (outside of the blood vessels) protein may be a sign of trouble. This is particularly true when protein is found in the urine. Normally, only water and crystalloid solutes are filtered from the blood as it passes through the kidney capillar-

ies (Fig. 2-14), but in certain cases of kidney infection the capillary membranes may be injured to such an extent that larger particles, such as proteins and even red blood cells, also may filter out and thus appear in the urine; these symptoms of kidney damage are referred to as *proteinuria* (protein in the urine) and *hematuria* (blood in the urine).

Diffusion

Diffusion is a physical process that involves the constant scattering or spreading out of molecules of gases or liquids until they are equally concentrated in all parts of the container. It is due to the fact that molecules are constantly moving, constantly bumping into one another and bouncing away. Thus they tend to scatter from areas where they are more highly concentrated to areas where they are less concentrated.

In the body there is diffusion of gases between the air sacs or alveoli of the lungs and the blood. Molecules of oxygen diffuse from the air sacs in the lungs into the blood, and carbon dioxide molecules diffuse from the blood into the air sacs in the lungs. When the blood reaches the capillaries in the tissues of the body, oxygen diffuses from the blood into the tissue fluid and on into tissue cells, while carbon dioxide diffuses from the tissue cells into the tissue fluid and on into the blood. In every instance the molecules diffuse from the region in which they are highly concentrated to the region in which they are less highly concentrated. A diagram of diffusion is shown in Figure 2-15.

Molecules diffuse easily through membranes

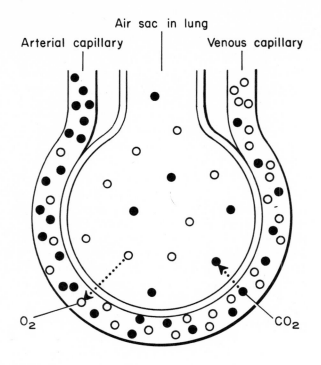

Fig. 2-15. Diffusion of gases in an air sac of the lung. In the diagram, circles represent oxygen, and dots represent carbon dioxide. The diffusion of carbon dioxide and oxygen is shown by changes in the number of dots and circles on the arterial and venous sides of the capillaries.

which are permeable to them. For example, crystalloid waste products produced by a cell have no difficulty in passing from the cell (where their concentration is great) through the cell membrane and into the tissue fluid (where their concentration is less), then through the capillary membrane into the blood stream; such substances are said to be *diffusible*. On the other hand, colloidal substances such as proteins, which are too large to pass through normal membranes, are said to be *nondiffusible*. Protoplasm, which is essentially protein in nature, is formed within the cell by various combinations of amino acids that are actively transported into the cell.

Osmosis

Osmosis is a physical process involving the passage of water through a semipermeable membrane that separates 2 solutions of different concentrations. A semipermeable membrane is one which is "partly permeable," in that it is permeable to water but either impermeable or only slightly

permeable to the solute. In osmosis, water moves from the weaker solution (where there are more water molecules) to the more concentrated solution (where there are fewer water molecules); thus water moves according to a *concentration gradient*. However, students frequently find it helpful to think of osmosis in terms of water being "pulled" from the weaker solution into the more concentrated solution in an attempt to equalize concentrations on both sides of the membrane, or of water being drawn into the concentrated solution in order to dilute it.

The force that causes this movement of water is referred to as osmotic pressure (or "pulling pressure"), and it varies directly with the number of solute particles in the solution. The more solute particles in any given solution, the higher the osmotic pressure; the fewer solute particles, the lower the osmotic pressure. For example, a 10 per cent NaCl solution contains more sodium and chloride ions than a 1 per cent solution and therefore, would have the greater osmotic pressure. A simple way of describing the process of osmosis is to say that "water goes where the most salt is to be found."

Osmosis can be demonstrated in the laboratory by the use of red blood cells and salt solutions of various strengths (Fig. 2-16). Normally, red blood cells are suspended in the plasma (liquid portion of the blood), the concentration of dissolved substances, such as salts, inside the red cell being the same as the concentration of dissolved substances in the plasma. When two solutions have the same concentration of dissolved substances they are said to be *isotonic*, that is, to have the same osmotic pressure. Since plasma is isotonic with the red blood cells, water moves freely in equal amounts in both directions across the cell membrane, and there is no change in the shape of the cell. However, if red cells are removed from the plasma and placed in a concentrated or **hypertonic** salt solution, water will be pulled from the cell into the salt solution. As a result, the cells become shrunken and appear to be knobby or *crenated*. On the other hand, if the cells are placed in a dilute or **hypotonic** solution, water will enter the cells causing them to swell until they burst and lose their "oxygen carrier," hemoglobin. This destruction of red blood cells with the loss of hemoglobin is called *hemolysis* (meaning "blood breakdown"). Crenation and hemolysis are illustrated in Figure 2-16.

Theoretically, only isotonic solutions should be injected into the blood stream (intravenously) in order to prevent undesirable shrinking or swelling of the red blood cells. However, both hypotonic and hypertonic solutions may be used on certain occasions; if these solutions are administered slowly and in relatively small amounts they will be safely mixed with the plasma. The two solutions used most frequently for intravenous injection (exclusive of whole blood and plasma) are 0.9 per cent sodium chloride, which is called physiologic or normal saline, and 5.0 per cent glucose. Both of these solutions are isotonic with the cells of the body.

Since osmotic pressure is directly related to the number of particles in solution, then it is logical to assume that the size of the solute particles would also play a part in the determination of this "pulling pressure." For example, a solution which contained 10 Gm. of a colloid would have a lower osmotic pressure than a solution which contained 10 Gm. of an electrolyte (such as NaCl), for the simple reason that colloids are large particles and there could be proportionately fewer of them in solution. However, the colloidal osmotic pressure of the blood is very important in the return of tissue fluid from the intercellular spaces. Since colloids are not diffusible, they are much more concentrated in the blood stream than in the tissue fluid; thus they exert a strong osmotic or "pulling pressure" on water molecules in the tissue fluid. Crystalloids, on the other hand, are diffusible; thus their concentration is practically the same on both sides of the capillary membrane, and they exert little or no effective osmotic pressure.

The exchange of water through capillary membranes is a fascinating process, and Figure 2-17 may help to clarify your understanding of the general principles involved. Note that we have two types of pressure at work for us: (1) the blood pressure, which is the hydrostatic or "pushing

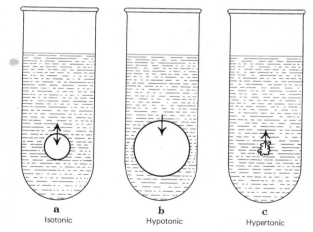

a
Isotonic

b
Hypotonic

c
Hypertonic

Fig. 2-16. Osmosis. (A) Red blood cells undergo no change in size in isotonic solutions. (B) They increase in size in hypotonic solutions. (C) They decrease in size in hypertonic solutions.

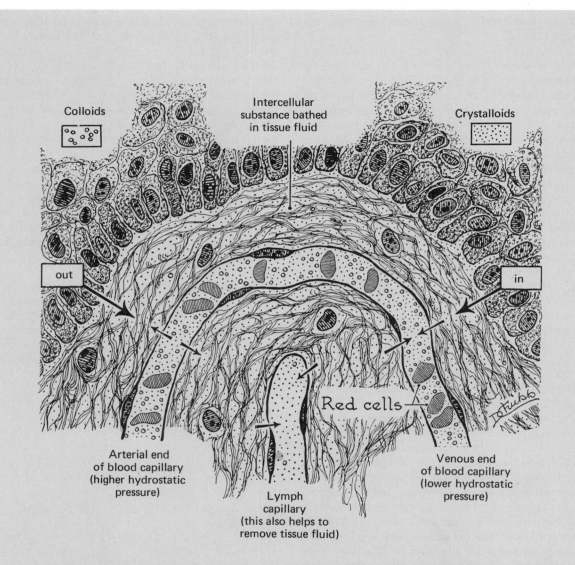

Fig. 2-17. A diagram to show how tissue fluid is formed by capillaries and absorbed by capillaries and lymphatics. The colloids of the blood are represented as small circles and the crystalloids of blood and tissue fluid as dots. Under normal conditions only a very little colloid escapes from most capillaries, and such colloid as escapes is returned to the circulation by way of the lymphatics. (Ham, A. W., and Leeson, T. S.: Histology, ed. 4, Philadelphia, Lippincott)

pressure" of the blood stream, and (2) the colloidal osmotic pressure, which is the "pulling pressure" exerted by colloids in the blood.

Blood pressure is primarily responsible for the formation of our tissue fluid. As blood flows away from its pressure source (the heart), its pressure becomes progressively lower; therefore, it is normally higher at the arterial end of the capillary (about 32 mm. Hg) than it is at the venous end (about 12 mm. Hg). This means that there is proportionately more filtration occurring at the arterial end of the capillary than at the venous end (Fig. 2-17).

The collodial osmotic pressure of the blood plays an important role in the return of tissue fluid to the blood stream. Since colloids, such as most of our blood proteins, are unable to cross normal membranes in any significant amount, their osmotic pressure remains essentially the same (about 22 mm. Hg) throughout the capillary bed. This means that water is being pulled in at approximately the same rate in all parts of the capillary. However, at the arterial end of the capillary the hydrostatic pressure of the blood is greater (32 mm. Hg) than the colloidal osmotic pressure (22 mm. Hg); therefore, the significant movement of water is from the blood into the tissue spaces. The reverse is true at the venous end of the capillary where the hydrostatic pressure has dropped (12 mm. Hg) and the collodial osmotic pressure remains the same (22 mm. Hg); the significant movement of water now is from the tissue spaces into the blood stream (Fig. 2-17).

There are several ways in which this dynamic fluid balance may be upset, but we shall mention only one at this time. For example, let us suppose that the blood protein level has fallen well below normal, as could happen in certain diseases of the kidney. With fewer protein molecules in the blood, the colloidal osmotic pressure would be proportionately reduced. Thus, the effective filtering pressure would be greater in all parts of the capillary, and water would be forced out into the tissues more rapidly than it could be pulled back into the blood. The end-result of this imbalance would be an accumulation of fluid in the tissue spaces; this condition is known as *edema*.

THE PRIMARY TISSUES

A tissue consists of a group of cells that are similar in structure and in intercellular substance, arranged in a characteristic pattern. In the human body there are 4 basic or primary tissues: epithelial, connective, muscular, and nervous tissue. The primary tissues, in turn, may be subdivided into various types, each type being specialized for the performance of a specific task or tasks.

Epithelial Tissue

Epithelial tissue covers the body surfaces and forms a lining for its cavities, including the tubular structures. In certain parts of the body epithelial tissue grows into the body substance to form structures called glands.

General Functions of Epithelial Tissue. The epithelial tissues of the body are concerned with protection, secretion, absorption, and filtration. For example, the outer layer of the skin (epidermis) offers *protection* from such things as bacterial invasion; cells in the respiratory tract, have fast-moving, hairlike projections (cilia) that are constantly at work sweeping dirt and dust particles out of the lungs. *Secretion* is a specialty of epithelial cells in the various glands of the body. Epithelial cells highly specialized for *absorption* are found in the small intestine and in the tubules of the kidneys. The formation of tissue fluid throughout the body depends very much upon the process of *filtration*, which occurs through the delicate epithelial tissue in the capillaries of the circulatory system.

Characteristics of Epithelial Tissue. The cells of epithelial tissues fit together so closely that there is no true intercellular substance other than certain structural components that hold the cells together. Epithelial tissues occur in the form of sheets or membranes that are not very strong. The important source of support comes from the underlying connective tissues to which the epithelial tissues are firmly attached by a permeable but "adhesive" *basement membrane* (Fig. 2-18).

Epithelial tissues have no blood vessels of their own; thus, they depend upon capillaries in the underlying connective tissue for supplies of food and oxygen and for the removal of waste products. Well nourished epithelial cells have an excellent capacity for regeneration, so that cells lost during the wear and tear of everyday living are readily replaced by mitosis (p. 26).

Types of Epithelial Tissue. The covering and lining division of epithelial tissue consists of two general classes: *simple* epithelium, which consists of one layer of cells; and *stratified* epithelium, which consists of more than one layer of cells. The terms squamous, cuboidal, and columnar indicate the general shape of the cells (in stratified tissue, these terms refer to the surface cells).

The glandular division of epithelial tissue forms the exocrine and some endocrine glands of the body. Endocrine glands pour their secretion into the blood stream, while the exocrine glands pour their secretion onto the surface from which they originated.

1. **Simple squamous epithelium** consists of one layer of thin, flat cells fitted together in such a way that they resemble a mosaic (Fig. 2-18). This type of epithelium is adapted for filtration and diffusion, rather than for withstanding wear and tear. Consequently, simple squamous epithelium lines the blood and lymph vessels—here it is called *endothelium;* in the microscopic capillaries this single layer of cells makes possible the formation of tissue fluid. The air spaces of the lungs also are lined with simple squamous epithelium, through which oxygen and carbon dioxide diffuse without difficulty.

2. **Simple cuboidal epithelium** consists of a single layer of cells that somewhat resemble tiny cubes when seen in a side view (Fig. 2-18). It is not found in very many places in the body—a few examples are the thyroid gland, the surface of the ovary, and a portion of the kidney tubules.

3. **Simple columnar epithelium** is composed of cells that are taller than they are wide (Fig. 2-18). These cells not only protect underlying tissues but also are specialized for additional functions. For example, consider the simple columnar epithelial lining of the small intestine, in which two types of cells are interspersed with one another. One type is specialized for the *selective absorption* of the products of digestion. A second type is specialized for the secretion of a slippery, protective substance called *mucus;* such a cell is called a *goblet cell,* because the nucleus lies near the basement membrane and the remainder of the cell is shaped like a goblet (Fig. 2-18). The mucus secreted by goblet cells keeps the epithelial surface moist.

Simple columnar epithelium also is in the uterus, in the uterine tubes, and in some of the respiratory passages. In addition to goblet cells, the epithelium in the aforementioned sites presents still another type of specialized cell, one that has hairlike processes on its free surface (Fig. 2-18); these processes are called *cilia,* and they act together to move particles and secretions, such as mucus, across the surface of the tissue. Repeatedly they bend down rapidly with a forceful stroke in one direction and then return to their original position. The movement passes over the ciliated surface in waves, as the cilia are rigid when bending down and limp when returning to the erect position.

4. **Pseudostratified columnar epithelium** is so named because it appears at first glance to be composed of several layers of cells (Fig. 2-18). However, closer inspection shows that although some of the cells in contact with the basement membrane do not reach the free surface of the tissue, most of the cells are tall, and do reach the surface. Both ciliated cells and goblet cells are seen in this epithelium, which lines most of the respiratory passages.

5. **Stratified epithelium** consists of more than one layer of cells and is named according to the shape of the cells in the top layer. This tissue serves to protect body surfaces that are subject to much wear and tear in daily living. As the surface cells are brushed off by friction, new ones are pushed up from below to take their place; this cell replacement is made possible by cell division taking place in the deepest layer of the tissue, in which cells are columnar in shape.

(a) *Stratified squamous keratinized* epithelium makes up the epidermis of the skin (Fig. 2-27). The superficial cells in this tissue are flattened, dead cells that have become fused together, form-

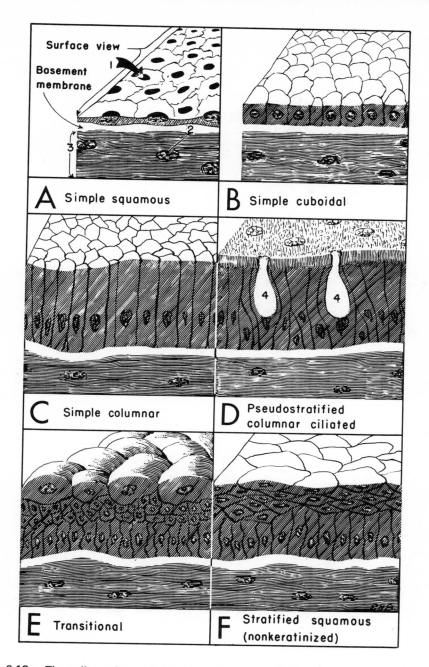

Fig. 2-18.   Three-dimensional diagrams illustrating the different types of epithelial membranes found on wet surfaces. (1) Nucleus of epithelial cell. (2) Cell of supporting connective tissue. (3) Connective tissue. (4) Goblet cell. The basement membrane is shown as a space merely to emphasize boundary between epithelial cells and connective tissue. (Modified from Ham, A. W.: Histology, ed. 2, Philadelphia, Lippincott)

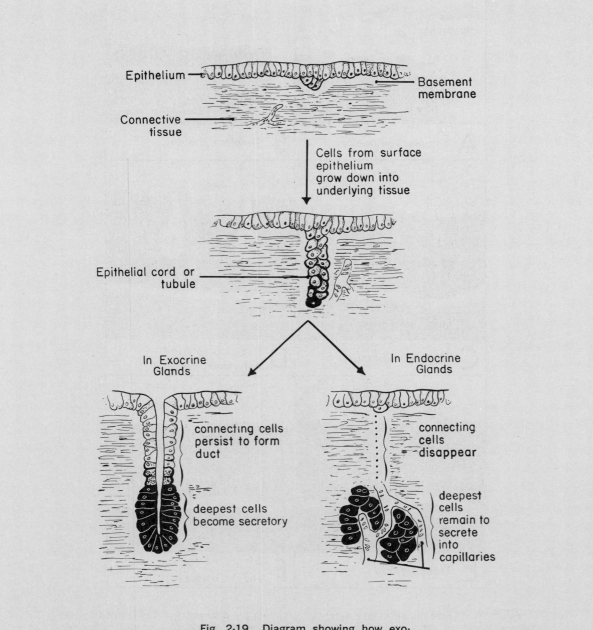

Fig. 2-19. Diagram showing how exocrine and some endocrine glands develop. (Modified from Ham, A. W.: Histology, ed. 2, Philadelphia, Lippincott)

ing a tough, waterproof layer of keratin material. The epidermis protects the underlying living tissues from a variety of injuries; it is described in more detail on page 48.

(b) *Stratified squamous nonkeratinized* epithelium also is protective in nature, but it differs from the keratinized tissue in that all of its cells are alive. Such epithelium is found on wet surfaces that are subjected to wear and tear, such as the inside of the mouth, where it provides protection from coarse foods.

(c) *Transitional epithelium* is a peculiar type of stratified epithelial tissue found in structures which are subjected to periodic distention, such as the urinary bladder. It is like stratified squamous nonkeratinizing epithelium except that the superficial cells are rounded when the bladder is empty and flattened when it is distended. In the latter case they are stretched and drawn out into squamous-like cells without breaking apart. (See Figs. 2-18 and 18-7).

6. **Glandular epithelium** gives rise to secretory units which are called glands. The mucus-secreting goblet cells described above cannot produce more than a small fraction of the various secretions needed in the body. To meet the needs for additional secretions, epithelial cells in many regions have turned inward from the covering or lining surfaces and grown into or invaded the underlying supportive connective tissue. The manner in which such masses of secreting cells (called glands) develop is shown in Figure 2-19. These cells are highly specialized to secrete; this means that they remove materials from the blood and manufacture new substances which they then extrude from their cytoplasm.

(a) *Endocrine Glands.* Some glands lose their connection with the epithelial surface from which they developed; consequently they possess no ducts through which they can extrude their secretions. The secretions which are produced by endocrine glands are extruded into blood or lymph. The endocrine glands comprise the endocrine system to which Chapter 19 is devoted.

(b) *Exocrine Glands.* The exocrine glands retain their connection with the epithelial surface from which they originated. The connections are called the ducts of the glands, and they convey the secretions from the glands to the surface. The secretory units are clusters of cells located at the ends of the ducts, and the shape of the unit determines the type of gland; Figure 2-20 illustrates various types of exocrine glands.

Connective Tissue

Connective tissue is the most abundant and the most widely distributed of all the primary tissues. It is found in all parts of the body.

General Functions of Connective Tissue. The connective tissues perform a variety of functions, ranging from broad areas of support, protection, and the binding together of other tissues, to the production of certain components of the blood, storage of fat, and protection of the body against bacterial invasion and disease. Some of these functions depend primarily upon the activities of special connective tissue cells, while others depend more upon the intercellular substance produced by the cells.

Characteristics of Connective Tissues. In addition to their widespread distribution in the body, connective tissues are characterized by vascularity; with a few exceptions—such as cartilage and tendons—connective tissues are abundantly supplied with blood vessels. These tissues also are characterized by the quantity and the quality of their intercellular substance. At one extreme are the blood-forming (hemopoietic) tissues, which consist almost entirely of cells; at the other extreme are connective tissues, such as bone and cartilage, which consist chiefly of intercellular substance. Between the two extremes are those tissues that are a representative mixture of cells and intercellular substance.

The intercellular substance, or matrix, is the nonliving material between the cells of connective tissue. It is produced by the cells and consists of two basic types: fibrous and amorphous (meaning without form).

Fibrous intercellular substance includes three types of fibers: collagenic, elastic and reticular; all 3 are protein in nature. Collagen is the most common protein in the body, and it is extremely

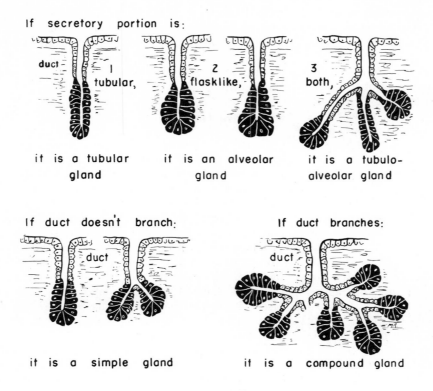

If secretory portion is:

duct — 1 tubular,   2 flasklike,   3 both,

it is a tubular
gland

it is an alveolar
gland

it is a tubulo-
alveolar gland

If duct doesn't branch:

duct

If duct branches:

duct

it is a simple gland

it is a compound gland

Fig. 2-20. Diagram showing the different kinds of secretory units of exocrine glands and the difference between simple and compound glands. (Modified from Ham, A. W.: Histology, ed. 2, Philadelphia, Lippincott)

tough. Therefore, *collagenic fibers,* also called white fibers, are strong and tough, yet flexible and resistant to a pulling force. *Elastic fibers* consist of the protein elastin; they permit connective tissue to be stretched and then return to the original form when the stretching force is removed. *Reticular fibers* are delicate fibers arranged in networks; they are found wherever connective tissue joins the other tissues, such as in or near basement membranes.

Amorphous intercellular substance is the background substance in which fibers and cells are embedded. It varies in consistency from a liquid (in blood), through a soft, jellylike material (in loose connective tissues), to the hard substance of bone.

The cells of connective tissue produce the intercellular substance, store fat, make new blood cells, eat bacteria and cell debris (phagocytosis), produce antibodies that give us immunity to cer-

tain diseases, and make heparin, which prevents the clotting of blood. Some of the specialized cells of connective tissue are described below.

1. *Fibroblasts* are the most numerous cells in connective tissue. They contain an abundance of rough-surfaced endoplasmic reticulum (p. 21). which indicates that they are active in the synthesis of protein for use in the extracellular environment; for example, they form the fibrous intercellular substance needed for growth and repair of tissues.

2. *Macrophages* or histiocytes are large ameboid cells that engage in phagocytosis, or the ingestion of bacteria, other cells, and any foreign material which enters the tissues. They are found in all loose connective tissue and are an important part of the *reticuloendothelial system;* this term is used to designate certain modified endothelial cells which occur in various parts of the body and have the ability to get rid of foreign matter

CONNECTIVE
TISSUE CELL

MIGRATORY
BLOOD CELLS

WHITE FIBERS

ELASTIC
FIBERS

Fig. 2-21. Preparation of ordinary loose connective tissue from subcutaneous area. Elastic fibers normally are straight; they are coiled here, due to the method of preparation. ×300.

Fig. 2-22. Adipose connective tissue from omentum. The fat cells are arranged as groups between bundles of fibers in intercellular substance. ×160.

which comes in contact with them. In addition to the macrophages in loose connective tissue, the reticuloendothelial system includes the cells of the spleen, the lymph nodes and the bone marrow, as well as the Kupffer cells in the liver. The main function of all these cells is phagocytosis, which means that they protect the body from injury by foreign substances, and they rid the body of worn-out red blood cells and other cellular debris.

3. *Mast cells* are connective tissue cells that are concerned with the production of heparin, an anticoagulant (p. 309). They also are believed to contain much of the histamine (an inflammatory substance) in the body. Inflammation is described on page 305.

4. *Fat cells* are fibroblasts which are specialized to store fat. Under the microscope these cells resemble a signet ring as the large fat droplet within each cell flattens the nucleus and the cytoplasm to one side.

5. *Plasma cells* are small rounded cells that are

the primary producers of circulating antibodies (gamma globulins, page 305). They develop most commonly in the loose connective tissues that support the wet epithelial membranes lining the respiratory and intestinal tracts. However, they also may develop in lymphatic tissue (p. 384) in any part of the body.

Types of Connective Tissue. The following tissues are found in the human body: ordinary loose connective tissue, adipose tissue, dense fibrous tissue, cartilage, bone, hemopoietic tissue, blood and lymph.

1. **Ordinary loose connective tissue** (*areolar*) contains all types of fibers loosely interwoven and embedded in a soft, jellylike background substance (Fig. 2-21). As its name suggests, loose connective tissue has a certain degree of flexibility; its intercellular substance is so arranged that the tissue can be stretched to some extent in various directions without being injured. This tissue is called "ordinary" because it is so abundant and so widely distributed throughout the body. It is found immediately beneath most epithelial membranes, and it serves as a delicate packing along the course of blood vessels, nerves, and the ducts of glands. In addition, it extends into and between various organs of the body. Loose connective tissue plays an important nutritive role in that it carries many capillaries, and its soft, jellylike substance is ideally suited for the diffusion of materials back and forth between the blood stream and neighboring tissue cells. This tissue, with its many macrophages and plasma cells, also serves as the body's second line of defense against bacteria that may penetrate the skin or mucous membranes.

2. **Adipose tissue** is a specialized variation of loose connective tissue. It consists primarily of closely packed fat cells with elastic and collagenic fibers running in all directions. Each specialized cell contains such a large droplet of fat that the nucleus and the cytoplasm are barely visible (Fig. 2-22). Adipose tissue is found under the skin, around the kidneys and the eyeballs, and as soft elastic pads between organs; it also forms padding around joints and is found in the marrow of our long bones. This fatty tissue of the body is a reserve food supply, an insulator against heat loss, and a support and protection for various organs.

3. **Dense fibrous connective tissue** differs from the loose variety in that its major function is performed by its intercellular substance; the cells that it contains are primarily concerned with producing that substance—i.e., collagenic and elastic fibers. In most dense connective tissue, collagenic fibers are more abundant than the elastic type; however, elastic fibers are prominent in such places as the walls of the trachea and the bronchial tubes of the respiratory system, and the walls of blood vessels, particularly the large arteries.

Tendons (attaching muscles to bones) and *ligaments* (holding bones together at joints) are both constructed primarily of collagenic fibers that are regularly arranged—that is, they run more or less in the same plane and in the same direction. This arrangement provides great strength and the ability to withstand tremendous pulling when force is applied in one general direction. On the other hand, when the fibers are irregularly arranged (i.e., run in different planes and directions), the tissue can withstand stretching in any direction (Fig. 2-23); such tissue is found in the deep layer of the skin, in the capsules of various organs, and as an outer wrapping (fascia) for muscles.

4. **Cartilage** or "gristle" is a special kind of dense connective tissue in which the shapeless intercellular substance exists in the form of a very firm jelly or gel, and the fibers form a dense network. Cartilage cells, called *chondrocytes*, lie in little cavities called lacunae, usually in groups of 2 or 4. There are no blood vessels in cartilage; its cellular nourishment and waste removal are accomplished by the diffusion of substances through the intercellular substance between the chondrocytes and capillaries located outside of the cartilaginous structure. The fibrous connective tissue membrane that covers cartilage is called the *perichondrium*.

Three types of cartilage occur in the body: hyaline, fibrous and elastic. *Hyaline cartilage* (Fig. 2-24) is the most common type; it is pearly white and glassy or translucent in appearance. It forms the skeleton in the embryo and provides models in which most of the bones develop. It covers the articulating ends of bones in movable joints, makes up the rib cartilages and the cartilages of the nose and the larynx.

Fibrous cartilage (fibrocartilage) is less firm than hyaline cartilage, but it has great strength owing to the regular arrangement of its collagenic fibers (Fig. 2-25). Probably the best known examples of fibrocartilage are the intervertebral disks, springy shock absorbers between the bodies of the vertebrae. The center of each disk is a soft mass (nucleus pulposus) which occasionally ruptures into the vertebral canal (p. 83). Fibrous cartilage also is found in the form of semilunar disks in the knee joint.

Elastic cartilage is more flexible than the other types due to the presence of a network of elastic fibers in its intercellular substance. It enters into the formation of several cartilaginous structures, such as the external ear and the epiglottis. Elastic cartilage allows some degree of change in these structures, yet strengthens them and maintains their shape.

5. **Osseous connective tissue** is most frequently referred to as "bone tissue." Its origin, structure and function are described in Chapter 3.

6. **Hemopoietic tissue, blood** and **lymph** are described in detail in Chapter 11.

Muscle tissue

The third primary tissue is muscle tissue, an amazing collection of highly specialized cells which have the capacity to shorten and thus produce movement of some body part. There are 3 distinct types of muscle tissue in the human body: skeletal, visceral or smooth, and cardiac muscle. For a complete description of these tissues your attention is directed to Chapter 4. Only a brief outline will be presented at this time as we survey body organization as a whole.

1. **Skeletal muscle,** attached to the skeleton, is a voluntary type of muscle tissue (under control of the conscious will). Contraction of skeletal muscle results in movement of external body parts, such as the extremities.

2. **Visceral** or **smooth muscle** is found in the

Fig. 2-23. Subcutaneous dense fibrous connective tissue, showing bundles cut in various directions, irregularly arranged.

walls of the internal organs and the blood vessels. It is an involuntary type of muscle tissue (not under conscious control). Contraction of visceral muscle results in such movements as the peristaltic waves in the stomach and the intestine during the digestion of food.

3. **Cardiac muscle** is found only in the walls of the heart. This involuntary type of muscle compresses the heart chambers and forces blood into the arteries.

Nerve tissue

Nerve tissue is the fourth primary tissue. It is composed of specialized cells which not only receive stimuli but also conduct impulses to and from all parts of the body. *Nerve cells* or *neurons* vary markedly from other cells in their appearance. For example, their cytoplasm is drawn out into long stringlike processes which may be several feet in length, although microscopic in diameter. Chapter 6 presents a complete description of this tissue which is so essential for the coordination and the correlation of all body activities.

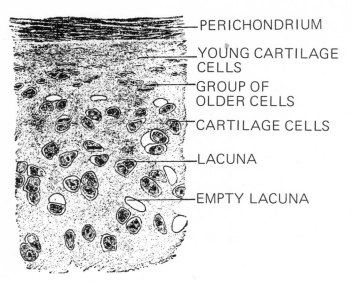

PERICHONDRIUM

YOUNG CARTILAGE CELLS

GROUP OF OLDER CELLS

CARTILAGE CELLS

LACUNA

EMPTY LACUNA

Fig. 2-24. Hyaline cartilage; cartilage cells are shown in lacunae; the matrix is firm and homogeneous. The perichondrium is shown. ×250.

Fig. 2-25. Fibrous cartilage. The matrix is filled with collagenic fibers. ×225.

HYALINE AREA SURROUNDING CARTILAGE CELLS

FIBROUS INTERCELLULAR SUBSTANCE

CARTILAGE CELLS

TISSUES AS BUILDING MATERIALS

We have seen how groups of cells band together to form tissues; now we shall see how various tissues are combined to form membranes, skin and the internal organs.

Membranes

The simplest combination of tissues is observed in the formation of membranes. A membrane is a sheet of tissues which covers or lines the body surface or divides organs into lobes.

Mucous membranes line body cavities and passageways which open to the outside world, such as the digestive tract, the respiratory passages, the urinary and the reproductive tracts. These membranes have epithelium on their free surface and a layer of connective tissue beneath. All mucous membranes contain a certain number of goblet cells which secrete the slippery, protective mucus, but the other types of cells may vary. For example, many of the cells in the respiratory passages are ciliated for the purpose of sweeping out mucus and particles of dirt, while the columnar cells of the intestine are specialized for the absorption of food.

Serous membranes line the closed cavities of the body (those that do not open to the outside world) and cover the various organs which are located within those cavities. These thin glistening membranes are composed of epithelium on the free surface, with connective tissue below. Cells in the surface layer secrete a slippery serous fluid which protects against friction when organs rub against the body wall or glide over one another. For example, the walls of both lung compartments of the thorax are lined with serous membrane (the parietal pleura), and each lung is covered with serous membrane (the visceral pleura); as the lungs expand with air, the slippery visceral layer glides against the equally slippery parietal layer with a minimum of friction. A similar arrangement of serous membranes, the pericardium and the peritoneum, protect the heart and the abdominal viscera, respectively.

Synovial membranes are composed entirely of

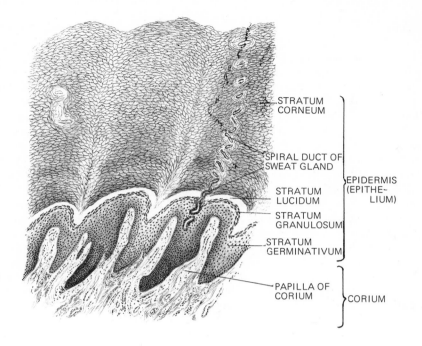

STRATUM
CORNEUM

SPIRAL DUCT OF
SWEAT GLAND

STRATUM
LUCIDUM

EPIDERMIS
(EPITHE-
LIUM)

STRATUM
GRANULOSUM

STRATUM
GERMINATIVUM

PAPILLA OF
CORIUM

CORIUM

Fig. 2-26. Section of skin from the sole of the foot, showing all the layers of the epidermis and a part of the corium. ×70.

connective tissue. Cells in the surface layer secrete a slippery fluid that has the consistency of raw egg white; this lubricant is called synovial fluid. Synovial membranes are associated with bones and joints (Chap. 3). For example, joint cavities are lined with these slippery membranes which permit movement of bones without friction.

The superficial fascia, or *subcutaneous tissue* is an extensive fibrous membrane which underlies the skin and forms a continuous sheet throughout the body. It is a combination of adipose and ordinary loose connective tissues and is attached firmly to the deep layer of the skin (dermis). The amount of adipose tissue varies in different persons but those who possess a generous amount are said to be "well padded." The superficial fascia attaches the skin to underlying structures, such as the deep fascia, the periosteum of bones, and the perichondrium of cartilage. However, the very continuity of these tissues may contribute to a serious spread of infection. For example, when bacteria enter the subcutaneous tissue through a break in the skin they are immediately attacked by the defensive macrophages in the areolar tissue. Should the bacteria win this preliminary battle, they may multiply and spread in all directions through the subcutaneous tissue, resulting in a diffuse and widespread inflammation called *cellulitis*. It is chiefly in the superficial fascia that abnormal collections of fluid (*edema*) occur.

The deep fascia lies under the superficial fascia and is composed of dense connective tissue. It contains no fat and is in close relation to bones, ligaments and muscles. Sheets of deep fascia are wrapped around muscles, supporting them and forming partitions between them. Deep fascia encloses glands and viscera, and it also forms sheaths for nerves and blood vessels.

Miscellaneous fibrous membranes, composed entirely of connective tissue, include such specialized structures as the *periosteum* (covering bone), the *dura mater* (covering the brain) and the *sclera* (outer covering of the eye); these will be described at a later time in connection with their related organs.

The skin

The skin, or integument, is much more than a simple "hide" which covers the body. It serves as an example of a more complex combination of tissues than that found in the membranes described above. Skin is subjected to many more "insults" than are the internal membranes, and its structure varies accordingly.

Structure of the Skin. The skin covers the entire surface of the body. It consists of two main layers which are quite different in character; these layers are the *epidermis* and the *dermis* which are firmly cemented together. However, excessive rubbing of the skin (as with poorly fitted shoes) may cause the epidermis to be forcibly separated from the dermis; tissue fluid accumulates in this area, further separating the two layers and resulting in a blister. Immediately under the dermis, but not part of the skin, is the subcutaneous tissue or superficial fascia, described previously as a fibrous membrane.

The **epidermis** is the thin surface layer of skin. It is composed of stratified squamous keratinizing epithelium which, when viewed under the microscope, is seen to consist of several distinct layers or strata of cells. Since epithelial tissues have no blood vessels, the only living cells are in the deepest layer which is nourished by tissue fluid from capillaries in the dermis. These cells are constantly undergoing mitosis, and the daughter cells are pushed upward toward the surface, away from their source of nourishment; as these cells die (from lack of tissue fluid) they undergo a chemical transformation and their soft protoplasm becomes keratinized, or cornified. Since the epidermis is exposed to the air, these horny waterproof cells prevent dehydration of the deeper layers.

The epidermis varies in thickness in different parts of the body. For example, it is thinnest on the eyelids and thickest on the palms and the soles. A person who spends many hours on his feet may develop calluses on his soles, as one who does difficult manual work may have calluses on his hands; this extra thickening of the epidermis offers additional protection to underlying tissues. Figure 2-26 illustrates the 4 layers of epidermis

present in skin on the sole of the foot. These layers are (1) *the stratum corneum* or horny layer, which consists of dead, keratinized cells; (2) *the stratum lucidum* and (3) *the stratum granulosum* which are middle layers where the epithelial cells gradually die and become keratinized; and (4) *the stratum germinativum* which is adjacent to the dermis and contains the only epidermal cells which can reproduce themselves. The cells in this deep layer also produce *melanin*, the pigment which is present in the skin of non-whites, and in the area of the nipple in white races; however, exposure of white skin to ultraviolet light will result in a production of melanin and the much sought after "sun tan." Freckles are merely irregular patches of melanin.

The **dermis,** also called the *corium* or true skin, is the inner layer of the skin. It is composed of connective tissues. The surface of the dermis is uneven due to the presence of conelike elevations, or papillae, which serve to attach it to the epidermis. If you look at your fingers and palms you can see ridges in the skin; these are the papillae of the dermis which project into the epidermis. The ridges develop during the third and fourth fetal months, and the pattern never changes except to enlarge. The unchanging pattern formed by these ridges is peculiar to the individual and is an excellent means of identification.

Both the papillary and the reticular layers of the dermis (Fig. 2-27) contain bundles of collagenic fibers; networks of elastic fibers are located between the bundles. The cells in this connective tissue are fibroblasts, fat cells and some macrophages. The fibers give strength, extensibility and elasticity to the skin. The extensibility of the skin is evident when one has swollen extremities; it is even more evident when the skin over the abdomen is stretched during pregnancy, in extreme obesity, or when there is an accumulation of a large amount of fluid in the abdomen. The stretched skin is smooth and glistening and can be injured by excessive stretching. The little tears which may occur during stretching remain visible afterward as silvery white streaks called *striae.*

In youth the skin is extensible and elastic, but as one grows older certain changes occur. The

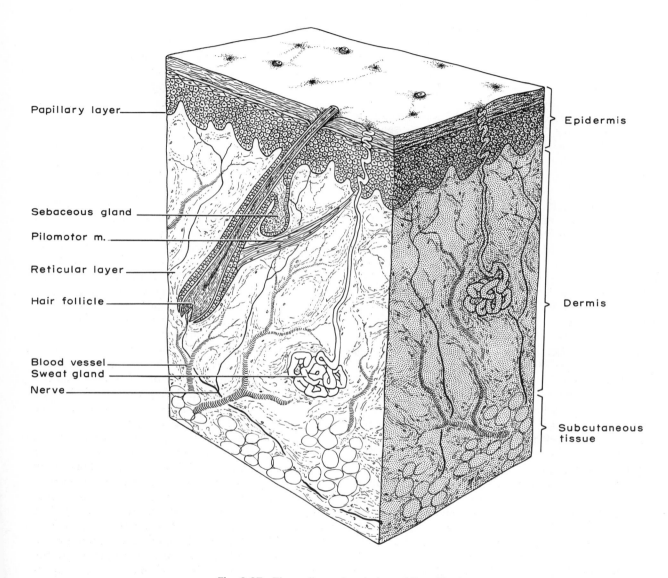

Papillary layer

Sebaceous gland

Pilomotor m.

Reticular layer

Hair follicle

Blood vessel

Sweat gland

Nerve

Epidermis

Dermis

Subcutaneous tissue

Fig. 2-27. Three-dimensional view of the skin.

skin becomes thinner, there are fewer elastic fibers and fat disappears from the subcutaneous tissue; this combination of events results in skin which is wrinkled in appearance.

The **blood supply** to skin is of great importance in the regulation of body temperature as well as for nourishment of the tissue cells. The arteries of the skin are arranged in the form of a network in the subcutaneous tissues just below the dermis. Branches from this network lead into capillary beds which permeate the dermis and ultimately drain into veins. The blood vessels of the skin are so numerous that they can hold a large proportion of the total blood supply of the body. When the skin is exposed to heat, or when the internal temperature of the body begins to rise, the small arteries of the skin dilate and allow more blood to flow through them, thus favoring the loss of heat from the body. On the other hand, when the skin is exposed to cold, or when the internal body temperature begins to drop, the vessels constrict and less blood flows through them; this means that less heat is lost from the body.

Interference with the blood supply to the skin will cause the death of cells and result in areas of ulceration. *Decubitus ulcers* (bedsores) may occur when patients spend prolonged periods of time in one position. The weight of the body exerts pressure on the skin, particularly where it lies over bony prominences, interfering with its blood supply and resulting in the death of tissue. Good nursing care, which includes frequent turning of the patient's body, alcohol rubs and keeping the skin clean and dry, helps to prevent this distressing condition.

The **nerve supply** of the skin consists of fibers which carry impulses to and from the central nervous system. The nerves which reach the skin from the central nervous system are distributed to the smooth muscle in the walls of the small arteries in the dermis, to the smooth muscle around the roots of the hairs and to the sweat glands of the skin. The nerves which carry messages from the skin to the central nervous system show specialized endings (receptors, p. 263) of many types. They are affected by changes in the environment of the individual, and the messages which they transmit to the central nervous system arouse sensations in the brain. By this means we acquire information about the world in the immediate vicinity of the body.

Appendages of the Skin. The cutaneous glands, the hair and the nails comprise the appendages of the skin. All are specializations or differentiations of the epidermis and are protective in nature.

The **cutaneous glands** are of 3 types: sebaceous, sweat and ceruminous glands. The *sebaceous glands* are found almost everywhere on the surface of the body, two prominent exceptions being the palms and the soles. These glands lie in the dermis, and their excretory ducts usually open into the necks of hair follicles, as shown in Figure 2-27. Sebaceous glands produce an oily secretion (called *sebum*) which prevents hair from becoming dry and brittle; it also forms an oily layer on the skin surface keeping it soft and helping to waterproof it. Persons with "lazy" sebaceous glands tend to have dry hair and skin, while those with active glands have hair and skin that are more oily. *Blackheads* are discolored accumulations of dried sebum. *Acne* (pimples) may be due to infection of sebaceous glands.

Sweat glands are distributed over the entire skin; they are most numerous in the axillae and on the palms, the soles and the forehead. It is estimated that there are about 2 million sweat glands in the skin of an adult. These glands are located in the dermis, and their ducts pass through the epidermis, in a spiral manner, to the surface of the skin where they open in pores.

Sweat glands are supplied by nerves which carry messages to promote perspiration when the outside temperature is high or when there is an elevation of body temperature. The main purpose of sweat glands is to act as an emergency mechanism when it is necessary for the body to lose heat by the evaporation of water from its surface. The pores of the sweat glands are rather prominent, and many persons use astringents on the skin to close the pores and make them appear smaller.

Ceruminous glands are modified sweat glands; they are found only in the skin of the passages leading into the ear (external auditory meatus). They secrete a yellow waxy substance (called *cerumen*) which helps to protect the tympanic membrane. However, if this wax accumulates in large amounts it may interfere with hearing.

The mammary glands, or breasts, are specialized cutaneous glands which produce milk for the nourishment of the young. They are described on page 588.

Hairs and hair follicles (Fig. 2-27) are epithelial structures. The follicles are formed by a downgrowth of cells of the epidermis into the dermis or into the subcutaneous tissue. Hair is formed by well nourished germinal cells in the deepest part of the follicle. As these cells divide, the daughter cells are pushed upward, getting farther and farther away from their source of nourishment; eventually the cells die and become keratinized.

A hair usually consists of a central core, or medulla, surrounded by a cortex. Hair color depends upon the quality and quantity of pigment (melanin) in the cortex. White hairs have no pigment—when they are mixed with pigmented hairs, the mixture that results is called "gray hair" (true gray hair is rare).

The root of a hair is that part embedded in the follicle (usually slanting from the perpendicular), while the shaft projects above the surface of the skin. Two or more sebaceous glands are associated with each follicle; they lie in a little triangle formed by the slanted follicle and a tiny bundle of smooth muscle fibers, the *arrector pili* or *pilomotor muscle.* One end of this involuntary muscle bundle is attached to the sheath of the follicle; the muscle then slants upward to the point at which its other end is attached to the papillary layer of the dermis. Contraction of this muscle results in two pronounced effects: first, because the muscle pulls on the deep part of the follicle, the hair is made to "stand on end" as the follicle becomes more perpendicular; second, as the muscle pulls on its place of attachment to the dermis it tends to produce a "dimple" in the skin and give the well-known appearance of "goose pimples." In addition, contraction of the muscle squeezes the sebaceous glands, forcing sebum into the follicle and onto the skin. Cold is an important stimulus that leads to the contraction of the pilomotor muscles.

Hairs are present over most of the body surface, with certain exceptions such as the palms and the soles, but are most abundant on the scalp. Straight or curly hair is related to the degree of curvature of the follicle and the form of the hair. If the follicle is unbent and the shaft is cylindrical, the hair is straight. If the follicle is bent and the shaft is flattened, the hair is curly.

Throughout life, one constantly loses hairs, but they are replaced by the continued division of epidermal cells in the germinal area. Cutting or shaving hair has no effect on its growth, the maximal rate being about ½ inch per month.

The nails are the horny scales of epidermis that overlie the dorsal surfaces of the fingers and the toes. The dermis, which the nail covers, is modified to form the nail bed. New formation of nail takes place in the epithelium at the proximal portion of the nail bed. As new formation takes place the nail moves forward and thus grows in length. The crescent at the base of the nail is called the lunula; it may be slightly or completely overlapped by the cuticle or *eponychium.*

Functions of the skin. The skin performs many essential functions, such as protection, temperature regulation and those of a sense organ. Relatively minor functions include the excretion of water and salts and the formation of vitamin D.

Protection of underlying tissues is an outstanding function of the intact skin. It acts as a mechanical barrier to prevent the invasion of bacteria and other foreign matter, and to prevent physical injury to the delicate tissues below. The skin is essentially a waterproof covering which makes it possible for the body to maintain a high content of water even in dry air. The importance of the skin in this respect is dramatically illustrated in the case of a person who suffers extensive burns over the entire body. Destruction of the skin results in such a rapid loss of fluid from the underlying tissues that the water balance of the entire body is upset; the victim may suffer complete circulatory collapse, and die. It might also be added that without this waterproof exterior we would be unable to swim in fresh water without becoming swollen, or in salt water without becoming shrunken.

Temperature regulation depends on several factors, but the skin plays an important role. Its many sweat glands constitute one of the mechanisms for cooling the body; the *evaporation* of sweat from the surface of the body facilitates a loss of heat when the environment becomes too warm. An even greater amount of body heat is lost through *radiation;* thus the amount of blood brought to the skin is an important factor in temperature regulation. When blood vessels are dilated, more heat is lost; when the vessels are constricted, less heat is lost.

The skin is a very efficient **sense organ,** containing nerve endings which are responsive to touch, pain and changes in temperature. It is an important source of information which enables us to withdraw from harmful stimuli (such as a hot stove) and to make other adjustments to the ever-changing world in which we live.

Other functions of the skin include the excretion of small amounts of nitrogenous waste products and NaCl in the sweat, the formation of vitamin D on exposure to the ultraviolet rays in sunlight, and the storage of water, sodium chloride and glucose.

Organs

As stated previously, tissues are combined to form organs. We have considered the structure of some of the tissues of the body and have had examples of simple combinations of tissues to form membranes, and a complex combination of tissues to form the skin. The next step in considering the organization of the body is to think of the component parts of organs.

An organ is a part of the body which performs a definite function. Organs have connective tissue frameworks, with special blood, lymph and nerve supplies, in addition to highly specialized cells which are characteristic for each organ. The specialized cells form the "parenchyma" of the organ, which is the important and predominant tissue. The accessory supporting tissues form the "stroma" of the organ. The stomach, the kidney and the liver are examples of organs.

THE SYSTEMS

The final units of organization in the body are called systems. A system is a group of organs, each of which contributes its share to the function of the whole. The systems of the body are skeletal, muscular, nervous, circulatory, respiratory, digestive, excretory, endocrine and reproductive.

The skeletal system includes not only the bones and the joints, but the strong ligaments that hold them together. This system provides a protective and supporting framework for the body as well as supplying a series of bony levers on which the skeletal muscles can act. Each bone is an organ, and connective tissue predominates in this system.

The muscular system is composed of 3 types of muscle plus the connective tissue necessary to "harness" the pulling power. Many movements of the body are due to the contraction of skeletal muscles which pull on the bones. Movement of food through the digestive tract depends on the contraction of visceral muscle, and blood is pumped around the body by cardiac muscle. Each muscle is an organ, and muscular tissue predominates in this system.

The nervous system is made up of the brain, the spinal cord and the peripheral nerves. The organs of special sense (e.g., the eye and ear) are included with the nervous system. This is the great correlating and controlling system of the body. Messages flash with great rapidity over all parts of this system, as over telephone and telegraph wires. The nervous system is intimately connected with all other systems and, by means of the organs of special sense, it is the source of information about the outside world and about one's own interior. Each part of the central nervous system is an organ. Nervous tissue predominates, and the cells are highly specialized for the conduction of messages.

The circulatory system comprises the heart, blood vessels, lymph vessels and nodes. The heart serves as the pump, while the blood vessels carry food and oxygen to all parts of the body and return wastes to the organs of excretion. The heart and each vessel are organs. Many types of tissue are present in the circulatory system, and many types of specialized cells are found.

The respiratory system comprises the respiratory passages and the lungs. It makes possible the oxygenation of the blood and the elimination of carbon dioxide. The lungs and each part of the passageway are organs, and many types of cells and tissues are found in this system.

The digestive system comprises the alimentary tract, its associated glands, the tongue and the teeth. It converts food into substances which can be absorbed and utilized by the various tissues of the body. Each part of the system, such as the stomach, the pancreas and the liver, is an organ. Many types of tissues and an even greater number of specialized cells are found in this system.

The excretory system proper includes the kidneys and the excretory ducts. Each kidney and ureter and the urinary bladder are organs. Nitrogenous waste, excess inorganic salts and water are eliminated by this system. Many types of tissues and cells are found in the excretory system.

The endocrine system comprises the glands of internal secretion. The pituitary and the adrenal glands are examples of the organs in this system, and the cells of each are highly specialized to produce their characteristic secretions (hormones). The function of this system is to provide chemical correlation which is just as important as nervous correlation, but much slower. In comparing the two, one might say that the speed of nervous correlation is like the telephone, while that of endocrine correlation is like the postal service.

The reproductive system is concerned with the perpetuation of the species. The organs of the male reproductive system include the testes (which produce sex cells called spermatozoa), a series of excretory ducts and various accessory structures. The female reproductive system consists of the ovaries (which produce sex cells called ova), uterine tubes, uterus, vagina and associated external structures. Many tissues are found in this system, and the cells in each are specialized to carry out their particular functions.

All of the systems are closely interrelated and coordinated for the sole purpose of maintaining homeostasis. As a successful baseball team requires the close cooperation of 9 different men, so the healthy body depends on the coordinated "teamwork" of its 9 systems.

Whenever something happens in one part of the body to disturb the existing condition, compensatory responses occur in other parts of the body to restore the original condition. This constant "give and take" between systems serves to maintain that dynamic equilibrium which we call homeostasis. For example, suppose that you suddenly look at your watch and see that it is time for class. You run up the steps, and your muscles require more oxygen than they had been using when you were sauntering along toward school. To supply extra oxygen, you breathe more rapidly, the heart beats faster, and the blood pressure rises in order to bring a more abundant supply of blood to the active muscles. You may feel warm and perspire by the time you reach the classroom. This is a brief list of the changes which occur during a bout of exercise.

As you would anticipate, damage to any part of the body has widespread effects on other parts. The whole field of medicine is concerned with the changes that occur in the human body when there is damage to such organs as the heart, the lungs or the liver. It is interesting to know that there are some organs which function for a time and then undergo "involution" or atrophy. For example, the ovaries in women cease to function after the menopause. Normal adjustments are made by the body when such organs undergo involution.

The beauty of the organization of the body should make a lasting impression on you. It is truly remarkable how well the body works if properly nourished and given adequate rest. It is equally remarkable how few difficulties are due to defective parts present at birth or to natural breakdowns of parts of the body before one reaches old age. Intricate integration and correlation of functions enable us to maintain life with a feeling of "well-being" and to perpetuate the species by reproduction.

SUMMARY

1. Cells, smallest units of life
2. Protoplasm
   A. Composition
      a. Inorganic compounds
      b. Organic compounds
   B. Importance of inorganic compounds
      a. Water: a solvent; high chemical stability; substances ionize in water; H^+ and OH^- involved in all chemical processes in cell; aids in regulation of body temperature
      b. Inorganic salts: maintenance of proper osmotic conditions; acid-base balance; clotting of blood; formation of bones, teeth, hemoglobin; normal functioning of muscle and nerve; electrolyte balance. Principal extracellular ions—sodium and chloride; intracellular ions chiefly potassium and phosphate
   C. Importance of organic compounds
      a. Proteins: framework of protoplasm; growth and repair of tissue
      b. Carbohydrates: primary source of energy; glucose is simple sugar in blood
      c. Lipids: source of energy; stored as adipose tissue (reserve food, protect and support organs, insulate); role in permeability of cell membrane
3. Cell structure
   A. Nucleus
      a. Control center
      b. DNA plays key role
   B. Cytoplasm
      a. Surrounds nucleus; concerned with functional activities of cell
      b. Contains centrioles, mitochondria, Golgi apparatus, endoplasmic reticulum, ribosomes, lysosomes
      c. RNA important in sythesis of protein
   C. Cell membrane
      a. Consists of lipo-proteins; pores between molecules allow passage of certain substances
      b. Selective permeability influenced by size of pores, lipid-solubility, electric charge on membrane and ion seeking entrance, electrolye balance; processes of passive and active transport
4. Cell division (mitosis)
   A. Provides for growth and repair
   B. DNA replicates prior to division
   C. Prophase, metaphase, anaphase, telophase
5. Protein synthesis
   A. m-RNA from DNA to ribosomes
   B. t-RNA picks up activated amino acids
   C. Assembly on ribosomes
6. Maintaining homeostasis in liquid cellular environment
   A. Tissue fluid serves as "middleman" between blood stream and cell
   B. Homeostasis, state of dynamic equilibrium in internal environment
   C. Circulatory "subway" system
      a. Transportation of materials throughout the body
      b. Closed circuit of tubes
      c. Capillaries: focal point of system
   D. Movement through membranes
      a. Filtration
      b. Diffusion
      c. Osmosis

d. Exchange of water through capillary membranes involves two pressures: blood pressure (hydrostatic or pushing pressure); colloidal osmotic pressure (pulling pressure); dynamic balance prevents accumulation of fluid

7. Primary tissues
    A. Epithelial
        a. Covers body and lines cavities; protect, secrete and absorb; no blood vessels
        b. Types: simple squamous, cuboidal, columnar; pseudostratified columnar; stratified squamous; transitional; glandular
    B. Connective
        a. Support, protect and bind together other body structures; store fat and produce new blood cells; most abundant of all primary tissues; excellent blood supply; fibrous and amorphous intercellular substance; fibroblasts, macrophages, mast, fat, plasma cells
        b. Types: ordinary loose, white fibrous, cartilage, osseous
    C. Muscle
        a. Cells have capacity to shorten; produce movement of body parts
        b. Types: skeletal, visceral or smooth, cardiac
    D. Nerve
        a. Nerve cells receive stimuli, conduct impulses to and from all parts of body
8. Tissues as building materials
    A. Membranes: sheets of tissues that cover or line cavities
        a. Mucous
        b. Serous

c. Synovial
d. Superficial fascia
e. Deep fascia
f. Periosteum, dura, sclera

B. Skin
    a. Epidermis is thin surface layer, consisting of stratified squamous epithelium; surface cells horny and keratinized; deep cells are living, undergo mitosis constantly; melanin is pigment. Dermis, or true skin, is inner layer; consists of connective tissues, subdivided into papillary and reticular layers.
    b. Blood supply abundant; important in temperature regulation
    c. Nerve supply to skin keeps us aware of environment
    d. Appendages: cutaneous glands, hair and nails
    e. Functions: protection, temperature regulation, sense organ, excretion of water and salts, formation of vitamin D, storage of water, sodium chloride and glucose

C. Organ
    a. A part of the body which performs a definite function; connective tissue framework
    b. Specialized cells form the parenchyma; accessory supporting structures form the stroma
    c. Examples: liver, kidney and stomach

9. Systems: skeletal, muscular, nervous, circulatory, respiratory, digestive, excretory, endocrine, reproductive
    A. All are closely interrelated and coordinated for purpose of maintaining homeostasis

PRACTICAL APPLICATIONS AND QUESTIONS

(Encircle the letter of the *best* answer to each question.)

Following the explosion of a hot water heater, Mr. J. B. was admitted to the hospital for treatment of severe burns that had destroyed the skin over one third of his body. Fluid was seeping from the burned surfaces, and he was very dehydrated. As part of his treatment he received intravenous injections of physiologic or normal saline.

1. Destruction of the skin involves which of the following primary tissues?
   a. adipose and fibrous
   b. muscular and epithelial
   c. connective and muscular
   d. epithelial and connective

2. Which layer of the skin, due to its waterproof nature, normally prevents the loss of tissue fluid?
   a. papillary
   b. reticular
   c. epidermis
   d. dermis

3. In the formation of tissue fluid, the physical process of filtration occurs because of different conditions which exist on two sides of a membrane; this would involve
   a. a difference in hydrostatic pressure
   b. molecular collisions
   c. a difference in fluid volume
   d. a difference in concentration of dissolved substances

4. Which of the following solutions are isotonic with red blood cells?
   a. 0.9% saline and 5.0% glucose
   b. 0.5% glucose and 0.9% saline
   c. 9.0% saline and 5.0% glucose
   d. 0.5% saline and 0.9% glucose

5. If hypotonic solutions were injected rapidly into Mr. J. B.'s blood stream, you would expect his red blood cells to become
   a. smaller
   b. sludged
   c. crenated
   d. hemolyzed

6. The repair of burned tissue and the growth of new tissue will be most dependent on the following food material:
   a. carbohydrate
   b. protein
   c. fat
   d. vitamins

7. Destruction of the skin may be followed by extensive infection if invading bacteria overcome the defensive macrophages in the
   a. epidermis
   b. serous membranes
   c. superficial fascia
   d. stratum germinativum

"Oh them bones, them dry bones..."

NEGRO SPIRITUAL

3

THE SKELETAL SYSTEM

All too often the words of the above song are taken quite literally by beginning students of anatomy and physiology. However, in the next few pages we hope to convince you that those 206 bones are not solid, inert masses. The latter impression is one that is all too frequently gained following examination of the typical skeleton in the classroom closet. Nothing could be further from the truth! Rather, these vital structures are dynamic little "factories" where millions of cells are busily engaged in work on a production line that would be the envy of any modern assembly plant.

For example, cells in the red bone marrow division *manufacture blood corpuscles* in fantastic quantities. It has been estimated that an average of one million wornout red blood corpuscles are destroyed every second of every day in the body; thus it is essential that an equal number of new ones be formed to replace them. Perhaps this will give some idea of the bustling activity that goes on within the bones.

Fig. 3-1. Anterior view of a long bone (femur) with cut-away section at distal end.

Fig. 3-2. Section of a flat bone; spongy or cancellous bone is shown, bounded above and below by layers of compact bone.

CLASSIFICATION OF BONES

Bones are classified on the basis of their shape rather than according to size. For example, the relatively small bones in your fingers are still referred to as "long bones." More attention will be given to structural details later on, but first let us consider the four classes as follows:

1. **Long bones** are found in the upper and the lower extremities; the only exceptions being the bones of the wrist, the ankle and the knee cap. A typical long bone consists of a shaft, or *diaphysis*, and two ends, or *epiphyses* (Fig. 3-1). The diaphysis is essentially a strong tube of compact bone with a roughly hollowed out space down the center. This space is referred to as the *medullary cavity*, and it is filled with yellow bone marrow. Each epiphysis consists of an outer compact shell with a spongy interior. In children, red bone marrow is found in all epiphyses, but it is eventually replaced by yellow marrow except in the proximal epiphyses of the adult arm and thigh bones.

2. **Short bones** are located in the wrist and the ankle. They might be described as cubical in shape and consist of spongy bone covered with a shell of compact bone.

3. **Flat bones** are relatively thin, each being composed of two plates of compact bone which enclose between them a layer of spongy bone (Fig. 3-2). The ribs and several of the skull bones are good examples of this type.

4. **Irregular bones** appear in various shapes and include all that are not in one of the preceding classes. For example, bones of the spinal column, the jaw, etc., are irregular bones. Bulky portions of these bones consist of spongy bone surrounded by a layer of compact bone, while the thinner parts may be composed of two plates of compact bone with a small amount of spongy bone between them.

Sesamoid bones, with the exception of the patella, or knee cap, are very small, rounded bones. They develop in the capsules of joints or in tendons, and their function is to reduce friction. The number of sesamoid bones is variable.

Less dramatic, but equally important, are the other functions of the skeleton. In combination with cartilaginous tissue it forms a solid *supporting framework* for the softer tissues and provides *protection* for them. Some parts of the skeletal system connect with each other in such a way that they form structures like cages or boxes in which internal organs are lodged. An example of this is the thorax, or chest, in which the lungs and the heart occupy a protected position. The skeleton also furnishes *surfaces for the attachment of muscles, tendons and ligaments,* which in turn pull on the individual bones and make it possible for us to move about. Thus one can see that bones and muscles are inseparable companions in the erect and moving body. It is only for ease of study that we consider them as individual units.

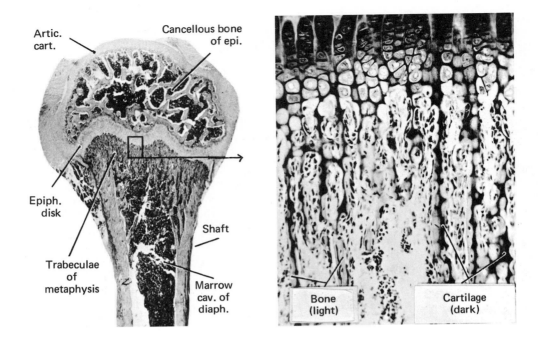

Fig. 3-3. At the left is a low-power photomicrograph of a longitudinal section cut through the end of a long bone of a growing rat. At this stage of development osteogenesis has spread out from the epiphyseal center of ossification so that only the articular cartilage above and the epiphyseal disk below remain cartilaginous. On the shaft side of the epiphyseal disk are trabeculae, which, as may be seen from the high-power picture on the right, consist of cartilage cores on which bone has been deposited. The cartilage cores of the trabeculae formerly were partitions between columns of cartilage cells in the epiphyseal disk. (Ham, A. W., and Leeson, T. S.: Histology, ed. 4, Philadelphia, Lippincott)

BONE FORMATION

To better understand the structural features of bone tissue, let us start at the very beginning of its formation when an embryo has been developing in its mother's uterus for approximately 2 months.

At the end of this 8-week period there is a complete little "skeleton," but it is composed entirely of *hyaline cartilage,* except for some of the face bones and the skull bones which are temporarily constructed of *fibrous membrane.* Obviously, cartilage and membrane cannot carry out the functions which we have ascribed to the skeleton; therefore, we shall now see what great changes are brought about in a relatively short period of time.

Intramembranous bone formation

Bones of the skull are formed by the intramembranous method and will be considered first. Try to visualize little "pieces" of membrane which are rough patterns for the bone-to-be. In the center of each individual membrane special bone-building cells, or **osteoblasts,** produce an intercellular substance in which calcium salts are deposited.

From this primary center, **ossification,** or bone formation, advances in radiating columns toward the edges of the membrane. However, the membrane also continues to grow for some time, and ossification of the skull bones is not yet complete when the baby is born. This is most noticeable at the "corners" of adjoining membranes and accounts for the "soft spots", or **fontanels,** which may be felt on an infant's head. Mothers often worry needlessly about injuring these areas when washing the baby's head or brushing the hair. They should be reassured that, with normal handling, the chance of injury is remote.

Eventually, ossification is completed. The cranial bones then consist of hard outer and inner plates of compact bone with spongy bone between. The latter layer is referred to as *diploë.*

Endochondral or cartilaginous bone formation

Most of the bones of our body are preformed in hyaline cartilage, and the endochondral or cartilaginous method of bone formation is responsible for converting these cartilage models into true bones. This process might be compared with the building of a bridge, in which a temporary wooden frame is erected first, and then gradually is replaced by a permanent steel structure.

Ossification begins soon after the second month of uterine life. The first change is an increase in the size of cartilage cells in certain areas. These areas, so far as long bones are concerned, are in the center of the shaft, or diaphysis, and in each end, or epiphysis. After the cartilage cells enlarge they begin to degenerate and, eventually, leave spaces into which move the osteoblasts, or bone-forming cells. The two processes go on simultaneously; that is, destruction of cartilage and formation of bone take place in adjacent areas, as illustrated in Figure 3-3. Bone formation spreads out from the centers of ossification in the diaphysis and the epiphyses until only two thin strips of cartilage remain, one at each end of the bone between the diaphysis and the epiphyses. These strips persist as **epiphyseal cartilages** until growth

of the bone is completed, at which time these cartilages also become transformed into bone, and the epiphyses are said to be "closed." The final stages in the replacement of cartilage occur long after birth in some bones.

GROWTH OF BONE

In Circumference. Bones grow in circumference by the deposit of bone beneath the periosteum by the appositional method or side to side application of successive layers. The deeper layer of the periosteum is composed of osteoblasts, which are responsible for the new bone that is formed (Fig. 3-4). As new bone is formed on the external surface, other cells called *osteoclasts* dissolve the bony tissue adjacent to the medullary cavity and in this way enlarge the marrow cavity to keep pace with the increase in circumference of the shaft.

In Length. Bones grow in length due to the activity of the cartilage cells in the epiphyseal cartilages and the replacement of these by osteoblasts. As ossification occurs in the cartilage adjacent to the shaft of the bone, new cartilage cells are formed at the distal end. The length of the shaft is increased in this manner, and growth in length continues until the epiphyses are closed, which means that all the cartilage has been transformed into bone. Cessation of growth in bones occurs at about 18 years in females and soon after 20 in males. An immature long bone is illustrated in Figure 3-5.

Certain *hormones,* chemical messengers produced by the endocrine glands, play a very prominent role in promoting or in inhibiting the growth of bone. For example, if there is an excessive amount of the pituitary "growth hormone," bones may continue to grow for a prolonged period of time. The resulting condition is referred to as *gigantism.*

"Bone-age" studies are often an important diagnostic tool in the evaluation of endocrine disturbances. X-ray pictures of the long bones of a child will show the presence of epiphyseal cartilages; they appear as dark lines on the relatively white

How a layer of bone is formed on a surface
(Appositional growth)

Fibrous layer
Osteogenic layer } of periosteum

Bone

Osteogenic cells proliferate
by mitosis

Fibrous layer unchanged

Deeper cells of thickened
osteogenic layer differentiate

into

osteoblasts, which begin to
form intercellular substance.

When surrounded by it they
are called osteocytes.

Bone

Fig. 3-4. Diagram of the process whereby bone increases in circumference. New layers of bone are produced by cells of the osteogenic layer of periosteum in appositional growth. (Modified from Ham, A. W.: Histology, ed. 2, Philadelphia, Lippincott)

Fig. 3-5. Immature bone. The epiphyseal cartilages separating the individual bone elements are shown. (A) Femur, showing diaphysis and epiphyses for head, trochanter and the lower end of the bone. (B) Hip bone; the epiphyseal cartilages at which growth is taking place between the ilium, the ischium and the pubis are shown. The relation of these parts in the formation of the acetabulum is indicated clearly. (C) Sacrum. Five individual vertebral elements which later fuse to form the sacrum are here shown separated by cartilages.

bone, since cartilage is of a lesser density. Normally, these cartilage bands become smaller and smaller as ossification proceeds, and an expert can tell the age of a child by just looking at x-ray pictures of the bones (Fig. 3-46). In certain abnormal conditions, however, the cartilage bands may continue to grow, and a youngster with a chronologic age of 12 years, for example, may have a "bone age" of only 8 years.

STRUCTURAL DETAILS

Composition of bone

Bone, or osseous connective tissue, is no different from other tissues insofar as it is maintained by living cells. However, we all know from personal experience that bone is hard and cannot be cut with a knife, while other tissues are soft and pliable. Therefore, the essential difference must lie in the composition of the *intercellular substance,* or *matrix.*

Osteocytes, or bone cells, are responsible for the maintenance of this matrix which is composed of various organic and inorganic constituents. The chief organic constituent is *collagen,* and the chief inorganic constituent is *calcium phosphate.* However, calcium is also present as carbonate and fluoride; magnesium and sodium are other inorganic components of bone.

These salts are constantly being deposited and constantly being withdrawn as the bone plays a part in maintaining the normal level of calcium in the blood stream. Various hormones, which we shall study at a later time, exert great influence on this continuous interchange of inorganic salts. For example, if the parathyroid glands are too active, the amount of calcium in the blood stream rises sharply. To meet this demand there may be a massive withdrawal of calcium from the bones, leaving them weak and subject to spontaneous fractures. **Fracture** is a term that refers to any break in a bone. It may be complete or only partial.

While the inorganic constituents make up approximately two thirds of the solid material in bone, the organic matter is no less important. If a

fresh bone is placed in dilute nitric acid, the inorganic salts will be removed. The remaining material still resembles a bone, but it is so flexible or "rubbery" that it can be tied in a knot. On the other hand, if a bone is placed over a hot flame, the organic matter will be removed, and the remaining bone is so brittle that it crumbles at the slightest touch. The conclusion to be drawn is obvious: there must be appropriate amounts of both organic and inorganic constituents if one is to have functional bone tissue for support and protection.

In *rickets* there is defective calcification of bones due to a disturbance in mineral metabolism. The bones remain soft, a condition which may result in bowlegs and malformations of the head, the chest and the pelvis. The cure and the prevention of rickets hinge on the intake of liberal amounts of calcium, phosphorus and vitamin D in the diet.

Thinking in terms of early bone formation and growth it is easy to understand why the bones of children normally contain more organic matter and less inorganic matter than the bones of adults. Consequently, since young bones are so much more flexible and less brittle, it stands to reason that children can better tolerate a tumble to the sidewalk. If a child's bone should happen to be fractured it would probably resemble the "splitting" that one encounters when trying to remove a branch from a growing bush; thus, the term *"green stick fracture"* is often used in such cases.

As one grows older the amount of inorganic matter increases in proportion to the organic matter. It is for this reason that the bones of the aged tend to be more brittle, to break easily, and to heal very slowly. Far more fractured hips are seen today than were seen a generation ago, since more people are living to a "ripe old age."

The haversian systems

One of the basic principles of physiology is that all living cells must constantly receive nourishment and eliminate waste products resulting from their metabolic processes. Osteocytes, the living bone cells, are no exception to this rule even

Outer circumferential lamellae

Fibrous layer of periosteum

Osteogenic layer of periosteum

Lacunae containing osteocytes

Canaliculi

Interstitial lamellae

Haversian system

Volkmann's canal

Haversian canal

Inner circumferential lamellae

Endosteum lining the marrow cavity

Blood vessels into marrow

Fig. 3-6. Haversian systems as seen in wedge-shaped section from a mature long bone drawn in three dimensions. The fibrous and osteogenic layers of periosteum, osteocytes in lacunae, haversian canals and Volkmann's canals are shown. Circumferential lamellae are shown at the boundaries, the outer toward the periosteum, and the inner toward the marrow cavity. Interstitial lamellae are shown between the haversian systems; these lamellae probably are the remains of former haversian systems. (Modified from Ham, A. W.: Histology, ed. 2, Philadelphia, Lippincott)

though they are surrounded by calcified intercellular substance. Fantastic systems of tiny canals permeate bone tissue and convey materials to and from every single osteocyte. These microscopic, functional units are known as haversian systems (Fig. 3-6).

When bone formation gets under way, the osteoblasts proceed to supervise the deposition of calcium salts on all sides, thus tending to wall themselves off in little lakes, or **lacunae** (Fig. 3-7). To prevent complete isolation, they send out little extensions of their cytoplasm (somewhat resembling the tentacles of an octopus). As the inorganic salts continue to be deposited, the presence of these cytoplasmic processes keeps microscopic channels, or **canaliculi**, open for the movement of tissue fluid. When bone formation is complete, the osteoblasts withdraw their little processes, but the bony tunnels remain. Unable to leave the lacunae, the osteoblasts, now referred to as **osteocytes**, assume the role of "maintenance cells" and supervise the constant interchange of inorganic salts in healthy adult bone.

The canaliculi extending from one lake, or lacuna, communicate with those from neighboring lacunae and form a network of permeating channels throughout the matrix (Fig. 3-8). This network has final connections with the central or **haversian canal** which contains the all-important blood vessels essential for the delivery of nutrients and the pick-up of wastes which move back and forth through the canaliculi according to the varying needs of the osteocytes.

Further examination of bone tissue will show that osteocytes are arranged in layers; one such layer of cells, together with the matrix around them, forms a sheet called a **lamella**. The lamella may then be arranged in one of two general designs, each of which gives rise to a characteristic type of bone structure. The first type is **cancellous** or *spongy bone,* in which the lamellae are arranged as a scaffolding or latticework of needle-shaped spicules of bone, with marrow-filled spaces between (Fig. 3-2). The second type is **compact bone,** in which the lamellae are arranged to form an apparently solid mass, as shown in Figure 3-6.

Fig. 3-7. Bone cells or osteocytes lying within lacunae in the matrix. ×700.

Fig. 3-8. Lacunae and canaliculi from dried bone (cut parallel with the lamellae). ×300.

Compact bone appears along lines of stress in the shaft of long bones and forms a protective outer shell in others. It is extremely strong and provides sturdy support as well as protection. Cancellous bone, on the other hand, is lighter in weight. It is found under the compact shell in short, flat, and irregular bones, and at the epiphyses of long bones where a relatively large area is needed for articulations. Were it not for this rather light but strong type of osseous tissue our bones would be unduly heavy.

Bone marrow

This interesting material arises from early embryonic structures and invades the cartilage as it is being replaced by bone. In adult bone, two types of marrow are present: red and yellow. *Yellow marrow* is found, especially, in the medullary cavities of long bones and consists largely of adipose tissue. *Red marrow* is found in the bodies of the vertebrae, diploë of the cranial bones, the sternum, the ribs and the proximal epiphyses of femur and humerus. The red marrow consists of a large number of cells contained in the meshes of a delicate connective tissue which is abundantly supplied with blood vessels.

Some of the *functions* of red bone marrow are:

1. Formation of the red blood cells which are so important in the transport of oxygen and carbon dioxide

2. Formation of some of the white blood cells (granular leukocytes), the most active of our "infection fighters"

3. Formation of thrombocytes, or platelets, which aid in the clotting of blood

4. Phagocytosis, the destruction of old, worn-out red blood cells and foreign particles

Red marrow is the only source of red blood cells and granular leukocytes after birth; consequently, improper functioning may lead to abnormalities such as certain types of anemia. In some areas, red marrow is changed to yellow marrow by the invasion of fat cells. This begins soon after birth, and, in the adult, red marrow is found only in those areas mentioned previously.

Coverings and blood supply

Our bones are almost completely covered with a dense fibrous membrane called the **periosteum,** the only exception being the joint, or articular, surface. Those areas where bones come into contact with each other (in freely movable joints) are covered with a cushion of hyaline cartilage referred to as the **articular cartilage** (Fig. 3-1). The periosteum is firmly attached by small thread-like fibers (of Sharpey) which actually penetrate the bone. Ligaments and tendons are also anchored securely to bone as their fibers interlace with those of the periosteum. The inner layer of the periosteum gives rise to the osteoblasts which are so important in the early growth of bone as well as in the repair of fractures which may occur when our bones are subjected to undue stress.

In addition to its aforementioned functions, the periosteum also plays an important role in the nourishment of bone tissue as a whole. Numerous **periosteal blood vessels** enter the bone through tiny openings (Volkmann's canals) which in turn connect with the central canals of the microscopic haversian systems (Fig. 3-6). The medullary cavity of long bones is supplied with blood by way of the **nutrient** or **medullary artery,** which enters the shaft at an oblique angle (Fig. 3-1). It then sends branches upward, downward, and into the adjacent bony tissue to *anastomose* (join) with the haversian vessels. Similar arteries supply the central parts of short, flat and irregular bones. Lymphatic vessels and nerves also have been traced into the substance of bone, offering even further proof that we are dealing with vital, dynamic tissue! And, like any other tissue of the body, a bone may become infected. The resulting inflammation of the bone and its marrow is called *osteomyelitis,* a very serious condition.

DESCRIPTIVE TERMS

When one examines the various bones of the skeleton it will be noted that many of them have marked projections, or processes. Some have depressions, or even a hole which further helps in their identification. Familiarity with the following

Fig. 3-9. The skeleton. The bones of the head and the trunk forming the axial skeleton, are shown in blue; and those of the extremities forming the appendicular skeleton, are shown in yellow.

terms should prove to be helpful when studying the bones.

head: a rounded end which extends from a constricted portion, or neck, and fits into a joint. For example, the *head of the femur,* or thigh bone (Fig. 3-52).

condyle: a slightly rounded projection for articulation (at a joint) with another bone. For example, the *condyles of the femur* which articulate with the tibia, or shin bone (Fig. 3-52).

crest: a ridge of bone to which muscles are attached. For example, the flaring upper border of the hip bone, the *iliac crest* (Fig. 3-47).

spine or spinous process: a relatively sharp projection for muscle attachments. For example, one can feel the *spinous processes* of the vertebrae just under the skin of the back (Figs. 3-30 and 3-31).

trochanter: a very large process to which muscles are attached. This is used to identify two large projections near the upper end of the femur, the *greater and the lesser trochanters* (Fig. 3-52).

tubercle: a small rounded projection for muscle attachment. For example, at the upper end of the humerus, or arm bone, one can find the *lesser tubercle* (Fig. 3-42).

tuberosity: a large, roughened projection to which muscles attach. For example, the *tuberosities of the ischium* (lower hip bone) help to bear the weight of your body as you sit in a chair while reading these lines (Fig. 3-47).

foramen: a hole in a bone. For example, the *foramen magnum* in the occipital bone of the skull (Fig. 3-15), through which the spinal cord passes.

fossa: a shallow or hollow place in a bone. For example, the *olecranon fossa* at the lower end of the humerus (Fig. 3-42).

sinus: an air-filled cavity in a bone. For example, the *maxillary sinus* in the upper jaw (Fig. 3-19).

meatus: a tube-shaped opening in a bone. For example, the external *auditory,* or *acoustic, meatus* which is the canal leading to the tympanic membrane (Fig. 3-13).

Other examples of projections and depressions will be encountered as you study the individual bones of the body.

THE SKELETON AS A WHOLE

The adult human skeleton is composed of 206 bones (excluding the small sesamoid bones which are variable). A greater number of bones may be seen in the skeleton of a newborn baby, but during normal growth and development some of these bones fuse, or unite, to form just one bone where previously there had been several.

For purposes of study, the skeleton is divided into two main parts. Logically, these divisions are as follows:

1. *The axial skeleton,* which is composed of the bones of the skull, the thorax and the vertebral column. These bones, 80 in number, form the *axis* of the body.

2. *The appendicular skeleton,* which consists of the bones of the shoulder, the upper extremities, the hips and the lower extremities. These bones, 126 in number, are attached to the axial skeleton as *appendages.*

The divisions of the skeleton are presented in color in Figure 3-9—the axial portion in blue, the appendicular in yellow. Details of individual bones will be shown at appropriate intervals as they are presented for consideration.

Study of the bones is much more interesting if one can locate the bones in his own body and, insofar as possible, feel their general outline. Examination of an actual skeleton also is quite helpful. *Osteology,* or the study of bones, is a distinct science in itself, so the following descriptions will necessarily be limited to those features which are most outstanding.

THE AXIAL SKELETON

Bones of the skull

A close examination of the skull will reveal 28 distinct bones. This number includes the 6 small bones of the middle ears which are concerned with the transmission of sound waves; they will be described in Chapter 10 on special senses. The remaining bones form the framework of the head and provide excellent protection for such important organs as the brain, the eyes and the

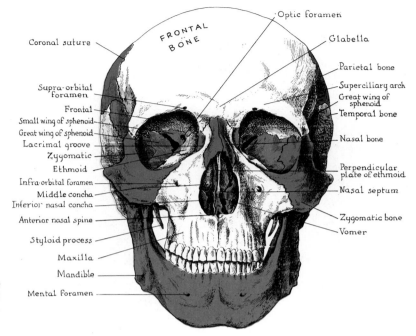

Coronal suture —
Supra-orbital foramen —
Frontal —
Small wing of sphenoid —
Great wing of sphenoid —
Lacrimal groove —
Zygomatic —
Ethmoid —
Infra-orbital foramen —
Middle concha —
Inferior nasal concha —
Anterior nasal spine —
Styloid process —
Maxilla —
Mandible —
Mental foramen —

FRONTAL BONE

Optic foramen
Glabella
Parietal bone
Superciliary arch
Great wing of sphenoid
Temporal bone
Nasal bone
Perpendicular plate of ethmoid
Nasal septum
Zygomatic bone
Vomer

Fig. 3-10. Anterior view of the skull, showing some of the cranial bones, the facial bones, the orbits, and part of the nasal cavity.

ears. With the exception of the lower jaw bone, which is freely movable, the skull bones are joined together and immovably fixed in position. These joints, or *sutures,* are described on page 78. To facilitate study, the bones of the skull will be considered in the following subdivisions: *the cranium,* (or brain box), *superficial bones of the face, and deeper bones of the face.*

1. The cranium

1 frontal	1 occipital
2 parietal	1 sphenoid
2 temporal	1 ethmoid

The frontal bone (Figs. 3-10 to 3-12) is shaped somewhat like a scoop; it forms the anterior roof of the skull, the forehead, and assists in the formation of the roof of the orbital and the nasal cavities. The *supraorbital margins* are arched rims of bone above the orbit where they afford consider-

able protection to the eye. They can be felt through the skin in the region of the eyebrows. The *superciliary ridges* are elevations above the orbital margins. Beneath these, within the bone, are the *frontal sinuses,* or air-filled cavities, which communicate with the nasal cavities.

The parietal bones, somewhat saucer-shaped, form much of the top and the sides of the cranium (Figs. 3-10 and 3-11).

The temporal bones are relatively complicated bones which form part of the sides and part of the base of the skull (Figs. 3-10 and 3-11). They articulate with the lower jaw, or mandible. For ease of description, each bone shall be divided into 4 parts: squamous, tympanic, mastoid and petrous (Figs. 3-12 to 3-14).

a. **Squamous portion:** a thin, flat plate of bone at the side of the skull. The *zygomatic process* projects forward from the lower lateral surface and articulates with the temporal process of the zygomatic, or cheek bone, to form the *zygomatic*

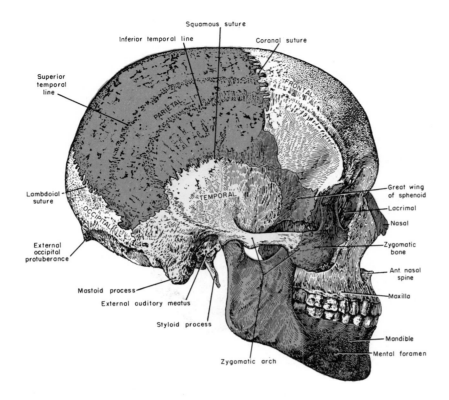

Fig. 3-11. Lateral view of the skull, showing some of the cranial and facial bones and sutures.

arch. The inferior surface is occupied largely by the *mandibular fossa* which receives the articular condyle of the mandible. This freely movable joint enables one to move the lower jaw when eating and talking.

b. **Tympanic portion:** a curved plate, inferior to the squamous portion. It makes up part of the wall of the *external acoustic meatus,* or bony canal of the external ear. This canal is closed at its medial end by the tympanic membrane.

c. **Mastoid portion:** posterior to the squamous and tympanic areas. The *mastoid process* projects downward immediately behind the external meatus; it contains many air spaces, referred to as *mastoid air cells,* which communicate with the middle ear. Infection of the latter (otitis media) may extend into the air cells causing *mastoiditis.* Only a thin plate of bone separates these air cells from the coverings of the brain, and infection may result in serious complications.

d. **Petrous portion:** a wedge-shaped mass of bone constituting part of the base of the skull. It contains the essential organs of hearing and position sense. On the cranial side can be seen the *internal acoustic meatus,* a foramen which allows passage of the facial and the acoustic nerves on their way to the brain. The *styloid process* projects downward from the inferior surface of the bone.

The occipital bone forms the back and a large part of the base of the skull (Figs. 3-11 and 3-12).

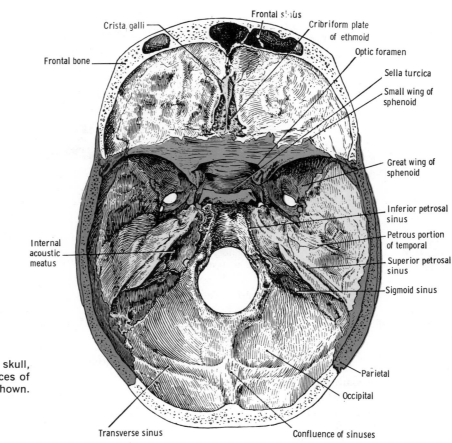

Crista galli

Frontal bone

Frontal sinus

Cribriform plate of ethmoid

Optic foramen

Sella turcica

Small wing of sphenoid

Great wing of sphenoid

Inferior petrosal sinus

Petrous portion of temporal

Superior petrosal sinus

Sigmoid sinus

Internal acoustic meatus

Parietal

Occipital

Transverse sinus

Confluence of sinuses

Fig. 3-12. View of base of skull, from above. The internal surfaces of some of the cranial bones are shown.

The *foramen magnum* is a large opening through which the spinal cord communicates with the brain (Fig. 3-15). On each side of the foramen magnum are the smooth *condyles* for articulation with the *atlas,* or first bone in the vertebral column. Nodding of the head, forward and backward, will demonstrate the action of this joint. The *external occipital protuberance* is a prominent elevation on the posterior aspect of the bone, in the midline. It can be felt as a definite bump just under the skin. The *superior nuchal line* is a curved ridge of bone passing laterally from the protuberance to the mastoid portion of the temporal bone.

The sphenoid bone is sometimes referred to as the "keystone" due to its central location and to its articulations with all of the other cranial bones (Figs. 3-12 and 3-14). When seen from above, the sphenoid fills the space between the orbital plates of the frontal bone anteriorly, the temporal and the occipital bones posteriorly. It bears some resemblance to a bat with its wings extended (Fig. 3-16). The middle portion or *body* contains the *sphenoid sinuses,* or air cells, which open into the nasal cavity. The upper surface presents a marked depression in the form of a saddle called the *sella turcica;* the pituitary gland lies in this depression. Extending laterally from the body are the 2 *great wings* and, above them, the 2 *small wings.* Projecting downward from the undersurface of the body and forming part of the lateral walls of the nasal cavity are the 2 *pterygoid processes.* These

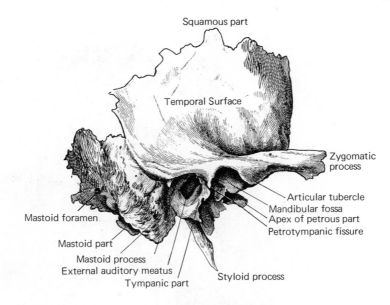

Squamous part

Temporal Surface

Zygomatic process

Articular tubercle
Mandibular fossa
Apex of petrous part
Petrotympanic fissure

Mastoid foramen

Mastoid part

Mastoid process
External auditory meatus
Tympanic part

Styloid process

Fig. 3-13. External view of right temporal bone.

would correspond to the "feet" of this bat-shaped bone.

The ethmoid bone is a light, cancellous bone located between the orbital cavities. Looking at the base of the skull from above (Fig. 3-12) one can see the *horizontal*, or *cribriform, plate*, which forms the roof of the nasal cavities and part of the base of the cranium. From the upper surface of this plate extends the *crista galli* (cock's comb), a triangular projection which provides a place for the attachment of the covering of the brain. Closer inspection of this plate will reveal many small openings, the *olfactory foramina*, through which pass the nerves of smell on their way to the brain. An anterior view of the skull (Fig. 3-10) will reveal the *perpendicular plate* as it forms the upper part of the nasal *septum*, or partition, which separates the nasal cavities. On each side, the *lateral masses* (Fig. 3-17) enter into the formation of the orbital cavity and lateral wall of the nose. They contain the *ethmoid sinuses*, or air cells, which open into the nasal cavities. Two scroll-like ridges of bone, the *superior* and the *middle conchae*, or *turbinates*, project medially from the lateral masses and serve to increase the total surface area of the nasal cavities (Fig. 3-18).

2. Superficial bones of the face

2 nasal   2 maxillae
2 zygomatic   1 mandible

The nasal bones are small oblong bones, which lie side by side, forming the so-called bridge of the nose (Fig. 3-10). The anterior portion of the nose, with which we are most familiar, is composed of cartilage and skin.

The zygomatic bone is the cheek bone, located at the upper and lateral part of the face (Fig. 3-10). In addition to forming the prominence of the cheek, it enters into formation of part of the lateral wall and the floor of the orbital cavity. It articulates posteriorly with the zygomatic process of the temporal bone. This union forms the prominent *zygomatic arch* which can be felt on the side of the face in front of the ear.

Maxilla is the term used in reference to the upper jaw as a whole. However, there are actually two *maxillae* which fuse in the midline (Fig. 3-10). They not only form part of the floor of the orbital cavities, but also the *horizontal*, or *palatine*, *processes* form the anterior three fourths of the roof of the mouth, or *hard palate*. Faulty union of these bones may result in a congenital

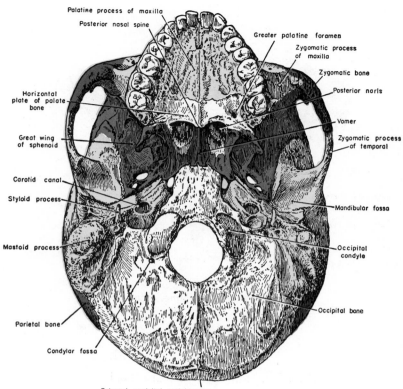

Palatine process of maxilla

Posterior nasal spine

Greater palatine foramen

Zygomatic process of maxilla

Zygomatic bone

Posterior naris

Horizontal plate of palate bone

Vomer

Zygomatic process of temporal

Great wing of sphenoid

Carotid canal

Styloid process

Mandibular fossa

Mastoid process

Occipital condyle

Occipital bone

Parietal bone

Condylar fossa

External occipital protuberance

Fig. 3-14. Base of the skull from below, with the lower jaw removed, showing some of the cranial bones and the bony roof of the mouth.

Superior nuchal line

External occipital protuberance

Inferior nuchal line

External occipital crest

Foramen magnum

Condyle

Jugular process

Jugular notch

Pharyngeal tubercle

Condyloid canal

Hypoglossal canal (probe in canal)

Fig. 3-15. External aspect of the occipital bone.

Fig. 3-16. The sphenoid bone, anterior view.

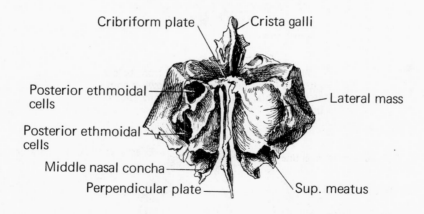

Fig. 3-17. The ethmoid bone, posterior
view. The left lateral mass has been opened
to show the posterior ethmoidal air cells or
sinuses.

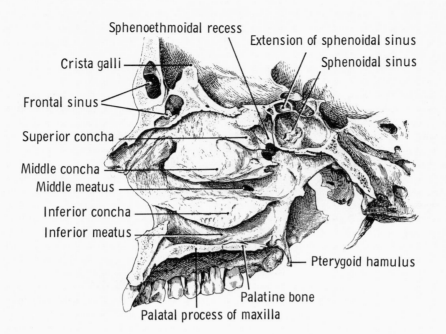

Fig. 3-18. Inner aspect of the lateral wall of the right nasal fossa.

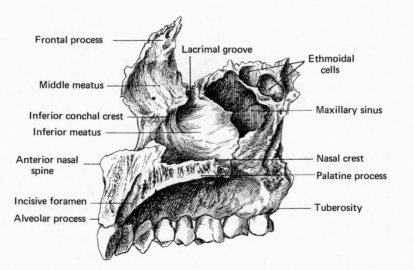

Fig. 3-19. Right maxilla, inner aspect, showing some of the ethmoidal cells and the maxillary sinus.

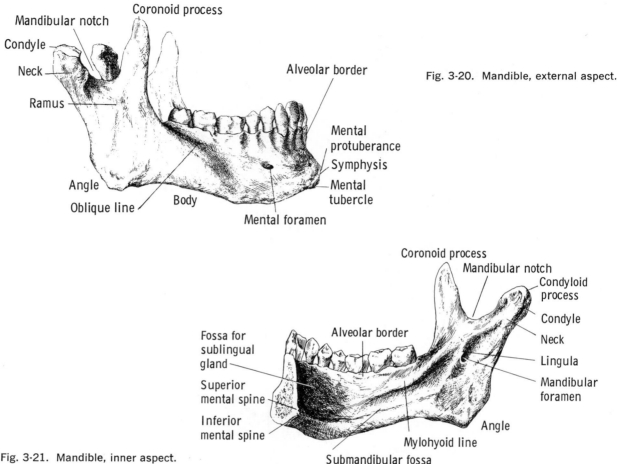

Fig. 3-20. Mandible, external aspect.

Fig. 3-21. Mandible, inner aspect.

deformity known as *cleft palate* in which there is an opening in the roof of the mouth. Infants born with this defect have difficulty in nursing, since their mouths communicate with the nasal cavities above, and air, rather than milk, is sucked in. The anterior and lateral aspects of the central portion, or *body,* form part of the face below the eye and above the teeth. On the medial aspect, the body forms part of the lateral wall of the nasal cavity. The *maxillary sinus,* or *antrum of Highmore,* is a large air space inside the body (Fig.

3-19); it opens into the nasal cavity. The *alveolar process* contains sockets for the upper teeth.

The mandible, or lower jaw, is the largest bone of the face (Figs. 3-11 and 3-20). Its horseshoe-shaped central portion is referred to as the *body,* and the upper margin or alveolar process contains sockets for the lower teeth. The *mental foramen* permits the passage of nerves and blood vessels to the chin. Extending upward from the posterior portion of the body are 2 *rami* (singular, *ramus*). Two prominent processes can be noted on top of

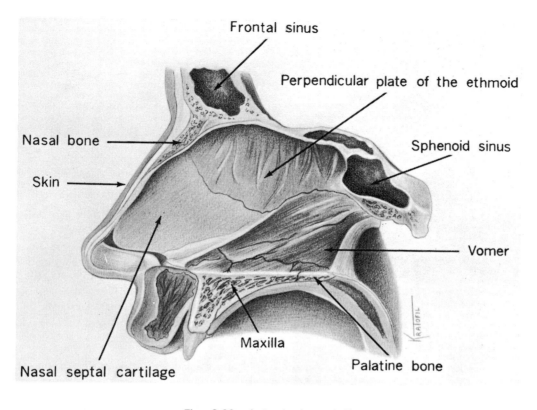

Frontal sinus

Perpendicular plate of the ethmoid

Nasal bone

Sphenoid sinus

Skin

Vomer

Maxilla

Nasal septal cartilage

Palatine bone

Fig. 3-22. Lateral view of the nasal septum showing relationship of bony and cartilaginous structures.

each ramus. The posterior or *condyloid process* articulates with the temporal bone to form the *temporomandibular joint,* the only movable joint of the skull. If a finger is placed just in front of the opening of the external ear, the condyle of the mandible can be felt sliding back and forth during movements of the lower jaw. The anterior or *coronoid process* provides a point of attachment for some of the muscles that move the jaw. On the inner side of the ramus is the *mandibular foramen* through which nerves and blood vessels pass to the lower teeth (Fig. 3-21). At birth, the mandible consists of 2 parts, but these fuse into one bone

during the first year. It undergoes several changes in shape as teeth erupt for the first and then the second time. In old age, after the teeth are lost, the alveolar process is absorbed, and the chin appears more prominent.

3. Deeper bones of the face

2 lacrimal   2 palatine
1 vomer   2 inferior conchae

The lacrimal bones are thin, fragile bones, about the size of a fingernail. They lie in the front part of the medial wall of the orbital cavity, just lateral

Fig. 3-23. Six children with microcephaly from the same family. (From Bartalos, M.:
Genetics in Medical Practice. Philadelphia, J. B. Lippincott, 1968)

and posterior to the nasal bones. Each lacrimal bone contains a groove which is part of the *lacrimal canal* from the orbit to the nasal cavity; the tear duct passes through this canal.

The **vomer,** shaped roughly like the blade of a plow, forms the lower back part of the nasal septum. It lies between the perpendicular plate of the ethmoid above and the maxillary and palatine bones below (Figs. 3-10 and 3-22).

The **palatine bones** are generally described as being L-shaped, but it must be kept in mind that the one on the left is reversed (i.e., ⌐). These bones are located at the back part of the nasal cavities between the maxillae and the pterygoid processes of the sphenoid. The upper end of each bone forms part of the floor of the orbital cavity; the upright portion forms part of the lateral wall of the nasal cavity; the horizontal section forms part of the floor of the nasal cavity and the posterior fourth of the hard palate (Fig. 3-14).

The **inferior conchae,** or *turbinates,* extend horizontally along the lateral wall of the nasal cavities (Fig. 3-18). Each is composed of a thin plate of

bone which is slightly curled upon itself, hence the expression "scroll-like" in shape.

The cranial sutures

Immovable articulations between the various cranial bones are referred to as sutures. The following may be seen either in Figure 3-11 or in Figure 3-24: (1) *coronal,* between the frontal and the parietal bones; (2) *lambdoidal,* between the parietal and the occipital bones; (3) *sagittal,* between the two parietal bones; and (4) *squamosal,* between part of the temporal and the parietal bones. These are the major sutures of the skull. In the newborn infant there is a frontal suture between the two halves of frontal bone; however, these halves unite in the second year, and the frontal suture is mentioned only to facilitate understanding of the anterior fontanel which is described below. Premature ossification of the sutures results in an abnormal smallness of the head, or *microcephaly* (Fig. 3-23). Such individuals are idiots as they have an arrested growth

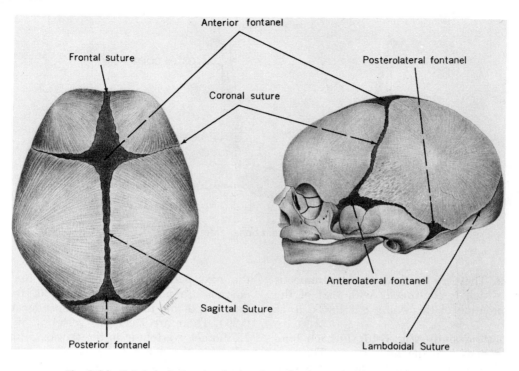

Fig. 3-24. Fetal skull showing fontanels and sutures. Left: superior aspect.
Right: lateral aspect.

of the brain as well as an arrested growth of the skull.

The fontanels

As mentioned previously (p. 61), ossification of the cranial bones is not yet complete at birth. The unossified membranous areas are referred to as fontanels. There are 6 such fontanels at the angles of the parietal bones (Fig. 3-24). The largest is the *anterior* fontanel, a diamond-shaped area at the junction of the sagittal, coronal, and frontal sutures; it usually closes at about 18 months of age. The *posterior* fontanel is a triangular space at the junction of the sagittal and lambdoidal sutures; it closes in about 6 to 8 weeks. The anterolateral fontanels, on each side, are at the junction of the frontal, the parietal, the sphenoid and the temporal bones. Similarly, the *posterolateral* fontanels are located at the junction of the temporal, the parietal and the occipital bones. The

lateral fontanels close within a few months after birth. The unossified cranial sutures and fontanels are of great importance during the birth of a baby. They allow for a certain amount of overriding of the cranial bones and a temporary molding of the baby's head as it passes through the narrow birth canal.

The air sinuses

You will recall that during the description of the bones of the skull it was noted that 4 of the cranial bones and 1 of the face bones contain air spaces, or *sinuses*. These spaces tend to decrease the weight of the skull and are important as resonance chambers in the production of voice. They may be divided into 2 groups:

1. **The paranasal sinuses** (Fig. 15-2), which communicate with the nasal cavity, include the *frontal*, the *maxillary*, the *sphenoid* and the *eth-*

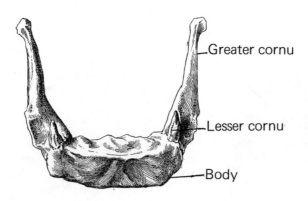

Greater cornu

Lesser cornu

Body

Fig. 3-25. The hyoid bone, anterior view.

moid sinuses. They are lined with ciliated mucous membrane which is continuous with that of the nose. Inflammation of this lining is referred to as sinusitis.

2. **The mastoid sinus** (Fig. 8-16), in each temporal bone, opens into the middle ear. The mucous membrane lining of these structures is continuous with that of the nasopharynx, or superior portion of the throat. Inflammation of this sinus is referred to as mastoiditis.

The hyoid bone

The hyoid is an isolated, U-shaped bone lying in the anterior part of the neck just below the chin. It consists of a central portion, or *body,* and 2 projections on either side called the *greater* and the *lesser cornua* (Fig. 3-25). The hyoid is suspended from the styloid processes of the temporal bones by the *stylohyoid ligaments.* It serves for the attachment of certain muscles which move the tongue and aid in speaking and swallowing.

Bones of the vertebral column

The vertebral column, or backbone, of an adult consists of 26 separate bony segments arranged in series to form a strong, flexible pillar. Children have 33 or 34 vertebrae, but some of these eventually fuse to form single segments as noted in the next paragraph. The bones of the vertebral column are named and numbered, from above downward, on the basis of their location (Fig. 3-26). There are 7 cervical vertebrae in the neck, 12 thoracic vertebrae in the thorax, 5 lumbar vertebrae in the small of the back, 1 sacrum (resulting from the fusion of 5 separate vertebrae), and 1 coccyx (resulting from the fusion of 4 or 5 vertebrae).

General structure of vertebrae

Although there are characteristic differences between bones in each of the aforementioned groups, there are marked similarities in general structure. Each vertebra, with the exception of the first 2 cervical, has a drum-shaped *body* located anteriorly where it serves as the weight-bearing part. An *intervertebral disk* of compressible fibrous cartilage acts as a cushion and shock absorber between each pair of vertebrae as their bodies are piled one on the other. Extending posteriorly from the body are two short thick projections, the *pedicles.* Arising from the pedicles are a pair of broad bony plates, the *laminae;* they meet and fuse in the midline posteriorly. If the laminae fail to unite, the resulting condition is referred to as *spina bifida;* the contents of the spinal canal, either the spinal cord or its coverings, or both, may protrude. From the junction of laminae the *spinous process* arises and projects backward and downward where it can usually be felt just under the skin of the back. *Transverse processes* extend laterally from the junction of pedicle and lamina on either side. These processes, as well as the spinous process, provide places for the attachment of muscles and ligaments. The large opening in the center of each vertebra is referred to as the *vertebral,* or *spinal, foramen,* and when all of the vertebrae are arranged in series we have provided a hollow bony cylinder which surrounds and protects the spinal cord. Facilitating movement of this bony column are the smooth articular surfaces on each vertebra. Two *superior articular processes* and two *inferior articular processes* project vertically near the junction of pedicles and laminae. In action, the inferior processes of one vertebra articulate with the superior processes of the vertebra immediately below, and so on down the column. In front of each of these joints can be seen an *intervertebral foramen,* or opening, through which emerges one of the spinal nerves as it leaves the vertebral cavity. These foramina can be noted between each two vertebrae in the column (Fig. 3-26).

Regional variations of vertebrae

The Cervical Vertebrae. This part of the vertebral column is extremely flexible, permitting a wide range of movement of the head and the neck. The 7 vertebrae are smaller than those lower in the column, but the main distinguishing characteristic is the presence of 3 foramina instead of only one. In addition to the usual *vertebral foramen,* there is an opening in each transverse process called the *transverse foramen* (Fig. 3-27) through which pass the vertebral arteries on their way to the brain.

The first 2 cervical vertebrae have additional distinctive features and have been given specific names. The **atlas,** or 1st cervical (Fig. 3-28), supports the head. (It was named for the Greek god who supposedly carried the world on his shoulders.) Having no body or spinous process it is little more than a bony ring which receives, on its superior articular surface, the condyles of the

First cervical
(atlas)

First
thoracic

First
lumbar

First
sacral

First
coccygeal

Fig. 3-26. Lateral view of adult vertebral column showing curves.

Fig. 3-27. Fourth cervical vertebra, superior aspect.

Spinous process
Vertebral foramen
Lamina
Pedicle
Inferior articular process
Superior articular process
Posterior tubercle of transverse process
Transverse foramen
Costal element
Body
Anterior tubercle of transverse process

Fig. 3-28. The atlas, superior aspect.

Posterior tubercle
Posterior arch
Groove for vertebral artery
Superior articular facet
Lateral mass
Vertebral foramen
Transverse process
Transverse foramen
Costal process
Facet of odontoid process of axis
Anterior arch
Anterior tubercle

Fig. 3-29. The axis, lateral view.

Odontoid process
Anterior articular facet
Superior articular surface
Spinous process
Inferior articular surface for third cervical vertebra
Body
Costotransverse foramen

occipital bone. By means of this joint you are able to rock your skull back and forth, as in nodding agreement. The 2nd cervical vertebra is called the **axis** (Fig. 3-29), and it is easily identified by the presence of a large toothlike projection, the *odontoid process,* which arises from the body. This process fits up into the anterior part of the atlas and forms the axis of rotation. As you turn your head from side to side, the atlas moves with the skull, and the two turn on the axis with the odontoid process serving as a pivot. The 7th cervical vertebra has a very prominent spinous process which can be felt at the nape of the neck.

The Thoracic Vertebrae. These vertebrae, 12 in number, become progressively larger from above downward. Their main distinguishing characteristic is the presence of smooth areas, or *facets,* on the body and transverse processes for articulation with the ribs (Fig. 3-30).

The Lumbar Vertebrae. Nearing the end of the column are the larger, heavier, lumbar vertebrae which are well equipped for weight-bearing (Fig. 3-31). Short spinous processes, gross size, plus the absence of transverse foramina and rib facets facilitate identification of these vertebrae.

The Sacrum. Formed by the fusion of 5 sacral vertebrae, this bone resembles a somewhat concave triangle, the base articulating with the 5th lumbar vertebra, the apex extending downward, and its concave surface facing forward. Wedged between the two hip bones, the sacrum fills in the back part of the bony pelvis (Fig. 3-48). The *sacral promontory* is a prominent lip at the upper anterior margin of the *body;* it is one of the important obstetric landmarks in determining the size of a pelvis for childbirth.

The Coccyx. Attached to the apex of the sacrum, the coccyx, or tail-bone, is formed by the fusion of 4 rudimentary vertebrae. This triangular bone is the last segment of the vertebral column (Fig. 3-26).

The vertebral column as a whole

The human vertebral column is a truly versatile arrangement of bony segments which are linked in series by ligaments. Not only does it provide the strength and rigidity necessary for *support* of the head, the trunk and the upper extremities, but it is also flexible to an amazing degree. One has merely to watch an acrobatic dancer for full appreciation of the mobility of this column. In addition to its supporting function, this hollow cylinder of bones effectively surrounds and *protects* the soft spinal cord as well as the origins of the 31 pairs of spinal nerves. Therefore, fractures of the vertebrae ("broken neck" or "broken back") may result in paralysis or even death, depending on the location and the severity of the fracture. Less serious, but extremely painful, is the so-called slipped or *ruptured disk* (technically called herniation of the nucleus pulposus). In these cases, the soft central portion of an intervertebral disk is forcibly pushed into the spinal canal where it presses on the spinal cord (Fig. 3-32) or on spinal nerve roots. This condition may be caused by a fall or by improper body mechanics when lifting heavy objects.

The normal curves of the vertebral column provide some of the resilience and spring so essential in walking and jumping. In a newborn infant the whole vertebral column is concave forward, a primary curve. When the infant begins to assume the erect posture, secondary curves, or those which are concave to the rear, may be noted. The vertebral column normally presents 4 curves (Fig. 3-26). The *thoracic* and the *sacral curves* are primary curves and are present at birth. The *cervical curve* appears when the infant begins to hold up his head at about 3 months, and the *lumbar curve* appears when the infant begins to walk. Figures 3-34 and 3-35 are x-rays of normal vertebral columns.

Exaggerated curves of the vertebral column may be due to disease, injury or, in some cases, to poor posture. An increase in the thoracic curve is called *kyphosis* or "hunchback" (Fig. 3-36). An increase in the lumbar curve is referred to as *lordosis* or "swayback." A lateral curvature, called *scoliosis,* is present to some degree in most persons; however, severe cases may require corrective surgery.

Ligaments of the vertebral column help to hold the bony segments in proper position as shown in

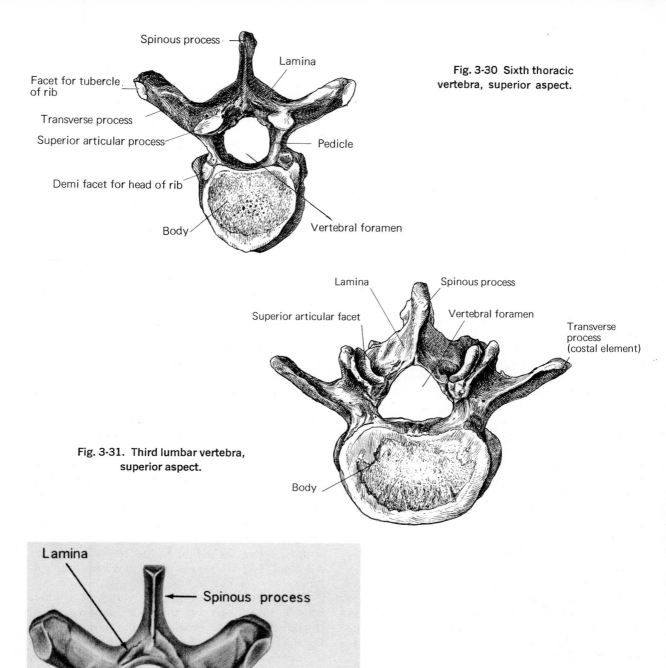

Spinous process

Lamina

Facet for tubercle of rib

Transverse process

Superior articular process

Demi facet for head of rib

Body

Pedicle

Vertebral foramen

Fig. 3-30 Sixth thoracic vertebra, superior aspect.

Lamina

Superior articular facet

Spinous process

Vertebral foramen

Transverse process (costal element)

Body

Fig. 3-31. Third lumbar vertebra, superior aspect.

Lamina

Spinous process

Spinal Cord

Intervertebral Disc

Fig. 3-32. Diagram of a ruptured intervertebral disk. The soft, central portion of the disk is shown protruding into the vertebral canal where it exerts pressure on the spinal cord.

Fig. 3-33. Sagittal section through part of the vertebral column, with the position of ligaments, intervertebral disks, bodies of vertebrae, spinous processes and intervertebral foramina indicated. (After Spalteholz)

Intervertebral disk

Body of vertebra

Ligament

Ligament

Ligament

Spinous process

Foramen for spinal nerve

Fig. 3-34. X-ray of vertebral column, lumbar and upper sacral regions. Retrograde pyelogram with ureteral catheter in place. Anteroposterior view. (From T. A. Pearson, M.D.)

Fig. 3-35. X-ray of vertebral column, lumbar region. Lateral view. Dark areas between bodies of vertebrae indicate position of intervertebral disks. (From T. A. Pearson, M.D.)

Fig. 3-36. X-ray showing kyphosis of the thoracic portion of vertebral column, with secondary changes on the anterior borders of the vertebrae. (From University of Minnesota Hospital)

Figure 3-33. These strong bands of connective tissue are somewhat extensible, and the intervertebral disks are compressible; thus, we are able to bend and to straighten our vertebral column within certain limits.

The *anterior longitudinal* ligament and the *posterior longitudinal* ligament connect the bodies of the vertebrae. They extend from the axis to the sacrum and might be compared with two long strips of adhesive tape—one extending along the anterior surface and one along the posterior surface of the vertebral bodies and disks.

Ligamenta flava are rather broad, thin ligaments which connect lamina to lamina from the axis down to the sacrum.

The *ligamentum nuchae* extends from the external occipital protuberance downward over the spinous processes to the 7th cervical vertebra. This ligament helps to support the weight of the head in four-legged animals such as cows and horses, but it is of less importance in man.

The *supraspinous ligament* connects the tips of the spinous processes from the 7th cervical vertebra downward to the sacrum.

Interspinous ligaments connect adjacent spinous processes between the tips and the lamina.

The bones of the thorax

Generally speaking, the thorax is a cone-shaped bony cage, narrow at the top and broad at its base. Twelve pairs of ribs form the bars of this cage, assisted by the sternum, or breastbone, anteriorly, and the 12 thoracic vertebrae posteriorly. It is covered with muscles and skin, and the floor is formed by the dome-shaped diaphragm. In fact, it is the upward curving of this muscular floor that makes it possible for the thorax to protect not only the heart and the lungs but also the liver and the stomach which lie immediately below the diaphragm in the upper part of the abdominal cavity. In addition to its protective function, the thorax plays an important role in the breathing process and helps to support the bones of the shoulder girdle.

The sternum lies in the midline in the front of the thorax; it is a flat, narrow bone about 6 inches

(15 cm.) long. It somewhat resembles a dagger in shape and is composed of 3 parts: the "handle" or *manubrium* above, the *body*, or gladiolus, in the middle, and the *xiphoid process*, below (Fig. 3-37). The clavicle and the first rib cartilage articulate with the manubrium, while the next 9 rib cartilages join the body, either directly or indirectly as will be described later. The point of union between the manubrium and the body forms the *sternal angle*, a relatively prominent ridge which can be felt just under the skin; it is an important landmark, since the second rib articulates with the sternum at this point. The superficial location of the sternum, as well as its structure, make it an excellent site for biopsy (examination of tissue from living subjects) of red bone marrow. This procedure is referred to as *sternal puncture* and is often of great value in the diagnosis of blood disorders such as the various types of anemia.

The ribs, 24 in number, are located 12 on each side of the thoracic cavity. They are slender, curved, and relatively flexible bones. All of the ribs are attached posteriorly to the thoracic vertebrae, but the anterior attachment varies. None of the ribs actually join the sternum directly; instead there are resilient bars of hyaline cartilage, the *costal cartilages,* which extend forward from the ends of the ribs (except the last 2 pairs) toward the sternum. The first 7 pairs of ribs are referred to as **true ribs,** since their costal cartilages actually reach the sternum. The next 3 pairs of ribs are called **false ribs,** since their costal cartilages turn upward to join the cartilage of the rib above. The last 2 pairs of ribs have no anterior attachment at all and are known as the **floating ribs** (Fig. 3-37). The spaces between the ribs are referred to as the *intercostal spaces;* muscles, blood vessels and nerves are located here.

A typical rib (Fig. 3-38) has a *head* and a tubercle which articulate with the facets on a thoracic vertebra. The *shaft* curves around the side of the chest, slanting downward and forward, making the sternal end lower than the vertebral end. The upper ribs are shorter than the lower, with the exception of the last two.

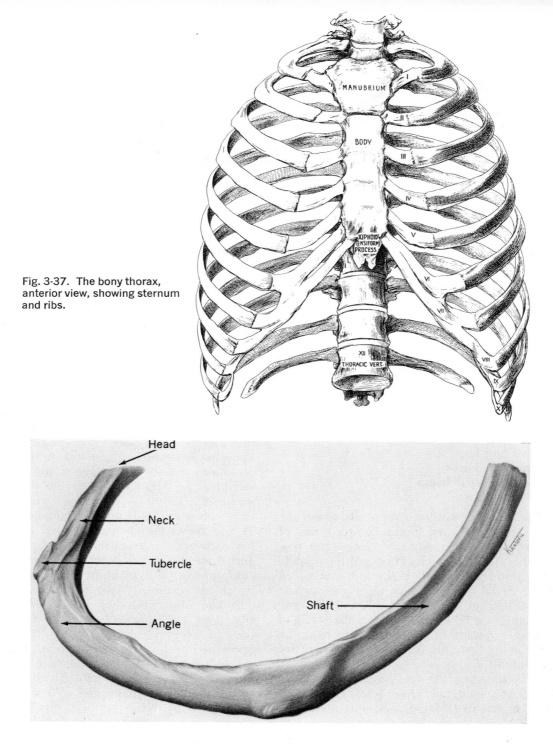

Fig. 3-37. The bony thorax, anterior view, showing sternum and ribs.

Fig. 3-38. Second rib, right side of body.

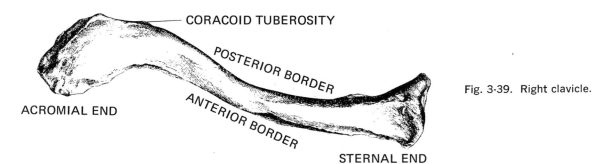

CORACOID TUBEROSITY

POSTERIOR BORDER

ANTERIOR BORDER

ACROMIAL END

STERNAL END

Fig. 3-39. Right clavicle.

THE APPENDICULAR SKELETON

Bones of the upper extremity

The 32 bones in each of the upper extremities may be divided into 4 groups for ease of study.
1. Shoulder girdle
   1 clavicle
   1 scapula
2. Arm
   1 humerus
3. Forearm
   1 ulna
   1 radius
4. Wrist and hand
   8 carpal bones
   5 metacarpal bones
   14 phalanges

1. **The Shoulder Girdle.** Despite its name, the shoulder *girdle* does not form a complete ring of bone but presents an especially large gap posteriorly between the medial border of the scapula and the vertebral column. This space is occupied by some of the muscles which move the scapula and contribute to the great mobility of the arm. The shoulder girdle serves to attach the bones of the upper extremity to the axial division of the skeleton and to provide places of attachment for many muscles.

The clavicle, or collar bone, is a slender bone with a double curvature (Fig. 3-39). It lies horizontally in the root of the neck, just above the first rib. Medially, the clavicle articulates with the sternum forming the *sternoclavicular joint,* the only bony joint between the shoulder girdle and the trunk; laterally it articulates with the acromial end of the scapula. Functionally, the clavicle serves to brace the shoulder. Fractures of this slender bone are fairly common when undue stress is applied along its shaft, as in falling heavily to one side and landing on the shoulder.

The scapula, or shoulder blade, is located on the upper back part of the thoracic cage. It is a rather flat, triangular-shaped bone which can be felt readily by reaching over the right shoulder with the left hand, placing it on the back, and then moving the right shoulder in various directions. One also may feel the prominent *spine* of the scapula (Fig. 3-40) as it passes across the upper posterior surface and ends in the large, flat *acromion process* which forms the tip of the shoulder and articulates with the clavicle. The acromion, as well as the clavicle, may be fractured when one falls on the shoulder. Figure 3-41 best shows the *glenoid cavity,* a smooth shallow socket that receives the head of the humerus. Just above the glenoid cavity can be seen the *coracoid process,* a hooked or beaklike projection, which curls forward beneath the clavicle.

2. **The Arm.** Extending from the shoulder to the elbow, the **humerus** is the largest and longest bone of the upper extremity (Fig. 3-42). At the upper end of the humerus is a rounded *head* that articulates with the glenoid cavity of the scapula, forming a ball-and-socket joint. The head is joined to the shaft by a constricted area known as the *anatomic neck.* Near this neck can be seen two eminences for muscle attachment: the *greater tubercle* on the lateral side, and the *lesser tubercle* on the anterior surface. The shaft of the humerus

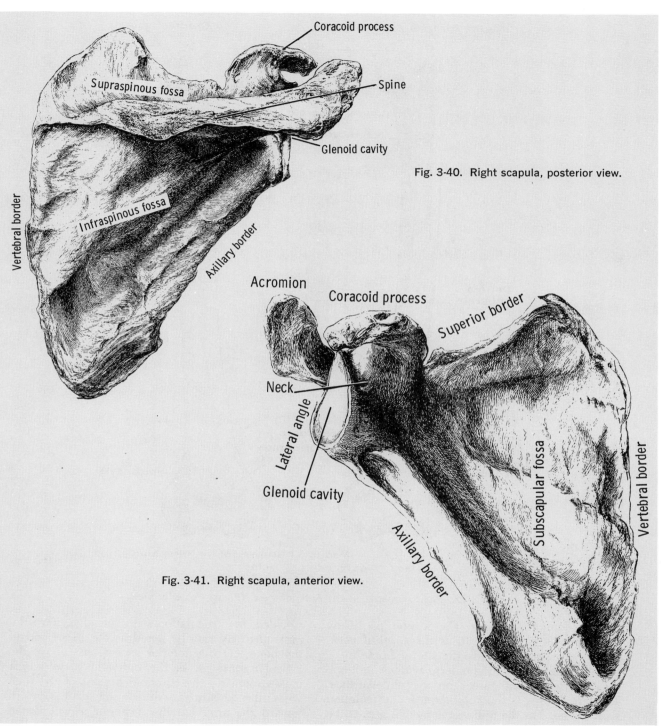

Coracoid process

Supraspinous fossa

Spine

Glenoid cavity

Fig. 3-40. Right scapula, posterior view.

Vertebral border

Infraspinous fossa

Axillary border

Acromion

Coracoid process

Superior border

Neck

Lateral angle

Glenoid cavity

Subscapular fossa

Vertebral border

Axillary border

Fig. 3-41. Right scapula, anterior view.

Fig. 3-42. Right humerus. (Left) Anterior view. (Right) Posterior view.

is rather long and slender. The portion just below the tubercles is referred to as the *surgical neck,* since it is most frequently the site of fracture.

The lower end of the humerus widens, and one can see two smooth areas on the undersurface. The lateral area is the *capitulum,* for articulation with the head of the radius; the medial area is the

trochlea, for articulation with the ulna. Two depressions may also be noted at the distal end of the bone. On the anterior aspect, just above the articular surfaces, is the *coronoid fossa* which makes room for the coronoid process of the ulna when the forearm is flexed, or bent upward toward the arm. On the posterior aspect is the

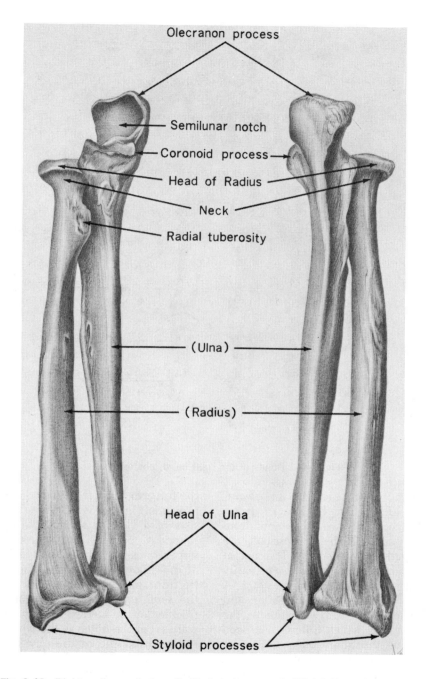

Fig. 3-43. Right radius and ulna. (Left) Anterior aspect. (Right) Posterior aspect.

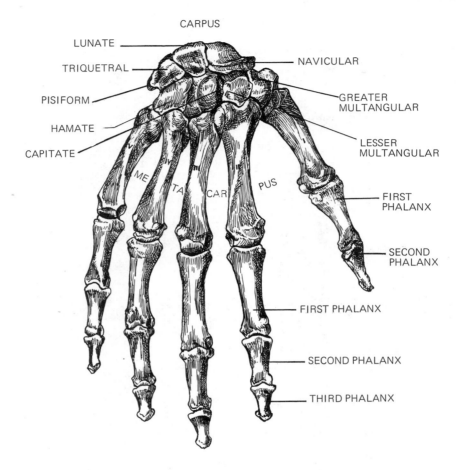

Fig. 3-44. Bones of the right hand, posterior view.

deep *olecranon fossa,* which receives the olecranon process of the ulna when the forearm is extended, or straightened. The two projections from the margins, on a line with the depressions, are the *medial* and the *lateral epicondyles.* The medial epicondyle is the more prominent and can easily be felt on the inner aspect of the elbow joint. A large nerve passes just below this projection and may be pinched when you bump your elbow; the strange tingling sensation which follows has been referred to as "hitting the funny bone."

3. **The Forearm. The ulna** lies on the medial or little finger side, of the forearm. It can be felt most easily through the skin on the posterior aspect of the forearm, from the tip of the elbow to the small projection in the wrist. The ulna (Fig. 3-43) consists of a slender shaft with an enlarged, hook-shaped upper end that is very distinctive. The upper, back part of the hook forms the prominence of the elbow and is called the *olecranon process.* In front of the olecranon is a concave surface, the *semi-lunar notch,* which articulates with the trochlea of the humerus. Curving upward and forward from the notch is the *coronoid process.*

The distal end of the ulna is small; it presents a knobbed portion, the *head,* and a downward projection on the medial side, the *styloid process.* On the lateral surface at both the upper and the

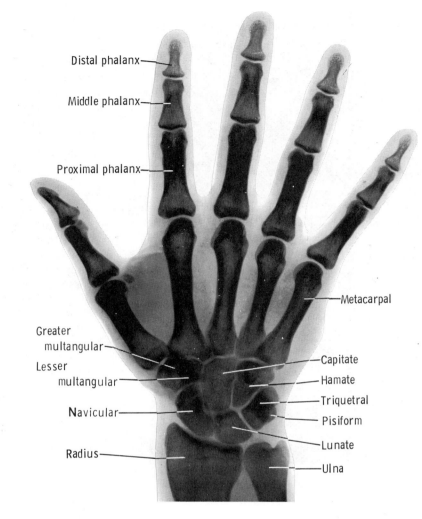

Distal phalanx

Middle phalanx

Proximal phalanx

Metacarpal

Greater
multangular

Lesser
multangular

Navicular

Radius

Capitate

Hamate

Triquetral

Pisiform

Lunate

Ulna

Fig. 3-45. X-ray of right
hand, posterior view, showing
bones. (Farris)

lower ends, are small, smooth areas for articulation with the radius. The ulna does not articulate directly with the wrist bones, but with a fibrocartilaginous disk instead.

The radius lies on the lateral, or thumb side, of the forearm. It is more difficult to feel than the ulna since it is better padded with muscles, except at the wrist. The radius consists of a shaft, with a small upper end and a large lower end (Fig. 3-43). Proximally, a disklike *head,* supported by a *neck,* articulates with the capitulum of the

humerus and the side of the ulna. The prominent *radial tuberosity* (for attachment of the biceps muscle) can be seen on the shaft just below the head. On the undersurface of the distal end is a smooth surface which articulates with two of the wrist bones and with the head of the ulna. The *styloid process* is lateral to the articular surface.

When the palm is up, or forward, the radius and the ulna are parallel; when the palm is turned down, or back, the lower end of the radius moves medially around the head of the ulna so that the

Fig. 3-46. X-ray of hand of 3-year old child, showing ossification in progress. (Temple Univ. Hosp.)

Proximal Row	Distal Row
1. navicular	5. greater multangular
2. lunate	6. lesser multangular
3. triquetral	7. capitate
4. pisiform	8. hamate

The carpal bones are bound firmly and closely together by ligaments.

The 5 **metacarpal bones** form the bony framework of the body of the hand; they are numbered from the lateral side (Fig. 3-44). These bones are relatively long and cylindrical, and their rounded distal ends form the knuckles. Proximally, the metacarpals articulate with the carpal bones and with each other; distally, they articulate with the first row of phalanges.

There are 14 **phalanges,** or finger bones, in each hand, 2 for the thumb, and 3 for each finger (Fig. 3-44). They are referred to as the first, or proximal; the second, or middle; and the third, or distal phalanx. Obviously, the thumb has only a proximal and a distal phalanx.

The carpals, the metacarpals and the phalanges (a total of 27 bones in each hand) are joined in such a way that each contributes to the dexterity and the mobility of the human hand. Of particular importance is the ability to place the thumb against the various fingers—one of many differences between man and the four-legged animals. X-ray studies of the hand are shown in Figures 3-45 and 3-46.

Bones of the Pelvis

The pelvis is a strong, bony ring somewhat resembling a basin. It is composed of 4 bones: the 2 hipbones, which form the front and the sides of the ring; the sacrum (wedged between the hipbones) and the coccyx which complete the ring posteriorly. (Note: the sacrum and the coccyx are described on page 83.)

The hipbone or **os coxae,** is a large, irregularly shaped bone. Each bone begins its development as 3 separate parts—the ilium, the ischium and the pubis. Eventually these segments fuse to form a solid bone, but the original names are retained for purposes of description. The lines of fusion are in the **acetabulum,** a prominent cup-

shafts of the 2 bones are crossed. A break in the lower third of the radius is referred to as *Colles' fracture.* It is one of the most common fractures and is caused by a fall on the palm of the hand, at which time the weight of the body is quite suddenly transmitted through the radius to the ground. The styloid process of the ulna also may be broken off due to the pull on its ligaments.

4. **The Wrist and the Hand.** The wrist contains 8 small **carpal bones,** arranged in two rows of 4 each (Fig. 3-44). Beginning on the lateral, or thumb side, in each row they are as follows:

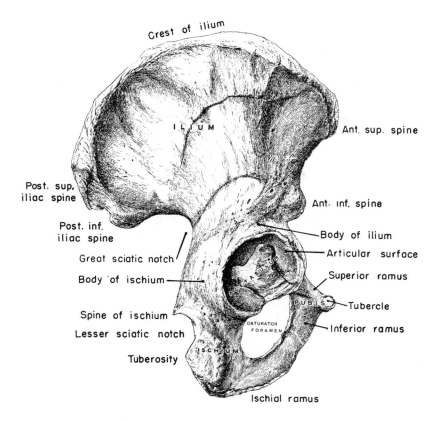

Fig. 3-47. Right hipbone, lateral aspect.

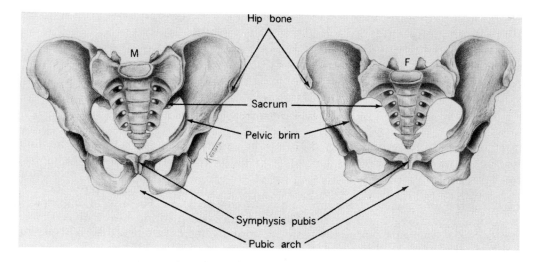

Fig. 3-48. Male and female pelves. (Left) Male pelvis, narrow, heavy and compact (Right) Female pelvis, broad, light and capacious.

Fig. 3-49. Midsagittal section of pelvis.

shaped socket on the lateral aspect (Fig. 3-47); the head of the femur articulates with the hipbone in this socket.

The upper, flared portion of the hipbone is the **ilium** which forms the prominence of the hip. The curved rim of the ilium, along the upper border, is called the *iliac crest;* this part can be felt easily near the level of the waist. At either end of the crest there are bony projections, but the more prominent one is the *anterior superior iliac spine* which serves as an important anatomic landmark

in surgery. The inner surface of the ilium is somewhat concave and contributes to the basinlike appearance of the pelvis. The articulation of the ilium with the sacrum, posteriorly, forms the *sacro-iliac joint.* The use of improper body mechanics when lifting heavy objects may result in torn ligaments around this joint—a very painful injury.

The ischium (Fig. 3-47) is the lowest and strongest portion of the hipbone. It extends downward from the acetabulum and expands into the large *ischial tuberosity* which helps to support the weight of the trunk when one sits down. Just above the tuberosity is a pointed projection, the *ischial spine,* which is an important landmark in obstetrics. A ramus, or branch, curves forward from the body of the ischium to join the pubis.

The anterior portion of the hipbone is called the **pubis.** It consists of two bars of bone, the *superior* and *inferior rami,* which meet in a flat *body.* Anteriorly, the body unites with its fellow in the mid-line, forming a joint known as the *symphysis pubis.* The *pubic arch* is the angle formed by the two inferior rami at this point. The superior ramus ascends to the ilium, and the inferior ramus descends to the ischium. The *obturator foramen* is a large hole in the hipbone, bounded by the pubis and the ischium.

The pelvis as a whole protects the urinary bladder, some of the reproductive organs, and the distal end of the large intestine; it serves also as a firm base by means of which the trunk can rest on the thighs when in a standing position, or on the ischial tuberosities when sitting down. Fractures of the pelvis are serious and painful injuries which often necessitate several weeks of rest in bed.

A curved line drawn from the sacral promontory downward and forward on each side (along the rounded ridges of the ilia) to the upper margin of the symphysis pubis helps to identify the boundaries of the *pelvic brim* (Fig. 3-48) which separates the greater from the lesser pelvis. The greater, or false, pelvis is the expanded portion above the brim, bounded by the flared portion of each ilium and by the muscular walls of the abdomen. The lesser, or true, pelvis lies below the brim; it is bounded in front and on the side by the pubis, the lower part of each ilium, and the ischium, and behind by the sacrum and the coccyx.

The true pelvis consists of an inlet, a cavity and an outlet. The *inlet,* or pelvic brim (Figs. 3-48 and 3-49), is of special importance during the birth of a baby; if any of its diameters are too small it may be impossible for the infants skull to enter the true pelvis for a "normal" or natural delivery. The cavity is a short, curved canal, considerably deeper in the region of the sacrum and

coccyx than in the region of the symphysis pubis (Fig. 3-49). The urinary bladder lies behind the symphysis pubis, and the rectum lies in the curve along the sacrum and coccyx. In women, the vagina lies between the urinary bladder and the rectum. The *outlet* is the space between the tip of the coccyx, behind, the ischial tuberosities, at the sides, and the pubic arch, in front. An x-ray of the pelvis is shown in Figure 3-50.

Differences Between the Male and the Female Pelvis. In women, the pelvis is adapted for pregnancy and childbirth, the bones being lighter and smoother, the cavity of the true pelvis roomier, the inlet and the outlet larger, and the coccyx more movable than in men. The female pelvis is broad and shallow with a wide pubic arch (greater than a right angle), while the male pelvis is narrow and deep with a pubic arch that is more pointed (less than a right angle). Figure 3-48 shows the male and the female pelves.

Bones of the lower extremity

The 30 bones of the lower extremity may be divided into 3 groups for ease of study.
1. Thigh
   1 femur
   1 patella (included here for convenience)
2. Leg
   1 tibia
   1 fibula
3. Foot
   7 tarsal bones
   5 metatarsal bones
   14 phalanges

1. **Bones of the Thigh. The femur** is the heaviest, longest and strongest bone in the body (Fig. 3-52). It transmits the entire weight of the trunk from hip to tibia and is covered so thickly with muscles it can be felt only near its ends. At the upper end of the femur is a rounded *head* supported by a constricted portion, or *neck,* which joins the cylindrical shaft at an angle. The head fits into the acetabulum of the hipbone, forming a deep articulation designed for the task of transmitting weight to the femur. The relatively long neck enables the femur to be moved freely even

Fig. 3-50. X-ray of pelvis. (From University of Minnesota Hospital)

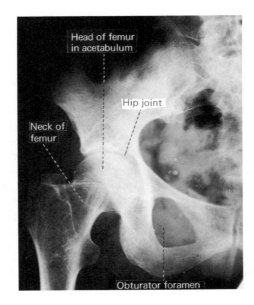

Fig. 3-51. X-ray of hip joint Arrangement of spicules visible in relation to lines of force. (From University of Minnesota Hospital)

Fig. 3-52. Right femur. (Left) Anterior aspect. (Right) Posterior aspect.

though the head is more or less buried. However, the angular junction with the shaft increases the risk of fracture, particularly in the aged person whose bones tend to become more brittle. A fracture through the neck of the femur is commonly referred to as a "broken hip." At the top of the shaft, on the lateral side, is a very large protuberance, the *greater trochanter,* which can be felt under the skin on the outer aspect of the upper thigh. The *lesser trochanter,* a smaller elevation, is on the medial side, below the neck. An x-ray of the hip joint is shown in Figure 3-51.

The *linea aspera,* a prominent ridge for the attachment of muscles, can be seen extending lengthwise on the posterior side of the shaft. At the lower end of the femur are two large, smooth bulges, the *medial* and the *lateral condyles,* which articulate with the tibia. They can be felt at the sides of the knee. The *intercondyloid fossa* is a

deep depression between the condyles posteriorly. On the anterior aspect is a smooth surface for articulation with the patella.

The patella, or knee cap (Figs. 3-53 and 3-54), forms the prominence in front of the knee. It is the largest sesamoid bone in the body and is embedded in the tendon of the quadriceps femoris (the principal anterior thigh muscle) where it crosses the knee to insert on the tibia. Its posterior surface is smooth for articulation with the femur. Functionally, the patella serves to protect the front of the knee joint, but, because of its position, it is frequently dislocated or even fractured.

2. **Bones of the Leg. The tibia,** or shin bone, is the medial and larger bone of the leg. It is second to the femur in length and transmits the weight of the trunk to the foot. The upper end of the tibia is quite broad and presents two masses of bone on either side, the *medial* and the *lateral condyles*

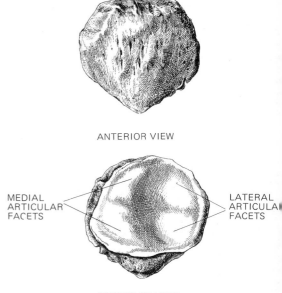

ANTERIOR VIEW

MEDIAL ARTICULAR FACETS

LATERAL ARTICULAR FACETS

POSTERIOR VIEW

Fig. 3-53. Right patella, anterior and posterior views.

Fig. 3-54. X-ray of knee. (Top, left) Anteroposterior and (top, right) lateral views in extreme extension. (Bottom) Lateral view, in extreme flexion. Position of patella is shown. (From University of Minnesota Hospital) (Farris)

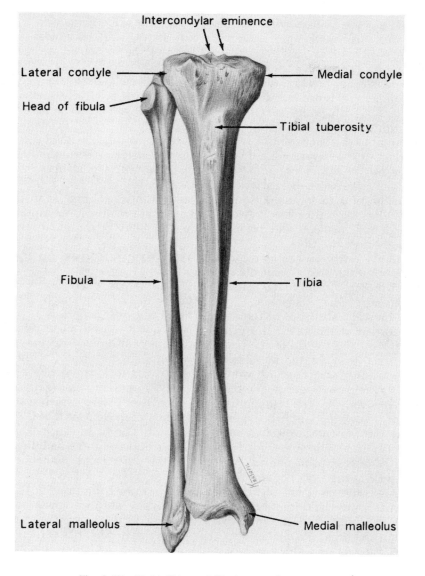

Fig. 3-55. Right tibia and fibula, anterior aspect.

(Fig. 3-55), the smooth upper surfaces of which articulate with the condyles of the femur. Between these surfaces is a projection called the *intercondylar eminence.* On the anterior surface, just below the condyles, there is a knoblike projection, called the tibial *tuberosity,* that can be felt just under the skin. The anterior border of the shaft is also quite superficial, and the overlying skin may be painfully bruised when we bump our shins.

The lower end of the tibia widens somewhat and has a smooth surface for articulation with the talus (a tarsal bone) below, and the fibula, laterally. A downward projection, the *medial malleolus,* forms the prominence on the inner aspect of the ankle; it can be identified easily as it lies just under the skin.

The fibula is a long, slender bone on the lateral side of the leg. The upper end is expanded slightly to form a *head* (Fig. 3-55) which articulates only with the tibia, not with the femur. The fibula does not enter into formation of the knee joint; it is not a weight-bearing bone. At the lower end, a downward projection, the *lateral malleolus,* forms the prominence on the outer aspect of the ankle joint by articulating with the tibia to form the side of the socket for the talus; the latter fits between the medial and the lateral malleoli and receives the weight of the body from the tibia.

Fracture of the fibula a few inches above the ankle and a splitting off of the medial malleolus of the tibia is referred to as *Pott's fracture;* it is usually caused by a sudden, sharp turn of the ankle.

3. **Bones of the Foot.** The structure of the foot is basically similar to that of the hand. However, the foot serves to support the weight of the body and to provide a strong lever for the muscles of the calf in walking, leaping, etc.; thus, we would expect the foot to be stronger and less mobile than the hand. Since arches provide great supporting strength in any type of construction, it is not surprising to note that the foot possesses two such curves: the *longitudinal arch,* which extends from heel to toe, and the *transverse,* or *metatarsal arch,* which extends crosswise in the foot. These springy arches are maintained by powerful ligaments, muscles and tendons which hold the bones in proper alignment. Weakening of these supportive structures may permit the arches to flatten out, a condition known as "flat feet" or "fallen arches."

Of the 7 **tarsal bones,** the uppermost is the *talus* (Fig. 3-56) which articulates with the tibia and the fibula as described previously. The largest and strongest of the tarsal bones is the *calcaneus,* or heel bone. It lies below and behind the talus and is shaped like the handle of a revolver. The calcaneus forms the base of the heel and transmits the weight of the body from the talus to the ground. The *cuboid,* which lies on the lateral side of the foot, articulates with the anterior end of the calcaneus, while the *navicular,* on the medial side, articulates with the anterior end of the talus. In front of the navicular are the 3 small *cuneiform bones.*

The 5 **metatarsal bones,** lying anterior to the tarsus, are relatively cylindrical and slightly curved (Fig. 3-56). The bases of the first 3 articulate with the cuneiform bones, and those of the outer 2 articulate with the cuboid. The heads of the 5 metatarsals form the ball of the foot.

There are 14 **phalanges** in each foot. Of these, 2 are in the great toe, and 3 in each of the other toes. In marked contrast to the hand, these phalanges are relatively unimportant due to the limited mobility of the great toe.

THE ARTICULATIONS, OR JOINTS

Those areas where bones come into close contact with one another are referred to as articulations, or joints. *Arthro-* is a combining form which is frequently used when referring to a joint; for example, arthrology is the branch of anatomy which deals specifically with the joints, and arthritis refers to inflammation of a joint, etc.

The bones are efficiently bound together by connective tissues which vary according to the amount of movement that is required at each type of joint. The body can make thousands of movements because of the mobility of most of its joints. On the other hand, immobility may be desirable in some areas, such as between the cranial bones which protect the brain.

For our purpose, joints are best classified according to the amount of movement which they permit. On this basis there are three classes: synarthroses, or immovable joints; amphiarthroses, or slightly movable joints; and diarthroses, or freely movable joints. Structural types will be included in the discussion of each class.

The synarthroses, or immovable joints

This class includes all joints in which the surfaces of the bones are in almost direct contact and in which there is no appreciable movement (as in the joints between the bones of the skull,

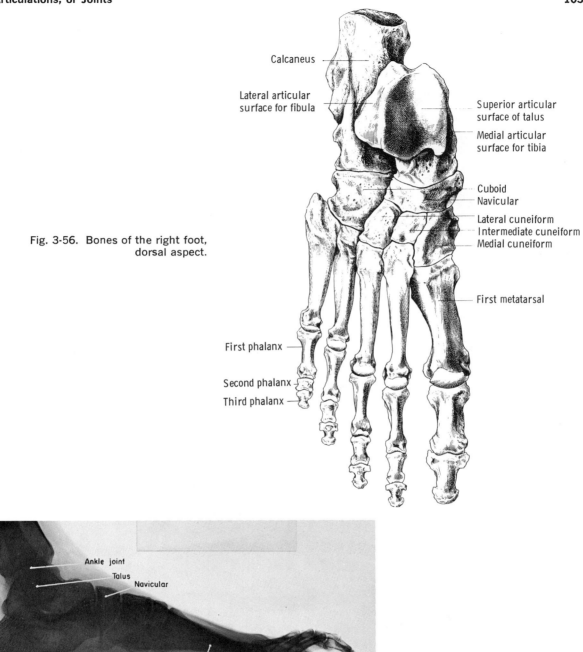

Calcaneus

Lateral articular
surface for fibula

Superior articular
surface of talus

Medial articular
surface for tibia

Cuboid
Navicular

Lateral cuneiform
Intermediate cuneiform
Medial cuneiform

First metatarsal

Fig. 3-56. Bones of the right foot,
dorsal aspect.

First phalanx

Second phalanx

Third phalanx

Ankle joint
Talus
Navicular

Calcaneus

Metatarsal

Phalanx

Fig. 3-57. X-ray of ankle and foot.
Lateral view. (From T. A. Pearson,
M.D.)

Fig. 3-58. Section across the sagittal suture.

Fig. 3-59. Diagrammatic section of a symphysis.

excepting the mandible). The bones are fastened together by fibrous tissue, by cartilage, or by bone itself as described below.

A *suture*, or sutura, is that type of articulation in which the adjoining margins of the bones are united by a thin layer of fibrous tissue. Some sutures consist of jagged, interlocking indentations and projections of the bone margins; others involve an overlapping of the margins; in either case the bones are slightly separated by a thin layer of fibrous tissue (Fig. 3-58).

A *synchondrosis* (meaning "together" and "cartilage") is a joint in which the connecting tissue is cartilage. This is a temporary form of joint, since the cartilage is eventually converted into bone. Examples are the joints between the epiphyses and the shafts of immature bones (Fig. 3-5). When growth is complete, the connecting link of cartilage undergoes ossification; the resulting bony joint is referred to as a *synostosis* (meaning "together" and "bone").

The amphiarthroses, or slightly movable joints

There are two types of amphiarthrotic joints, the symphysis and the syndesmosis. Functionally, the sacro-iliac joint has only limited movement and belongs in this group; structurally, it is a synovial joint which will be described later.

In a *symphysis* articulation the adjoining bony surfaces are connected by broad, flattened disks of fibrocartilage (Fig. 3-59). Examples are: the symphysis pubis in the pelvis, and the intervertebral disks between the bodies of vertebrae. While sitting in a chair, turn your trunk from side to side; the action takes place along the entire vertebral column, since each vertebra can move only slightly.

The *syndesmosis* joint is one in which the bone margins are united by dense fibrous tissue, as between the lower ends of the tibia and the fibula.

The diarthroses or freely movable joints

Most of the joints in the body belong to this class and are so constructed as to provide great freedom of movement, the hip and the shoulder being the most movable of all. For example, you can swing your upper extremity around in great circles, and, with practice you can do almost the same thing with your lower extremity by swinging it from the hip. Other joints, such as the elbow, may not permit movement in so many planes, but they are still freely movable.

Structurally, all diarthroses are classified as **synovial joints,** or those in which fluid is present in a closed cavity between 2 bones. In a typical joint (Fig. 3-60) a thin layer of hyaline cartilage, the *articular cartilage,* serves to cushion the end of each bone as contact is made in the joint. A strong *capsule,* or envelope, of fibrous tissue surrounds the joint as a whole and is firmly attached to both bones, thus helping to hold them together. Lining this joint capsule is a *synovial membrane* which provides a built-in lubricating system as it secretes the slippery synovial fluid, or *synovia,* (meaning "with egg," since it resembles egg white in consistency). Just as the moving parts of an automobile must be kept lubricated if they are to run smoothly and with a minimum of wear, so our joints must be similarly protected.

Where additional strength is to be desired, such as in the hip and the knee joints, ligaments are found within the joint itself, binding one bone firmly to the other; these are referred to as *interosseous ligaments.* Even though joints are further strengthened by overlying muscles and tendons, it is still possible for the bones to become completely separated and displaced; this injury is referred to as a *dislocation* or *luxation.* An incomplete or partial dislocation is called a *subluxation* of the joint. A *sprain* refers to the wrenching of a joint, during which the attachments are stretched or torn, but there is no displacement of the bones. The knee joint, in addition to its interosseous ligaments, contains two semilunar disks of articular cartilage, the medial and the lateral *menisci.* Sudden twisting or wrenching of the knee joint may result in the detachment of one or both of these cartilages, a fairly common injury, especially among athletes.

While freely movable joints are basically similar in structure, there are distinct variations in the

Fig. 3-60. Structure of synovial joint, semidiagrammatic. Joint cavity shown enlarged. (Top) Hip joint. (Right) Relations of the bones which articulate at the acetabulum. (Bottom) Mandibular joint. (Right) Relations of the bones which articulate. This joint is modified by an articular disk with which each articular cartilage normally is in contact.

shape of the articulating surfaces, and it is on this basis that we may divide them into the following subgroups:

1. *Ball - and - socket joint* (enarthrosis). The rounded head of one bone is received into a cuplike cavity in the other, as at the hip and the shoulder. These joints permit angular movement in all directions, and axial rotation as well.

2. *Hinge joint* (ginglymus). A convex cylindrical surface meets a concave cylindrical surface in such a way as to permit movement only in one plane, forward and backward. The elbow, the knee, the ankle and the interphalangeal joints are examples of hinge joints.

3. *Condyloid joint* (ellipsoidal). An oval-shaped articular surface fits into an elliptical cavity in such a way as to permit angular movement in all planes, but no axial rotation. The wrist joint, between the radius and the carpal bones, is a good example.

4. *Pivot joint* (trochoid or rotary). Movement in this type of joint is limited to rotation, as one bone turns about another. For example, the atlas rotates around the odontoid process of the axis when one turns his head from side to side. If it were not for this type of joint in the forearm (between the radius and the ulna) we would be unable to turn a doorknob or to use a screwdriver.

5. *Saddle joint*. The end of one bone is convex in one direction and concave in the other, while the end of the other bone is exactly the opposite. Observe the great range of movement possible at the carpo-metacarpal joint at the base of your thumb; this is a saddle joint.

6. *Gliding joint* (arthrodia). This type is best seen between the various carpal bones at the wrist and the tarsal bones of the foot where the articular surfaces permit one bone to glide against the other.

Movements Possible at Diarthrotic Joints. The movements of the head, trunk, and extremities result chiefly from the revolving of joint surfaces. These surfaces revolve around axes that are located in or near the joint and produce distinct kinds of movement. However, it is to be noted that these movements are often combined in the various joints. Seldom is only one type of motion found in any particular joint.

Angular Movement. As the name implies, angular movement is the type that changes the angle between bones. It may be divided into 4 kinds:

1. *Flexion* decreases the angle between bones or brings the bones closer together, as in bending the fingers to close your hand. One might think of this in terms of moving a body part forward from the anatomic position, except in the case of the knee and the foot joints where movement is to the rear. When we are standing in the erect position, the foot is normally in a state of flexion. Further flexion of the foot is referred to as *dorsiflexion*.

2. *Extension* increases the angle between bones or separates them more widely, as in straightening the fingers to open the hand. When one stands in the anatomic position, all parts of the body are in a state of extension, except the foot. In the latter case we often use the term *plantar flexion,* rather than extension, and such movement results in our standing on "tip toes." Extreme extension of a body part, as in arching the back, is referred to as *hyperextension.*

3. *Abduction* is movement away from the midsagittal plane of the body, as in moving the arm straight out to the side.

4. *Adduction* is movement toward the midsagittal plane, as in bringing the arm back to the side of the body.

NOTE: Movements of the digits are exceptions, as the point of reference is the median longitudinal axis of the hand or the foot rather than the midline of the body; therefore, abduction would be a spreading of the fingers or toes, while adduction would refer to pulling them back together.

Circumduction. When all of the angular movements are combined in succession so that the distal end of an extremity describes a circle and the shaft of the extremity describes the surface of a cone, the resulting movement is referred to as circumduction. For example, if one stands with arm outstretched at the blackboard and draws a large circle, the upper extremity must go through flexion, abduction, extension and adduction successively.

Rotation. In this movement there is a revolving or twisting of a part of the body around the longitudinal axis of that part with no change in its position. For example, when one turns his head from one side to the other (as when indicating disagreement), the atlas is rotating around the axis. Rotation also is possible at the shoulder and the hip joints. *Internal,* or *medial* rotation involves the twisting or rotating of a part toward the midsagittal plane of the body, as when standing with the toes of each foot pointed inward ("pigeon-toed") instead of forward. *External,* or *lateral* rotation involves the twisting or rotating of a part away from the midsagittal plane of the body, as when standing with the toes directed outward instead of forward.

Special Movements. There are special movements of the forearm, the ankle, the lower jaw and the clavicle.

1. *Supination* is the movement that brings the forearm into the anatomic position, with the palm forward and the radius and the ulna parallel.

2. *Pronation* is the act of turning the palm down, or backward; the radius is crossed over the ulna.

Demonstrate these movements on yourself by holding one forearm with the opposite hand, then turning your palm downward and upward several times; you can feel the radius change its position with respect to the ulna.

3. *Inversion* is the act of turning the sole of the foot inward.

4. *Eversion* is the act of turning the sole of the foot outward.

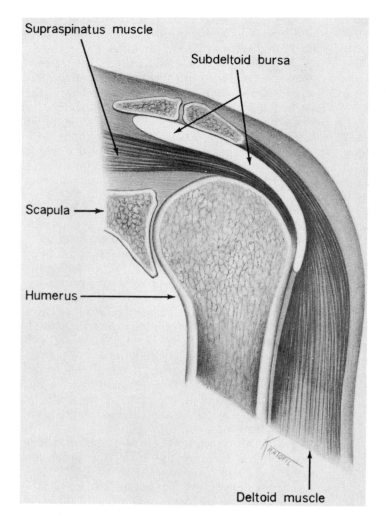

Fig. 3-61. Diagrammatic section of shoulder joint, showing the subdeltoid bursa.

Most of us have a moderate amount of inversion or eversion at all times. Examine the heels of your shoes. If they are worn down on the outer edge, it indicates that you walk with your feet slightly inverted, but if the wear is on the inner edge, then the tendency is toward eversion. *Clubfoot,* or talipes, is a term used in reference to various types of foot deformities; for example, a radical amount of inversion is referred to as talipes varus, while radical eversion is called talipes valgus.

5. *Protraction* is the act of moving a part forward, as in sticking out your tongue or your jaw.

6. *Retraction* refers to the act of drawing a part back.

The bursae

Structure. The bursae (singular, bursa, meaning "a purse") are small clefts, or fissures, lined with synovial membrane which thus converts them into closed sacs containing synovial fluid.

Location and Function. Bursae are found in those areas where pressure is exerted during the movement of body parts; for example, between bones and their overlying skin, muscles or tendons (Fig. 3-61). These little sacs act as slippery cushions which tend to reduce friction between the moving parts, and they are named according to their location. A few of the more important bursae are: acromial, subdeltoid, subscapular, olecranon and prepatellar.

Injury to bursae may result in inflammation, or *bursitis,* and one finds it extremely painful to move the affected part. The prepatellar bursa, due to its location between the skin and the patella, is frequently injured by those who work for prolonged periods in the kneeling position; the resulting irritation and enlargement of this bursa is popularly called "housemaid's knee." A *bunion* is a swelling of a bursa of the foot, particularly at the metatarso-phalangeal joint of the great toe, which is then forced outward, making the joint unduly prominent. It may develop as a result of pressure or friction from improperly fitted shoes.

SUMMARY

1. Functions of the skeleton
   A. Produce blood cells
   B. Support body
   C. Attachment of muscles and tendons
   D. Protect internal organs
2. Classification on basis of shape
   A. Long bones (e.g., humerus)
   B. Short bones (e.g., carpals)
   C. Flat bones (e.g., sternum)
   D. Irregular bones (e.g., vertebrae)
   E. Sesamoid bones (e.g., patella)
3. Bone formation
   A. Intramembranous
   B. Endochondral or cartilaginous
4. Growth of bone: circumference, length
5. Structural details
   A. Composition
      a. Inorganic
      b. Organic
   B. The haversian system

   C. Bone marrow—red and yellow
   D. Coverings and blood supply
      a. Periosteum
      b. Articular cartilage
      c. Periosteal blood vessels
      d. Nutrient or medullary artery
6. Descriptive terms
   A. Projections: head, condyle, crest, spine, trochanter, tubercle, tuberosity
   B. Depressions and openings: foramen, fossa, sinus, meatus
7. Skeleton as a whole—206 bones in adult
   A. Divisions: axial and appendicular
8. Axial skeleton
   A. Skull
      a. Cranium: frontal, parietal, temporal, occipital, sphenoid, ethmoid
      b. Superficial bones of face: nasal, zygomatic, maxillae, mandible
      c. Deeper bones of face; lacrimal, vomer, palatine, inferior conchae
   B. Cranial sutures
      a. Immovable joints
      b. Coronal, lambdoidal, sagittal, squamosal
   C. Fontanels
      a. Incomplete ossification of skull bones at birth
      b. Anterior, posterior, anterolateral, posterolateral
   D. Air sinuses: paranasal: frontal, maxillary, sphenoid, ethmoid; mastoid of temporal bone
   E. Hyoid bone
   F. Vertebral column
      a. Adult and child
      b. General structure of vertebrae
      c. Regional variations
      d. Column as a whole
   G. Thorax: bony cage, sternum, ribs
9. Appendicular skeleton
   A. Upper extremity
      a. Shoulder girdle: clavicle, scapula
      b. Arm: humerus
      c. Forearm: ulna, radius
      d. Wrist and hand: carpals, metacarpals, phalanges

B. Pelvis
  a. Hipbone (ilium, ischium, pubis)
  b. As a whole: hipbones, sacrum and coccyx
C. Lower extremity
  a. Thigh: femur, patella
  b. Leg: tibia, fibula
  c. Foot: tarsals, metatarsals, phalanges
10. Articulations (joints)
  A. Classification
    a. Synarthroses—immovable
    b. Amphiarthroses—slightly movable
    c. Diarthroses—freely movable
  B. Movements at diarthrotic joints
    a. Angular: flexion, extension, abduction, adduction
    b. Circumduction
    c. Rotation
    d. Special: supination, pronation, inversion, eversion, protraction, retraction
  C. Bursae
    a. Clefts lined with synovial membrane; reduce friction between moving parts
    b. Named for location under muscles, tendons, bones, e.g., acromial, subdeltoid, olecranon, prepatellar, etc.

PRACTICAL APPLICATIONS AND QUESTIONS

(Encircle the letter of the *best* answer to each question.)

A. *When his horse bolted suddenly, Mr. J. fell heavily to the ground. At the hospital it was discovered that he had two ruptured, or herniated, intervertebral disks which were protruding into the cervical portion of the vertebral canal. The surgeon performed a laminectomy so that the disks could be removed.*

1. Intervertebral disks normally serve as cushions between the
   a. pedicles
   b. spinous processes
   c. bodies
   d. lamina

2. These joints are classified as
   a. diarthroses
   b. synarthroses
   c. amphiarthroses
   d. none of these

3. Disks that protrude into the cervical portion of the vertebral canal may exert harmful pressure on the
   a. lungs
   b. ribs
   c. spinal cord
   d. brain

4. In performing a laminectomy which of the following structures would the doctor remove?
   a. anterior part of a vertebra
   b. posterior part of a vertebra
   c. transverse processes of a vertebra
   d. rib facets of a vertebra

B. *Mrs. K., a 76-year-old woman, fell down the cellar stairs. X-ray examination revealed a definite fracture of the right hip and a possible fracture of the medial bone in the right leg.*

1. The bones of elderly individuals are fractured more readily than are those of children because
   a. they contain proportionately more inorganic salts which causes them to be hard and brittle
   b. they are worn thin after years of hard work
   c. they are more fragile due to removal of calcium and phosphorus
   d. they have more spongy bone than do those of young people

2. The hip joint is an example of
   a. a hinge joint
   b. a gliding joint
   c. a ball-and-socket joint
   d. a pivot joint

3. Mrs. K's fracture involved a splintering of the rounded projection of the femur which articu-

lates with the socket in the hipbone. The doctor referred to this projection as the
- a. greater trochanter
- b. lesser trochanter
- c. head
- d. acetabulum

4. The medial leg bone involved in this fall would be the
- a. talus
- b. patella
- c. fibula
- d. tibia

5. Which of the following movements would be possible at both the hip and the knee joints?
- a. flexion and adduction
- b. abduction and extension
- c. circumduction and rotation
- d. flexion and extension

6. Students examined Mrs. K's x-ray pictures and observed the characteristics of a female pelvis. In comparing the male and the female pelves it can be said that
- a. the female pelvis has a wider pubic arch than the male
- b. the bones of the female pelvis are large and heavy
- c. the male pelvis is broad and shallow
- d. the female pelvis has more bones than the male pelvis

C. Mrs. M. was very interested in the growth and development of her 3-month-old son. She noted that his skull bones were not yet solid, that his extremities were growing longer, and that he was attempting to hold his head erect.

1. The soft places in an infant's head are called
- a. sutures
- b. fontanels
- c. fissures
- d. fossae

2. One of the normal curvatures of the vertebral column develops as the child begins to hold up his head; this is the
- a. lateral curve
- b. cervical curve
- c. thoracic curve
- d. lumbar curve

3. Long bones grow in length primarily due to activity of the
- a. medullary cavity
- b. periosteum
- c. articular cartilage
- d. epiphyseal cartilage

4. Usually, growth of the long bones is complete by the age of
- a. 12 to 14 years
- b. 18 to 20 years
- c. 25 to 30 years
- d. 35 to 40 years

MUSCLE TISSUE

Were it not for muscle tissue, our bones and joints would be quite useless, food could not move through the digestive tract, and blood could not circulate through the vessels of the body. In short, movement of any type would be impossible, and life as we know it could not exist.

Muscle tissue is most famous for its ability to *contract,* or to shorten, thus *producing movement* of internal and external body parts. For example, one very important activity begins long before you are born and continues until your last minute of life; this vital movement is the contraction of heart muscle which results in the pumping of blood to all parts of your body. A fetus also can move its extremities several months before birth; when this begins, the mother says that she "feels life" and knows that the fetus is alive within her body. Other important movements are those related to breathing, or getting oxygen into and carbon dioxide out of the lungs. The first gasp or cry of the newborn infant indicates that the muscles of respiration have begun to function.

Soon after birth we find other important muscular activity getting under way, activity over which we have no voluntary control: the movement of food material along the gastrointestinal tract, the emptying of the bowel, the transport of urine from the kidneys to the urinary bladder, and then the emptying of this bladder. These activities are made possible by muscle tissue which is located in the walls of various organs.

The developing child's mastery of the muscles that move his extremities is fascinating to watch. Within a few months after birth the infant learns to hold his spoon and then his cup. The *maintenance of posture* is another important accomplishment; first the child learns to control those muscles that enable him to sit and then to stand erect. A little later he learns to walk and to run. But it takes several years before movements can be so coordinated as to permit the child to button his clothes, tie his shoe strings and write his own name. Still more years are necessary before muscular control permits such things as playing the piano, fingering a violin or using a typewriter. In fact, some persons who are "all thumbs" may never acquire skill in using their hands for delicate work such as threading needles, sewing a fine seam or using small tools of any kind.

In addition to the work accomplished by its contraction, another important function of muscle tissue is the *production of heat*. The chemical changes which occur during muscle contraction produce much of the heat that is needed to maintain our normal body temperature. For example, when you "shiver" in cold weather, you are experiencing involuntary contractions of certain muscles; this is the body's attempt to produce more heat and keep you warm.

The above examples will give you an idea of the variety of activities carried out by muscle tissue, and help you more fully to appreciate muscles that are functioning normally. Consider what a difference it would make in our lives if we could not walk, talk, feed ourselves or perform the hundreds of tasks that make up a day's work. It is also easy to see how complicated life would be if certain muscles became *paralyzed*, or unable to function. For example, poliomyelitis is a disease that may paralyze many muscles, including those of respiration, and require that the victim be placed in an "iron lung" which will do the work normally done by his respiratory muscles.

TYPES OF MUSCLE TISSUE

Muscles serve as the "engines" of our body and are so constructed as to provide varying degrees of speed and power. There are three types of muscle tissue (skeletal, smooth and cardiac), each being uniquely designed for the performance of a certain type of work.

Skeletal muscle

Skeletal muscles are attached to the bones, cover the skeleton and give shape to the body, as well as making it possible for us to move about during our work and play. This type of muscle also is referred to as **striated,** due to the striped appearance of its individual fibers when seen under a microscope. A third name, **voluntary,** is sometimes used to indicate that this type of muscle is under the control of our conscious will. Skeletal muscle tissue is like a highspeed "hot rod" engine; it can develop great power but runs for relatively short periods of time.

Nonstriated or smooth muscle

Smooth muscle is very prominent in the walls of viscera such as the stomach, the intestine, the urinary-bladder, etc. For this reason it is sometimes called **visceral** muscle. Smooth muscle also occurs in the walls of blood vessels, in glands and in the skin. When seen under the microscope, it appears to be smooth, or nonstriated, since it lacks the characteristic striped appearance of other muscle tissue. The term **involuntary** is used to indicate that this type of muscle is not subject to our conscious control. Smooth muscle might be compared with the engine of a freight elevator; geared for slow speed and heavy duty, it continues to function day after day in a slow but steady manner.

Cardiac muscle

This highly specialized tissue is found only in the walls of the heart, hence the name cardiac muscle. It too is **involuntary** as we have no con-

Fig. 4-1. Longitudinal section of striated muscle showing cross-striations and the nuclei at the periphery. ×275.

Fig. 4-2. Smooth muscle from the intestine. Several isolated cells are seen at the top. ×200.

scious control of its activity. When seen under the microscope, cardiac muscle is a branching network of fibers which are striated. Our cardiac "engine" works steadily day after day, and yet it is capable of vigorous response for short periods, such as when we make a dash for the bus or run up a flight of stairs.

STRUCTURE OF MUSCLE TISSUE

Microscopic structure

Skeletal muscle cells are drawn out into long threadlike cylinders which vary in length from 1 to 40 mm. (Fig. 4-1). Since their length is relatively so much greater than their diameter, these cells are often referred to as muscle *fibers*. Each fiber is wrapped in a delicate connective tissue sheath, called the endomysium ("within muscle"), which contains a network of capillaries for nourishment of the fiber. The cell membrane is called *sarcolemma* (sarco, meaning flesh, and lemma, meaning husk). Skeletal muscle fibers are multi-

nucleated, their many nuclei lying between the sarcolemma and the *sarcoplasm* (muscle cytoplasm). Embedded in the sarcoplasm and running the entire length of the cell are many fine fibers which are called myofibrils. Each myofibril, in turn, consists of *actin* and *myosin* filaments, the large protein molecules that are ultimately responsible for muscle contraction. Figure 4-8 illustrates one contractile unit (called a *sarcomere*), of a myofibril. The arrangement of actin and myosin contribute to the alternating light and dark sections that are responsible for the characteristic striated appearance of skeletal muscle tissue. A network of tubules, the sarcoplasmic reticulum, extends between the myofibrils; this network provides the "plumbing" needed for the distribution of substances that are required for contraction of the myofibrils. Numerous mitochondria also are found in the sarcoplasm.

Smooth muscle cells are spindle-shaped, which means that they are long and tapering (Fig. 4-2). Each cell, or fiber, has a single nucleus which is centrally located. The length of smooth muscle

Fig. 4-3. Human cardiac muscle. Branching fibers, centrally placed nuclei, striations and intercalated disks are evident. ×375.

fibers varies markedly in different parts of the body. In the walls of tiny blood vessels we find the shortest fibers—only 0.02 mm. long, or 1/50 as long as the shortest skeletal muscle fiber. The longest fibers are found in the walls of a pregnant uterus, in which they may be 0.5 mm. long, but they still are shorter than the shortest skeletal fiber. Myofibrils are present in the sarcoplasm, but they are nonstriated in appearance. Smooth muscle has an abundant blood supply.

Cardiac muscle cells are roughly quadrangular in shape with a single central nucleus (Fig. 4-3). The cells are arranged end to end and end to side, forming a network of branching fibers. The dark-stained bands noted at intervals are called *intercalated discs,* and studies with the electron microscope indicate that they represent cell boundaries. This latticework arrangement of cardiac cells forms a *functional syncytium,* so that impulses transmitted over the membrane of any single fiber spread to all of the fibers (i.e., either of the atria or of the ventricles, as described in more detail in Chapter 12). Myofibrils are pres-

ent, as are the transverse striations mentioned previously. Mitochondria are particularly abundant in the sarcoplasm of cardiac muscle. This important muscle tissue also has an excellent blood supply, which is essential to life itself. Any disease process that interferes with this blood supply may result in a "heart attack."

Gross structure

All muscles contain connective tissues that not only provide for the support and the nourishment of working fibers, but also help to direct their "pull" into the performance of specific tasks such as moving an arm, emptying the stomach, etc.

Each **skeletal muscle** has an outer sheath or "overcoat" of connective tissue called the *epimysium* ("upon muscle"). Extending inward from the epimysium are little partitions of connective tissue which divide the muscle into bundles, or *fasciculi;* these partitions are called *perimysium* ("around muscle"), since they surround bundles of muscle fibers. Endomysium surrounds indi-

Fig. 4-4. Diagram of a cross section of a skeletal muscle, showing the connective tissue component. An enlarged cross section of a single muscle fiber (cell) is shown by the arrow at the right. The cell contains many nuclei located peripherally just under the cell membrane or sarcolemma. The myofibrils are organelles in the cytoplasm or sarcoplasm. (Modified from Ham, A. W.: Histology, ed. 2, Philadelphia, Lippincott)

Fig. 4-5. Motor end-plates or neuromuscular junctions in striated muscle. ×135.

vidual fibers as previously noted in the discussion of microscopic features. A diagrammatic cross section of skeletal muscle is shown in Figure 4-4. The epimysium, the perimysium and the endo-mysium all are continuous with the tendon which merges with the periosteum of the bone to which a muscle is attached and on which it exerts its pull when contracting. In fact, the connective tissue component of skeletal muscle has been compared with a harness, by means of which the pull exerted by a horse can be brought to bear on a wagon.

Smooth muscle tissue is arranged in sheets or bundles which form contractile layers in the walls of blood vessels and viscera. The cells of one layer lie in a circular plane while those of another layer lie in a longitudinal plane. These layers in turn are bound firmly to other components of the wall by connective tissue. Contraction of muscle fibers of the layers results in various changes in the shape and size of organs as needed to carry out body functions. For example, when one looks at a bright light, it is smooth muscle that automatically decreases the size of the pupil and regulates the amount of light that can enter the eye.

Cardiac muscle tissue is composed of bundles which are arranged concentrically as spirals or figures-of-eight so that when contraction occurs, the cavities of the heart are temporarily obliterated and blood is forced out. The muscle tissue of the upper chambers (atria) is not continuous with that of the lower chambers (ventricles), but the two groups work in close harmony, as described in Chapter 12.

Chemical composition of muscle tissue

Muscle tissue contains about 75 per cent water and 20 per cent protein; *actin* and *myosin* (functionally associated as actomyosin) are the main proteins composing the contractile elements of muscle. The remaining 5 per cent is made up of carbohydrates, lipids, inorganic salts and nonprotein nitrogenous compounds. The composition differs widely in different species and in different muscles in the same animal. Carbohydrate is present in the form of glycogen and glucose. Present in small amounts, but of great importance, are the nonprotein nitrogenous substances adenosine-triphosphate (ATP) and phosphocreatine. These chemical constituents will be considered further during discussion of muscle contraction.

NERVE SUPPLY OF MUSCLE TISSUE

All three types of muscle tissue are supplied with nerve fibers that carry messages to and from the central nervous system (brain and spinal cord). These fibers are classified as afferent and efferent.

Afferent or sensory nerves

Afferent nerve fibers are those that convey messages from muscle tissue to the central nervous system (CNS), thus supplying "headquarters" with information regarding the activity in outlying muscular areas. For example, **somatic afferent** fibers from muscle spindles keep the CNS informed about the degree of contraction of all *skeletal muscles;* such information is essential if we are to maintain our equilibrium and to coordinate all muscular movements. **Visceral afferent** fibers keep the CNS informed about the condition of cells in *smooth muscle* and *cardiac muscle.* For example, excessive contraction (spasm-cramp) or excessive stretching (distention) of smooth muscle will arouse sensations of pain. If the intestine is distended with gas that cannot escape by the rectum, pain results; as you may know, gas pains can be very severe. When the gas escapes, either spontaneously or after the insertion of a rectal tube, the distention is relieved and the pain disappears. Information sent to the brain from cardiac muscle usually is concerned with the amount of oxygen being supplied to the cells. When the heart muscle fails to get enough oxygen to carry out its work efficiently, one may feel a sharp warning pain in the chest, a symptom that is referred to as *angina pectoris.*

Efferent nerves

Efferent nerve fibers convey messages from CNS "headquarters" to each type of muscular tissue. As you might expect, these messages are of great importance in "ordering" the muscle cells to contract or, in certain cases, to relax.

Messages to *skeletal muscles* travel over **somatic efferent** nerve fibers which deliver the order for contraction. The point of contact between muscle and nerve is referred to as the *neuromuscular junction*, the *myoneural junction* or the *motor end plate* (Fig. 4-5). The individual nerve fibers supply varying numbers of muscle fibers. In muscles in which fine, accurate movements are essential, such as in the muscles that move the eyes, each nerve fiber supplies only 3 to 6 muscle fibers. On the other hand, in muscles in which such fine control is unnecessary, as in the muscles of the leg, each nerve fiber divides extensively and supplies as many as 150 muscle fibers. A nerve cell, its outgoing fiber and all the muscle fibers supplied constitute a **motor unit.** Each skeletal muscle is made up of an enormous number of motor units.

Skeletal muscle is completely dependent on its nerve supply, and, should these efferent fibers be destroyed through injury or disease, the end-result will be paralysis, as in poliomyelitis. Since paralyzed muscles cannot be used voluntarily, they undergo *atrophy* (wasting or decrease in size) unless properly treated. Much of the training and the treatment of poliomyelitis victims is directed toward the prevention of atrophy of the involved muscles. In most of the involved muscles only a few of the motor units are affected, and with training the surviving units can be made to contract at will. Atrophy will occur, likewise, in muscles rendered immobile by splints or casts, or if their tendons are cut. When muscles cannot be contracted voluntarily, they should be massaged, exercised by passive movements or stimulated to contract by electrical methods. This is a part of the field of physical medicine or physiotherapy. Remarkable progress has been made, especially in the treatment of poliomyelitis and the spastic paralyses in children following birth injuries.

Messages to *smooth muscle* and to *cardiac muscle* travel over **visceral efferent** or *autonomic* nerves (p. 250). In contrast to skeletal muscles, which contract only when they receive orders from the CNS, smooth muscle and cardiac muscle may contract quite independently of such messages. However, there are times when the activity of these tissues must be temporarily increased or decreased, and messages from the CNS are essential on such occasions. To meet this dual need, there is a double nerve supply to smooth muscle and to cardiac muscle; one nerve supply carries orders for an increase in the activity that is already going on, and the other for a decrease in such activity. This regulation of activity is entirely unconscious, and we have no voluntary control over it.

PHYSIOLOGIC PROPERTIES OF MUSCLE TISSUE

All three types of muscle tissue have the same fundamental properties:

1. Excitability (irritability), or the capacity to respond to a stimulus
2. Contractility, or the capacity to shorten
3. Tonus, or the capacity to maintain a state of steady, partial contraction
4. Extensibility, or the capacity to stretch when force is applied
5. Elasticity, or the capacity to regain original form when the force is removed

Excitability

The capacity to respond to a change in the environment (i.e., a stimulus) is referred to as excitability. This property is highly developed in muscle fibers and in nerve fibers (p. 190), as both are capable of transmitting electrochemical impulses along their membranes. The details of electrical membrane potentials are not within the scope of this textbook, but a few broad, general statements will lay the groundwork for an understanding of how muscle and nerve fibers respond to stimuli.

Polarization. The outer surface of a resting fiber or cell membrane bears a positive electrical

Fig. 4-6. Diagram illustrating membrane theory of impulse conduction. Above: resting fiber. Below: conducting fiber.

charge, while the inner surface bears a negative charge (Fig. 4-6); this polarization is caused primarily by the relative impermeability of the membrane to sodium ions plus the action of the sodium "pump," as previously described on page 24. However, various stimuli (e.g., chemical, electrical, thermal, and so on) may temporarily alter the membrane so that it becomes more permeable, allowing sodium ions to rush into the cell, and potassium ions to leak out of the cell. The instantaneous result is a reversal of the electrical potential or a **depolarization** of the membrane, as the outer surface becomes electronegative while the inner surface becomes electropositive. Within a fraction of a second after depolarization takes place, the membrane again becomes relatively impermeable to sodium ions and the normal resting membrane potential is restored, a process that is called **repolarization.** Depolarization begins at the point at which the membrane is first disturbed, then spreads to adjacent areas in such a way that successive portions of the membrane become depolarized (Fig. 4-6). This transmission of a wave of depolarization, accompanied by an action current, is called an impulse; if it occurs over a nerve fiber it is called a *nerve impulse,* while over a muscle fiber it is referred to as a *muscle impulse.*

Stimuli. We shall now consider the various factors or stimuli that serve to excite the three types of muscle tissue. In the intact body, skeletal muscles are excited exclusively by nerve impulses coming from the brain and the spinal cord. If such impulses fail to reach them, they will be completely relaxed and unable to respond.

Smooth muscle responds to a great variety of stimuli, such as distention, temperature changes and nerve impulses. So far as temperature is concerned, the application of cold increases the activity of smooth muscles. In fact, an ice pack can have detrimental effects if it stimulates activity in the intestine when an inflamed and swollen appendix is at the point of bursting. The effect of heat varies with the speed of application. If smooth muscle is heated rapidly, it contracts, but if heated slowly, the muscle relaxes. Thus the response of smooth muscle to heat depends not only on the elevation of temperature but also on the rapidity with which the temperature is raised.

In addition to the stimuli listed above, smooth muscle is sensitive to changes in the composition of the blood or the tissue fluid that bathes it. Hormones, vitamins, drugs, salts, acids and bases may affect the activity of smooth muscle.

Smooth muscle in certain parts of the body displays the property of **rhythmicity** or "automaticity"; this refers to a repetitive discharge of

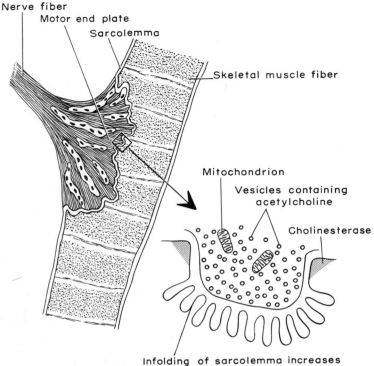

Nerve fiber
Motor end plate
Sarcolemma

Skeletal muscle fiber

Mitochondrion
Vesicles containing
acetylcholine

Cholinesterase

Infolding of sarcolemma increases
surface area for contact with
acetylcholine

Fig. 4-7. Neuromuscular junction. Diagram of a single motor end plate in striated muscle. The general appearance of the junction as a whole is shown on the left. The arrow indicates a small section of the end plate and sarcolemma that has been even more greatly enlarged. Modified from Guyton: Textbook of Medical Physiology. ed. 3. Philadelphia, W. B. Saunders, 1966.

action currents. The smooth muscle fiber membrane is naturally permeable enough to allow automatic depolarization, followed by repolarization. This self-excitatory process plays an important part in promoting peristalsis (p. 484) along various tubular structures.

Cardiac muscle is duly famous for its rhythmicity (see above) which develops as soon as the heart is formed in the embryo and long before any nerves have grown out to it. However, when the nerve supply is established, the heart will respond to nerve impulses which order an increase or a decrease in its rate and force of contraction. Cardiac muscle also may be stimulated by mechanical, electrical, thermal and chemical agents. Doctors frequently make a life-saving practical application of these facts when a patient's heart suddenly stops beating for no apparent reason (*cardiac arrest*). For example, the heart may be stimulated by firm, rhythmic pressure on the sternum (external cardiac massage). If the chest is open, the doctor may rhythmically squeeze the heart with his hand, or he may use a special machine that sends an electrical current through the walls of the heart. In any case, he is depending on the property of excitability of cardiac muscle as he endeavors to re-establish the heart beat.

Neuromuscular transmission. As noted in the preceding discussion, all three types of muscle tissue can be excited by nerve impulses. Because this is of fundamental importance insofar as skeletal muscle is concerned, we shall discuss briefly the neuromuscular transmission of impulses. Although we do not yet fully understand all of the details, we do know that when nerve impulses reach a neuromuscular junction in skeletal muscle, a chemical substance, acetylcholine, is released by the end plate of the nerve fiber (Fig. 4-7). **Acetylcholine** excites the muscle fiber and initiates the process of contraction. Within a fraction of a second acetylcholine is destroyed by the enzyme *cholinesterase;* this prevents re-excitation of the muscle until the arrival of another nerve impulse. The chemical excitation of smooth muscle and cardiac muscle follows a similar pattern, but it is best described after study of the autonomic division of the nervous system (p. 248).

Certain drugs, such as curare and similar muscle relaxants, can block the passage of nerve impulses at neuromuscular junctions, thus temporarily preventing the contraction of the muscles. Used in conjunction with various types of anesthetics, these drugs produce excellent muscular relaxation; this is very important to the surgeon who has made an incision through the strong muscles of the abdominal wall and is trying to examine the internal organs. Perhaps you are wondering about the effect of these drugs on the muscles of respiration. For some unknown reason, the muscles of the abdominal wall and the extremities respond to smaller doses of curarelike drugs than do the muscles of respiration. However, if larger doses are administered, the respiratory muscles also will be paralyzed; in such cases artificial respiration must be given until the effects of the drug wear off, usually within 5 minutes.

Myasthenia gravis is a condition characterized by weakness of skeletal muscles due to blocking of nerve impulses at the neuromuscular junction. It usually begins first in muscles of the face, then it spreads to other muscles until the patient is eventually incapacitated. Recent studies have shown that this disease causes specific changes in the terminal nerve fibers and the motor end plates; these changes may be responsible for the improper transmission of impulses from the CNS to the muscles.

Contractility

When appropriately stimulated, all muscle cells or fibers have the capacity to shorten, or contract. However, before one can fully appreciate the over-all sequence of events involved in muscle contraction, there must be some understanding of the basic molecular changes that take place, as well as the all-important sources of energy for those changes.

Molecular changes. In the earlier discussion of the microscopic structure of muscle tissue (p. 114) it was noted that each muscle fiber contains many myofibrils embedded in the sarcoplasm. Each myofibril, in turn, consists of myosin and actin filaments, the large protein molecules that are ultimately responsible for muscle contraction. These filaments are more precisely arranged in skeletal and cardiac muscle than they are in smooth muscle, but the contractile process appears to be essentially the same in all 3 types of muscle tissue. The precise arrangement of the actin and myosin filaments in skeletal muscle is shown diagrammatically in Figure 4-8. Note that the thick filaments (myosin) are arranged longitudinally in the middle of the relaxed sarcomere, but do not reach the ends of the sarcomere. On the other hand, the thin filaments (actin) extend from the ends (Z bands) of the sarcomere, but do not reach the middle. Contraction of the sarcomere takes place when there is an interaction between these filaments, causing the thin actin filaments to move inward among the myosin filaments and pull with them the Z bands to which they are attached. The chemical changes involved in this process are extremely complex and not yet completely understood. However, this "actomyosin team" is so strong that it can move loads many times its own weight; pound for pound, it packs more power than any engine yet designed by man.

Energy Sources. The immediate energy source for the contractile process is **adenosine triphosphate (ATP).** This energy-rich phosphate compound sometimes is referred to as the "spark plug" of the muscular engine. When a muscle cell is stimulated, an enzyme causes one of ATP's 3 phosphate radicals to split off, leaving *adenosine diphosphate* or *ADP;* during this splitting process a burst of energy is released (Fig. 4-9). The ultramicroscopic "sparks" of energy from a variable number of ATP units power the interaction between actin and myosin, causing the fiber to shorten.

Within a fraction of a second after the contractile process ends the ADP is converted back to ATP. Most of this immediate reconversion occurs when ADP reacts with **phosphocreatine**, another high-energy compound found in the sarcoplasm. Phosphocreatine is present in muscle in far greater concentration than is ATP, but its energy must be "funneled" through ATP before it can be utilized by the muscle fiber.

ADP + Phosphocreatine → ATP + Creatine

Some ADP also diffuses out of the myofibril and into the mitochondria, where foods are being oxidized in the citric acid cycle—a complex series of chemical reactions that not only require a constant supply of oxygen but also liberate large quantities of energy for the formation of ATP (p. 502). However, these oxidative processes do not produce ATP in the quantity needed during prolonged muscular activity, and the available ATP would soon be used up were it not immediately resynthesized by the interaction of ADP and phosphocreatine. During periods of rest, when energy requirements are reduced, enough ATP is formed by the aforementioned oxidative processes in the mitochondria to convert the creatine back to phos-

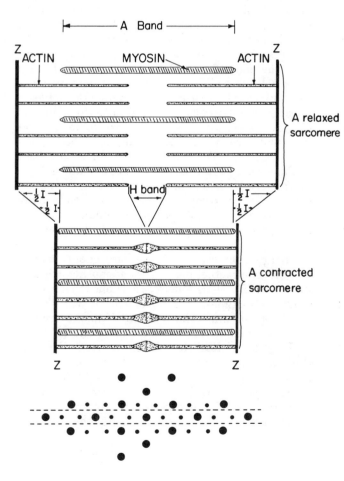

Fig. 4-8. Diagram of actin and myosin filaments in one sarcomere, or contractile unit, of a myofibril in skeletal muscle. Contraction occurs when the thin actin filaments move inward among the myosin filaments and pull with them the Z bands to which they are attached. The small diagram below the sarcomere illustrates a longitudinal section through the A band, showing two fine filaments between each pair of coarse ones. (Diagrams based on the sliding-filament hypothesis of H. E. Huxley: Ham, A. W. and Leeson, T. S.: Histology, ed. 4, Fig. 260A, p. 428, Philadelphia, Lippincott Co.)

phocreatine, thus re-charging the chemical "battery" of the muscular engine.

Another source of energy for muscular contraction is found in the *anaerobic breakdown of carbohydrates*. Through a complex series of chemical reactions, not requiring the simultaneous use of oxygen, glycogen and glucose are broken down to *pyruvic acid;* during this process a relatively small amount of ATP is formed (Fig. 4-10). However, during strenuous exercise even this small amount of ATP is of considerable importance.

The course of events following the formation of pyruvic acid depends on whether or not oxygen is available in sufficient quantities for the amount of work being done. For example, during moderate activity one is able to breathe in enough oxygen so that some of the pyruvic acid is oxidized to CO_2 and H_2O with the liberation of sufficient energy to convert the remaining pyruvic acid back to glycogen. Exercise physiologists sometimes refer to this as the "steady state" (Fig. 4-10). On the other hand, during bursts of strenuous activity (such as running up a flight of stairs) a person cannot breathe in oxygen rapidly enough to handle the increasing amounts of pyruvic acid being produced in the hard working muscular engines. Under these conditions pyruvic acid is converted to *lactic acid,* which begins to accumulate in the body. As lactic acid accumulates the person is said to be running up an *oxygen debt.* (Fig. 4-11). However, nature has decreed that one must repay this obligation, so a person will be "out of breath" until the debt is paid in full (Fig. 4-12). During this period of rapid breathing the lactic acid is changed back to pyruvic acid, some

Fig. 4-10. A summary of the highlights of anaerobic and aerobic pathways in the breakdown of carbohydrate leading to the formation of ATP. This figure also illustrates "the steady state" (i.e. during moderate exercise sufficient oxygen is available to oxidize pyruvic acid and prevent the formation of any significant amount of lactic acid).

Fig. 4-11. "Oxygen debt." During severe exercise the aerobic phase lags behind the more rapid anaerobic phase and lactic acid begins to accumulate. The oxygen debt must be repaid by rapid breathing, or muscle fatigue will result.

Fig. 4-12. Repayment of "oxygen debt." During the period of rest and rapid breathing, lactic acid is oxidized to pyruvic acid. About 20% of this pyruvic acid then is oxidized to CO_2 and H_2O with the production of energy for conversion of the remaining pyruvic acid to glycogen.

Adenosine — $PO_4 \sim PO_4 \sim PO_4$ ⇌ (enzyme) Adenosine — $PO_4 \sim PO_4 + PO_4 +$ Energy (7 Cal.)

ATP   ADP

Fig. 4-9. Schematic representation of the reversible action between adenosine triphosphate (ATP) and adenosine diphosphate (ADP). The symbol $\sim$ represents high energy bonds between phosphate radicals. Splitting of a high energy bond releases 7 calories of energy, as when the above reaction proceeds to the right. When ADP is reconverted to ATP, as the reaction proceeds to the left, 7 calories of energy are required for the PO_4 bonding process.

of which is then oxidized to provide energy for the conversion of the remainder to glycogen, as well as for the restoration of phosphocreatine and ATP, as previously noted. Thus the oxidative processes in the mitochondria serve not only to recharge the cellular "batteries" but also to prevent the accumulation of lactic acid and help prevent the depletion of one's glycogen "fuel supply."

If for any reason a person is unable to repay his oxygen debt and prevent the accumulation of lactic acid, *muscle fatigue* will result. Excessive amounts of lactic acid tend to depress the activity in muscle cells, leading to decreased irritability and interfering with their ability to contract. Therefore, if the recovery phase lags too far behind the contraction phase, the muscles will be physically unable to respond in their usual efficient manner, thus "forcing" one to stop his activity and rest until conditions return to normal.

Heat production is an important consideration in the functioning of any engine, and muscles are no exception. Most of the energy liberated during muscle contraction appears as heat, but only a small part (20-30%) can be converted to work; muscular efficiency is roughly the same as an ordinary steam engine in that respect. However, at this point the comparison breaks down, since most of the remaining heat is used for the very important and useful purpose of maintaining body temperature.

In extremely hot weather we often tend to reduce our muscular activity, wear lightweight clothing to facilitate heat dissipation, and "take things easy." On the other hand, when cold weather arrives we put on heavier clothing to prevent heat loss, and move briskly in an effort to generate even more body heat. If we cannot do this, nature will take a hand in our affairs and increase heat production by making us "shiver."

Heat production does not stop when we go to bed at night, but it is greatly reduced. While we are asleep, a certain amount of heat is produced by the constant activity of respiratory muscles, the heart muscle and smooth muscle in the walls of blood vessels and various organs.

In concluding this discussion of the property of contractility, we present a brief description of the over-all sequence of events that follows excitation of a muscle fiber. The various types of contractions and the strength of contractions will be considered later in the chapter.

Contraction of Skeletal Muscle. As previously described on page 119, the excitation of a muscle fiber results in a wave of depolarization, accompanied by an action current that spreads throughout the entire fiber. It is believed that the related change in membrane permeability permits the temporary escape of *calcium ions* from a "relaxing substance" in the sarcoplasmic reticulum. These calcium ions, in turn, probably serve to activate an enzyme that causes the breakdown of ATP to ADP. The burst of energy liberated during this breakdown then powers the interaction between actin and myosin, thus causing the fiber to contract. One attractive theory attempting to explain this event suggests that the energy liberated from ATP sets up electrical forces between actin and myosin, thus "drawing" them together.

Within a fraction of a second after the action current ends, the calcium ions again become firmly bound to the "relaxing factor" in the sarcoplasmic reticulum. The fiber then remains in a relaxed state until another action current is initiated.

Contraction of smooth muscle. The actual contractile process in smooth muscle is apparently the same as in skeletal muscle, the only significant difference being in the timing of the process. For example, the development of a contraction in smooth muscle is much slower than in skeletal muscle, and relaxation at the end of contraction is equally slow, possibly owing to the development of much stronger bonds between the actin and myosin. This feature may help to explain why smooth muscle can maintain a considerable amount of tension over long periods of time without using much ATP energy, which is quite unlike skeletal muscle.

Contraction of Cardiac Muscle. Because cardiac muscle is striated like skeletal muscle, and has the same arrangement of actin, myosin and sarcoplasmic reticulum, the basic mechanism of contraction is essentially the same. However, there are certain important differences in the manner of excitation and in the duration of depolarization. These will be described in Chapter 12, which deals exclusively with the heart.

Muscle tone, or tonus

All healthy muscles exhibit the property of tonus which is a state of steady, partial contraction, varying in degree but present at all times.

Tonus in **skeletal muscle** is due to the stretch reflex (an involuntary response to the stretching of muscle fibers); this means that it is completely dependent on the central nervous system for maintenance. Our skeletal muscles are so arranged in the body that they are held in slight stretch over the joints; this is particularly true of the "extensor" muscles that enable us to stand erect. Many sensitive nerve endings (receptors) are located in each fiber, and these are stimulated by any stretching of the muscle across a joint. As a result of this stimulation, nerve impulses are sent in to the CNS which, in turn, causes impulses to be sent back to the part of the muscle that is being stretched, ordering contraction of the fibers.

During the maintenance of tonus, groups of motor units work in relays or shifts. This means that one group of motor units is active for a short period of time; when this group relaxes, another group becomes active.

Muscle tone is often reduced when one is in poor health, and particularly so when prolonged bed rest is necessary. Such persons should have assistance when getting out of bed for the first time; otherwise they may suffer a fall as their weakened muscles fail to support the body weight. Early ambulation of hospital patients markedly reduces this hazard.

Tonus in **smooth muscle** differs widely from that in skeletal muscle and is entirely independent of the nervous system. However, smooth muscle is extremely sensitive to the chemical composition of its environment. The response to any particular stimulus may be rhythmic contraction, an increase in tonus or a decrease in tonus (relaxation). In fact, a given stimulus which produces contraction under some circumstances may produce relaxation under other circumstances, depending on the condition of the muscle itself and its environment. Even though smooth muscle has the same fundamental properties as skeletal and cardiac muscle, it is not as uniform or as constant in its reactions because it is influenced by such a large number of extrinsic factors.

Smooth muscle tonus is influenced markedly by the presence of drugs in the tissue fluid bathing the muscle fibers. Figure 4-13 illustrates the effect of epinephrine (Adrenaline) and pituitrin on the tonus of a strip of smooth muscle taken from a rat.

Fig. 4-13. Smooth muscle from a strip of rat uterus. Three normal, spontaneous contractions are shown at the left. When epinephrine was added, complete inhibition resulted. With the addition of pituitrin, the contractions began again with an increase in tonus. When this was washed out (right), the normal contractions began.

NORMAL   Epinephrine added   Pituitrin added   Washing   NORMAL

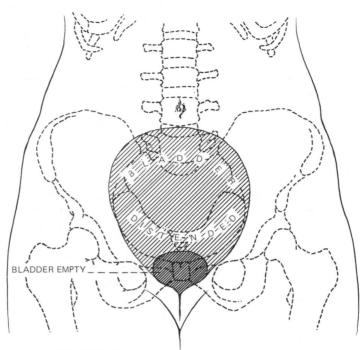

BLADDER EMPTY

Fig. 4-14. Urinary bladder, empty and distended.

The curarelike drugs, in addition to their paralyzing effect on skeletal muscle, lead to a temporary loss of tone and activity in the intestinal tract, the blood vessels and the smooth muscle generally.

Tonus in **cardiac muscle** is independent of nerve impulses and is synonymous with its general physiologic condition. When the heart is in good condition it has a high tonus and empties itself almost completely with each beat. A heart in poor condition is dilated at the end of each beat and contains a large amount of residual blood.

Extensibility and elasticity

All types of muscle tissue have the capacity to stretch when force is applied and to regain their original form when the force is removed. From a practical standpoint these properties are extremely important in that they lessen the danger of muscle rupture during times of great stress. The fact also has been established that muscle contracts more forcibly when it is slightly stretched.

The extensibility of smooth muscle, in particular, is truly remarkable. For example, this property makes possible the increase in size of the urinary bladder as urine accumulates. If the bladder could not distend, there would be a constant dribbling of urine instead of a periodic emptying of the bladder. Figure 4-14 illustrates the bladder in an empty and in a markedly distended condition. Distention of such a degree as illustrated is serious and occurs only under abnormal circumstances. Normally, as the bladder is moderately distended the sense of fullness in the bladder merges into pain, and the bladder is emptied long before it is stretched to a dangerous extent. Abnormal distention occurs in an unconscious person if the bladder is not emptied by catheterization at intervals.

MECHANICAL PHENOMENA OF CONTRACTION

Much of our knowledge of muscular contraction has been gained from laboratory studies of an isolated muscle (gastrocnemius) taken from the leg of a frog. The muscle is suspended between a clamp and a writing lever tipped with a stylus. The stylus rests against a drum, and, as the drum turns, any movement of the muscle is graphically recorded (Fig. 4-15). Such muscles will respond to many types of stimulation, such as the application of a hot wire, a pinch, a crystal of salt and a strong salt solution, but the stimulus of preference is an electric shock. Electrical stimuli are least harmful, most easily regulated and most like nerve impulses which stimulate muscles in the intact body. Consequently, the discussion that follows is based on the results of electrical stimulation.

Types of contractions

If a single electric shock is sent through the muscle, it responds by giving one contraction which is called a *simple twitch*. A possible example of this in our own bodies might be the involuntary blinking movement of the eye, but the rest of our movements are far more complex. A record of the simple twitch is shown on the drum in Figure 4-15. Note that a short period of time elapses after the stimulus is applied and before the muscle contracts; then the lever describes a curve. The period of time between the application of the stimulus and the beginning of the contraction is called the *latent period*. The time during which the muscle is shortening is called the *contraction period* and that during which the muscle is lengthening is called the *relaxation period*. The duration of each of these periods varies with the muscle studied. For example, Figure 4-16 illustrates the comparative times of three different muscles; a muscle which moves the eyeball, and two calf muscles which move the foot. As one would expect, the eye muscle is most rapid in its response while the calf muscles are proportionately slower, in accordance with the function which each performs in the body.

Fig. 4-15. Simple twitch of frog muscle following a single electrical stimulus.
(A) Latent period, (B) period of contraction, and (C) period of relaxation.

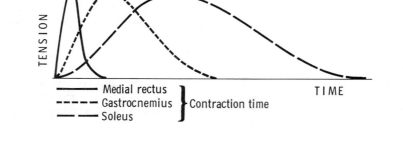

TENSION

TIME

———— Medial rectus
- - - - Gastrocnemius } Contraction time
— — — Soleus

Fig. 4-16. Relative durations of simple twitches of different types of skeletal muscles. The medial rectus of the eye is rapid in its responses. The soleus twitch is of long duration. The gastrocnemius is intermediate. (Redrawn from Fulton, J. F.: Textbook of Physiology (Howell), Philadelphia, Saunders)

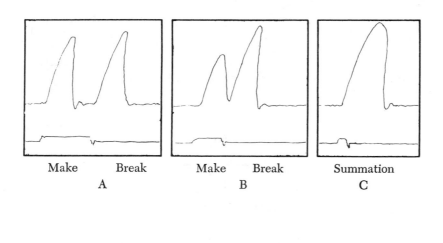

Make   Break
A

Make   Break
B

Summation
C

Fig. 4-17. Summation of skeletal muscle contractions. (Left) Stimuli far apart; two single twitches. (Center) Stimuli closer together; beginning summation. (Right) Stimuli very close together; complete summation.

3/sec.   4/sec.   6/sec.   8/sec.   16/sec.

Fig. 4-18. Tetanic contractions of skeletal muscles. (Left to right) Shocks at the rate of 3 per second produce individual twitches. There are incomplete tetanic contractions when shocks come at the rate of 4, 6 and 8 per second. Complete tetanic contraction results when shocks occur at the rate of 16 per second.

We shall now leave the simple twitch and consider the results that follow the application of two stimuli in quick succession. If the second stimulus follows the first too quickly, the muscle will not respond to the second one. We know from this fact that there is a short *refractory period* following stimulation of skeletal muscle, during which it will not respond to a second stimulus, no matter how strong that stimulus is.

If a little more time is allowed to elapse between the first and the second stimulus (that is, if time for recovery of excitability is allowed, or if we wait until the refractory period is over), the muscle responds to both the first and the second stimulus, and the second response is added to the first, producing a higher contraction called a *summation* (Fig. 4-17).

If the muscle is bombarded with a series of stimuli in rapid succession, there is a sustained contraction with no apparent relaxation. This response is called a *complete tetanic contraction,* or *tetanus* (Fig. 4-18). (NOTE: This should not be confused with the disease entity known as *tetanus,* or "lockjaw." Victims of this dread condition do have sustained tetanic contractions, but the problem lies in their inability to end them voluntarily. Many muscles are involved, but those which cause the jaws to be clamped shut are responsible for the common expression "lockjaw.") The rate at which stimuli need to be applied to produce complete tetanus varies in different muscles. In the soleus muscle of a mammal, complete tetanic contractions are produced when the rate of stimulation is about 30 per second; in the extrinsic eye muscles about 350 stimuli per second are required to produce complete tetanic contractions. In any event, our normal body movements depend on these smooth contractions rather than simple twitches. Tetanus is closely related to muscle tone, but in the latter case only a few motor units are stimulated at one time so that no actual movement occurs.

Not all muscular contractions result in actual shortening of fibers and movement of some body part. For example, if you push against a stone wall there will be no appreciable movement; yet your muscles are expending a great deal of energy. At

Fig. 4-19. Effect of altering strength of stimulus in skeletal and cardiac muscles. In skeletal, with increasing strength of stimulus, the contractions are higher and higher, due to more motor units being brought into action, until finally all the units are active. In cardiac muscle, every contraction is maximal, regardless of the strength of the stimulus, due to the network of branching fibers. The figures indicate the distance between the secondary and primary coils of the inductorium; the smaller the distance, the stronger the current.

such times there is a marked increase in tonus but little shortening; such contractions are called *isometric*. When a reasonable load is to be moved, tonus is relatively unchanged, but the muscle shortens. The latter is referred to as an *isotonic* contraction.

Strength of contractions

Various factors may alter the strength of contraction of any muscle. Some of these will be mentioned briefly.

Satisfactory metabolic conditions tend to strengthen contractions. Such conditions exist when adequate food and oxygen are available, when lactic acid is efficiently oxidized, and when waste products are removed promptly.

The strength of the stimulus can alter the strength of contraction. A minimal stimulus is the weakest one that will initiate the contraction of a muscle fiber, which contraction also will be weak. As the strength of the stimulus is increased, the height of contraction becomes greater and greater until the maximal response is obtained. This

change in the height of contraction of skeletal muscle with increasing strength of stimulation is due to the fact that more and more motor units are brought into action as the stimulus is increased. Keep in mind that this is true only for skeletal muscle. If the same experiment is carried out on an isolated quiescent ventricle of the heart (one that is no longer beating spontaneously), it will be noted that the height of contractions is the same whether minimal or maximal stimuli are used. Since cardiac muscle fibers form a functional syncytium, and since there are no motor units as in skeletal muscle, the entire muscle mass behaves as a unit. The responses of skeletal and cardiac muscle obtained by increasing strengths of stimuli are shown in Figure 4-19. In the intact body we can execute contractions of different strengths by using varying numbers of motor units. In other words, we can grade our muscle contractions; we use few units in weak contractions and more units in strong contractions.

The rate of stimulation (as measured by action currents in a single motor nerve fiber) increases from 5 to 50 per second as voluntary contractions progress from weak to strong. Some motor units

Fig. 4-20. Effect of load on simple muscle twitch. The figures indicate the load in grams. The tuning fork is vibrating at the rate of 100/sec.

Fig. 4-21. Effect of altering the temperature on simple muscle twitch. Temperature expressed in degrees Centigrade.

respond at only 8 stimuli per second, others at 12, and so on, up to 50 per second. This results in *asynchronism,* the net result of which is a smooth contraction. If all of the motor units in use contracted and relaxed at the same rate, the result would be a series of jerks, instead of a smooth contraction. In pathologic cases this condition does exist and is called *clonus.*

The weight of the load imposed on a muscle, when increased to optimal limits, will stretch the fibers and cause the muscle to contract more forcibly. However, as the load is gradually increased, the latent period becomes longer, the height of the contraction lower, and the relaxation faster (Fig. 4-20).

The temperature of the fluid which bathes the muscle influences contractions. As the muscle is warmed the latent period becomes shorter, the height of contraction greater, and the relaxation more rapid. Cooling the muscle has the opposite effect. The form of the curve at different temperatures is shown in Figure 4-21. Athletes are well aware of these facts and no doubt you have noticed their "warm-up" exercises before contests which require muscular effort. Another familiar sight is the baseball pitcher who wears a jacket between innings, even though the weather is warm, to prevent his arm muscles from "cooling out" and contracting less efficiently.

Hypertrophy (increase in size) of muscle occurs with repeated use, and the larger the muscle, the greater the strength of its contractions. Therefore, exercise is essential in strengthening muscles that have become weakened through disuse while in splints or casts.

Fatigue of muscle cells reduces the strength of contraction. Accumulation of excessive amounts of lactic acid is probably a key factor in the intact body (p. 124). However, if you continue to stimulate a frog's muscle after removing it from the body, fatigue will occur, since it is no longer being supplied with oxygen and food, and its waste products are not being removed.

As fatigue progresses, the latent period becomes longer, the height of contraction less, and relaxation slower. You can tell by the shape of the curve if a muscle is fresh or fatigued (Fig. 4-22). As fatigue begins, the first apparent change is a failure to relax completely; later the other changes appear. In fact, human beings find it difficult to relax if they permit themselves to become "too tired."

Pathologic contractions

A **spasm** is a sudden involuntary contraction of a skeletal muscle. If persistent, it is called a tonic spasm or *cramp.* If the spasm is characterized by

Fig. 4-22. Muscle twitches showing fatigue due to repeated stimulation. The first six contractions are numbered. (Evans, C. L.: Starling's Principles of Human Physiology. London, Churchill)

alternate contraction and relaxation, it is called a clonic spasm or *clonus*. Spasms may occur in smooth muscle, also. In this case, the spasm is evident as a transitory constriction of a passage, a duct or an orifice, an example of this being the spasm during the passage of a gallstone or a kidney stone. Spasmodic contractions are accompanied by pain.

Fasciculation is the contraction of some motor units whose nerve cells are undergoing pathologic changes; it resembles localized shivering in some respects and is evident in superficial muscles just under the skin.

Fibrillation is the uncoordinated contraction of individual fibers; therefore, the whole muscle does not contract. This cannot be seen readily in muscles under the skin, but if it happens to involve the tongue muscles it can be seen as a quivering of parts of the protruded tongue. When fibrillation occurs in cardiac muscle, the heart seems to tremble or to be in a state of continuous convulsive movement; if this involves the lower chambers (ventricles) of the heart, death is usually quite sudden.

SUMMARY

1. Muscle function
   A. Movement: voluntary; involuntary
   B. Production of heat (body temperature)
2. Types of muscle tissue
   A. Striated or skeletal: attached to bones; give shape to body; voluntary
   B. Nonstriated or smooth: in walls of viscera and skin; involuntary
   C. Cardiac: in walls of heart; involuntary; striated
3. Structure of muscle tissue
   A. Microscopic
      a. Skeletal muscle: cells (fibers) thread-like cylinders; multinucleated; sarcolemma; sarcoplasm; myofibrils contain actin and myosin (contractile material of cell)
      b. Smooth muscle: spindle-shaped cells; single nucleus; nonstriated myofibrils contain actin and myosin

   c. Cardiac muscle: cells quadrangular; form network of branching fibers; intercalated discs; functional syncytium; blood supply essential to life
   B. Gross structure
      a. Connective tissues provide support and nourishment
      b. Skeletal muscle: covered by epimysium; partitioned into bundles by perimysium; individual fibers surrounded by endomysium; attached to tendons or bones by connective tissue "harness"
      c. Smooth muscle: arranged in sheets or bundles; in circular or longitudinal plane; produces changes in size and shape of organs
      d. Cardiac muscle: composed of bundles; arranged in spirals or figures-of-eight; contraction obliterates cavities and empties them; muscle of atria not continuous with ventricles
   C. Chemical composition: 75% water; 20% protein; carbohydrate as glycogen and glucose; ATP and phosphocreatine chief NPN substances
4. Nerve supply of muscle tissue:
   A. Afferent or sensory fibers
      a. Somatic afferent inform CNS about degree of contraction of skeletal muscles
      b. Visceral afferent inform CNS about condition of cells in smooth and cardiac muscle
   B. Efferent fibers
      a. Messages to skeletal muscles over somatic efferent fibers; motor unit is nerve cell, its fiber and all muscle fibers supplied by it; nerve injury results in paralysis
      b. Messages to smooth and cardiac muscle over visceral efferent fibers; most organs have double nerve supply; may contract independently of nerve supply (automaticity)
5. Physiologic properties of muscle tissue
   A. Excitability or irritability
      a. Capacity to respond to stimulus

b. Polarization; depolarization; repolarization

c. Stimuli: nerve impulses, distention, temperature change, composition of blood; rhythmicity

d. Neuromuscular transmission: acetylcholine; cholinesterase; muscle relaxants

B. Contractility

  a. Capacity to shorten

  b. Molecular changes: interaction between actin and myosin

  c. Energy sources: immediate source is ATP; phosphocreatine aids restoration of ATP; oxidative processes of citric acid cycle; anaerobic breakdown of carbohydrate; steady state; oxygen debt; repayment of oxygen debt; fatigue

  d. Heat production

  e. Calcium ions related to "relaxing substance"

C. Muscle tone or tonus

  a. State of steady, partial contraction present in muscle at all times

  b. In skeletal muscle due to stretch reflex; dependent on nerve supply

  c. In smooth muscle: independent of nerve supply; widely fluctuating; greatly influenced by chemical composition of environment

  d. In cardiac muscle: independent of nerve supply; synonymous with general physiologic condition

D. Extensibility and elasticity

  a. Capacity to stretch when force applied and to regain original form when force removed

  b. Prevents muscle rupture under stress; most marked in smooth muscle

6. Mechanical phenomena of contraction

A. Types of contraction

  a. Simple twitch—single contraction followed by relaxation

    (1) Latent period

    (2) Contraction period

    (3) Relaxation period

  b. Refractory period

  c. Summation

  d. Tetanic contraction — smooth, sustained, no apparent relaxation; makes possible all normal body movements

  e. Isometric contraction — increase in tonus, length unchanged

  f. Isotonic contraction—muscle shortens, tonus unchanged

B. Strength of contraction affected by

  a. General metabolic conditions

  b. Strength of stimulus

  c. Rate at which stimulus is applied

  d. Weight of the load to be moved

  e. Temperature of fluid around muscle fibers

  f. Size of muscle

  g. Fatigue

C. Pathologic contractions: spasm, fasciculation, fibrillation

---

PRACTICAL APPLICATIONS AND QUESTIONS

(Encircle the letter of the *best* answer to each question.)

A. As B. J. walked out of the house she noticed that her bus was just pulling away from the curb. Running at full speed she managed to catch it at the next stop. However, she was breathing rapidly and her muscles "seemed so weak" that she had difficulty in getting aboard.

1. Which of the following delivered orders for the contraction of her skeletal muscles?

  a. somatic afferent fibers

  b. visceral afferent fibers

  c. somatic efferent fibers

  d. visceral efferent fibers

2. Substances which tend to *decrease* in quantity during strenuous spurts of exercise are

  a. carbon dioxide, oxygen and water

  b. oxygen, glycogen and ATP

  c. water, carbon dioxide and glycogen

  d. ATP, lactic acid and oxygen

3. Even though the spurt of exercise was completed, B. J. was still breathing rapidly because
    a. lactic acid concentration was low
    b. glycogen was being oxidized to glucose
    c. excessive amounts of pyruvic acid were present
    d. she was repaying her oxygen debt

4. Which of the following reactions require the presence of oxygen?
    a. lactic acid $\rightarrow$ pyruvic acid $\rightarrow$ CO_2 + H_2O + energy
    b. glycogen $\rightarrow$ glucose $\rightarrow$ pyruvic acid
    c. ATP $\rightarrow$ ADP + energy for contraction
    d. glucose $\rightarrow$ pyruvic acid $\rightarrow$ lactic acid

5. The sensation of weakness which she experienced after the exercise was due to
    a. increased blood supply to the muscles
    b. excessive amounts of pyruvic acid within the muscles
    c. increased heat production by the muscles
    d. accumulation of lactic acid within the muscles

B. *G. L., a cross-country runner, was struck by an automobile. He suffered an injury to the nerve supply in his right arm.*

1. What symptom would you expect him to observe in his arm muscles immediately after the accident?
    a. increased muscle tone
    b. hypertrophy
    c. tetanic contractions
    d. paralysis

2. Because of their regular exercise and training athletes have good muscle tone. Tonus may be defined as
    a. the ability of muscles to stretch when force is applied
    b. a state of steady partial contraction
    c. sustained contraction
    d. a quick contraction followed by relaxation

3. The maintenance of skeletal muscle tone is
    a. entirely dependent on the CNS
    b. not essential for everyday activities
    c. independent of any reflex action
    d. under our conscious control

4. While G. L. was being treated by a physiotherapist he learned that the strength of a muscular contraction is decreased by
    a. warming the muscle
    b. rapid application of stimuli
    c. hypertrophy
    d. atrophy

5

"A hard task and the muscle to achieve it..."

THE TEAMSTER ● *HENRY H. BASHFORD*

THE SKELETAL MUSCLES

Over 600 skeletal muscles are under our command as we move about at work and play. Varying in size, shape, power and method of attachment, these muscular engines enable us to execute all manner of voluntary movements. They also make up the so-called red meat of the body, comprising about 36 per cent of the body weight in women and 42 per cent in men. The combined weight of all the skeletal muscles in the body is about 3 times as great as that of all the bones.

Naming the skeletal muscles

Each skeletal muscle in the body has a name; many of these are now in English, others are still in Latin. Learning the names of some of the more important skeletal muscles will be an easier task if you understand that names have been assigned in a logical manner. The following list of ways in which muscles are named will include specific examples of each.

1. *Location:* intercostal muscles (between the ribs); brachii (region of the arm); tibialis posterior (behind the tibia)

2. *Direction of fibers:* rectus (straight); transversus (across); obliquus (in an oblique direction)

3. *Action:* adductor, flexor and levator (lifter)

4. *Shape or Size:* deltoid (from Greek letter *delta*); trapezius (like a trapezoid); maximus (largest); minimus (smallest); longus (long); brevis (short)

5. *Number of heads of origin:* biceps (2 heads); triceps (3 heads); quadriceps (4 heads)

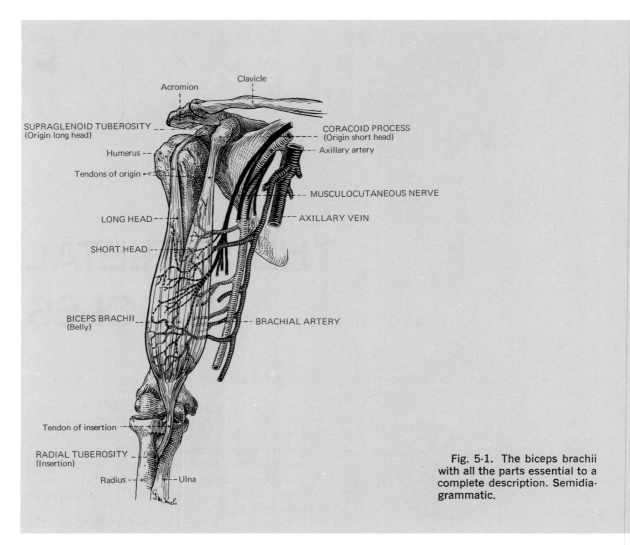

Fig. 5-1. The biceps brachii with all the parts essential to a complete description. Semidiagrammatic.

6. *Points of attachment:* sternocleidomastoid (sternum, clavicle, mastoid process of temporal bone); sacrospinalis (sacrum and vertebrae of spinal column)

As you progress in your study of the muscles you will discover that some names are combinations of two of the above, such as adductor magnus, biceps brachii and rectus abdominis.

Parts of a skeletal muscle

The end of the skeletal muscle that is the relatively more fixed point of attachment is called the *origin*. The end that is freely movable is called the *insertion*. When the muscle contracts, the insertion is pulled toward the origin. However, you will note later that the origin is fixed absolutely in

Fig. 5-2. Diagram of a longitudinal section of a muscle showing its termination in a tendon. The sarcolemma, the endomysium, the perimysium and the epimysium are continuous with the connective tissue of the tendon. The connective tissue forms a harness, against which the pull of contracting muscle fibers is exerted. (Modified from Ham, A. W.: Histology, ed. 2, Philadelphia, Lippincott)

Fig. 5-3. Diagram of coordinated movement. (Left) In flexion of the forearm the biceps brachii is contracted and the triceps is inhibited. (Right) In extension, the reverse condition holds. (Redrawn from Keith)

only a small number of muscles, such as those of the face. In many other muscles, the origin and the insertion are "functionally" interchangeable, which means that these can "act from either end." For example, muscles which pull the thigh up toward the trunk also may pull the trunk down toward the thigh, as in bending forward. That portion of the muscle between the origin and the

insertion is called the *body* or *belly* of the muscle. The parts of a typical muscle (biceps brachii) are shown in Figure 5-1.

Attachments of skeletal muscles

Extensions of the connective tissue of muscle attach the muscles to bone, cartilage, skin, mucous

Fig. 5-4. Muscles of the body, anterior view.

Sternocleidomastoid
Splenius capitis

Trapezius

Rhomboid major

Teres minor
Teres major

Latissimus dorsi

External abdominal
oblique

Gluteus medius

Gluteus maximus

Gracilis

Adductor magnus

Semitendinosus

Biceps femoris (long head)

Semimembranosus

Plantaris

Gastrocnemius

Soleus
Peroneus longus
Flexor digitorum longus
Peroneus brevis
Calcaneus tendon (Achilles)

Deltoid

Triceps brachii (long head)

Triceps brachii (lateral head)

Brachioradialis
Extensor carpi radialis
longus
Anconeus

Flexor carpi ulnaris
Extensor carpi ulnaris
Extensor digitorum
communis
Extensor carpi radialis
brevis
Abductor pollicis longus

Extensor pollicis brevis

Iliotibial band

Biceps femoris (short head)

Fig. 5-5. Muscles of the body, posterior view.

membrane or fasciae. The attachments to periosteum of bone or perichondrium of cartilage are broad. This type of attachment is found in the intercostal muscles and in some of the muscles attached to the shoulder and the hip girdles.

The connective tissue may be prolonged in the form of tendons, as shown in Figure 5-2. Tendons attach to bone, cartilage or other structures. They vary greatly in appearance; many of them resemble glistening white cords, some are like flat ribbons, and others are broad sheets called *aponeuroses*. In each case the type of attachment is best suited to the particular work which that muscle performs. Tendons are extremely strong, and severe stress will usually result in a broken bone rather than a torn tendon.

Muscles are separated from one another and held in position by sheets of tough fibrous connective tissue (deep fascia). *Bursae*, the closed sacs that contain a small amount of fluid (see p. 108), serve to reduce friction in areas where there are gliding movements between muscles and their underlying parts. Important bursae are found at the elbow, the shoulder, the hip and the knee.

Skeletal muscle action

Skeletal muscles are responsible for the movements of parts of the body or the body as a whole and are used in both voluntary and reflex movements. When muscles contract, they become shorter and thus exert a pull on their attachments. Most skeletal muscles are attached to bones (which function as levers) and move those bones at the joints (which serve as fulcrums). Muscles usually do not lie directly over the part that is to be moved; instead they are located above or below it, in front of or behind it, depending on the desired movement. For example, the muscle bodies which move the forearm are located in the region of the arm, their tendons crossing the elbow joint to insert on the bones of the forearm.

Many skeletal muscles are arranged in pairs; when one of a pair contracts the other muscle of the pair relaxes. The first is called the **prime mover,** and the second the **antagonist**. The relaxa-

tion of the antagonist makes possible coordinated movement. A diagram of coordinated movement is illustrated in Figure 5-3. When the opposite movement is performed, the prime mover becomes the antagonist, and vice versa.

When you wish to perform a particular act, such as rubbing your eye, the act as a whole is thought of, and you do not analyze it into the individual muscles that you are going to use. Even our simplest acts require the coordinated use of many muscles in different functional capacities; this is essential to the precision of the act. Other muscles act as **synergists** (meaning "working together") and enable the prime movers to perform the desired act efficiently and smoothly. In some instances, the synergists control the position of intermediate joints, so that the prime mover may exert its action on a distal joint. Suppose you wish to clench your hand; in order to do this the prime movers flex the fingers and the antagonists (extensors of the fingers) relax. The synergistic muscles fix the wrist in the extended position. If you have something in your hand which someone wants to take from you, he will flex your wrist, and your grip will be lost, since your fingers will no longer remain flexed. Even though he knows nothing of prime movers, antagonists and synergists, he can get what he wants by interfering with the coordinated movements that accompany clenching your hand.

Study of individual muscles

Due to limitations of space only a few of the more than 600 skeletal muscles can be described in any detail. For a more complete listing of these muscles your attention is called to the Table of Muscles at the end of this chapter. Figures 5-4 and 5-5 will give you an idea of the muscles of the body as a whole.

As you begin to learn the names and the locations of prominent muscles, try to visualize them in relation to your own body. Movements of many of the muscles described in this chapter can be seen and felt through the skin, particularly if you make the muscles "work" for you. For example, the biceps brachii flexes the forearm and supinates

Fig. 5-6. Superficial dissection of the head, showing the muscles of facial expression.

the hand; to increase its work, have a friend hold your hand and resist these movements. Note the muscle activity under the skin of your arm.

Learning the location of a muscle also will help you to analyze its main action. For example, the triceps brachii lies on the posterior aspect of the arm, and its tendon of insertion crosses *behind* the elbow joint on its way to the ulna. Since *muscles can only pull* (not push), the action here would necessarily be extension of the forearm. Understanding this basic principle is essential for learning the action of any muscle.

MUSCLES OF THE HEAD AND THE NECK

Included in this group will be some of the more prominent muscles concerned with facial expression, movements of the eyeball, mastication and movements of the head as a whole.

Movement related to facial expression

The epicranius (occipitofrontalis) is a broad musculofibrous sheet that covers the top and the sides of the skull; it is composed of two muscular portions, the frontalis and the occipitalis, connected by a fibrous sheet called the *epicranial aponeurosis* or *galea aponeurotica* (Fig. 5-6). The *frontalis,* which arises from the aponeurosis and inserts into the skin in the region of the eyebrows, raises the eyebrows and wrinkles the skin of the forehead. It is used in expressing both attention and surprise; if its action is exaggerated it gives rise to the expression of fright or horror. The *occipitalis* arises from the occipital bone and the mastoid process and inserts into the aponeurosis; it draws the scalp backward.

The orbicularis oculi is a flat, elliptical muscle that sweeps around the circumference of the orbit (Fig. 5-6). Its main action is to constrict the opening into the orbit, shut out light and protect the eye against the entrance of foreign bodies. It arises from the nasal portion of the frontal bone and the frontal process of the maxilla. The fibers extend laterally, occupy the eyelids, encircle the orbit, and extend into the temporal region and the cheek. When only part of the muscle is working, the eyelids are closed gently as in sleep. When more fibers are called into action, the eyelids are

LEVATOR PALPEBRAE SUPERIORIS
SUPERIOR OBLIQUE
SUPERIOR RECTUS
LATERAL RECTUS (CUT)
MEDIAL RECTUS
OPTIC NERVE
STUMP OF EXTERNAL RECTUS

FRONTAL SINUS
TROCHLEA
INSERTION OF LEVATOR PALPEBRAE SUPERIORIS INTO UPPER TARSAL PLATE
EYE LIDS TURNED ASIDE
INFERIOR OBLIQUE
MAXILLARY SINUS

INFERIOR RECTUS

Fig. 5-7. Lateral view of extrinsic eye muscles after removal of outer wall of orbit; levator of upper eyelid has been pulled upward and inward. Portion of external or lateral rectus is removed. Maxillary and frontal sinuses are shown opened.

closed firmly, as when looking into the sun; tissues overhanging the orbit are lowered while the skin of the cheek is raised, producing the familiar wrinkles or "crows feet" that radiate from the corner of the eye.

The **levator palpebrae superioris** ("lifter of the upper eyelid") is the antagonist of the orbicularis oculi. It arises from the back of the orbit and passes forward to be inserted into the tarsal plate (dense connective tissue in the upper lid) as shown in Figure 5-7. This muscle opens the eye by drawing the upper eyelid upward and backward.

The **orbicularis oris** consists of numerous layers of muscle fibers that surround the opening of the mouth and extend in different directions (Fig. 5-6). It is composed partly of fibers derived from other facial muscles, which are inserted into the lips, and partly of fibers distinctive of the lips. This muscle closes the lips and compresses them against the teeth; it also may cause protrusion or pouting of the lips.

The **buccinator** (Figs. 5-6 and 5-8) is the muscle coat of the cheeks. It arises from the max-illa and the mandible and extends forward to be inserted into the sides of the mouth. This muscle draws the corner of the mouth laterally, pulls the lips against the teeth and flattens the cheek. It aids in mastication, swallowing, whistling and blowing wind instruments. It prevents food from being pocketed between the teeth and the cheek. When the cheeks have been distended with air, the buccinator muscles expel it between the lips, as in blowing the trumpet, from which the muscle derived its name.

The **zygomatic muscle** arises from the zygomatic bone and inserts into the orbicularis oris (Fig. 5-6). It raises the corner of the mouth and draws it laterally, as in smiling and laughing.

The **platysma** is a broad sheet of muscle that lies just under the skin in the anterolateral region of the neck (Fig. 5-6). Its fibers arise from fascia covering the pectoral and the deltoid muscles and extend obliquely upward across the clavicle to insert on the mandible and into the skin around the mouth. The platysma is a muscle of facial expression which acts particularly on the skin of the lower lip and the neck. It wrinkles the skin of the

Fig. 5-8. Lateral aspect of the skull with the temporal, the masseter, the buccinator and the orbicularis oris muscles in place.

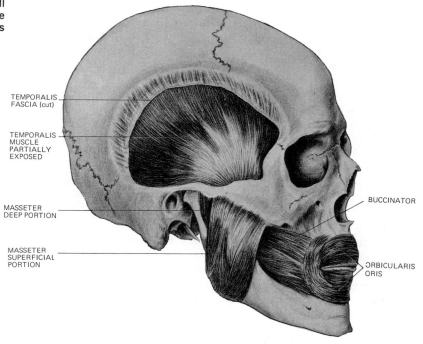

TEMPORALIS FASCIA (cut)

TEMPORALIS MUSCLE PARTIALLY EXPOSED

MASSETER DEEP PORTION

MASSETER SUPERFICIAL PORTION

BUCCINATOR

ORBICULARIS ORIS

neck, depresses the corner of the mouth and expresses melancholy, sadness, fright and suffering. It also relieves the pressure on the veins that lie under it and thus aids the circulation of the blood.

Many other facial muscles help in the expression of various emotions and in emphasizing spoken words. If you watch the faces of your classmates you will see how frequently their expressions change due to the varying activities of these muscles. Look in the mirror and assume various facial expressions, such as smiling, frowning and determination; note which muscles are called into action.

Movement of the eyeball

There are 6 muscles that control the movement of the eyeball and make it possible for us to glance in all directions without moving the head (Fig. 5-7). The 4 rectus muscles arise from the margin of the optic foramen at the apex of the orbital cavity. Each muscle extends forward to insert into the sclera (outer coat) of the eyeball on four different sides as indicated by their names, i.e., superior, inferior, medial and lateral recti.

The superior rectus directs the eyeball upward as in looking at the ceiling, and the **inferior rectus** turns the eyeball downward, as in looking at the floor. The **medial rectus** directs the eyeball inward, and, working with its fellow on the opposite side, enables one to gaze at near objects. The **lateral rectus** directs the eyeball outward; it normally works with the medial rectus of the other eye, as in glancing to one side.

There are 2 oblique muscles (superior and inferior) which work with a high degree of coordination as they tend to rotate the eyeball on its axis. The **superior oblique** arises at the apex of the orbit, extends forward and passes through a ring of cartilage at the upper medial angle of the orbit. This determines the direction of its pull, which is downward and laterally, with a medial rotation. The **inferior oblique** arises from the medial part of the orbital floor and curves around the under portion of the eyeball to insert on the lateral aspect of the sclera; it turns the eyeball upward and laterally, with a lateral rotation.

Strabismus refers to a deviation of one of the eyes from its proper direction; it may be due to a muscle defect or to a lack of coordination in the movement of the two eyes. For example, if one or both eyes are turned inward ("crosseyed"), the defect is referred to as *convergent strabismus,* and if one or both eyes are turned outward ("wall-eyed"), it is referred to as *divergent strabismus.*

Movement of the mandible and the tongue

Chewing and swallowing of food are made possible by the coordinated action of many muscles.

The masseter (Fig. 5-8) arises from the zygomatic arch and is inserted on the lateral surface of the ramus and the angle of the mandible. If you close your jaws tightly you can feel this muscle while it is in action; it appears as a bulging mass near the angle of the jaw.

The temporal muscle (Fig. 5-8) is a fan-shaped muscle that arises from the temporal fossa, extends downward beneath the zygomatic arch and inserts on the coronoid process of the mandible. If the jaws are closed firmly, the temporal muscle bulges out in the temple.

The pterygoids (Fig. 5-9) are deeply placed and extend from the under aspect of the skull to the medial surface of the ramus of the mandible. The *external pterygoid* muscle assists in opening the mouth. The side-to-side movements, such as occur in grinding the teeth, are produced by the pterygoid muscles of the two sides acting in alternation. If the external pterygoids of the two sides act together, they protrude the jaw.

The muscles of mastication enable one to close the mouth and clench the teeth. Normally, we keep the mouth closed; it is remarkable how the expression can change by merely opening the mouth. When the muscles are relaxed, the mandible drops, due to the pull of gravity.

Movements of the tongue are important in speaking, in keeping food between the teeth during mastication, and in the process of swallowing.

The most characteristic feature of the tongue is its mobility. It is composed of a compact mass of interwoven muscle fibers covered with mucous membrane. There are 2 groups of muscles in the tongue, the intrinsic and the extrinsic.

The intrinsic muscles lie entirely within the tongue and are responsible for its mobility and changes in general shape. The intrinsic muscles are important in speaking, mastication and swallowing.

The extrinsic muscles arise outside the tongue and insert into it (Fig. 5-10).

The genioglossus forms part of the body of the tongue. It arises from the mandible, behind the point of the chin, and spreads out in a fanlike manner to be inserted along the whole length of the undersurface of the tongue. It performs various functions according to the part of it that contracts. The anterior fibers withdraw the tongue into the mouth and depress its tip; the middle fibers draw the base of the tongue forward and protrude it from the mouth. If the 2 genioglossus muscles act along their entire length, they draw the tongue downward. When this is done, the superior surface of the tongue becomes concave, like a channel. Fluids readily pass along this channel toward the pharynx during the act of sucking.

The styloglossus (Fig. 5-10) arises from the styloid process of the temporal bone and is inserted into the whole length of the side and the underpart of the tongue. The styloglossus muscles retract the tongue, elevate the margins and raise the base of the tongue.

Movement of the head and the neck

Many muscles are involved in movement of the head as a whole. The sternocleidomastoid and the semispinalis capitis are typical examples.

The sternocleidomastoid (Figs. 5-11 and 5-13) is a strong, bandlike muscle that lies superficially across the side of the neck. It can be palpated in its entire length if you resist the pressure of one hand under your chin. It arises from the upper border of the sternum and the clavicle and extends obliquely upward and backward to be in-

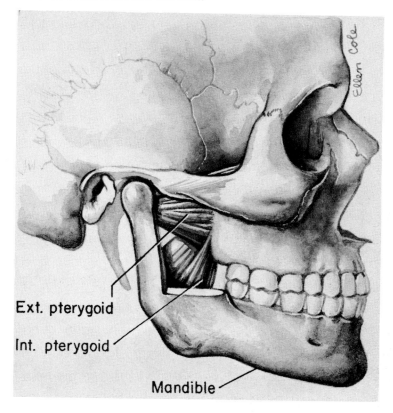

Ext. pterygoid

Int. pterygoid

Mandible

Fig. 5-9. The pterygoid muscles; a portion of the ramus of the mandible has been cut away.

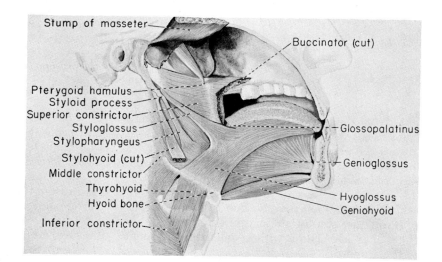

Fig. 5-10. Pharyngeal muscles and extrinsic muscles of the tongue.

Stump of masseter

Buccinator (cut)

Pterygoid hamulus
Styloid process
Superior constrictor
Styloglossus
Stylopharyngeus
Stylohyoid (cut)
Middle constrictor
Thyrohyoid
Hyoid bone
Inferior constrictor

Glossopalatinus

Genioglossus

Hyoglossus
Geniohyoid

Fig. 5-11. Muscles of neck, thorax, and arm—anterior
view. Certain superficial muscles have been removed (left
side), so that deep muscles may better be visualized.

serted on the mastoid process of the temporal
bone. The sternocleidomastoid draws the head
toward the shoulder of the same side and rotates
the head so as to carry the face toward the opposite side. When the head is abnormally fixed in
this position one is said to have *torticollis or wry
neck;* this condition may be due to injury or disease of the sternocleidomastoid muscle, either
alone or in association with a similar involvement
of the trapezius.

If the 2 sternocleidomastoid muscles act together,
they flex the cervical part of the vertebral column
and bring the head forward. If the head is fixed,
these muscles elevate the thorax and, in this way,
aid in forced inspiration.

The semispinalis capitis (Figs. 5-12 and 5-14)
arises from the last 5 cervical and upper 5 thoracic
vertebrae; it extends upward to insert on the occipital bone. When these two muscles act together
they extend the head, but if one acts alone, it bends
the head to that side and rotates it so that the
face is turned to the opposite side.

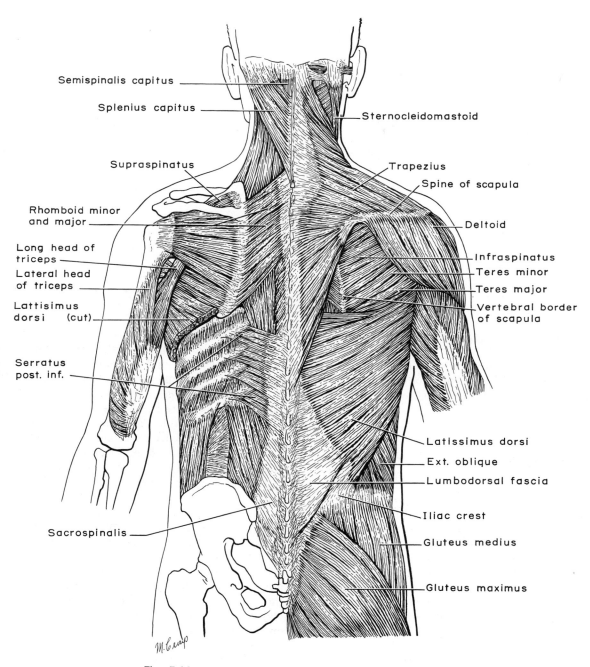

Semispinalis capitus

Splenius capitus

Sternocleidomastoid

Supraspinatus

Trapezius

Spine of scapula

Rhomboid minor
and major

Deltoid

Long head of
triceps

Infraspinatus

Lateral head
of triceps

Teres minor

Teres major

Lattisimus
dorsi   (cut)

Vertebral border
of scapula

Serratus
post. inf.

Latissimus dorsi

Ext. oblique

Lumbodorsal fascia

Iliac crest

Gluteus medius

Sacrospinalis

Gluteus maximus

Fig. 5-12. Muscles of neck, thorax, and arm—posterior
view. Certain superficial muscles have been removed (left
side), so that deep muscles may better be visualized.

Mastoid process

Sternal end of clavicle

Manubrium of sternum

Fig. 5-13.
The sternocleidomastoid muscles.

MUSCLES OF THE UPPER EXTREMITY

The muscles of the upper extremities are used in writing, eating, manipulating tools and machines, climbing, defending, attacking and innumerable other activities. They even play a part in expressing one's emotions.

Movement of the shoulder and the arm

The shoulder joint has the widest range of movement of all the joints due to its large humeral head, shallow socket and loose capsule. In addition, muscles which change the position of the scapula further increase this range of movement. The scapula can be moved forward, backward, upward, downward and rotated as it follows the movements of the arm. The head of the humerus is kept in the glenoid cavity during these movements. The arm can be abducted, adducted, flexed, extended and rotated at the shoulder joint.

Perform the following acts, and in each case try to determine the direction of the movements of the arms and the shoulders: fold your arms across your chest; make yourself round-shoul-

dered; throw out your chest and throw your shoulders back; tie your shoestrings; scratch your back; place a book on your head and move your arms in various directions without dropping the book. If you have been a careful observer during the above acts you noted that one muscle takes part in several acts, and that different parts of one muscle may take part in opposite acts, according to variations in the relative fixation of the attachments.

The trapezius is a very large muscle that lies superficially at the back of the neck and the upper part of the thorax (Figs. 5-12 and 5-15). The right and the left trapezius muscles together form a trapezoid, which is the reason the muscle was so named. Each trapezius arises from, or has its origin from, the occipital bone, the ligamentum nuchae, the spines of the 7th cervical and all of the thoracic vertebrae. Each is inserted on the clavicle, the acromion and the spine of the scapula on its own side.

The degree of contraction of the trapezius muscles determines the position of the shoulders. Depending on which part of the muscle is more fixed, the trapezius can take part in many acts, such as

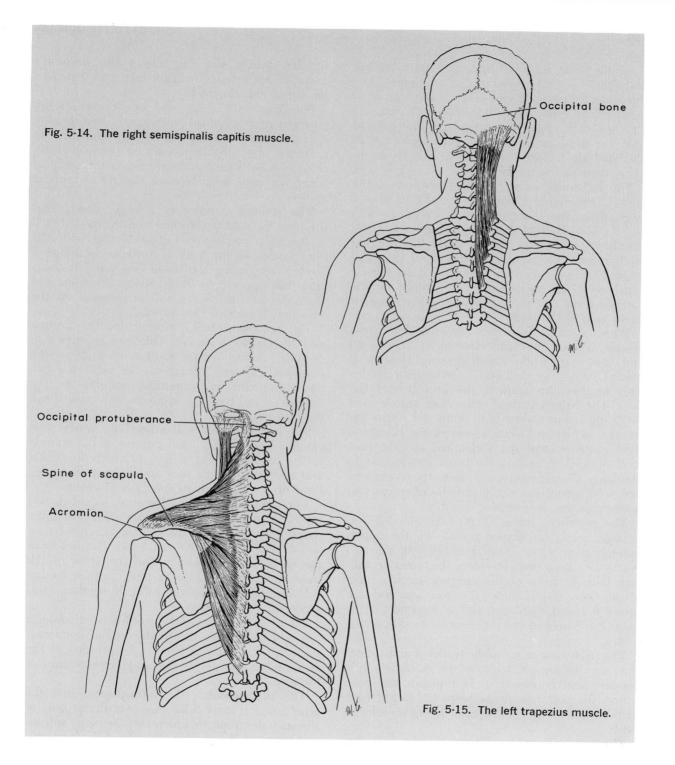

Fig. 5-14. The right semispinalis capitis muscle.

Occipital bone

Occipital protuberance

Spine of scapula

Acromion

Fig. 5-15. The left trapezius muscle.

(1) pulling the scapulae back and thus bracing the shoulders, (2) raising and shrugging the shoulders, (3) extending the head, and (4) turning the head from side to side. When all parts act together, they rotate the scapulae so that we can raise our arms as in reaching for objects on an overhead shelf. *Stiff neck* may be due to an inflammation of the trapezius.

The latissimus dorsi (meaning "widest of the back") is shown in Figures 5-12 and 5-16. It is a large, flat, triangular muscle that covers the loin and the lower half of the thoracic region. It arises mainly from the spines of the lower thoracic, the lumbar and the sacral vertebrae and the iliac crest. The fibers of each latissimus dorsi muscle converge to a narrow tendon and insert on the anterior surface of the upper part of the humerus on its side of the body.

With the trunk fixed, the latissimus dorsi powerfully extends the arm, drawing it downward and backward while simultaneously rotating it inward as in the well-known swimming stroke. This muscle also adducts the arm behind the back. The latissimus dorsi is the chief muscle used in giving a downward blow with the upper extremity. When both arms are fixed, the latissimus dorsi muscles assist the abdominal and the pectoral muscles in pulling the trunk forward, as in climbing. These muscles also raise the lower ribs and, in this way, can act as muscles of respiration when a person is breathing forcibly.

The pectoralis major (Figs. 5-11 and 5-17) is a large, thick, fan-shaped muscle on the upper, anterior part of the chest. The fibers of the two pectoralis major muscles form the anterior axillary folds in front of the armpits. Each muscle arises from the clavicle, the sternum and the upper 6 costal cartilages and is inserted on the greater tubercle of the humerus of its side of the body.

The pectoralis major adducts, flexes and rotates the humerus inward. It draws the shoulder girdle forward and depresses it. If the arm has been raised, the pectoralis major helps to bring it back to the side. These are the chief flying muscles in birds.

The pectoralis minor (Fig. 5-11) is a thin, triangular muscle that lies under the pectoralis major. It pulls the scapula forward and depresses the tip of the shoulder.

Both pectoralis major and minor muscles are removed during *radical mastectomy,* an extensive operation for cancer of the breast. Postoperative exercises are very important for such persons, since muscles which formerly acted primarily as synergists now must assume the role of prime movers.

The serratus anterior is a large muscle that occupies the side of the chest and the medial wall of the axilla or armpit (Figs. 5-11 and 5-18). Its fibers arise like the teeth of a saw or in a jagged fashion, suggesting the name "serratus." It arises from the upper 8 or 9 ribs along the front and the sides of the thorax and is inserted on the vertebral border of the scapula.

The serratus anterior muscles are the fixation muscles for the scapulae. They are important in pushing, during which motion they carry the scapulae forward. These muscles assist the trapezius muscles in supporting weights on the shoulders, and they aid in raising the arms above the horizontal level.

The coracobrachialis is a bandlike muscle that extends from the coracoid process of the scapula to the humerus (Fig. 5-19). It assists in flexion and adduction of the arm and helps to keep the head of the humerus in the glenoid cavity.

The deltoid is a thick, powerful, shield-shaped muscle that covers the shoulder joint and gives roundness to the upper part of the arm just below the shoulder (Figs. 5-11 and 5-20). It arises from the clavicle, the acromion and the spine of the scapula. Its fibers unite to form a thick tendon that inserts on the deltoid tubercle on the lateral aspect of the humerus.

When the whole deltoid contracts, it abducts the arm and raises it laterally to the horizontal position. The anterior fibers aid in flexion of the arm, and the posterior fibers aid in extension of the arm.

The supraspinatus, the **infraspinatus** and the **teres minor** (Figure 5-12) pass over the capsule of the shoulder joint, to which their tendons adhere, and insert on the greater tubercle of the humerus.

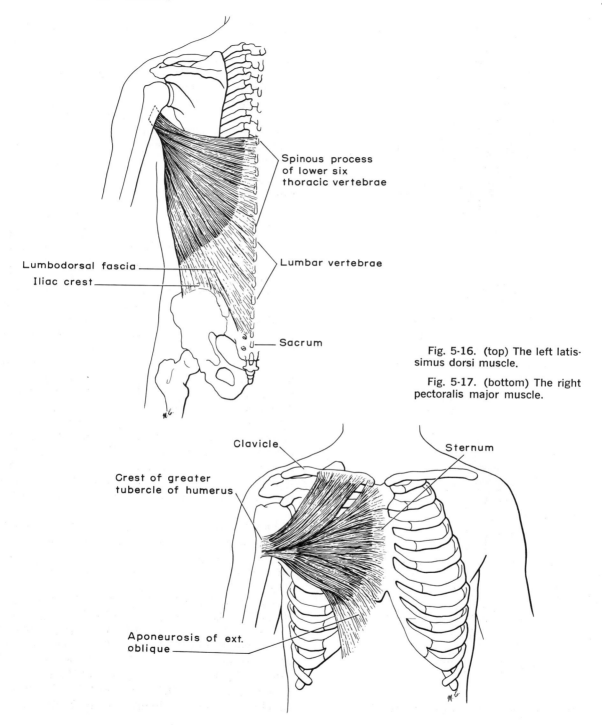

Spinous process
of lower six
thoracic vertebrae

Lumbar vertebrae

Lumbodorsal fascia

Iliac crest

Sacrum

Fig. 5-16. (top) The left latissimus dorsi muscle.

Fig. 5-17. (bottom) The right
pectoralis major muscle.

Clavicle

Sternum

Crest of greater
tubercle of humerus

Aponeurosis of ext.
oblique

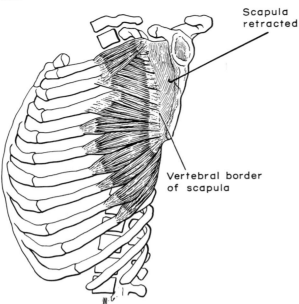

Scapula
retracted

Vertebral border
of scapula

Fig. 5-18. The left serratus anterior muscle.

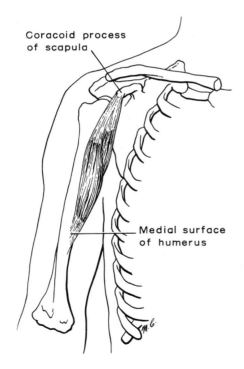

Coracoid process
of scapula

Medial surface
of humerus

Fig. 5-19. The right coracobrachialis muscle.

They help to protect the shoulder joint, as well as to assist in lateral rotation of the arm. The supraspinatus, in addition, aids the deltoid in abducting the arm and helps to fix the head of the humerus in the glenoid cavity.

The teres major (Fig. 5-12) arises from the axillary border of the scapula and ascends to the upper, anterior surface of the humerus. This thick, flat muscle extends the arm and adducts it behind the back.

Movement of the forearm and the hand

The biceps brachii (Figs. 5-1 and 5-11) is a large, conspicuous muscle which small boys like to show when boasting of their physical strength. It lies anterior to the humerus and forms a large part of the substance of the arm. As indicated by the name, the biceps brachii has 2 heads of origin; the long head arises from the upper margin of the glenoid cavity, and the short head from the tip of the coracoid process of the scapula. Both heads insert by way of a single tendon on the tuberosity at the proximal end of the radius. The biceps brachii assists in flexion of the forearm and is a powerful supinator of the hand (Fig. 5-21). Action of this muscle can be studied best by placing the fingers of the opposite hand on the anterior surface of the arm and then flexing the forearm. While maintaining the flexed position, rapidly alternate supination and pronation of the hand and feel the activity of this muscle. Note that flexion is most powerful when the hand is supinated.

The brachialis (Figs. 5-11 and 5-22) extends from the distal, anterior half of the humerus to the coronoid process of the ulna, covering and protecting the front of the elbow joint. It is a powerful flexor of the forearm.

The triceps brachii (Figs. 5-12 and 5-23) is a single muscle on the posterior aspect of the arm, but it arises by 3 heads: 2 from the humerus and a long one from the scapula. The common tendon of insertion crosses behind the elbow joint and attaches to the olecranon process of the ulna. The triceps brachii is the antagonist of the biceps brachii and the brachialis, which means that it

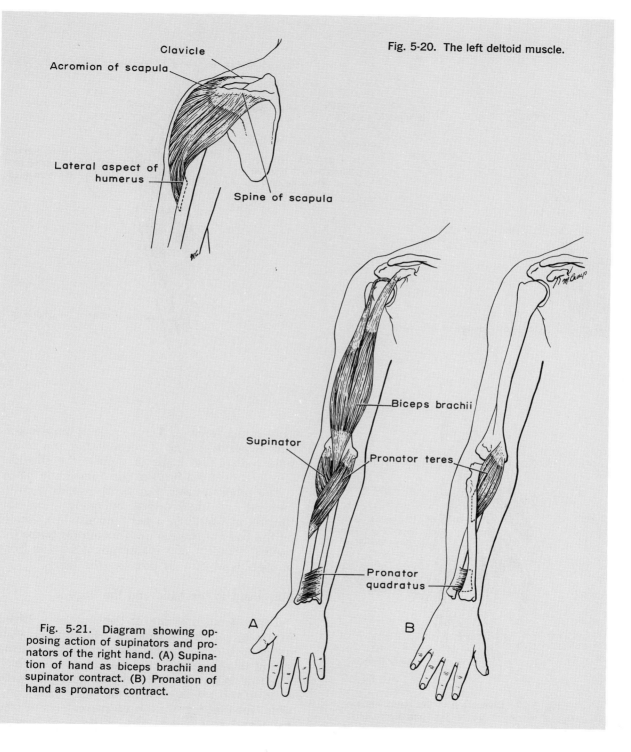

Fig. 5-20. The left deltoid muscle.

Clavicle

Acromion of scapula

Spine of scapula

Lateral aspect of humerus

Biceps brachii

Supinator

Pronator teres

Pronator quadratus

A

B

Fig. 5-21. Diagram showing opposing action of supinators and pronators of the right hand. (A) Supination of hand as biceps brachii and supinator contract. (B) Pronation of hand as pronators contract.

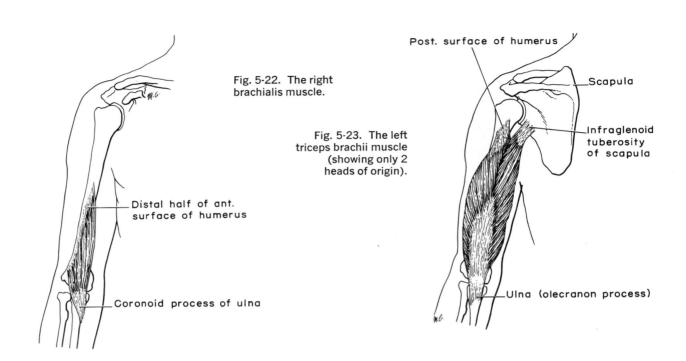

Fig. 5-22. The right brachialis muscle.

Fig. 5-23. The left triceps brachii muscle (showing only 2 heads of origin).

Post. surface of humerus

Scapula

Infraglenoid tuberosity of scapula

Ulna (olecranon process)

Distal half of ant. surface of humerus

Coronoid process of ulna

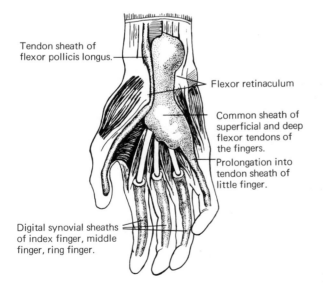

Tendon sheath of flexor pollicis longus.

Flexor retinaculum

Common sheath of superficial and deep flexor tendons of the fingers.

Prolongation into tendon sheath of little finger.

Digital synovial sheaths of index finger, middle finger, ring finger.

Fig. 5-24. Dissection of the palm, showing sheaths of flexor tendons artificially distended.

extends the forearm. This muscle is very important in pushing, since it converts the arm into a solid rod. It also helps to support the shoulder joint and hold the head of the humerus in place.

The pronator teres (Fig. 5-21) extends from its humeral and ulnar origins obliquely across the forearm and ends in a flat tendon which inserts on the body of the radius. This muscle forms the medial boundary of the antecubital fossa in front of the elbow joint. It pronates the hand.

Movement of the hand and the fingers

For a detailed listing of the muscles involved in movement of the hand and the fingers, your attention is called to the Table of Muscles at the end of this chapter. Contraction of muscles which originate in the forearm and pull across the wrist joint, together with those in the hand, makes possible an amazing variety of movements of the hand and the fingers. For purposes of general

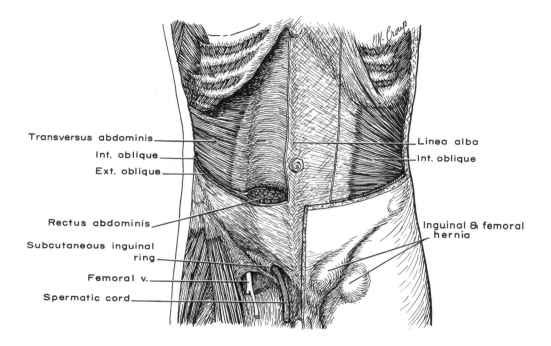

Transversus abdominis

Int. oblique

Ext. oblique

Rectus abdominis

Subcutaneous inguinal ring

Femoral v.

Spermatic cord

Linea alba

Int. oblique

Inguinal & femoral hernia

Fig. 5-25. Muscles of the anterolateral abdominal wall; inguinal and femoral hernias shown on left side of body.

description the muscles of the forearm may be divided into two subgroups: anteromedial and posterolateral.

The anteromedial muscles of the forearm, crossing in front of the wrist joint, are pronators and flexors of the hand and the fingers. The **posterolateral muscles,** crossing the posterior aspect of the wrist joint, are supinators and extensors of the hand and the fingers. Feel the movement of these muscles under the skin of your forearm while opening and closing the hand.

While flexing and extending the fingers, note the numerous tendons which are usually visible as well as palpable at the hand and the wrist. These glistening white cords are encased in slippery synovial tendon sheaths which reduce friction between the moving tendons and the stationary bones. Figure 5-24 illustrates the artificially distended sheaths of the flexor tendons of the right hand.

Injuries of the hand may easily sever the tendons of the muscles of the forearm. Repair after such lacerations must be exact in order for normal movements to be restored. When such repairs are attempted in outpatient clinics, sometimes wrong tendons have been sutured together. Generally it is realized that it is imperative to do such repairs on tendons of the wrist and the hand in the operating room where better facilities are available. Infection in the hand may travel along the tendon sheaths producing a *tenosynovitis,* or inflammation of a tendon and its sheath. Another complication, one that frequently follows fracture of the distal end of the radius, is stiffness of the wrist and the fingers due to adhesions (sticking together) of the extensor tendons and their sheaths to surrounding structures.

The thenar eminence (thumb side of the palm) is made up of muscles that arise from the carpus and the metacarpus and insert on the metacarpal and first phalanx of the thumb. A similar group about the little finger makes up the **hypothenar eminence.** These muscle groups can be seen in Figure 5-24 but they are not labeled. These muscles of the hand act on the 1st and the 5th metacarpal bones and bring the thumb and the little finger into contact with each other. Observe all the intricate movements that you can perform with your thumb and fingers. The free movements of the thumb are of great importance in the human hand, and many are distinctly characteristic of man.

MUSCLES OF THE TRUNK

The muscles of the trunk will be considered in the following groups: (1) muscles of respiration, (2) muscles of the abdominal wall, (3) muscles of the pelvic floor, and (4) deep muscles of the back.

Muscles of respiration

The diaphragm and the external intercostals are the chief muscles of respiration. Other muscles of the thorax, the neck and the abdomen play a relatively minor role in normal breathing, but they may become very important when breathing is labored or forced in any way (p. 445).

The external intercostals fill in the spaces between the ribs (Fig. 5-27). They arise from the lower portions of the first 11 ribs, and the fibers extend downward and forward to be inserted on the upper borders of the ribs below. These muscles play an important part in respiration by enlarging the thoracic cavity from side to side and from front to back as they elevate the ribs.

The internal intercostals (Fig. 5-27) lie under cover of the external intercostals and are similar to them, except in the direction of their fibers, which pass downward and backward. These muscles probably depress the ribs to some extent and may decrease the size of the thorax.

The diaphragm is a dome-shaped muscular partition which completely separates the thoracic and the abdominal cavities (Fig. 1-5). The heart and the lungs rest on the upper, convex surface of this muscle as it forms the floor of the thoracic cavity.

The lower, concave surface forms the roof of the abdominal cavity (Fig. 5-28), lying directly over the liver on the right side and over the spleen and the stomach on the left side. The central portion of the diaphragm is composed of fibrous tissue and is called the *central tendon*. The peripheral muscular portion of the diaphragm arises from the xiphoid process of the sternum, the costal margins of the lower 6 ribs and the vertebral column. The fibers converge to be inserted into the central tendon. There are 3 large openings in the diaphragm; one transmits the vagus nerves and the esophagus; the second transmits the aorta, azygos vein and the thoracic duct, and the third transmits the inferior vena cava.

When the muscular fibers of the diaphragm contract, the central portion is pulled downward, and thus the thoracic cavity above is enlarged from top to bottom. Because of this, the diaphragm is the principal muscle of inspiration. The level of the dome is changing constantly during respiratory movements. Also, its level varies with the amount of distention of the stomach and the intestines. When one is standing or sitting, the diaphragm descends to a lower level than when one is lying down, the abdominal organs tending to pull the diaphragm down in the first case and to push it up in the second. Therefore, patients who are in respiratory distress will breathe more easily if the head of the bed is elevated so as to support them in a sitting position.

Muscles of the abdominal wall

The anterolateral abdominal wall is composed of 4 pairs of flat muscles. Each muscle is enclosed by fascia which continues beyond the muscle to form aponeuroses. Fusion of right and left aponeuroses occurs in the midline from sternum to pubis and forms a sort of seam called the *linea alba* (meaning "white line") (Fig. 5-25).

The external oblique is the strongest and most superficial muscle of the lateral abdominal wall. It is a broad, thin, muscular sheet, as shown in Figure 5-25. It is composed of muscular tissue on the lateral wall and an aponeurosis on the anterior wall of the abdomen. It arises from the

Fig. 5-26. Transverse section of the anterolateral abdominal wall showing arrangement of muscular layers.

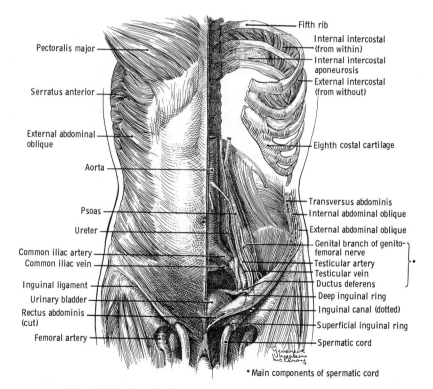

Fig. 5-27. Inguinal canal, spermatic cord and contents. Greater part of abdominal wall removed on left side to expose these structures. Intercostal muscles shown in their relationship to ribs from within and from without. Superficial muscles of abdomen and thorax shown on right side of the body.

DIAPHRAGM (OUTER SURFACE)

VENA CAVA INFERIOR

AORTA

TWELFTH RIB

CRUS OF DIAPHRAGM

PSOAS MINOR

ILIOPSOAS { PSOAS MAJOR

ILIACUS

OBTURATOR EXTERNUS

ADDUCTOR BREVIS

ADDUCTOR MAGNUS

VASTUS INTERMEDIUS

VASTUS LATERALIS (CUT)

RECTAS FEMORIS (CUT)

VASTUS MEDIALIS (CUT)

LIGAMENTUM PATELLAE

SARTORIUS (INSERTION)

ESOPHAGUS

CENTRAL TENDON OF DIAPHRAGM

DIAPHRAGM (INNER SURFACE)

QUADRATUS LUMBORUM

INGUINAL LIGAMENT

GLUTEUS MINIMUS

PECTINEUS

ADDUCTOR LONGUS (CUT)

OBTURATOR EXTERNUS

GRACILIS

ADDUCTOR LONGUS (CUT)

SARTORIUS

RECTUS FEMORIS

VASTUS LATERALIS

VASTUS MEDIALIS

TENDON OF QUADRICEPS FEMORIS

PATELLA

Fig. 5-28. Diaphragm, anterior view, with a portion removed to show the inner surface, with central tendon and openings. Most of the muscles of the abdomen and upper right thigh have been removed to show the relations of the deeper muscles to the skeleton. The superficial muscles are shown on the left thigh.

sides of the lower 8 ribs by slips that interlace with those of the serratus anterior. The fibers extend downward and forward to be inserted on the iliac crest, the anterior superior iliac spine and the pubic tubercle. Between the iliac spine and the pubic tubercle, the lower border of the muscle has no bony attachment but folds back on itself (like the hem on a dress) to form a thick band called the *inguinal ligament* (Figs. 5-27 and 5-28), an important anatomic landmark.

The large aponeurosis of the external oblique muscle forms part of the anterior abdominal wall and inserts into the linea alba. The **subcutaneous or superficial inguinal ring** is an opening in the aponeurosis just above and lateral to the pubic tubercle (Fig. 5-25); it is one of the weak places in the abdominal wall.

The posterior portions of the external oblique muscles are overlapped by the latissimus dorsi muscles.

The internal oblique muscle (Fig. 5-22) also is a broad, thin sheet of muscular tissue. It is located between the external oblique and the transversus abdominis muscles. It arises from the lumbar fascia, part of the iliac crest and lateral two thirds of the inguinal ligament. The fibers extend upward and forward. Some are inserted on the cartilages of the 7th, the 8th and the 9th ribs; the remainder of the fibers spread out like a fan and become an aponeurosis, which inserts into the linea alba. The lower part of the aponeurosis inserts on the pubic bone; the upper part splits to enclose the rectus abdominis before it reaches the linea alba.

The transversus abdominis (Fig. 5-25) is deeply placed in the lateral abdominal wall. It arises from the iliac crest, the inguinal ligament, the deep fascia of the back and the lower ribs. The fibers pass directly forward around the abdominal wall to form what has been called a "living girdle." They end in an aponeurosis which helps to form the sheath of the rectus abdominis before inserting into the xiphoid process, the linea alba and the pubic bone. There is an opening in the aponeurosis of the transversus abdominis halfway between the anterior superior iliac spine and the pubis. This opening is called the **abdominal or deep inguinal ring** (Fig. 5-27); it is another of the weak places in the abdominal wall. The fibrous sheet internal to the transversus abdominis muscle is called the transversus fascia, and internal to this fascia is the serous membrane known as the peritoneum (p. 459).

The external oblique, the internal oblique and the transversus muscles, with their aponeuroses, form a triple wall for the abdomen (Fig. 5-26). The muscle fibers run in 3 directions and greatly strengthen the wall.

The rectus abdominis muscle (Fig. 5-25) is a long, straplike muscle that arises from the pubic bone and its ligaments. It widens as it extends upward to be inserted on the anterior surface of the xiphoid process and the costal cartilages of the 5th, the 6th and the 7th ribs. It is entirely enclosed in the sheath formed by the aponeuroses of the muscles of the lateral wall of the abdomen.

Functions of the anterolateral abdominal wall muscles include: (1) protection of the underlying viscera, (2) providing aid in expelling substances from the body by compressing the abdominal cavity and increasing the intra-abdominal pressure (e.g., coughing, vomiting, defecation and childbirth), and (3) assistance in bending the body forward or flexing the vertebral column. These muscles are antagonists of the diaphragm, relaxing as it contracts and contracting as it relaxes.

The inguinal canal is an oblique tunnel about 4 cm. long which passes through the lower abdominal wall parallel with, and a little above, the inguinal ligament. The inguinal canal extends from the abdominal inguinal ring to the subcutaneous inguinal ring, as shown in Figure 5-27. It transmits the spermatic cord (p. 575) in the male, and the round ligament of the uterus (p. 581) in the female.

Weak places in the abdominal wall include: (1) the subcutaneous and the abdominal inguinal rings, as described above; (2) the femoral ring, the oval upper end of the femoral canal, lying behind the inguinal ligament; and (3) the umbilicus, a puckered scar that marks the closure of the umbilical opening of the fetus.

Owing to the upright position of man, the pressure of the weight of the abdominal viscera falls on the ventral part of the abdominal wall. As one stands, any weak places in this portion of the wall will be put under added strain.

Hernia (rupture) refers to the abnormal protrusion of an organ or part of an organ through the wall of the cavity that normally contains it. This term is most frequently applied to the protrusion of an organ (usually the small intestine) through one of the weak places in the abdominal wall. If such herniation occurs at the umbilicus, it is referred to as an umbilical hernia; if in the area of the inguinal rings, an inguinal hernia, or in the femoral ring, a femoral hernia (Fig. 5-25).

The basic underlying cause of any hernia is a sudden or prolonged increase in the intra-abdominal pressure. Decreased muscle tone in the abdominal wall which may follow an illness or occur naturally in older persons can be a contributing factor. Activities which promote the occurrence of a hernia are those that increase the pressure of abdominal viscera against the ventral body wall, e.g., coughing, heavy lifting or straining.

Muscles of the posterior abdominal wall assist in movements of the vertebral column and the thigh. The **quadratus lumborum** (Fig. 5-28) lies lateral to the vertebral column and extends from the last rib to the iliac crest; the kidneys are in close relationship to this muscle. In addition to its respiratory function of fixing and depressing the last rib and helping to anchor the diaphragm, the quadratus lumborum also aids in flexing the vertebral column. The **iliopsoas muscle** is described with those of the lower extremity (p. 164).

Muscles of the pelvic floor

The outlet of the true pelvis (p. 97) is closed by a shallow hammock of muscles and fascia which form the pelvic floor (Fig. 5-29). They are an extremely important group of muscles, for on them rests part of the weight of the abdominal and the pelvic viscera.

The levator ani muscle arises from the pubis and the spine of the ischium; its fibers extend downward, backward and toward the midline. The posterior fibers are inserted on the coccyx; the anterior fibers unite with those from the opposite side forming a seam in the midline. These muscles constrict the lower part of the rectum and pull it forward, thus aiding in defecation.

The coccygeus muscle arises from the spine of the ischium and inserts on the sacrum and the coccyx. The coccygeus and the levator ani provide support for the pelvic viscera and resist increases in intra-abdominal pressure. These muscles are occasionally stretched and torn during childbirth.

The external anal sphincter is a relatively funnel-shaped muscle which surrounds the anal canal. It is attached to the coccyx and to the skin surrounding the anus. This important sphincter muscle keeps the anal canal and the anus closed; like all skeletal muscle, it is under control of the conscious will.

Deep muscles of the back

The deep muscles of the back lie on either side of the vertebral column and form a complex group. They are attached to the sacrum, to the ilium, to the spines, the transverse and the articular processes and the laminae of the lumbar, the thoracic and the cervical vertebrae and to the posterior aspects of the ribs and the base of the skull. They are the splenius capitis and cervicis, the sacrospinalis, the semispinalis, the multifidus, the rotatores, the interspinales and the intertransversarii muscles. Only the sacrospinalis will be described.

The sacrospinalis is the longest muscle in the body. It is an elongated muscular mass, consisting of separate slips, which extends from the sacrum to the skull (Fig. 5-12). It arises from the lower and posterior part of the sacrum, the posterior portion of the iliac crests and the spines of the lumbar and the lower 2 thoracic vertebrae. It "climbs" the back in a series of columns and extends as high as the cervical vertebrae and the temporal bone. The lateral muscular column is called the *iliocostalis* muscle; and the medial is called the *longissimus* muscle. The sacrospinalis muscle is attached on the ribs and the vertebrae all the way up the back to the mastoid process of the temporal bone.

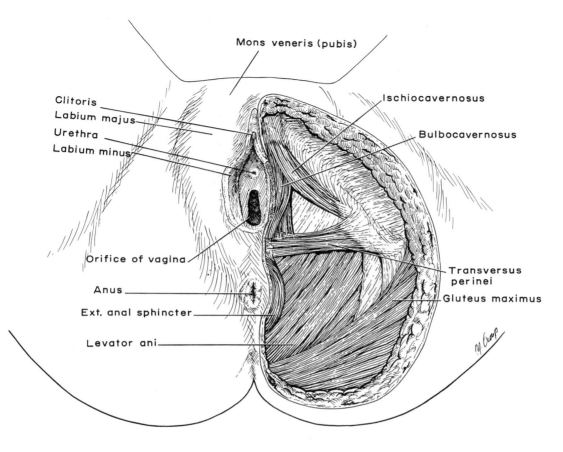

Fig. 5-29. Muscles of the pelvic floor (female perineum).

The sacrospinalis helps to maintain the vertebral column in the erect posture. At certain times these muscles bend the trunk backward. This occurs when it is necessary to counterbalance the effect of weight at the front of the body, such as in pregnancy. Since the vertebral column is drawn backward in pregnancy, the gait is peculiar and very characteristic.

If the sacrospinalis of one side acts alone, it bends the vertebral column to that side. You can note the great flexibility of the vertebral column if you extend, flex, abduct and adduct it. The cervical and the lumbar regions possess the greatest freedom of movement.

MUSCLES OF THE LOWER EXTREMITY

The muscles of the lower extremity are used chiefly to support the body in the standing position and are specialized for locomotion. Movements of the pelvic girdle as a whole are greatly restricted.

When sitting, the pelvis is flexed, and the weight of the body is transmitted through the sacrum and the hip bones to the ischial tuberosities. When standing, the pelvis is extended, and the weight of the body is transmitted to the femoral bones through the acetabula. When walking, the pelvis is rotated forward toward the limb that is being moved forward.

GLUTEUS MAXIMUS

SARTORIUS

RECTUS FEMORIS

VASTUS LATERALIS

ILIOTIBIAL BAND

BICEPS FEMORIS (LONGHEAD)

BICEPS FEMORIS (SHORT HEAD)

QUADRICEPS FEMORIS TENDON

PATELLA

LIGAMENTUM PATELLE

GASTROCNEMIUS

SOLEUS

PERONCUS LONGUS

TIBIALIS ANTERIOR

EXTENSOR DIGITORUM LONGUS

PERONCUS BREVIS

a

EXTENSOR DIGITORUM LONGUS

PERONEUS BREVIS TENDON

PERONCUS TERTIUS

TIBIALIS ANTERIOR

EXTENSOR HALLUCIS LONGUS

ILIACUS
PSOAS } ILIOPSOAS

PIRIFORMIS

COCCYGEUS

OBTURATOR INTERNUS

GLUTEUS MAXIMUS

ADDUCTOR MAGNUS

SARTORIUS

ADDUCTOR LONGUS

SEMITENDINOSUS

RECTUS FEMORIS

GRACILIS

VASTUS MEDIALIS

SEMIMEMBRANOSUS

GASTROCNEMIUS

SOLEUS

FLEXOR DIGITORUM LONGUS

TIBIALIS POSTERIOR

FLEXOR HALLUCIS LONGUS

b

FLEXOR DIGITORUM LONGUS TENDON

Fig. 5-30. (Left) Muscles of hip, thigh and leg, seen from the lateral view. (Right) Muscles of hip, thigh and leg seen from the medial view. The muscles which originate from the walls of the pelvis are shown. The relations of tendons to the ankle and digits are shown.

GLUTEUS MAXIMUS
GLUTEUS MEDIUS
PIRIFORMIS
GEMELLI
OBTURATOR INTERNUS
BURSA
ADDUCTOR MAGNUS
VASTUS LATERALIS
BICEPS FEMORIS (LONG HEAD)
SEMITENDINOSUS
GRACILIS
SEMIMEMBRANOSUS
POPLITEAL SPACE
PLANTARIS
GASTROCNEMIUS (CUT)
PLANTARIS TENDON
SOLEUS
TENDO ACHILLIS

GLUTEUS MINIMUS
SACROTUBEROUS LIGAMENT
QUADRATUS FEMORIS
GLUTEUS MAXIMUS (INSERTION)
VASTUS LATERALIS
ADDUCTOR MAGNUS
BICEPS FEMORIS (LONG HEAD)
VASTUS MEDIALIS
SEMIMEMBRANOSUS TENDON
POPLITEUS
TIBIALIS POSTERIOR
FLEXOR HALLUCIS LONGUS
PERONEUS LONGUS
FLEXOR DIGITORUM LONGUS
PERONEUS BREVIS
TIBIALIS POSTERIOR TENDON
TENDO ACHILLIS

a   b

Fig. 5-31. (Left) Superficial muscles of the posterior aspect of hip, thigh and leg. Gluteus maximus cut and turned aside and belly of gastrocnemius removed to show deeper muscles. (Right) Deep muscles of hip, thigh and leg. Certain muscles have been removed and others cut to expose the various bones.

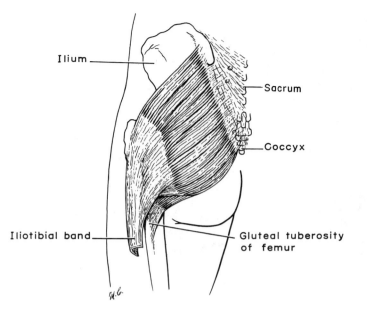

Fig. 5-32. The left gluteus
maximus muscle.

Movement of the thigh

The hip joint is a ball-and-socket joint that permits free movement in all directions, except as
limited by muscles around it. Flexion and extension make possible such acts as walking and running. Abduction, adduction, circumduction and
rotation also occur and are important in balancing
the body during all activity.

The iliopsoas is a compound muscle. Its parts,
the psoas major and the iliacus, are illustrated in
Figure 5-28. The iliac portion arises from the
iliac fossa, and the psoas major arises from the
lumbar vertebrae. The fibers combine and pass
along the brim of the pelvis to the front of the
thigh, where they wind around the neck of the
femur and insert on the lesser trochanter of the
femur. This muscle is a powerful flexor of the
thigh. When standing, it helps to hold the trunk
erect by keeping it from falling backward. When
the femur is fixed, the iliopsoas bends the lumbar
portion of the vertebral column forward and tilts
the pelvis forward. It is used in raising the trunk
from the recumbent position.

The gluteus maximus (Figs. 5-30 and 5-32, *left*)
is a broad, thick, fleshy, quadrilateral muscle that
forms much of the buttock. Its fibers are very
coarse. The large size of the gluteus maximus is
characteristic of man and is associated with walking in the upright position. When the pelvis is
fixed, the gluteus maximus is a very powerful extensor of the thigh. When the femur is fixed, the
gluteus maximus supports the pelvis and the trunk
on the femur, as in standing on one leg. When
you rise to a standing position, after stooping
over, you can feel the powerful action of the gluteal muscles. The gluteus maximus helps to rotate
the lower extremity outward. It is used in walking up stairs and in climbing hills, and you may
notice soreness after undue climbing. This large
muscle is frequently selected as the site for intramuscular injections of various drugs.

The gluteus medius and **gluteus minimus** are
located under the maximus, extending from the
outer surface of the ilium to the greater trochanter
of the femur (Fig. 5-31). These muscles abduct
the thigh and rotate it medially.

The adductor group consists of 3 muscles: the

adductors longus, brevis and magnus. They arise from the pubis and the ischium and insert on the linea aspera of the femur (Fig. 5-28). These important muscles adduct and flex the thigh as in grasping a saddle between the knees when riding horseback.

Movement of the thigh and the leg

The sartorius (Fig. 5-28) is a long muscle, narrow and ribbonlike. It arises from the anterior superior spine of the ilium, extends obliquely across the upper part of the thigh from the lateral to the medial side and is inserted on the upper part of the medial surface of the tibia. It is used in crossing the legs, as tailors of old used to sit cross-legged on the floor or the table (which explains the origin of the name). It flexes and rotates the thigh laterally; also, it flexes the leg.

The quadriceps femoris is the large fleshy mass covering the front and the sides of the femur. It is composed of 4 parts: the rectus femoris, which arises from the ilium, and the vasti (lateralis, medialis and intermedius), which arise from the femur, as shown in Figures 5-28 and 5-33). There is a common tendon of insertion for the 4 parts, and in this tendon, which is closely applied to the capsule of the knee joint, is the patella. The tendon is inserted on the tubercle of the tibia. The chief action is extension of the leg, but it also helps to keep the femur erect on the tibia; this means that the quadriceps is important in both walking and standing. The rectus femoris portion of the muscle flexes the thigh.

The hamstring muscles are the biceps femoris, the semitendinosis and the semimembranosis. These muscles extend from the ischial tuberosity to the proximal ends of the fibula and the tibia (Fig. 5-31). You can feel the tendons of the hamstring muscles as ridges behind the knee where they help to form the boundaries of the popliteal space (the diamond-shaped area back of the knee). The main action of the hamstrings is to flex the leg on the thigh. Extreme relaxation of these muscles is required for such exercises as touching the toes without bending the knees and for doing the high kick.

Movement of the leg and the foot

Since the muscles of the leg are responsible for the movements of the foot and the toes, it is important to have the movements clearly in mind before describing the muscles. In the foot, upward movement at the ankle joint is called *dorsal flexion* of the foot, and downward movement at the ankle joint is called *plantar flexion* (extension) of the foot. Upward movement of the toes is called *extension* and downward movement is called *flexion* of the toes. In other words, upward and downward movements at the ankle and the metatarsophalangeal joints are described by different terms. Turning the sole of the foot inward is called *inversion* and turning it outward is called *eversion*.

The tibialis anterior (Figs. 5-4 and 5-34) originates from the lateral condyle and the shaft of the tibia; its tendon of insertion crosses over the front of the tibia and attaches to the first metatarsal and the first cuneiform bones. This muscle dorsally flexes and inverts the foot. Poliomyelitis seems to affect the tibialis anterior more frequently than any other muscle of the lower extremity, resulting in a condition known as "foot drop" (inability to pull the foot up toward the shin). These patients have difficulty in walking due to failure of the foot to clear the ground on the forward step; to compensate for this defect they walk with a characteristic "high step and flop" of the affected foot.

The tibialis posterior (Figs. 5-30 and 5-31) arises from the posterior surfaces of the tibia and the fibula; its tendon passes behind the medial malleolus to insert on several of the tarsal bones (navicular, calcaneus, cuneiforms and cuboid) and on the base of the 2nd, the 3rd and the 4th metatarsal bones. It plantar flexes (extends) and inverts the foot. The tendon of the tibialis posterior is an important factor in the maintenance of the longitudinal arch of the foot (p. 168).

The peroneus longus, (Figs. 5-30 and 5-35) on the lateral aspect of the leg, originates from the head and the lateral surface of the fibula; it ends in a long tendon which passes behind the lateral malleolus, crosses the sole of the foot obliquely and inserts on the first cuneiform and the base of

Fig. 5-33. The right quadriceps femoris muscle, showing 3 heads of origin (vastus intermedius is not visible).

Ant. inf. iliac spine

Rectus femoris

Vastus lateralis

Vastus medialis

Lateral condyle and proximal half of lateral surface of tibia

Patella

Tuberosity of tibia

Fig. 5-34. The right tibialis anterior.

Proximal end of first metatarsal and first cuneiform

Fig. 5-35. The left peroneus longus muscle.

Fig. 5-36. The right gastrocnemius and soleus muscles.

the 1st metatarsal bone. This muscle plantar flexes and everts the foot; it is an antagonist of the tibialis anterior. The peroneus longus helps to maintain the transverse arch of the foot (p. 168).

The gastrocnemius and the **soleus** are superficial muscles that form the powerful muscular mass referred to as the calf of the leg. The 2 heads of the gastrocnemius arise from the condyles of the femur (Figs. 5-30 and 5-36), while the soleus arises from the upper ends of the tibia and the fibula (Fig. 5-31) underneath the gastrocnemius.

Both muscles insert on the calcaneus by way of the *tendon of Achilles,* the thickest and strongest tendon in the body, and they are the chief plantar flexors of the foot at the ankle joint. These powerful muscles are used in standing, walking and leaping. In walking, they raise the heel from the ground; the body is supported on that foot, and the opposite limb is free to be carried forward. These muscles enable one to stand on the tips of the toes; consequently, they are greatly over-developed in toe dancers.

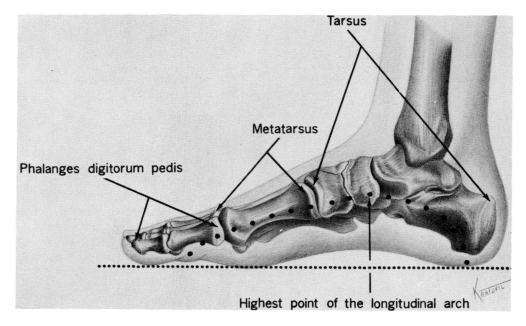

Tarsus

Metatarsus

Phalanges digitorum pedis

Fig. 5-37. Medial aspect of the foot and the ankle. Longitudinal arch indicated by curved series of dots.

Highest point of the longitudinal arch

Movement of the toes

Deep in the sole of the foot, there are numerous muscles that act on the toes. Flexion, extension, abduction and adduction occur, but these movements are quite limited in comparison with those of the fingers. For a listing of muscles in this group consult the Table of Muscles at the end of the chapter.

The arches of the foot

The human foot is unique among all feet in the animal kingdom in that it is arched. Some of the advantages of this arched state are as follows: it distributes body weight over the foot, provides strength and rigidity for use of the foot as a lever and also a protected space for the soft structures of the sole (blood vessels and nerves), provides a resilient spring, in harmony with the muscles, to absorb jarring shocks.

The bones of the arch are supported by a posterior base (the calcaneus) and an anterior base (the metatarsal heads). On the medial aspect of the foot, the calcaneus extends upward and forward, carrying the talus above and in front of it.

The talus forms the highest point of the arch and is the keystone. From the talus, moving downward and forward in order, are the navicular, the 3 cuneiforms and the 3 medial metatarsals whose heads meet the ground (Fig. 5-37). Laterally, the arch is much lower. The calcaneus rises to meet the cuboid which in turn is directed downward and forward to the lateral 2 metatarsals, their heads meeting the ground. This placement of bones between the calcaneus and the metatarsal bones is called the **longitudinal arch.** The foot also shows a **transverse arch,** formed by the metatarsal bones in front and the distal row of tarsals behind.

Support of the arches depends on various ligaments and muscles, the latter being of paramount importance. For example, the tibialis anterior braces the keystone of the arch and supports it from above; the tibialis posterior braces the tarsal bones and supports the arch from below; the peroneus longus crosses under the sole of the foot and forms a sling that helps to maintain the transverse arch.

The strength of the muscles supporting the arches should be increased by proper exercises and massage. This is particularly important for

Fig. 5-38. X-ray of bones of the left foot; flatfoot. Courtesy of Michael R. Marino, D.S.P., Pittsburgh, Pa.

Fig. 5-39. Prints of right foot, showing (left to right) high arch, moderate arch, low arch and flatfoot, respectively.

those who must spend long hours on their feet. Nurses, teachers, policemen and others who do a great deal of walking and standing often find that the supporting muscles and ligaments of the arches are unable to meet the demands placed on them. When this occurs, the arch sags downward and may disappear entirely, resulting in *"flatfoot"* (Fig. 5-38). Figure 5-39 shows prints of the right foot with high, normal and low arches, and flatfoot.

SUMMARY

1. Naming the skeletal muscles
   A. Location: e.g., intercostals
   B. Direction of fibers: e.g., transversus
   C. Action: e.g., flexor
   D. Shape or size: e.g., deltoid, maximus, brevis
   E. Number of heads of origin: e.g., biceps
   F. Points of attachment: e.g., sternocleidomastoid
2. Parts of a skeletal muscle
   A. Origin—more fixed point of attachment
   B. Insertion—more movable point of attachment
   C. Body or belly—portion of muscle between origin and insertion
3. Skeletal muscle action
   A. Muscles become shorter when they contract and exert pull on attachments
   a. Most muscles attached to bones which act as levers
   b. Bones moved at joints which serve as fulcrums
   c. Muscle bodies usually lie above or below, in front of or behind the part to be moved
   B. Many muscles arranged in pairs
   a. Prime mover contracts
   b. Antagonist relaxes
   C. Synergists work with prime movers and help them
4. Study of individual muscles
   A. Consult Table of Muscles at end of chapter
   B. Visualize muscles in relation to your own body
   a. See and feel them under the skin when possible
   b. "Make them work for you" by resisting their movements

PRACTICAL APPLICATIONS AND QUESTIONS

Assume the various positions shown on page 171, and in each case identify (A) the type of movement, and (B) the names of one or two muscles whose contraction makes possible that particular action.

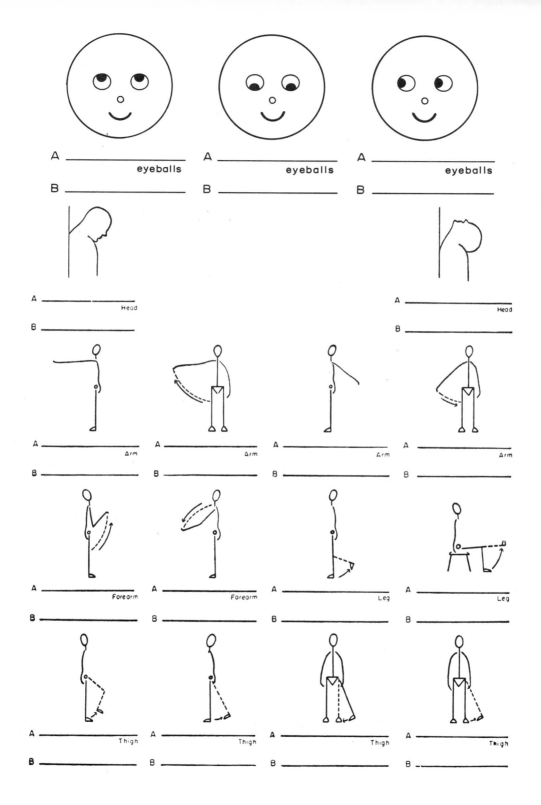

A _____ eyeballs

B _____

A _____ eyeballs

B _____

A _____ eyeballs

B _____

A _____ Head

B _____

A _____ Head

B _____

A _____ Arm

B _____

A _____ Arm

B _____

A _____ Arm

B _____

A _____ Arm

B _____

A _____ Forearm

B _____

A _____ Forearm

B _____

A _____ Leg

B _____

A _____ Leg

B _____

A _____ Thigh

B _____

A _____ Thigh

B _____

A _____ Thigh

B _____

A _____ Thigh

B _____

TABLE OF MUSCLES

The name, origin, insertion, nerve supply and action of certain additional muscles are included in the following table. Those muscles which have been described in the text are printed in **boldface** type.

Muscle	Origin	Insertion	Innervation and Action
MUSCLES OF THE HEAD AND THE NECK			
Movements related to facial expression			
Occipitalis	Superior nuchal line of occipital bone	Epicranial aponeurosis	Facial nerve. Tenses epicranial aponeurosis and draws scalp backward.
Frontalis	Epicranial aponeurosis	Skin of eyebrow and of root of nose	Facial nerve. Elevates eyebrow; wrinkles forehead.
Levator palpebrae superioris	Margin of optic foramen	Upper eyelid	Oculomotor nerve. Raises upper lid.
Orbicularis oculi	Medial palpebral ligament, frontal bone, and maxilla	Lateral and medial palpebral ligaments; some fibers encircle eye	Facial nerve. Closes eyelids; stretches skin of forehead.
Corrugator	Frontal bone	Skin of eyebrow	Facial nerve. Draws skin of brow downward and medially, as in frowning.
Procerus	Cartilages of nose	Skin over root of nose	Facial nerve. Draws skin of forehead down.
Nasalis	Maxilla above incisor and canine teeth; dorsum of nose	Skin of nasolabial groove and margin of nostril	Facial nerve. Draws wings of nose laterally and upward; constricts nostrils.
Orbicularis oris	Various muscles running into lip	Fibers surround oral opening, forming a sphincter	Facial nerve. Draws lips together.
Quadratus labii superioris			
Angular head	Root of nose	Alar cartilage; upper lip	Facial nerve. The whole muscle raises the upper lip. The angular head also lifts the wings of the nose.
Infra-orbital head	Maxilla below orbit	Upper lip	
Zygomatic head	Zygomatic bone	Upper lip	
Quadratus labii inferioris	Mandible below canine and premolar teeth	Lower lip	Facial nerve. Draws lower lip downward.

Muscle	Origin	Insertion	Innervation and Action
Incisivus labii (inferior and superior)	Maxilla and mandible, near canine and lateral incisor teeth	Orbicularis oris muscle	Facial nerve. Draws corners of lips medially.
Zygomatic	Zygomatic bone	Orbicularis oris muscle	Facial nerve. Raises corner of mouth and draws it laterally.
Canine	Canine fossa of maxilla	Orbicularis oris muscle	Facial nerve. Raises corner of mouth and draws it medially.
Risorius	Subcutaneous tissue over parotid gland	Skin and mucous membrane at corner of mouth	Facial nerve. Draws corner of mouth laterally.
Triangularis	Mandible below canine, premolar and first molar teeth	Orbicularis oris muscle	Facial nerve. Draws corner of mouth downward.
Buccinator	Maxilla, mandible, and pterygomandibular raphe	Orbicularis oris muscle and skin of lips	Facial nerve. Draws corner of mouth laterally; pulls lips and cheek against teeth.
Mentalis	Mandible, below lower lateral incisor	Skin of chin	Facial nerve. Draws up skin of chin.
Platysma	Fascia of upper pectoral and deltoid muscles	Lower border of mandible; skin of lower part of cheek and corner of mouth	Facial nerve. Wrinkles skin of neck; depresses corner of mouth.
Movement of the eyeball			
Superior rectus	Margin of optic foramen	Eyeball, above pupil	Oculomotor nerve. Turns eyeball upward.
Medial rectus	Margin of optic foramen	Eyeball, medial to pupil	Oculomotor nerve. Turns eyeball medially.
Inferior rectus	Margin of optic foramen	Eyeball, below pupil	Oculomotor nerve. Turns eyeball downward.
Lateral rectus	Margin of optic foramen	Eyeball, lateral to pupil	Abducens nerve. Turns eyeball laterally.
Superior oblique	Margin of optic foramen	Lateral side of eyeball	Trochlear nerve. Turns eyeball downward and laterally. Rotates medially.
Inferior oblique	Medial part of floor of orbit	Lateral side of eyeball	Oculomotor nerve. Turns eyeball upward and laterally. Rotates laterally.

Muscle	Origin	Insertion	Innervation and Action
Movement of the mandible, the tongue and the pharynx			
Masseter	Zygomatic arch	Lateral surface of ramus of mandible	Masticator or motor root of trigeminal nerve. Raises mandible and draws it forward.
Temporal	Temporal fossa of temporal bone	Coronoid process of mandible	Masticator or motor root of trigeminal nerve. Raises mandible.
External pterygoid	Lateral pterygoid plate, sphenoid and palatine bones	Neck of condyle of mandible	Masticator or motor root of trigeminal nerve. Draws mandible forward and sideward; aids in opening mouth.
Internal pterygoid	Maxilla and palatine bone	Medial surface of ramus of mandible	Masticator or motor root of trigeminal nerve. Draws mandible upward and sideward.
Genioglossus	Spine of mandible, near midline	Fascia of tongue; hyoid bone	Hypoglossal nerve. Anterior fibers retract tongue; remainder draws it forward and depresses its tip. Draws hyoid bone upward and forward.
Hyoglossus	Body and great cornu of hyoid bone	Fascia of tongue	Hypoglossal nerve. Depresses side of tongue and retracts it.
Styloglossus	Styloid process of temporal bone	Side of tongue	Hypoglossal nerve. Draws tongue backward.
Glossopalatinus	Aponeurosis of soft palate	Side and under surface of tongue	Pharyngeal plexus (vagus nerve). Draws side of tongue upward and soft palate downward. Constricts faucial isthmus.
Inferior constrictor of pharynx	Lateral surfaces of thyroid and cricoid cartilages	Dorsal part of pharynx	Pharyngeal plexus. Constricts pharynx; aids in swallowing.
Middle constrictor of pharynx	Greater and lesser cornua of hyoid bone; stylohyoid ligament	Dorsal part of pharynx; occipital bone	Pharyngeal plexus. Constricts pharynx; aids in swallowing.
Superior constrictor of pharynx	Pterygoid process, pterygomandibular raphe, and mylohyoid ridge of mandible	Dorsal part of pharynx; occipital bone	Pharyngeal plexus. Constricts pharynx; aids in swallowing.
Stylopharyngeus	Styloid process of temporal bone	Thyroid cartilage and lateral wall of pharynx	Glossopharyngeal nerve. Lifts pharynx in act of swallowing.

Muscle	Origin	Insertion	Innervation and Action
Pharyngo-palatine	Aponeurosis of soft palate and cartilage of auditory tube	Thyroid cartilage and lateral wall of pharynx	Pharyngeal plexus (vagus nerve). Closes opening between nasal and oral pharynx; depresses soft palate.
Levator veli palatini	Under surface of temporal bone and cartilage of auditory tube	Aponeurosis of soft palate	Pharyngeal plexus (vagus nerve). Raises soft palate; narrows pharyngeal opening of auditory tube.

Movement of the head and the neck

Muscle	Origin	Insertion	Innervation and Action
Sternocleido-mastoid	Manubrium of sternum and medial third of clavicle	Mastoid process and occipital bone	Accessory, 2nd and 3rd cervical nerves. Bends head and neck toward shoulder; rotates head toward opposite side. Both sides acting together flex the neck and bring the head forward.
Semispinalis capitis	Last 5 cervical and upper 5 thoracic vertebrae	Occipital bone, between inferior and superior nuchal lines	Posterior rami of upper 5 cervical nerves. Extends head and bends it laterally.
Longus coli	Lower 5 cervical and first 3 thoracic vertebrae	Upper 6 cervical vertebrae	Second to 6th cervical nerves. Flexes neck.
Longus capitis	Transverse processes of 3rd to 6th cervical vertebrae	Basilar part of occipital bone	First 4 cervical nerves. Flexes head and rotates it toward same side.
Rectus capitis anterior	Lateral part of atlas	Basilar part of occipital bone	First cervical nerve. Flexes head and rotates it toward same side.
Rectus capitis lateralis	Transverse process of atlas	Lateral part of occipital bone	First cervical nerve. Bends head to side.
Rectus capitis posterior major	Spine of axis	Inferior nuchal line of occipital bone	Suboccipital nerve. Extends and rotates head.
Rectus capitis posterior minor	Posterior tubercle of atlas	Inferior nuchal line of occipital bone	Suboccipital nerve. Extends head.
Obliquus capitis inferior	Spine of axis	Transverse process of atlas	Suboccipital nerve. Rotates head.
Obliquus capitis superior	Transverse process of atlas	Inferior nuchal line of occipital bone	Suboccipital nerve. Extends head.

175

Muscle	Origin	Insertion	Innervation and Action
MUSCLES OF THE UPPER EXTREMITY			
Movement of the shoulder and the arm			
Trapezius	Occipital bone, nuchal ligament, 7th cervical and all thoracic vertebrae	Lateral third of clavicle, acromion, and lateral part of spine of scapula	Accessory, 2nd, 3rd, and 4th cervical nerves. Upper part raises shoulder, extends head, bends head toward shoulder, and turns head toward opposite side. Lower part draws scapula downward and inward, rotating the inferior angle laterally. The whole muscle rotates the scapula so that the lateral angle points upward.
Latissimus dorsi	Spines of last 6 thoracic and upper lumbar vertebrae, lumbodorsal fascia, and crest of ilium	Anterior surface of upper part of humerus	Thoracodorsal nerve. Adducts, extends, and rotates arm medially. Depresses shoulder.
Levator scapulae	Transverse processes of first 4 cervical vertebrae	Upper part of vertebral border of scapula	Third and 4th cervical nerves. Draws scapula upward.
Minor rhomboid	Nuchal ligament, last cervical, and first thoracic vertebrae	Vertebral border of scapula	Dorsal scapular nerve. Draw scapula upward and medially. Rotate it so as to depress the tip of the shoulder.
Major rhomboid	Upper 4 thoracic vertebrae	Vertebral border of scapula	
Pectoralis major	Cartilages of 2nd to 6th ribs, sternum, and medial half of clavicle	Humerus, on a line extending downward from the greater tubercle	Anterior thoracic nerves (medial and lateral). Adducts, flexes and rotates arm medially.
Pectoralis minor	Second to 5th ribs, near their cartilages	Coracoid process of scapula	Medial anterior thoracic nerve. Pulls scapula forward.
Subclavius	First rib near its cartilage	Lower surface of clavicle	Fifth cervical nerve. Depresses scapula and shoulder.
Serratus anterior	Lateral surfaces of upper 8 or 9 ribs	Vertebral border of scapula	Long thoracic nerve. Draws scapula forward and laterally; rotates it so as to raise the tip of the shoulder.
Coraco-brachialis	Coracoid process of scapula	Middle third of humerus	Musculocutaneous nerve. Adducts and flexes arm. Aids in medial rotation of the arm.

Muscle	Origin	Insertion	Innervation and Action
Deltoid	Spine of scapula, acromion, and lateral part of clavicle	Deltoid tubercle of humerus	Axillary nerve. Abducts arm; anterior part flexes and rotates arm medially; posterior part extends and rotates arm laterally.
Supraspinatus	Supraspinous fossa of scapula	Greater tubercle of humerus	Suprascapular nerve. Abducts arm.
Infraspinatus	Infraspinous fossa of scapula	Greater tubercle of humerus	Suprascapular nerve. Rotates arm laterally.
Teres major	Axillary border of scapula	Anterior surface of upper part of humerus	Lower subscapular nerve. Adducts, extends, and rotates arm medially.
Teres minor	Axillary border of scapula	Greater tubercle of humerus	Axillary nerve. Rotates arm laterally
Subscapularis	Subscapular fossa of scapula	Lesser tubercle of humerus	Subscapular nerves. Rotates arm medially; holds humerus in glenoid cavity.

Movement of the forearm and the hand

Muscle	Origin	Insertion	Innervation and Action
Biceps brachii	Short head from coracoid process; long head from scapula above glenoid fossa	Tubercle on proximal end of radius	Musculocutaneous nerve. Flexes and supinates forearm; flexes and rotates arm medially; long head abducts, short head adducts the arm.
Brachialis	Ventral surface of distal half of humerus	Tubercle on proximal end of ulna	Musculocutaneous nerve. Flexes forearm.
Triceps brachii	Long head from infraglenoid tubercle of scapula. Lateral and medial heads from posterior surface of humerus	Olecranon of ulna	Radial nerve. Extends forearm. Long head also extends and adducts the arm.
Pronator teres	Medial epicondyle of humerus and coronoid process of ulna	Middle third of lateral surface of radius	Median nerve. Pronates and flexes forearm.
Supinator	Lateral epicondyle of humerus; proximal 5th of ulna	Proximal third of radius	Radial nerve. Supinates forearm.
Anconeus	Lateral epicondyle of humerus	Proximal part of ulna	Radial nerve. Extends forearm.
Brachioradialis	Ridge above lateral epicondyle of humerus	Proximal part of styloid process of radius	Radial nerve. Flexes forearm.

Muscle	Origin	Insertion	Innervation and Action
Pronator quadratus	Distal 4th of volar surface of ulna	Distal fourth of volar surface of radius	Median nerve. Pronates the forearm.

Movement of the hand and the fingers

Muscle	Origin	Insertion	Innervation and Action
Flexor carpi radialis	Medial epicondyle of humerus	Base of second metacarpal	Median nerve. Flexes and abducts the hand.
Palmaris longus	Medial epicondyle of humerus	Fascia of palm	Median nerve. Flexes the hand.
Flexor carpi ulnaris	Medial epicondyle of humerus and proximal two thirds of ulna	Pisiform, hamate and 5th metacarpal	Ulnar nerve. Flexes and adducts the hand.
Flexor digitorum sublimis	Medial epicondyle of humerus, coronoid process of ulna, and proximal part of radius	Volar surfaces of 2nd phalanges of fingers	Median nerve. Flexes fingers and hand.
Flexor digitorum profundus	Proximal three fourths of ulna and interosseous membrane	Volar surfaces of 3rd phalanges of fingers	Median and ulnar nerves. Flexes fingers and hand.
Flexor pollicis longus	Volar surface of radius and interosseous membrane	Terminal phalanx of thumb	Median nerve. Flexes thumb.
Extensor carpi radialis longus	Ridge above lateral epicondyle of humerus	Base of 2nd metacarpal	Radial nerve. Extends and abducts hand.
Extensor carpi radialis brevis	Lateral epicondyle of humerus	Bases of 2nd and 3rd metacarpals	Radial nerve. Extends and abducts hand.
Extensor digitorum communis	Lateral epicondyle of humerus	By 4 tendons into phalanges of fingers	Radial nerve. Extends wrist and fingers.
Extensor digiti quinti proprius	Septum separating it from extensor digitorum communis	Phalanges of little finger	Radial nerve. Extends little finger.
Extensor carpi ulnaris	Lateral epicondyle of humerus; proximal three fourths of ulna	Base of 5th metacarpal	Radial nerve. Extends and adducts hand and 5th metacarpal.
Abductor pollicis longus	Dorsal surface of ulna, radius, and interosseous membrane	Base of 1st metacarpal	Radial nerve. Abducts the thumb.

Muscle	Origin	Insertion	Innervation and Action
Extensor pollicis brevis	Middle part of dorsal surface of radius and interosseous membrane	Base of 1st phalanx of thumb	Radial nerve. Extends thumb and abducts 1st metacarpal.
Extensor pollicis longus	Middle 3rd of dorsal surface of ulna and interosseous membrane	Base of 2nd phalanx of thumb	Radial nerve. Extends 2nd phalanx of thumb.
Extensor indicis proprius	Distal 3rd of dorsal surface of ulna and interosseous membrane	Aponeurosis on dorsal surface of index finger	Radial nerve. Extends index finger.
THE THENAR MUSCLES			
Abductor pollicis brevis	Transverse carpal ligament and lateral part of carpus	Base of 1st phalanx of thumb	Median nerve. Abducts thumb; flexes the 1st and extends the 2nd phalanx.
Flexor pollicis brevis	Transverse carpal ligament; distal row of carpal bones	Base of 1st phalanx of thumb	Median nerve. Flexes and adducts the thumb.
Opponens pollicis	Transverse carpal ligament and greater multangular bone	Lateral border of metacarpal of thumb	Median nerve. Flexes, adducts, and rotates thumb medially.
Adductor pollicis	Second and 3rd metacarpals, capitate, and ligaments	Base of 1st phalanx of thumb	Ulnar nerve. Adducts and flexes the thumb.
THE HYPOTHENAR MUSCLES			
Palmaris brevis	Palmar aponeurosis	Skin of medial side of palm	Ulnar nerve. Draws skin of medial side of hand toward center.
Abductor digiti quinti	Pisiform bone and ligaments	First phalanx of little finger	Ulnar nerve. Abducts little finger; flexes the 1st phalanx of little finger.
Flexor digiti quinti brevis	Transverse carpal ligament and hamate bone	First phalanx of little finger	Ulnar nerve. Flexes 1st phalanx of little finger.
Opponens digiti quinti	Transverse carpal ligament and hamate bone	Fifth metacarpal	Ulnar nerve. Flexes and adducts little finger.

Muscle	Origin	Insertion	Innervation and Action
THE INTERMEDIATE MUSCLES			
Lumbricales (4)	Tendons of flexor digitorum profundus	Tendons of extensor digitorum communis	Ulnar nerve, except the lateral 2 lumbricales, which are supplied by the median nerve. All flex the 1st and extend the 2nd and the 3rd phalanges. Lumbricales draw fingers toward thumb. Volar interossei draw fingers toward middle finger, and dorsal interossei draw fingers away from middle finger.
Interossei volares (4)	First, 2nd, 4th, and 5th metacarpals	First phalanx of thumb, index, ring, and little fingers	
Interossei dorsales (4)	Adjacent sides of metacarpal bones	First phalanx of middle 3 fingers, 2 muscles inserting on middle finger	

MUSCLES OF THE TRUNK
The muscles of respiration

Muscle	Origin	Insertion	Innervation and Action
External intercostal	Lower border of each rib	Upper border of next rib	Intercostal nerves. Elevate ribs and enlarge thorax.
Internal intercostal	Lower border of each rib	Upper border of next rib	Intercostal nerves. Contract thorax (probably).
Diaphragm	Xiphoid process, lower 6 ribs and their cartilages, lumbar vertebrae	Central tendon of diaphragm	Phrenic nerve. Expands thorax; compresses contents of abdominal cavity.
Levatores costarum	Transverse processes of thoracic vertebrae	Next lower rib	Intercostal nerves. Bend vertebral column laterally; extend and rotate it.
Transversus thoracis	Dorsal surface of lower half of sternum	Cartilages of 2nd to 6th ribs	Second to 6th intercostal nerves. Depresses ribs (in expiration).
Serratus posterior superior	Nuchal ligament and upper 3 thoracic vertebrae	Second to 5th ribs	Upper 4 intercostal nerves. Raises ribs, in this way enlarges thorax.
Serratus posterior inferior	Last 3 thoracic and first 2 lumbar vertebrae	Last 4 ribs	Ninth to 11th intercostal nerves. Draws lower ribs outward; enlarges thorax.
Anterior scalene	Transverse processes of 4th to 6th cervical vertebrae	First rib	Fifth, 6th, and 7th cervical nerves. Raises 1st rib and bends neck to same side.
Middle scalene	Transverse processes of 3rd to 7th cervical vertebrae	First and 2nd ribs	Fourth to 8th cervical nerves. Raises 1st and 2nd ribs; bends neck to same side.

180

Muscle	Origin	Insertion	Innervation and Action
Posterior scalene	Transverse processes of 5th and 6th cervical vertebrae	Second rib	Seventh or 8th cervical nerves. Action is the same as that of the scalenus medius. All scalene muscles aid in forced inspiration.

Muscles of the abdominal wall

Muscle	Origin	Insertion	Innervation and Action
External oblique	Lower 8 ribs	Iliac crest, inguinal ligament and linea alba	Lower 7 intercostal nerves and iliohypogastric nerve. Compresses abdomen; flexes and rotates vertebral column.
Internal oblique	Inguinal ligament, iliac crest, and lumbodorsal fascia	Lower 3 ribs, linea alba, and pubic bone	Iliohypogastric, ilio-inguinal, and last 3 intercostal nerves. Compresses abdomen; flexes and rotates vertebral column.
Cremaster	Upper border of inguinal ligament	Pubic tubercle	Genitofemoral nerve. Lifts testis toward subcutaneous inguinal ring.
Transversus abdominis	Lower 6 ribs, lumbodorsal fascia, iliac crest, and inguinal ligament	Linea alba and pubic tubercle	Iliohypogastric, ilio-inguinal, genitofemoral, and last 5 intercostal nerves. Compresses abdomen.
Rectus abdominis	Symphysis pubis and body of pubis	Fifth to 7th costal cartilages; xiphoid process	Lower 6 intercostal nerves. Depresses thorax; flexes vertebral column and pelvis.
Pyramidalis	Body of pubis	Linea alba	Last thoracic nerve. Tenses linea alba.
Quadratus lumborus	Iliac crest, lower 3 lumbar vertebrae	Upper 3 lumbar vertebrae, 12th rib	First 3 or 4 lumbar nerves. Flexes vertebral column laterally; extends vertebral column.

Muscles of the pelvic floor and the perineum

Muscle	Origin	Insertion	Innervation and Action
Levator ani	Body of pubis, ischial spine, and obturator fascia	Coccyx and raphe joining coccyx to rectum	Fourth sacral nerve. Flexes coccyx; raises anus; resists downward pressure of abdominal viscera.
Coccygeus	Ischial spine	Fourth and 5th sacral vertebrae and coccyx	Third and 4th sacral nerves. Flexes and abducts coccyx.
External anal sphincter	Fibers of this muscle surround the anus and are attached to the skin and to the coccyx		Inferior hemorrhoidal nerves. Keeps anus closed.
Transversus perinei profundus	Inferior ischial ramus	Fibers interdigitate in midline	Perineal nerve. Draws back central tendon of perineum.
Sphincter urogenitalis	Pubic ramus	Fibers interdigitate in midline, some encircle urethra	Perineal nerve. Compresses the urethra; compresses vagina or Cowper's glands.

Muscle	Origin	Insertion	Innervation and Action
Ischiocavernosus	Ischial tuberosity and inferior ischial ramus	Crus penis (in male) Crus clitoridis (female)	Perineal nerve. Constricts crus penis (or clitoridis).
Bulbocavernosus	Median raphe on ventral side of bulb; central tendon of perineum	Dense tissue covering root of penis	Perineal nerve. Compresses bulb of urethra.
Transversus perinei superficialis	Ischial tuberosity	Central tendon of perineum	Perineal nerve. Fixes central tendon of perineum.

Deep muscles of the back

Muscle	Origin	Insertion	Innervation and Action
Splenius cervicis	Third to 6th thoracic vertebrae	Upper 2 or 3 cervical vertebrae	Posterior rami of 2nd, 3rd, and 4th cervical nerves. Bend and rotate head toward the side of the muscle which is acting.
Splenius capitis	Nuchal ligament and upper thoracic vertebrae	Mastoid process and occipital bone	
Sacrospinalis (iliocostalis, longissimus, spinalis)	Ilium, sacrum, lumbar, thoracic, and last 4 cervical vertebrae, posterior parts of ribs	Lumbar, thoracic, and cervical vertebrae; posterior parts of all ribs; mastoid process	Posterior rami of spinal nerves from 1st cervical to 5th lumbar. Bends head and vertebral column to side. Extends head and vertebral column.
Semispinalis cervicis and dorsi	All thoracic vertebrae	Lower 6 cervical and upper 5 thoracic vertebrae	Posterior rami of 3rd to 6th cervical and 3rd to 6th thoracic nerves. Extend and rotate vertebral column.
Multifidus	Iliac crest, sacrum, and all vertebrae below 4th cervical	Spines of vertebrae up to 2nd cervical	Posterior rami of spinal nerves. Extends and rotates the vertebral column.
Rotatores	Transverse processes of vertebrae	Next vertebrae above	Posterior rami of spinal nerves. Extend and rotate vertebral column.
Interspinales	Spines of vertebrae	Spines of next vertebrae above	Posterior rami of spinal nerves. Extend vertebral column.
Intertransversarii	Transverse processes of vertebrae	Transverse processes of next vertebrae	Posterior rami of spinal nerves. Bend vertebral column to side.

Muscle	Origin	Insertion	Innervation and Action
MUSCLES OF THE LOWER EXTREMITY			
Movement of the thigh			
Gluteus maximus	Iliac crest, lateral surface of ilium, sacrum, coccyx, and sacrotuberous ligament	Iliotibial band and gluteal tuberosity of femur	Inferior gluteal nerve. Extends thigh; rotates thigh laterally.
Gluteus medius	Lateral surface of ilium	Great trochanter of femur	Superior gluteal nerve. Abducts thigh; aids in rotation.
Gluteus minimis	Lateral surface of ilium; capsule of hip joint	Great trochanter of femur	Superior gluteal nerve. Abducts and rotates thigh medially.
Tensor fasciae latae	Anterior part of iliac crest	Iliotibial band	Superior gluteal nerve. Tenses fascia lata; flexes, abducts, and rotates thigh medially.
Piriformis	Ventral surface of sacrum and sacrotuberous ligament	Great trochanter of femur	First or 2nd sacral nerve, or both. Extends, abducts, and rotates thigh laterally.
Obturator internus	Pelvic surface of pubis, ischium, and obturator membrane	Trochanteric fossa of femur	Fourth lumbar to 2nd sacral nerves. Rotates thigh laterally.
Quadratus femoris	Ischial tuberosity	Line below great trochanter of femur	Fourth lumbar to 1st sacral nerves. Rotates thigh laterally.
Gemellus superior	Ischial spine	With obturator internus	Nerve to obturator internus ⎫
Gemellus inferior	Ischial tuberosity	With obturator internus	Nerve to quadratus femoris ⎬ Rotate thigh laterally.
Psoas major	Bodies of 12th thoracic to 5th lumbar vertebrae and intervertebral disks	Small trochanter of femur	Second to 4th lumbar nerves. Flexes thigh; adducts and rotates it medially.
Iliacus	Iliac fossa of ilium	Small trochanter of femur	Femoral nerve. Flexes thigh; adducts and rotates it medially.
Iliopsoas	**The iliacus and psoas major muscles are often considered together as the iliopsoas.**		
Psoas minor	Twelfth thoracic and 1st lumbar vertebrae	Iliopectineal eminence of os coxae	First and 2nd lumbar nerves. Flexes the pelvis.

183

Muscle	Origin	Insertion	Innervation and Action
Pectineus	Crest of pubis	Pectineal line of femur, below small trochanter	Femoral nerve. Flexes and adducts thigh.
Adductor longus	Superior ramus of pubis	Middle third of linea aspera of femur	Obturator nerve. Adducts, flexes and rotates thigh laterally.
Adductor brevis	Inferior ramus of pubis	Upper third of linea aspera of femur	Obturator nerve. Adducts thigh.
Adductor magnus	Rami of pubis and ischium, and ischial tuberosity	Linea aspera of femur; tubercle above medial condyle	Obturator and sciatic nerves. Adducts thigh; aids in flexion, extension, and lateral rotation.
Obturator externus	Lateral surface of pubis, ischium, and obturator membrane	Trochanteric fossa of femur	Obturator nerve. Rotates thigh laterally; aids in adduction.

Movement of the leg and the thigh

Muscle	Origin	Insertion	Innervation and Action
Gracilis	Rami of pubis and ischium	Tibia, below medial condyle	Obturator nerve. Adducts thigh; rotates thigh medially; flexes leg.
Sartorius	Anterior superior iliac spine	Medial surface of proximal end of tibia	Femoral nerve. Flexes thigh and leg; rotates thigh laterally.
Quadriceps femoris	Arises by 4 heads from ilium and femur	Tuberosity of tibia, through a common tendon	Femoral nerve. All parts extend leg. Rectus femoris flexes thigh.
Rectus femoris	Anterior inferior iliac spine	Common tendon	
Vastus medialis	Medial lip of linea aspera	Common tendon	
Vastus lateralis	Lateral lip of linea aspera	Common tendon	
Vastus intermedius	Anterior surface of femur	Common tendon	

The Hamstrings

Muscle	Origin	Insertion	Innervation and Action
Biceps femoris	Long head from ischial tuberosity; short head from middle third of linea aspera	Head of fibula; lateral condyle of tibia	Sciatic nerve. Flexes leg and rotates it laterally; long head also extends and adducts thigh.
Semitendinosus	Ischial tuberosity	Proximal part of medial surface of tibia	Sciatic nerve. Flexes leg and rotates it medially; extends and adducts thigh and rotates it medially.

Muscle	Origin	Insertion	Innervation and Action
Semimembranosus	Ischial tuberosity	Medial condyle of tibia	Sciatic nerve. Flexes leg and rotates it medially; extends and adducts thigh and rotates it medially.

Movement of the leg and the foot

Muscle	Origin	Insertion	Innervation and Action
Gastrocnemius	Medial and lateral condyles of femur	Calcaneus, through tendon of Achilles	Tibial nerve. Flexes leg; plantar flexes, adducts, and inverts foot.
Soleus	Head and proximal 3rd of fibula, and middle 3rd of tibia	Calcaneus, through tendon of Achilles	Tibial nerve. Plantar flexes, adducts, and inverts foot.
Plantaris	Line above lateral condyle of femur	Through a slender tendon terminating in the fibrous tissue of the heel	Tibial nerve. Flexes leg and plantar flexes foot. Its action is very weak.
Popliteus	Lateral condyle of femur	Proximal 4th of tibia	Tibial nerve. Flexes leg and rotates it medially.
Flexor digitorum longus	Dorsal surface of tibia and fascia covering tibialis posterior	Phalanges of lateral 4 toes	Tibial nerve. Flexes digits; plantar flexes and inverts foot.
Flexor hallucis longus	Distal two thirds of fibula and fascia covering tibialis posterior	Terminal phalanx of big toe	Tibial nerve. Flexes big toe; plantar flexes and inverts foot.
Posterior tibial	Posterior surfaces of tibia, fibula, and interosseous membrane	Navicular, cuboid, and all cuneiform bones; 2nd to 4th metatarsals	Tibial nerve. Adducts, plantar flexes, and inverts foot.
Anterior tibial	Lateral condyle and proximal part of tibia and interosseous membrane	First cuneiform and base of 1st metatarsal	Deep peroneal nerve. Dorsal flexes and inverts foot.
Extensor digitorum longus	Lateral condyle of tibia, interosseous membrane, and shaft of fibula	Phalanges of 4 lateral toes	Deep peroneal nerve. Dorsal flexes foot; everts foot and extends toes.
Peroneus tertius	Distal 3rd of fibula and interosseous membrane	Base of 5th metatarsal (and 4th)	Deep peroneal nerve. Dorsal flexes foot and everts it.
Extensor hallucis longus	Middle half of fibula; distal half of interosseous membrane	Second phalanx of big toe	Deep peroneal nerve. Extends big toe, dorsal flexes foot and inverts sole.

Muscle	Origin	Insertion	Innervation and Action
Peroneus longus	Lateral condyle of tibia, head and shaft of fibula, and intermuscular septum	First cuneiform and base of 1st metatarsal	Common peroneal nerve. Plantar flexes, abducts, and everts foot. Supports arch of foot.
Peroneus brevis	Middle 3rd of fibula, and intermuscular septa	Tuberosity of 5th metatarsal	Superficial peroneal nerve. Everts foot; aids in extension. (Plantar flexion.)
Movement of the toes			
Extensor digitorum brevis	Calcaneus and cruciate ligament	Phalanges of medial 4 toes	Deep peroneal nerve. Extends medial 4 toes.
Quadratus plantae	Calcaneus and ligaments	Tendon of flexor digitorum longus	Lateral plantar nerve. Aids flexor digitorum longus.
Flexor digitorum brevis	Calcaneus, plantar aponeurosis, and septa	Phalanges of lateral 4 toes	Medial plantar nerve. Flexes toes.
Abductor hallucis	Calcaneus and ligaments	First phalanx of big toe	Medial plantar nerve. Abducts big toe.
Flexor hallucis brevis	Cuneiform bones and ligaments	First phalanx of big toe	Medial plantar nerve. Flexes 1st phalanx of big toe.
Adductor hallucis			
Oblique head	Cuboid, 3rd cuneiform, 2nd and 3rd metatarsals, and ligaments	First phalanx of big toe	Lateral plantar nerve. Adduct big toe; aid in flexion of big toe. Transverse head holds heads of metatarsal bones together.
Transverse head	Capsules of metatarsophalangeal joints	Sheath of tendon of flexor hallucis longus	
Abductor digiti quinti	Calcaneus and fascia of sole	First phalanx of little toe	Lateral plantar nerve. Abducts and flexes little toe.
Flexor digiti quinti brevis	Cuboid and 5th metatarsal	First phalanx of little toe	Lateral plantar nerve. Abducts and flexes little toe.
Opponens digiti quinti	Cuboid	Fifth metatarsal	Lateral plantar nerve. Draws little toe medially and plantarward.
Lumbricales (4)	Tendons of flexor digitorum longus	Phalanges of lateral 4 toes	Medial plantar nerve to most medial lumbrical. Others by lateral plantar nerve. These muscles flex the 1st phalanx. Dorsal interossei abduct from, plantar interossei adduct toward, 2nd toe. Lumbricales extend 2nd phalanges.
Interossei dorsales (4)	Metatarsal bones and ligaments	Phalanges of middle 3 toes	
Interossei plantares (4)	Metatarsal bones and ligaments	Medial side of phalanges of digits	

"Sow a Thought, and you reap an Act;
Sow an Act, and you reap a Habit;
Sow a Habit, and you reap a Character;
Sow a Character, and you reap a Destiny."

OF UNKNOWN AUTHORSHIP

6

ORGANIZATION OF THE NERVOUS SYSTEM

At this very moment your body is being bombarded with stimuli of many kinds, and you are making constant adjustments (either consciously or unconsciously) to these environmental changes. For example, if the light rays reflected from this page are too bright, you may unknowingly begin to squint, i.e., to partly close your eyes; as the chair seems to become "harder" you may shift and squirm around to relieve the pressure on various parts of your anatomy. Microscopic "sentries" (nerve endings) in all parts of the body are constantly reporting on conditions in their area, constantly informing "headquarters" (the brain and the spinal cord) of any changes that may require some type of positive action on the part of your body.

The following sequence of events will serve to illustrate the comprehensive way in which our nervous system functions. While chewing a piece of candy you become aware of a severe toothache. Since this is the fourth time that sweets have caused such a pain, you realize that the possibility of a cavity must no longer be ignored. A telephone call to the dentist results in an immediate appointment. As you hurry toward his office, worrying about the expense of filling the tooth, and the possibility of losing it, you step off the curb to cross the street, without your usual vigilance.

There is an immediate screech of brakes, and you are back on the sidewalk in a flash, trembling, perspiring, your knees shaking, and your heart pounding "like a trip-hammer." You feel so weak that a few minutes elapse before you can continue on your way.

In terms of functions of the nervous system, the sweet saliva penetrated a crack in the enamel of a tooth and reached the nerve endings. This constituted a change in the environment of those "sentries," and they swiftly notified the brain of that fact.

When the impulses reached the brain they produced a sensation of pain. The recognition of pain, together with the memory of the three previous similar experiences, and your knowledge of the consequences of neglected cavities, led to the decision to attend to the situation without further delay. However, while crossing the street, you were so busy thinking about the consequences of the toothache that you were heedless of what you were doing. The screech of brakes was a startling change in the external environment, and impulses flashed to your brain which instantaneously cancelled the original order to cross the street. At the same time a new set of impulses started the emergency response which enabled you to jump back to the safety of the sidewalk before you were really aware of what had happened.

From this experience we might summarize some of the basic functions of the nervous system as follows:

1. The conversion of stimuli to nerve impulses which are then conducted to the central nervous system (CNS)

2. The interpretation of incoming impulses and the making of decisions about them on the basis of memory

3. The "sorting out" of incoming impulses; unimportant ones being ignored, and important ones receiving immediate attention

4. The dispatching of nerve impulses from the CNS to "effectors" (muscle tissue and glands) which carry out orders for appropriate response to a stimulus. In this case, your responses to the toothache consisted of telephoning the dentist and walking toward his office, which involved chiefly the skeletal muscles. However, your responses to the screech of brakes involved not only skeletal muscles but also other effectors, as evidenced by the pounding of your heart and an increased flow of perspiration.

The final scene in this drama of response to a stimulus consists of a full awareness of what has happened. Impulses are transmitted from the active effectors back to the brain, informing it that assignments have been or are being carried out. You know that your skeletal muscles are quivering, that your heart is pounding, and that you have narrowly escaped serious injury or even death. While you continue to tremble, this experience is vividly stored in your memory, and it will be some time before you again step off the curb without giving it more thought.

GENERAL PLAN OF THE NERVOUS SYSTEM

Mechanisms of correlation

Just as a large city relies heavily on the telephone system to help in the correlation of its many activities, so does the human body rely on the nervous system. A complex network of peripheral nerve fibers, similar to telephone wires, connects all parts of the body with the CNS which serves as a "switchboard." Nerve impulses travel over these living "wires" at a tremendous rate of speed and enable us to make rapid adjustments in both the external and the internal environment of the body.

The endocrine system, in contrast to the nervous system, resembles the slower moving postal service of a city, but it also plays an important role in the field of communication and correlation. Chemical messengers (hormones) secreted by the endocrine glands are carried in the blood stream to all parts of the body where they influence various activities. These specialized glands are described in Chapter 19.

Divisions of the nervous system

The nervous system is the most highly organized system of the body, and all of its parts function as an inseparable unit. However, for purposes of study we must first consider individual structures if we are to understand the unified whole.

Organs of this system may be classified according to their location or according to their function.

1. **Anatomic divisions:**
   a. *The central nervous system* (CNS) consists of the brain within the skull, and the spinal cord within the vertebral canal.
   b. *The peripheral nervous system* consists of those nerves that connect the CNS with the body wall and with the viscera; these are the cranial and the spinal nerves.
2. **Physiologic divisions:**
   a. *The cerebrospinal* or *"voluntary"* nervous system consists of those nerve fibers that connect the CNS with structures of the body wall (e.g., skeletal muscles and the skin); therefore, this division also is known as the *somatic* system.
   b. *The autonomic* or *"involuntary"* nervous system consists of those fibers that connect the CNS with smooth muscle, cardiac muscle and glands. It also is referred to as the *visceral* system, as it supplies the internal organs.

Regardless of the classification which may be used, one must never forget the basic unity of the nervous system. For example, one part of our nervous system coordinates the activities involved in external processes related to the seeking, preparing and eating of food, while another part is concerned with the coordination of internal processes such as digestion, respiration and circulation of blood, all of which are essential for the nourishment of individual cells. The ultimate goal of all parts of the nervous system is the same as that of every other system—the maintenance of homeostasis!

STRUCTURE OF NERVOUS TISSUE

The structural features of the nervous system include the nerve cells, or neurons, and a variety of supporting cells referred to as *neuroglia*. Although neuroglia in the CNS serves the same general function as connective tissue in other organs, one should be aware of the fact that neuroglia is extremely delicate, inasmuch as it does not have any tough intercellular substance such as collagen or elastin. Thus, when one examines fresh brain and spinal cord tissues they are soft and jellylike.

The Neuron

Neurons, or nerve cells, are microscopic units of structure uniquely adapted to conduct impulses accompanied by action currents (p. 119) over their entire length, which may be only a fraction of an inch or as much as 3 or 4 feet in some parts of the body. Although neurons vary in size and shape, they have certain basic similarities, in that each consists of a cell body and elongated processes.

The cell body is that part of a neuron that contains the nucleus. The nucleus, in turn, contains fine granules of chromatin and one (or more) large nucleoli. Fine fibrils, referred to as *neurofibrils*, form a network in the granular cytoplasm of the cell body and extend into the cell processes. Scattered throughout the cytoplasm are *Nissl bodies*, irregular clumps of chromidial substance (Fig. 6-1). Numerous free ribosomes are associated with the Nissl bodies. It is believed that they are concerned with the continuous formation of protein molecules needed to replace those that are used by the neuron in various metabolic activities. The synthesized protein that streams out into the axon is called *axoplasm*. Mitochondria and the Golgi apparatus also are present in the cytoplasm.

An intact, well nourished cell body is essential to the life of the neuron as a whole. If the cell body dies, the remainder of the neuron also dies and can never be replaced, because these specialized cells cannot reproduce themselves. Therefore, this vital portion of each neuron is located in a relatively protected area; cell bodies are found only within the gray matter of the brain, in the spinal cord, and in ganglia (small nodules of nervous tissue lying close to the CNS).

The cell processes are elongated extensions of

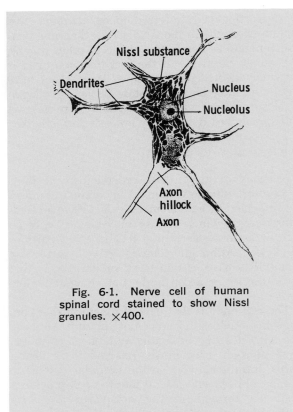

Fig. 6-1. Nerve cell of human spinal cord stained to show Nissl granules. ×400.

Fig. 6-2. Nerve fibers. (Top) Myelinated fiber. (Bottom) Unmyelinated fibers.

the cell body, and it is this anatomic feature that gives the neuron its unique appearance; no other cells in the body have such a "drawn out" shape. These processes also are referred to as **nerve fibers.** *Dendrites* (meaning "tree-like") are those fibers that carry impulses toward the cell body, and they vary greatly in different types of neurons. For example, some dendrites are very long and branch only at the end, while others are short and branch freely. An *axon* is the fiber that carries impulses away from the cell body; it frequently has one or more side branches (collaterals) that come off at right angles. Each neuron has only one axon, and this fiber may be long or short depending on the location of its cell body.

Both dendrites and axons may develop *sheaths* which completely envelop them, or they may remain "naked" (i.e., they consist only of a conducting core or axis cylinder). The sheaths which envelop certain fibers are of 2 types: myelin and neurilemma (also spelled neurolemma).

The myelin sheath is a white, lipid and protein substance that surrounds many of the nerve fibers of the body. However it is not a continuous sheath, as it is interrupted at intervals by constrictions called the *nodes of Ranvier.* Myelin is an excellent insulator that prevents almost all flow of sodium and potassium ions. Thus the uninsulated areas at the nodes of Ranvier play an important role in the conduction of nerve impulses, as will be described presently.

Cell processes supplied with myelin sheaths are referred to as *myelinated* or white fibers, and those that lack such a sheath are called *unmyelinated* or gray fibers (Fig. 6-2). Both myelinated and unmyelinated fibers are found in the peripheral nerve trunks. Within the CNS itself, bundles of myelinated fibers form the so-called *white matter* of the brain and the spinal cord. Conversely, the *gray matter* of the CNS consists of unmyelinated fibers and cell bodies of certain neurons.

The neurilemma sheath is a delicate sheet of protoplasm formed by special cells (Schwann cells) that wrap themselves around peripheral nerve fibers; it ends at the point at which a fiber enters or leaves the CNS. The neurilemma of unmyelinated fibers is wrapped directly around the axis cylinder; on myelinated fibers it surrounds the myelin and comes into contact with the axis cylinder only at the nodes of Ranvier. The neurilemma sheath cells play an important part in the myelination of peripheral nerve fibers (it is believed that neuroglia cells perform a similar function in regard to the myelination of fibers within the CNS, in which neurilemma is absent).

The neurilemma sheath probably plays a protective role and aids in maintaining the integrity of normally functioning nerve fibers. However, following injury to a fiber, the neurilemma assumes added importance because it is essential for regeneration of the fiber. Figure 6-7 illustrates in diagrammatic form the changes that occur in a nerve when it is cut and when it regenerates. Briefly, if a nerve fiber is crushed or cut, so that it is no longer connected to its cell body, the cytoplasm and the myelin in the distal stump degenerate and are engulfed by phagocytic cells. Meanwhile, if the cut ends are not too widely separated, neurilemma sheath cells grow into the cut and unite the stumps. The nerve fibers in the proximal stump that are still connected to their cell bodies then send "buds" or "sprouts" into the network of sheath cells; many of these "buds" become obstructed, but some of them do grow through the old area of injury and down into the cords of neurilemma sheath cells waiting to enfold them and complete the repair process. Regeneration is a slow process and, depending upon the length of the injured fibers, may require many weeks or months. Within the brain and the spinal cord, where there is no neurilemma, there is no regeneration of injured fibers.

Functional classification of neurons

1. **Afferent** (sensory) neurons (Fig. 6-3a) transmit impulses from the periphery to the CNS. Specialized *receptors* or sense organs (located on the distal ends of the dendrites) are excited by stimuli; this *excitatory state* or *nerve impulse* then sweeps over the neuron to the CNS.

2. **Efferent** neurons transmit impulses from the central nervous system to some effector (muscle

Fig. 6-3. Diagram of typical neurons: a. afferent or sensory; b. efferent or motor. Sheaths are not shown.

or gland). There are 4 types of efferent neurons: *motor neurons* (Fig. 6-3b) carry impulses that lead to the contraction of skeletal muscles; *secretory neurons* transmit impulses that provoke the secretion of glands; *accelerator* and *inhibitory neurons supply* smooth muscle and cardiac muscle with impulses that speed or slow activities respectively. The point of contact between nerve fiber and effector is called the *neuro-effector junction.* (NOTE: the terms neuromuscular or myoneural junctions are limited to muscle tissue; they are not applicable to glands).

3. **Central** or *intermediate* neurons transmit impulses from one part of the brain or the spinal cord to another. Consequently, their processes do not leave the CNS. These neurons also may be called *internuncial* or *association neurons.*

Structural classification of neurons

1. **Unipolar** neurons have only one process extending from the cell body, but this process divides into a central and a peripheral branch (Fig. 6-3a); the central branch is the axon, and the peripheral branch functions as a dendrite.

2. **Bipolar** neurons have two processes, a single dendrite and a single axon (Fig. 6-4).

3. **Multipolar** neurons have several dendrites and one axon (Fig. 6-5).

Fig. 6-4. Bipolar neurons: a. from olfactory mucous membrane; b. from retina.

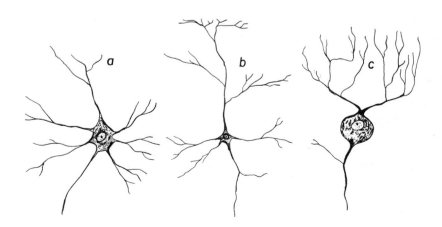

Fig. 6-5. Multipolar neurons. (a) From spinal cord. (b) From cerebral cortex. (c) From cerebellar cortex.

SPINAL
GANGLION

AFFERENT
NEURON

Epineurium
Perineurium   A
Endoneurium   PERIPHERAL
Fascicles   NERVE

SENSORY
ENDING

ANTERIOR
HORN CELL

EFFERENT
NEURON

NODE OF RANVIER

ONE NERVE FIBER
Axon
Myelin sheath
Neurolemma
(Sheath of Schwann)

MOTOR ENDING

Fig. 6-6. Diagram showing the various parts of a sizable peripheral nerve, individual nerve fibers and nerve endings.

Synapses

The entire nervous system is composed of chains of neurons, but there is no anatomic continuity between them. This means that neurofibrils do not extend from one neuron into the next. Each neuron is a separate unit, but it is in contact with other neurons. The points of contact are called *synapses*. The term synapse was derived from a Greek word that means "to clasp," as one would clasp hands with a friend. Although the hands would be in contact, there would be no continuity of the flesh.

Because impulses are transmitted away from cell bodies over axons, a synapse is necessarily an area of contact between the axon of one neuron and one of the dendrites or the cell body of the next; *an impulse can pass only from axon to dendrite* or to cell body *across a synapse* (the law of forward conduction). Synapses are found only in the gray matter of the CNS and in autonomic ganglia.

Nerves and tracts

Peripheral nerves, such as the sciatic, are composed of an infinite number of nerve fibers; these fibers are arranged in related bundles, much like the wires in a large telephone cable. Individual nerve fibers (axons and dendrites of various neurons) are bound to one another by delicate connective tissue called *endoneurium*. Groups of these individual fibers are bundled together and surrounded by stronger connective tissue which is called *perineurium*. When several nerve fiber bundles are grouped and bound together by *epineurium*, the resulting organ is called a **nerve** (Fig. 6-6).

Within the CNS, bundles of nerve fibers are referred to as **tracts** rather than as nerves. However, both nerves and tracts appear white to the naked eye, since most of their individual fibers are myelinated.

With respect to function, peripheral nerves are divided into 4 types:

Somatic afferent nerves carry impulses from the skin, the skeletal muscles, tendons and joints to the CNS.

Somatic efferent nerves carry impulses from the CNS to the skeletal muscles.

Visceral afferent fibers carry impulses from the viscera to the CNS.

Visceral efferent fibers carry impulses from the CNS to smooth muscle, cardiac muscle and glands.

Neuritis is a term which refers to either inflam-

PROXIMAL STUMP   DISTAL STUMP

Degeneration of axon
and myelin for short
distance proximal to
cut

Fragmentation of axon and myelin

Schwann cells, mostly from
distal side, grow into cut and
unite stumps

Macrophages engulf degenerated
axon and myelin.
Schwann cells grow,
thicken, and form cords in shrinking
endoneurial tubes.

Axons send many buds
into network of Schwann
cells between stump. Many
are obstructed but....

....some delicate axons
enter endoneurial tubes
and lie beside cords of
Schwann cells.

Axons continue to push along endoneurial
tubes of distal stump and are enfolded by
Schwann cells after which new myelin is formed.

Fig. 6-7. Degeneration and regeneration of a severed
nerve. Diagram showing the changes that occur in a nerve
when it is severed and then regenerates.

matory or degenerative lesions of a nerve. It may result in pain, hypersensitivity, loss of sensation, muscular paralysis and atrophy.

Neuralgia is the condition in which there are severe paroxysmal pains along the course of a nerve; there is no structural change in the nerve, as in neuritis. The pain is sharp and stabbing in type.

PHYSIOLOGY OF NERVOUS TISSUE

Total functioning of the nervous system depends not only on the structural integrity of neurons but also on their highly developed physiologic properties of excitability and conductivity. From receptor to effector, the transmission of nerve impulses is a complicated process, and only a brief summary is within the scope of this textbook.

The reflex arc and act

Reflex arcs are the *functional units* of the nervous system as they provide pathways over which nerve impulses travel from receptors to effectors. The activity that results from the passage of impulses over a reflex arc is called a *reflex act* or simply a *reflex*. Generally speaking, a reflex is a response to a stimulus, but the term usually means only our involuntary responses. We may or may not be aware of reflex activities, but they occur without any conscious assistance on our part.

The basic components of a typical reflex arc consist of:

1. The *receptor* (sense organ) that is excited by an appropriate stimulus

2. The *afferent neuron* which transmits the impulse (excitatory state) from the receptor to the CNS

3. The *central* or *internuncial neuron* which transmits the impulse from afferent to the efferent neuron (NOTE: the great majority of reflex arcs involve many neurons; there are relatively few 2-neuron arcs in which afferent and efferent neurons synapse directly.)

4. The *efferent neuron* which transmits the impulse from the CNS to the effector

5. The *synapses,* or points of contact between related neurons (i.e., between 2 and 3, and 3 and 4 above).

6. The *neuroeffector junction* or point of contact between the efferent fiber and the effector that brings about a response.

For example, when your hand touches a hot stove it is withdrawn swiftly. In terms of the reflex arc the following sequence of events occurs in just a fraction of a second. Special heat receptors in the skin are stimulated by the hot stove, and the resulting nerve impulse flashes over the dendrite, the cell body and the axon of an afferent neuron into the dorsal horn of spinal gray matter. At this point, the nerve impulse crosses the synapse between the axon of the afferent neuron and the dendrite of a central neuron; continuing along the dendrite, the cell body and the axon of this central neuron, the impulse then crosses another synapse to the dendrite of an efferent neuron in the ventral horn of spinal gray matter. Speedily moving along the dendrite, the cell body and the axon of this motor neuron, the nerve impulse reaches the motor end plate in a skeletal muscle, activating the contractile protoplasm and enabling you to withdraw from the harmful stimulus. Figures 6-8 and 6-9 illustrate simple reflex arcs.

Characteristics of Nerve Tissue

The two outstanding characteristics of nerve tissue are excitability and conductivity. Both are inseparably related to depolarization and repolarization of cell membranes, as previously described on page 119, you may find it helpful to review this material before proceeding.

Excitability is the capacity to be affected by a stimulus (i.e., a change in the environment), and neurons may be stimulated at any point along their entire length. Many persons discover this fact for themselves when they accidently strike an elbow (or "funny bone") in such a way that the ulnar nerve is pinched. The resulting waves of depolarization, or nerve impulses, spread in both directions from the point of stimulation; within a fraction of a second there may be a

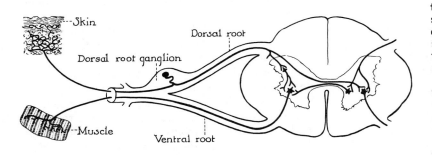

Skin

Dorsal root

Dorsal root ganglion

Muscle

Ventral root

Fig. 6-8. Diagrammatic section through the spinal cord to illustrate a simple reflex arc. Dendrites of the afferent neuron transmit impulses from the skin to the cell body in the ganglion on the dorsal root of a spinal nerve. The axon transmits impulses on to the spinal cord in which they are transferred over synapses to internuncial neurons (and commissural neurons). From the internuncial neuron the impulses are relayed to the efferent neuron, by means of which they reach the effector muscle. (Based on Ranson)

twitch of certain forearm muscles, and one is aware of a sensation that is sometimes described as "pins and needles" in the little finger and the ring finger of the hand. However, under normal conditions nerve impulses of the reflex arc originate in the receptors. The physiologic property of *excitability* is most highly developed in these afferent nerve endings, and the *threshold* or *minimal stimulus* (weakest stimulus that will excite the receptor) is very low. Each receptor, except those for pain, is specialized for the reception of a particular type of stimulus which is called its *adequate stimulus*. For example, light rays are the adequate stimuli for the receptors of vision, and sound waves for those of hearing.

There is no completely satisfactory classification of receptors, but the following one is useful. Those receptors which are affected by changes in the external environment are called *exteroceptors* and are concerned with touch, cutaneous pain, heat, cold, smell, vision and hearing. Those receptors which respond to changes in skeletal muscles, tendons, joints and the labyrinth of the inner ear (semicircular ducts and utricle, pp. 291, 292) are called *proprioceptors* and are concerned with muscle sense, sense of position and movement of the body in space. Those receptors which respond to changes in the viscera are called *interoceptors* and are concerned with visceral pain, hunger and thirst.

Receptors not only initiate the involuntary reflex acts, but they also help to keep the brain informed of environmental changes that require some voluntary response in making adjustments. If the weather suddenly turns cold, your receptors may start the reflex that results in shivering, but you will *consciously* go home to secure heavier clothing.

Conductivity, the ability to transmit nerve impulses, is a highly developed property of nerve tissue. Because of this property the CNS is informed of all changes in the environment, and then may dispatch "orders" to various effectors to make necessary adjustments. There is no visible change in a nerve fiber as it conducts an impulse, but various types of investigation have led to the establishment of certain facts and theories regarding conduction. A few of these will be summarized briefly.

1. *A nerve impulse is self-propagating.* This means that as one portion of neuron becomes depolarized it serves as a stimulus for the depolarization of adjacent portions. Thus, once an action current is started, the wave of depolarization will sweep over the entire membrane (the all-or-nothing law).

2. *The electric changes* related to depolarization and repolarization were previously described on page 119. At this point we would like to add that the action currents or impulses that sweep over

Fig. 6-9. Diagrams illustrating reflex arcs involving 2 and 3 neurons, respectively. Notice that the cell body of the afferent (sensory) neuron is situated in the posterior root ganglion outside the central nervous system. (Ham, Arthur W.: Histology, ed. 5, Philadelphia, Lippincott)

nerve fibers may be recorded and studied. Records of the so-called "brain waves" are really records of electrical changes in the brain. Such records are called **electro-encephalograms.** They are of great diagnostic importance in the study of brain disorders. However, it should be noted that whether nerve impulses are traveling over central or peripheral nerve fibers the *electrochemical disturbances* involved are identical. The reason we have a sensation of pain from an impulse in one fiber and a contraction of a muscle in another is because of the location of the endings of the two fibers. It is possible to have sensations of pain only in the brain, and to have contraction only in a muscle. Impulses may be compared with electric currents flowing through wires. In one case the current will produce heat and toast bread; in a second case it will ring a doorbell. The electric current is the same in each wire; the difference is in the ending to which it is conducted.

3. *A nerve impulse travels at a definite speed* that depends upon the size of the fiber. Large, myelinated fibers conduct more rapidly than do small, naked fibers. As previously noted, myelin is an insulator that interferes with the flow of sodium and potassium ions; thus depolarization occurs only at the uninsulated areas or nodes of Ranvier. It is believed that the high velocity of conduction in myelinated fibers exists because the impulse "jumps" from node to node rather than passing over the entire fiber. Studies have shown that the very large fibers can conduct impulses as rapidly as 120 meters per second (a distance longer than a football field). This is a slower rate than that at which sound waves travel, but even in a man who is 6 feet tall, the impulses could travel in large afferent nerve fibers from toes to brain and back to the toes over large efferent fibers in less than one twentieth of a second. On the other hand, the smallest fibers conduct impulses as slowly as 0.5 meter per second (about the distance from the foot to the knee).

4. After a nerve fiber conducts one impulse, a short interval of time must pass before it can conduct another. This period is called the *absolute refractory period.* No stimulus, however strong, can force the nerve fiber to conduct a second impulse before it has recovered from the effects of the first. Perhaps this time is essential for the potassium ions to re-enter the axis cylinder and for the sodium ions to leave. In any case, each impulse is a separate or distinct event; there is no fusion of impulses, thus there is nothing comparable with tetanic contractions in skeletal muscle.

A nerve fiber never seems to be "pushed to its limit," so far as conduction of impulses is concerned. If a weak constant stimulus is applied to a nerve fiber it may conduct 2 impulses per second; if a very strong constant stimulus is applied, the nerve may conduct as many as 50 impulses per second. However, since the recovery period is very short, it is calculated that a nerve fiber could conduct between 1,000 and 2,000 impulses per second, but we seem unable to force it to carry the maximal number.

5. *The chemical changes* that occur in nerve fibers during the conduction of impulses are not completely understood. There is a greater use of oxygen and increased production of carbon dioxide; glucose is used during conduction, and some ammonia is produced. However, explanations of the chemical changes that accompany activity in nerve fibers are not nearly as well worked out as they are for skeletal muscle activity. The important thing to keep in mind is the fact that the all-important brain cells depend as much on glucose as on oxygen; deprivation of either one or both can result in serious brain damage.

6. *Thermal changes* accompany conduction of nerve impulses, but the amount of heat produced is only 1/10,000 of that which results from the contraction of an equal weight of muscle. In other words, you never will become overheated from thinking as you might from vigorous exercise.

7. *The transmission of nerve impulses at synapses depends* upon chemical substances liberated by excitatory and inhibitory neurons. The axons of these "incoming" neurons are in contact with the dendrites or the cell bodies of "outgoing" neurons, but there is no continuity of protoplasm;

the microscopic space that exists between the 2 neurons is called the synaptic cleft. As a nerve impulse sweeps over the axon of an incoming fiber, it triggers the release of a *chemical transmitter substance* at the end of the axon; this chemical substance diffuses into the synaptic cleft, where it then serves to excite the next neuron, or to inhibit it, as the case may be.

At excitatory synapses, the transmitter substance depolarizes the cell membrane of the outgoing neuron and thus triggers a nerve impulse. *At inhibitory synapses,* it is believed that the chemical substance makes the neuron's internal voltage even more negative than usual. This opposes depolarization. There is no difference in the electrical impulses that are carried by excitatory and inhibitory fibers. They achieve opposite effects because of the release of different chemical transmitter substances at their synaptic endings. It is believed that many different chemical transmitter substances are liberated at synapses throughout the nervous system, but their precise chemical nature is not yet known. However, one such substance, acetylcholine, is fairly well recognized as an excitatory transmitter at synapses in autonomic ganglia (p. 256) and in certain parts of the CNS; acetylcholine was previously described in terms of the neuromuscular transmission of impulses (p. 120 and Fig. 4-7).

Because all reflex arcs involve a variable number of synapses, we shall summarize some of their more important properties. Impulses can pass in only one direction across a synapse, from the axon of the first neuron to the dendrite or cell body of the next neuron. Conduction is slower at synapses than along the nerve fiber, as there is a variable amount of resistance to the transmission of nerve impulses. However, repetition of an act results in increased ease of transmission at the synapses; this is known as *facilitation* and is the basis of habit formation. For example, when one is learning to play the piano, great thought and concentration are required at first, but with practice the finger movements become increasingly easy.

In comparison with other parts of a reflex arc, the synapse is most susceptible to a lack of oxygen, to fatigue, to various drugs, and so on. For ex-

ample, strychnine blocks the action of inhibitory transmitter substance, and, in the absence of normal inhibition, the effects of the excitatory transmitter become overwhelming; as a result, neurons become so excited that they fire repetitively, causing uncoordinated muscular contractions known as convulsions.

Reaction time

The time which elapses between the application of a stimulus and the start of a response is referred to as *reaction time.* This time will vary in different individuals under different conditions. Some of the factors which will cause variations in reaction time are:

1. The strength of the stimulus
2. The nature of the stimulus (e.g., sound, pain, etc.)
3. The number of synapses through which the impulse must travel
4. The condition of those synapses (e.g., fatigue, drugs, alcohol, etc., may delay transmission of impulses and increase the reaction time.)

SUMMARY

1. Basic functions of the nervous system
   A. Convert stimuli to nerve impulses and conduct to CNS
   B. Interpretation of incoming impulses and decision making
   C. "Sorting out" of impulses
   D. Dispatching impulses to effectors
   E. Awareness of body activities
2. General plan of the nervous system
   A. Mechanisms of correlation
      a. Nervous system
      b. Endocrine system
   B. Divisions of the nervous system
      a. Anatomic
         (1) Central: brain and spinal cord
         (2) Peripheral: cranial and spinal nerves
      b. Physiologic
         (1) Cerebrospinal or "voluntary:" Somatic

(2) Autonomic or involuntary: visceral

C. Ultimate goal of nervous system—maintenance of homeostasis

3. Structure of nervous tissue
   A. Neuron
      a. Cell body: contains nucleus; essential to life of neuron
      b. Cell processes: extensions of cell body; dendrites and axons
      c. Myelin sheath: serves as insulator; fibers possessing this sheath, myelinated, those without, unmyelinated
      d. Neurilemma sheath: essential for regeneration of injured fibers
   B. Functional classification of neurons
      a. Afferent or sensory: conduct from periphery to CNS
      b. Efferent: conduct from CNS to effectors
      c. Central or association: transmit impulses from one part of brain and cord to another
   C. Structural classification of neurons
      a. Unipolar
      b. Bipolar
      c. Multipolar
   D. Synapses
      a. Points of contact between neurons
      b. No anatomic continuity
      c. Impulse passes only from axon to dendrite or to cell body of next neuron
   E. Nerves and Tracts
      a. Nerves composed of peripheral fibers bundled together; endoneurium, perineurium, epineurium
      b. Tracts are fiber bundles within the CNS
      c. Functional types of peripheral nerves
         (1) Somatic afferent
         (2) Somatic efferent
         (3) Visceral afferent
         (4) Visceral efferent

4. Physiology of nervous tissue
   A. Reflex arcs
      a. Functional units of nervous system
      b. Activity resulting from passage of impulses over reflex arc called reflex act
      c. Basic components

(1) Receptor and afferent neuron
(2) Central or association neuron
(3) Efferent neuron and neuroeffector junction
(4) Synapses between related neurons

B. Excitability of nerve tissue
   a. Nerve fiber may be stimulated at any point, but receptor usually starts impulses involved in reflex acts
   b. Property of excitability most highly developed in receptor
   c. Must have adequate stimulus
   d. Classification of receptors: exteroceptors; proprioceptors; interoceptors

C. Conductivity of nerve tissue
   a. Capable of transmitting nerve impulses
   b. Impulse is self-propagating
   c. Electrical changes accompany passage of impulse; electroencephalograms — records of electrical changes in brain
   d. Impulse travels at a definite speed; larger fibers conduct more rapidly
   e. Refractory period
   f. Chemical changes occur in conducting fibers, heat produced
   g. Thermal changes
   h. Transmission at synapses depends upon excitatory and inhibitory transmitter substances; synapse more susceptible than nerve fibers; conduction is slower

D. Reaction time
   a. That between application of stimulus and start of response

PRACTICAL APPLICATIONS AND QUESTIONS

(Encircle the letter of the *best* answer to each of the following questions.)

A few drops of boiling water splashed on V. W.'s hand while she was cutting chunks of meat and dropping them into the kettle. Jerking away from this painful stimulus she gashed her wrist with the knife and severed a large nerve.

1. The hot water stimulated specialized nerve endings in her skin which in turn generated nerve impulses. These endings are called
   a. exteroceptors
   b. interoceptors
   c. proprioceptors
   d. motor end plates

2. Nerve impulses which originate in the periphery are conducted to the CNS over
   a. efferent neurons
   b. central neurons
   c. associational neurons
   d. afferent neurons

3. Nerve impulses are conducted at great speed over reflex arc components, but there is some slowing when they pass across the
   a. cell bodies
   b. synapses
   c. afferent fibers
   d. efferent fibers

4. Which of the following is essential to the life of a neuron?
   a. axon
   b. dendrite
   c. myelin
   d. cell body

5. The doctor sewed together the cut ends of the nerve by placing stitches in the outer covering or
   a. perineurium
   b. epineurium
   c. endoneurium
   d. neuroglia

6. After sewing the nerve, the doctor assured V. W. that she probably would recover good function
   a. the next day
   b. in 10 days
   c. in a few months
   d. in a few years

7. Which of the following is essential for the regeneration of injured nerve fibers?
   a. neurilemma sheath
   b. myelin sheath
   c. gray matter
   d. white matter

7

*"Oh the nerves, the nerves;
the mysteries of this machine called man!"*

THE CHIMES ● CHARLES DICKENS

THE SPINAL CORD AND SPINAL NERVES

THE SPINAL CORD

The spinal cord and its 31 pairs of nerves might be roughly compared with a telephone switchboard and its miles of cables. As you dial the telephone number of a friend, electrical impulses flash over wires to the central switchboard; from here they are routed over appropriate circuits to still other wires that lead to the bell in your friend's telephone. For more complicated calls, the services of special operators and supervisors are required. In a similar manner the spinal cord serves as a "switchboard" for the nerve impulses which are transmitted over the millions of fibers in our spinal nerve "cables." Many of our daily activities are carried out more or less "automatically" without any special thought processes; however, they are always being monitored and influenced by special "operators" and "supervisors" through a more complicated switchboard, the brain.

Location and description

The spinal cord (continuous with the brain stem) begins at the level of the foramen magnum and extends downward through the vertebral canal to the level of the disk between the first and the second lumbar vertebrae (Fig. 7-1).

This elongated cylindrical mass of nervous tissue consists of **31 segments,** each of which gives rise to a pair of spinal nerves. The spinal cord is conspicuously enlarged in two regions: the **cervical enlargement** gives origin to nerves which supply the upper extremities, and the **lumbar enlargement** gives origin to nerves which supply the lower extremities.

Extending the full length of the spinal cord are two clefts that partially divide the spinal cord into right and left halves. The *ventral median fissure* is a relatively deep cleft that effectively separates the anterior portions of the cord. Posteriorly, separation is achieved by a partition

First cervical vertebra —

First thoracic vertebra —

Twelfth thoracic vertebra —

First lumbar vertebra —

Fifth lumbar vertebra —

First sacral nerve —

Cauda equina

Sacrum { (sacral and

coccygeal nerves)

— Medulla

— First cervical nerve

— Eighth cervical nerve

— First thoracic nerve

— Dural sheath

— Twelfth thoracic nerve

— First lumbar nerve

— Fifth lumbar nerve

— End of dural sheath

— Fifth sacral nerve

— Coccygeal nerve

— Coccyx

Fig. 7-1. Spinal cord enclosed in unopened dural sheath,
lying within the vertebral canal. The neural arches are completely removed on the left side, partially on the right, to
expose the dorsal surface of the dura. The bundle of nerve
roots below the dural sac forms the cauda equina.

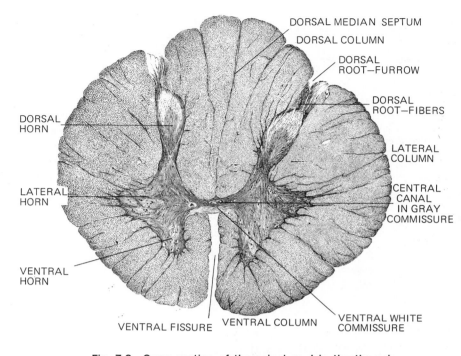

DORSAL MEDIAN SEPTUM
DORSAL COLUMN
DORSAL ROOT—FURROW
DORSAL ROOT—FIBERS
LATERAL COLUMN
CENTRAL CANAL IN GRAY COMMISSURE
DORSAL HORN
LATERAL HORN
VENTRAL HORN
VENTRAL FISSURE
VENTRAL COLUMN
VENTRAL WHITE COMMISSURE

Fig. 7-2. Cross section of the spinal cord in the thoracic region, showing the H-shaped gray matter, surrounded by white matter. ×13.

which is called the *dorsal median septum.* In the central midportion of the cord, a narrow bridge (commissure) of gray and white fibers, surrounding the central canal, serves to join the two halves (Fig. 7-2). The central canal contains cerebrospinal fluid (p. 236).

Coverings of the spinal cord

In addition to the bony vertebral column, the spinal cord is covered and protected by 3 **meninges,** or membranes, (Fig. 7-3) which are downward extensions of those which cover the brain.

The dura mater ("hard mother") is the outermost membrane, and it is composed of dense fibrous connective tissue. This tough, tubular sheath extends downward to the level of the second sacral segment where it ends as a blind sac. The dura mater also covers the spinal nerve roots

as they leave the spinal cord and extend to the intervertebral foramina.

The space between the walls of the vertebral canal and the outer surface of the dura mater is called the *epidural* or *extradural space;* it contains a network of blood vessels and adipose and areolar connective tissue. The *subdural space* is that between the inner surface of the dura and the underlying arachnoid membrane; it is quite limited and contains only a small amount of fluid.

The arachnoid membrane ("like a spider web") is a thin, transparent sheath which lies immediately under the dura and follows it to the end of the dural sac. The innermost layer of the meninges, called the **pia mater** ("gentle mother"), is very closely applied to the spinal cord. This delicate membrane contains many blood vessels and plays an important part in the nourishment of cells within the spinal cord.

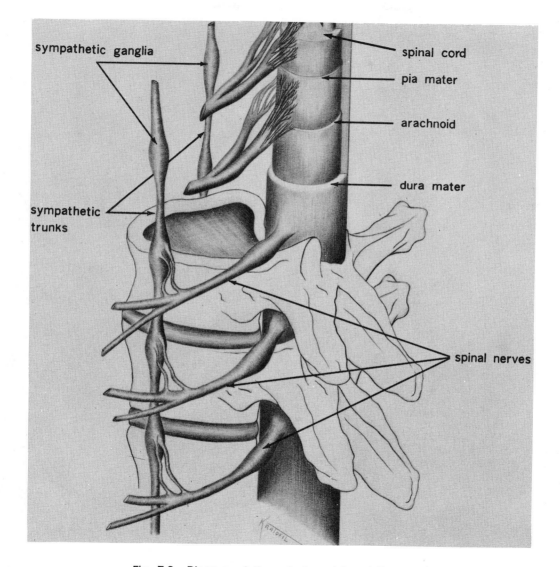

Fig. 7-3. Diagram of the spinal cord in relation to the meninges and to the bony vertebral canal. Spinal nerve branches and connections with sympathetic chain ganglia also are shown.

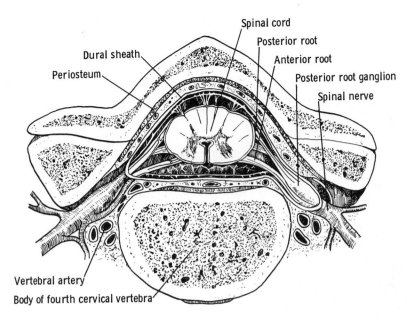

Spinal cord
Posterior root
Anterior root
Posterior root ganglion
Spinal nerve
Dural sheath
Periosteum
Vertebral artery
Body of fourth cervical vertebra

Fig. 7-4. Cross section of vertebral column at the level of the 4th cervical vertebra, showing spinal cord in position.

Fig. 7-5. Cross section of the spinal cord. On the right, the principal conduction pathways are shown; of these, 1, 2, 5, 6 and 7 are ascending, and 3, 4 and 8 are descending tracts. On the left, the functions of the various tracts are indicated. Diagrammatic. All tracts are bilateral.

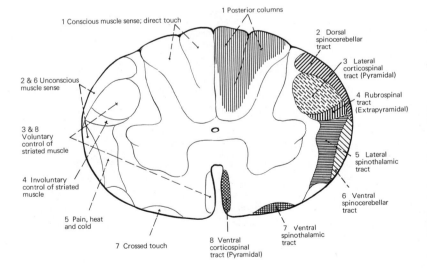

1 Posterior columns
1 Conscious muscle sense; direct touch
2 Dorsal spinocerebellar tract
3 Lateral corticospinal tract (Pyramidal)
4 Rubrospinal tract (Extrapyramidal)
2 & 6 Unconscious muscle sense
5 Lateral spinothalamic tract
3 & 8 Voluntary control of striated muscle
6 Ventral spinocerebellar tract
4 Involuntary control of striated muscle
7 Ventral spinothalamic tract
5 Pain, heat and cold
8 Ventral corticospinal tract (Pyramidal)
7 Crossed touch

The **subarachnoid space** is a relatively roomy area between the arachnoid and the pia mater. It is filled with a liquid commonly called the *spinal fluid;* however, a more accurate term is **cerebrospinal fluid,** since it also is found in the cranial subarachnoid spaces. Analysis of this fluid is a valuable diagnostic aid in many cases, and samples may be obtained by spinal tap or lumbar puncture. This procedure requires the insertion of a long needle between the 3rd and the 4th (sometimes the 4th and the 5th) lumbar vertebrae and into the subarachnoid space. Since the spinal cord ends at the level of the disk between the 1st and the 2nd lumbar vertebrae, there is little danger of striking it with the needle. The formation, the circulation and the functions of cerebrospinal fluid are described on page 236.

Inflammation of the meninges is called **meningitis.** It may involve the dura only, or it may involve the arachnoid and the pia mater. It may be due to a variety of infectious agents, such as the tubercle bacillus, meningococcus, streptococcus or staphylococcus.

Internal structure

In cross section the spinal cord presents a somewhat oval-shaped appearance. It is seen to contain an "H"-shaped mass of gray matter which is surrounded by white matter (Figs. 7-2 and 7-4).

The **gray matter** of the spinal cord is composed of cell bodies and unmyelinated nerve fibers. For descriptive purposes, the columns of the "H" are referred to as the right and left anterior or ventral horns, the lateral horns and the posterior or dorsal horns (Fig. 7-2).

The **white matter** of the spinal cord consists primarily of myelinated fibers in a network of neuroglia. These fibers serve to link various segments of the spinal cord and to connect the spinal cord with the brain. The white matter in each half of the cord is divided into 3 columns (or funiculi): the anterior, the lateral and the posterior columns (Fig. 7-2). Each column is subdivided into *tracts* which are merely large bundles of nerve fibers arranged in functional groups (Fig. 7-5). *Ascending tracts* transmit impulses to the brain, and *descending tracts* transmit impulses from the brain to various levels of the spinal cord.

THE SPINAL NERVES

There are 31 pairs of spinal nerves, and each pair is numbered according to the level of the spinal cord segment from which it originates. There are 8 pairs of cervical nerves, 12 pairs of thoracic, 5 pairs of lumbar, 5 pairs of sacral and 1 pair of coccygeal nerves.

Origin of spinal nerves

Each spinal nerve arises by 2 roots: a posterior or dorsal root and an anterior or ventral root (Figs. 6-8 and 7-4).

1. **The dorsal root** of a spinal nerve may also be called the *sensory root,* since it contains afferent nerve fibers that conduct nerve impulses to the spinal cord. On each dorsal root there is a marked swelling called the **dorsal root ganglion,** or *spinal ganglion,* which contains the cell bodies of both somatic and visceral afferent neurons. The axons of these afferent neurons extend into the dorsal gray matter of the spinal cord.

2. **The ventral root** of a spinal nerve may also be referred to as the *motor root;* it contains efferent fibers that conduct impulses away from the spinal cord. The dendrites and the cell bodies of somatic efferent neurons are located in the anterior horns of gray matter in the cord. Figure 6-8 illustrates the synaptic connections between related neurons of the spinal nerve roots. Cell bodies of visceral efferent neurons are located in the lateral horns, as described in Chapter 9.

The dorsal and the ventral roots extend to the intervertebral foramen which corresponds to their spinal cord segment of origin. Early in fetal life, the spinal cord and the vertebral column are the same length, but soon the vertebral column begins to elongate more rapidly than the cord. Because of this difference in growth, the cord segments are displaced upward from their corresponding vertebrae, the discrepancy being greatest at the lower end of the cord. Since the spinal cord ends in the upper lumbar region of the vertebral column, the lower lumbar, sacral and coccygeal nerve roots

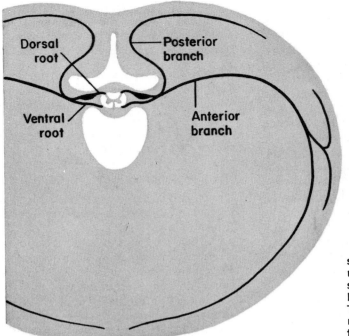

Fig. 7-6. Schematic cross section through vertebral column and left side of trunk showing anterior and posterior branches of one spinal nerve. The spinal cord and the spinal nerve roots can be seen within the vertebral canal.

must descend further and further to reach their respective intervertebral foramina (Fig. 7-1). This "drooping" of lower nerve roots somewhat resembles the tail of a horse, and thus it has been named the *cauda equina* ("tail, horse").

As a dorsal and ventral root reach their intervertebral foramen they unite to form a **spinal nerve,** as shown in Figure 7-4. Therefore, all spinal nerves are *mixed* nerves, since they contain both sensory and motor fibers for the conduction of nerve impulses between the spinal cord and the periphery. Severing of a spinal nerve results in paralysis of muscle and loss of sensation in the areas supplied by the nerve.

Distribution of spinal nerves

As each spinal nerve emerges from the intervertebral foramen a small *meningeal branch* is given off; this branch re-enters the vertebral canal, where it innervates the vertebrae, ligaments, and blood vessels of the spinal cord and the meninges. The two *primary branches,* however, are the anterior and the posterior rami (Fig. 7-6).

The posterior rami consist of those motor and sensory fibers that supply the skin and the longitudinal muscles of the back.

The anterior rami are larger than the posterior; they consist of motor and sensory fibers which supply all of the structures of the extremities and the lateral and the anterior portions of the trunk. However, the anterior rami (except those of 11 thoracic nerves) do not go directly to skin or muscle; they first combine in such a way as to form complicated networks of nerve fibers which are called **plexuses.** Emerging from each plexus are nerves which are named according to the general region which they supply (e.g., ulnar, femoral, etc.). Each of these nerves, in turn, may have numerous branches which are named for the structure which they supply, such as articular, muscular or cutaneous branches.

The thoracic and upper lumbar spinal nerves also give rise to *white rami* (visceral efferent branches) or preganglionic autonomic nerve fibers; these fibers are described in Chapter 9.

The Cervical Plexus. The anterior rami of the first 4 cervical spinal nerves combine to form the cervical plexus which lies deep in the neck on each side (Fig. 7-7). Branches from this plexus are distributed to the muscles and the skin of the neck and the posterior part of the scalp. The **phrenic nerve,** composed of fibers from the 3rd, the 4th and the 5th cervical spinal nerves, is the most important branch of the cervical plexus, as it supplies motor fibers to the muscular *diaphragm.* Crushing of the spinal cord above the level of phrenic nerve origin, as in the case of a "broken neck," will result in respiratory paralysis and death, since "orders" from the brain no longer can reach the phrenic nerves, and the diaphragm ceases to contract.

The Brachial Plexus. The anterior rami of the last 4 cervical and the 1st thoracic spinal nerves combine to form the brachial plexus (Fig. 7-8) which supplies a number of neck and shoulder muscles in addition to the entire upper extremity. The chief nerves that emerge from this plexus, on each side of the body, are (1) the **musculocutaneous,** which supplies motor fibers to the anterior arm muscles (e.g., biceps brachii) and sensory fibers to the skin of the lateral forearm; (2) the **median** nerve, which supplies motor fibers to flexor muscles in the anterolateral aspect of the forearm and the hand, and sensory fibers to the skin in the radial half of the palm; (3) the **ulnar** nerve, which supplies motor fibers to the flexor muscles in the anteromedial aspect of the forearm and the hand, and sensory fibers to the skin of the same region; and (4) the **radial** nerve (largest branch of the plexus) which supplies motor fibers to the muscles and sensory fibers to the skin on the posterior aspect of the arm, the forearm and the hand. The distribution of these nerves is shown in Figure 7-9. When you strike your elbow and feel the tingling and the pain in the forearm you say that you have hit your "funny bone," but you really have given a mechanical stimulus or blow to the ulnar nerve as it passes superficially between the medial epicondyle of the humerus and the olecranon process of the ulna.

Injuries to the nerves that supply the upper extremities are not uncommon. For example, the improper use of crutches may cause undue pressure on the nerves in the axilla, resulting in a temporary paralysis, mainly of structures supplied by the *radial nerve.* The most characteristic sign of radial nerve damage is an inability to extend the hand at the wrist, a condition that is called "wrist drop."

When the *median nerve* alone is damaged, there is inability to pronate the forearm or to flex the wrist properly, since the pronators and most of the flexors are supplied by it. The second phalanges of the middle and the index fingers cannot be flexed. The thumb cannot be flexed and abducted, which is one of the most characteristic features of the normal hand. The ability to appose the thumb to any one of the fingers, as is done in picking up very small objects, is lost.

After damage to the *ulnar nerve,* flexion and adduction of the wrist are impaired. There is difficulty in spreading the fingers; the hand is clawed. When both the ulnar and the median nerves are injured at the wrist, as is frequently the case, all small muscles of the hand are paralyzed.

The Intercostal Nerves. The anterior rami of the 12 thoracic spinal nerves (except for the 1st) follow a simple segmental pattern and do not enter into the formation of plexuses. They are referred to as intercostal nerves, since they run through the intercostal spaces in the thorax. These nerves supply motor fibers to the intercostal muscles and to the muscles of the abdominal wall, as well as sensory fibers to the overlying skin.

The Lumbar Plexus. The anterior rami of the first 4 lumbar spinal nerves combine to form the lumbar plexus (Fig. 7-8). Nerves derived from this plexus supply motor and sensory fibers to the structures of the lower abdominal wall, the external genitalia and part of the lower extremity. The **femoral nerve,** largest branch of the plexus, supplies motor fibers to the iliopsoas and the quadriceps femoris muscles, and sensory fibers to skin on the anteromedial aspect of the thigh. The *saphenous nerve* is a long cutaneous branch of the femoral which supplies the skin overlying the

Fig.7-7. Distribution of certain peripheral
nerves seen from dorsal view.

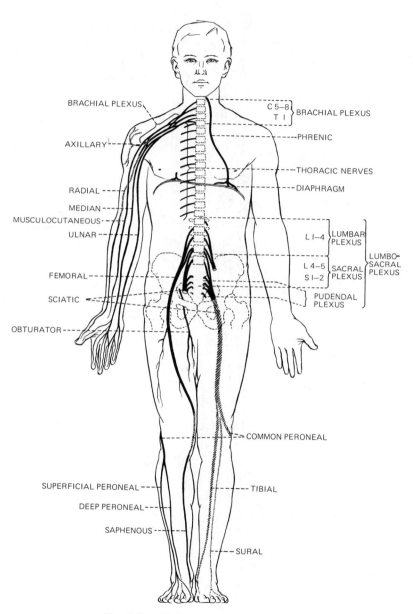

Fig. 7-8. Diagrammatic distribution of certain peripheral nerves projected on the ventral surface.

Median nerve

Ulnar nerve

Deltoideus

Musculo-cutaneous
nerve, ant.
and post. brs.

Biceps brachii
tendon

Radial nerve

Articular branches
of median nerve

Superficial
radial nerve

Extensor carpi
rad. longus

Ulnar nerve

Radial artery

Brachio-radialis

Palmar cutaneous
br. of ulnar

Flexor carpi
radialis

Median nerve

Deep br. of
ulnar nerve

Digital brs. of
median nerve

Digital brs. of
ulnar nerve

Fig. 7-9. Dissection of anterior surface of right upper extremity, showing course and distribution of parts of radial, ulnar and median nerves.

medial aspect of the leg and the foot. The *obturator nerve* supplies motor fibers to the adductor muscles of the thigh.

Injuries to the femoral nerve may result from pelvic tumors or fractures of the pelvis and the upper femur. In such an event, there is inability to extend the leg, and sensation is lost in those skin areas supplied by the nerve. If the injury is high enough to involve the iliopsoas, there is inability to flex the thigh.

The Sacral Plexus. The anterior rami of the 4th and the 5th lumbar and the first 3 sacral spinal nerves enter into formation of the sacral plexus (Fig. 7-8). Branches from this plexus supply motor and sensory fibers to structures in the buttocks, the perineum (area between pubis and coccyx) and the lower extremities. The **sciatic nerve**, largest and longest nerve in the body, is the main branch of the sacral plexus. Covered by the gluteus maximus muscle, this great nerve curves downward through the buttock, resting on the posterior surface of the ischium, between the ischial tuberosity and the greater trochanter of the femur. It then descends through the thigh, supplying branches to the hamstring muscles and the overlying skin before it divides into the tibial (medial popliteal) and the common peroneal (lateral popliteal) nerves (Fig. 7-10).

The *tibial nerve* supplies the posterior calf muscles concerned with plantar flexion and inversion of the foot and with plantar flexion of the toes. The *common peroneal nerve* supplies the lateral and anterior muscles of the leg and the dorsal muscles of the foot, effecting dorsal flexion and eversion of the foot.

Injury to the sciatic nerve may result from a herniated intervertebral disk, a dislocated hip, compression by the pregnant uterus, or injections of various drugs into or near the nerve. In adults, the upper outer quadrant of the buttocks is a recommended site for intramuscular injections. However, it is essential that the person giving the injection knows the location of the underlying sciatic nerve and how to select the proper site for insertion of the needle. The classic method of dividing the buttocks into 4 quadrants by intersecting perpendicular lines may be dangerous,

Fig. 7-10. Deep dissection of posterior surface of right thigh, showing sciatic nerve dividing into peroneal and tibial nerves.

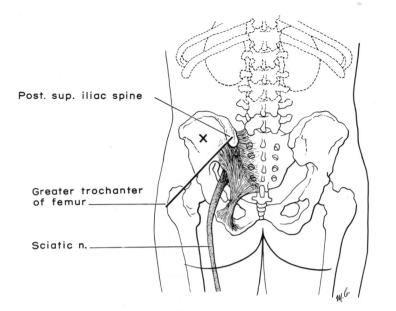

Post. sup. iliac spine

Greater trochanter
of femur

Sciatic n.

Fig. 7-11. Diagram of landmarks for the injection of intramuscular medications in the gluteal region. An injection that is lateral and superior to a line drawn from the posterior superior iliac spine to the greater trochanter of the femur will be removed from the course of the sciatic nerve; the letter x indicates one such site.

because of the absence of well defined landmarks for locating the vertical line. Daniel J. Hanson, M.D., recommends the following minor modification for locating the injection site: "A line drawn from the posterior superior iliac spine to the greater trochanter of the femur is lateral to and parallel with the course of the sciatic nerve. Any injection lateral and superior to this line will be removed from the course of the sciatic nerve and will be within the region of the greatest gluteal mass . . ." (Fig. 7-11). Should the sciatic nerve be injured by drug injection, experience has shown that the common peroneal nerve fibers (located on the lateral side of the sciatic trunk) usually suffer the greater damage, resulting in "foot drop" due to paralysis of the dorsiflexor muscles of the foot and the toes.

Sciatica is one type of neuritis. This condition is characterized by sharp, shooting pain along the course of the sciatic nerve; there may be tenderness, numbness and tingling in addition to the pain. If this inflammatory condition persists, there may be atrophy or "wasting" of those muscles supplied by the nerve.

The Pudendal Plexus. The anterior rami of the 2nd, the 3rd and the 4th sacral spinal nerves con-

tribute fibers to this plexus. The *pudendal nerve* is the largest branch, and it supplies the levator ani muscle, the skin and other structures of the perineum. This nerve may be blocked by drugs to facilitate childbirth.

FUNCTIONS OF THE SPINAL CORD

The spinal cord serves as a center for spinal reflexes and as a conduction pathway to and from the brain.

Reflex center

The reflex arc (p. 195) depends not only on afferent and efferent fibers but also on a central structure where these fibers can be connected; the spinal cord serves this function for first level, or spinal cord reflexes. Second and third level reflexes involve centers in the brain and are described in Chapter 8.

Examples of spinal reflexes are the *stretch reflexes* and the *flexor reflexes*. The "knee jerk" is an example of the stretch reflex, and one that you can demonstrate easily on your own body. Sit with the thighs crossed so that one leg swings free of the floor in a relaxed manner; with the side of your hand, strike the patellar tendon (just below the knee cap) and note the involuntary extension of the leg. When this tendon is struck, the quadriceps muscle of the thigh is stretched slightly, and proprioceptors are stimulated. Impulses travel from these receptors in the muscle over dendrites in the femoral nerve to cell bodies in the dorsal root ganglion and then over the axons to synapses in the ventral horn of gray matter. Since the stretch reflex is a two-neuron circuit, central cells are not required, and impulses travel directly to the dendrites of motor cell bodies in the ventral horn, pass over the dendrites and the cell bodies and on to the axons and to the muscle fibers of the quadriceps femoris muscle, causing contraction. Probably 3 segments of the spinal cord in the lumbar region and hundreds of incoming and outgoing fibers are involved in this reflex. It is due to stretch reflexes in our extensor muscles (those that oppose gravity) that we are able to maintain the standing position.

Not all spinal reflexes are so simple as the knee jerk, as will be noted in the following illustration. Suppose that as you step out of bed expecting to put your feet into your bedroom slippers you encounter a sharp object with one foot. You withdraw that foot, put your weight on the other leg and grab something to keep from falling, and you note that your heart is beating faster and more forcibly than usual. In this case there was a stimulation of the receptors in one foot, and the impulses passed to the spinal cord. Some impulses were transferred directly to efferent neurons and sent back immediately to the skeletal muscles to cause that foot to be withdrawn from the harmful object. This is a *flexor reflex*. Other impulses were sent to the muscles of the opposite leg, to enable you to maintain your balance, and to the upper extremities, to enable you to hold on to something to prevent a fall. The entire spinal cord from the sacral to the cervical region is involved in this response. Even cell bodies of autonomic neurons received impulses which caused the heart to beat faster. While all of this was going on in the spinal cord, impulses were arriving at the brain which made you conscious of the pain in the foot after it had been withdrawn from the stimulus. Flexor reflexes are protective in nature and help to guard us from harm; they are fundamental to preservation of life.

Testing of various reflexes is an important part of any physical examination. If they are normal it indicates that the muscles themselves, the nerve fibers which carry impulses to the CNS, the reflex centers of the CNS and the nerve fibers which carry impulses from the CNS to the muscles all are working properly (Fig. 6-9).

Spinal reflexes may be brought about as a result of stimuli outside of the body or inside the body, and they may involve skeletal muscle, smooth muscle, heart muscle and glands.

Conduction pathway

In its function as a conduction pathway to and from the brain, the spinal cord makes use of tracts. Ascending tracts transmit impulses to the brain, and descending tracts transmit impulses from the brain to various levels of the spinal cord. In many cases, the tracts of the spinal cord are given names that indicate the origin and the destination of the constituent fibers.

The ascending pathways in each side of the spinal cord consist of the posterior columns, the spinocerebellar and the spinothalamic tracts (Fig. 7-5).

1. The **posterior columns** (fasciculus gracilis and fasciculus cuneatus) consist of axons of cell bodies in the dorsal root ganglia. These axons ascend to the medulla, where they synapse with other neurons which cross to the opposite side. Eventually nerve impulses reach the highest centers of the brain, and the medullary crossing of fibers means that impulses from the right side of the body are transmitted to the left side of the brain, while impulses from the left side of the body reach the right side of the brain. Some of the impulses which travel over fibers in this tract were originally started by proprioceptors in skeletal muscle, tendons and joints; these are impulses of *"conscious muscle sense,"* which means that when

they reach the brain they give rise to sensations of body position and movement. Other fibers in the posterior columns conduct impulses from exteroceptors for touch and pressure. When these impulses reach the brain, one is able to recognize the size, shape and texture of objects; one also is able to localize the exact part of the body that is touched.

Injury to the posterior columns results in ataxic movements, since proprioceptive impulses cannot reach the brain. This patient cannot tell where his body parts are without looking at them; he walks on a wide base, slapping his feet on the floor, and usually watches his legs so that he will know where they are. In the dark, or with his eyes closed, he may fall. There also is an impairment of touch discrimination and precise localization. Vertebral fractures, tumors and diseases such as syphilis of the spinal cord (tabes dorsalis) may lead to posterior column damage.

2. The **spinocerebellar tracts** (dorsal and ventral) consist of axons which arise from central cell bodies in the spinal cord and end in the cerebellum; the majority of these fibers are uncrossed. Nerve impulses that travel in these tracts originate in proprioceptors in muscles, tendons and joints, as do those that travel in the posterior columns; however, synaptic connections and final destination differ, as spinocerebellar impulses do not reach the conscious centers of the brain. These tracts transmit impulses concerned with *"unconscious muscle sense"* and play an important part in reflex adjustments of posture and muscle tone.

Injury to these tracts leads to uncoordinated voluntary movements, chiefly because of abnormal tone in the skeletal muscles.

3. The **spinothalamic tracts** consist of axons that arise from central cell bodies in the spinal cord and end in the thalamus (a relay station in the brain). Other neurons connect the thalamus with sensory areas in the brain. The *ventral spinothalamic* tract transmits impulses concerned with crude touch and pressure sensations, while fibers in the *lateral spinothalamic tract* transmit impulses concerned with *pain and temperature* sensations. These impulses arise from exteroceptors in the skin and travel over afferent neurons which synapse

with the spinothalamic neurons in the dorsal gray matter of the cord. The axons of these central neurons cross to the opposite side of the cord before ascending to the thalamus.

The lateral spinothalamic tracts may be intentionally cut by a surgical procedure called *chordotomy*. This operation often makes life bearable for those who suffer from intractable pain (that which cannot be relieved by drugs) as a result of cancer. There is no sensation of pain if the pathways that transmit impulses from the diseased area are cut. However, one must keep in mind the fact that temperature sensations also are abolished, and the person may be burned by hot water bottles or heating pads unless care is exercised.

The descending pathways in each side of the spinal cord consist of two groups of tracts: the pyramidal and the extrapyramidal tracts (Fig. 7-5).

1. The **pyramidal** or **corticospinal tracts** are bundles of axons that arise from cell bodies in the motor areas of the frontal lobes of the brain and eventually end in the spinal cord segments. These tracts are the most important and prominent of all the descending bundles, each consisting of over 1 million fibers. Most of the corticospinal fibers cross in the medulla and descend as the large *lateral corticospinal* (crossed pyramidal) tract in each side of the spinal cord; during the descent, each tract gradually diminishes in size as fibers leave to terminate in the ventral gray matter. Those fibers that do not cross in the medulla continue as the smaller ventral corticospinal tracts; some of these fibers cross at each segment of the spinal cord, and all of them ultimately terminate in the ventral gray matter.

The corticospinal tracts conduct impulses from the brain to motor neurons in the ventral gray matter of the spinal cord, which in turn conduct the impulses to skeletal muscles and bring about our fine *voluntary movements,* especially those of the fingers, the hand, etc., which enable us to acquire various skills.

Due to the crossing of fibers, the left half of the brain controls the skeletal muscles on the right side of the body, and the right side of the brain controls the left side of the body.

2. The **extrapyramidal tracts** (meaning "outside" of the pyramidal) are composed of fibers which arise from the lower levels of the brain and descend through the cord to synapse with the ventral horn cells. Thus we can see that these busy ventral horn cells are truly "the final common path" to our skeletal muscles; they are stimulated not only by afferent neurons in segmental reflexes, but also by pyramidal and extrapyramidal fibers from the brain.

Although the extrapyramidal fibers are primarily concerned with *involuntary* or unconscious skeletal muscle coordination and the reflex control of equilibrium, they also may produce some of the gross movements that are of a voluntary nature. This latter function assumes added importance following injury to the pyramidal tracts; while fine isolated movements of the extremities are severely and permanently affected, there is a recovery of some of the grosser movements, probably due in part to greater use of the extrapyramidal tracts.

The brain cells and their axons in the descending tracts are called "upper motor neurons" in contrast to the ventral horn cells of the spinal cord which are called "lower motor neurons." Injury to upper motor neurons results in a spastic type of paralysis, the skeletal muscles becoming stiff and resisting passive movements. On the other hand, when lower motor neurons are injured, a flaccid paralysis results; the skeletal muscles become soft and flabby, even reflex movements are absent, and the muscles eventually atrophy.

Injury to the spinal cord

Bullet wounds and fracture dislocations of vertebrae may result in a *transection* or severing of the spinal cord. In such a case, the skeletal muscles below the level of injury are paralyzed, and sensation is abolished as all descending and ascending pathways are interrupted. If the transection occurs below the 5th cervical segment, the phrenic nerves to the diaphragm will not be affected and the patient will continue to breathe. However, paralysis below this point is complete,

and even spinal reflexes are temporarily abolished. This severe depression or collapse of cord function is known as "spinal shock" and is believed to be due to loss of stimulation from higher levels.

Limited reflex activity within the isolated spinal cord segments will reappear within a variable period of time; however, muscle tone and the deep reflexes are greatly increased in intensity. The uncontrolled muscle tone leads to alternating spasms of the flexor and the extensor muscles, but eventually one group or the other will predominate. It is believed that the position assumed by the extremities during the early stages of paralysis is an important factor in determining whether flexor or extensor spasms will eventually predominate.

The nursing care of such a patient presents many problems, particularly if the injury is high enough to involve the upper extremities. This patient is completely helpless; he can breathe and talk, his heart beats, and the blood circulates, but he cannot walk, feed himself or scratch his nose when it itches. Bladder and rectal functions also are greatly disturbed in all transections of the cord as voluntary control is lost. The nurse plays an important role in proper positioning of the patient, and in the prevention of decubitus ulcers and urinary tract infection. Kidney infection is a serious complication of spinal cord transection. Since a "cord bladder" does not empty completely, there is residual urine in which bacteria may flourish, and the resulting infection may spread up the ureters to the kidneys. However, the advent of antibiotic drugs has changed the picture greatly, and spinal cord damage does not necessarily mean an early death.

Because of the persistent efforts of dedicated members of the medical and allied health professions, many of these patients can be rehabilitated to an amazing degree. This is particularly true of those whose spinal cord injury is below the midthoracic region. A large percentage of these persons can be taught to walk with the aid of braces and crutches, and many of them can become completely self-supporting. One must never lose sight of these facts when encouraging and working with those who have suffered a spinal cord injury.

SUMMARY

1. Spinal cord
   A. Location and description
      a. From foramen magnum to level of disk between L-1 and L-2
      b. 31 segments, each gives rise to pair of nerves
      c. Cervical enlargement: origin of nerves to upper extremity
      d. Lumbar enlargement: origin of nerves to lower extremity
      e. Ventral median fissure separates anterior portions of cord
      f. Dorsal median septum separates posterior portions of cord
      g. Bridge of gray and white fibers joins two halves of cord in midportion
   B. Coverings of the cord
      a. Dura mater, outer covering
      b. Arachnoid membrane, middle covering
      c. Pia mater, innermost covering
      d. Subarachnoid space between arachnoid and pia mater; contains cerebrospinal fluid
   C. Internal structure
      a. In cross section—H-shaped mass of gray matter; unmyelinated fibers and cell bodies
      b. White matter surrounds gray; myelinated fibers in network of neuroglia
2. Spinal nerves
   A. Origin
      a. Dorsal root contains afferent fibers
         (1) Dorsal root ganglion, contains cell bodies of afferent neurons
         (2) Fibers may synapse with central neurons or ascend to brain
      b. Ventral root contains efferent fibers
      c. The two roots extend to intervertebral foramen; drooping of lower roots called cauda equina
      d. Roots unite to form spinal nerves
   B. Distribution of spinal nerves
      a. Each branches after leaving intervertebral foramen
      b. Posterior rami supply skin and muscles of back
      c. Anterior rami supply extremities, lateral and anterior portions of trunk; rami enter into formation of plexuses
      d. Cervical plexus: supplies muscles and skin of neck and posterior scalp; phrenic nerve to diaphragm
      e. Brachial plexus: supplies neck and shoulder muscles and upper extremity;
         (1) Musculocutaneous nerve to anterior arm muscles
         (2) Median nerve to anterolateral forearm and hand
         (3) Ulnar nerve to anteromedial forearm and hand
         (4) Radial nerve to posterior arm, forearm and hand
      f. Intercostal nerves to intercostal muscles and muscles of abdominal wall
      g. Lumbar plexus: femoral nerve to iliopsoas and quadriceps; obturator nerve to adductor muscles of thigh
      h. Sacral plexus: sciatic nerve supplies hamstrings and muscles of leg and foot; tibial and common peroneal are main branches
      i. Pudendal plexus: pudendal nerve to levator ani muscle and perineum

3. Functions of spinal cord
   A. Reflex center
      a. Provides central point for synaptic connections between afferent and efferent neurons
      b. Stretch reflexes
      c. Flexor reflexes
   B. Conduction pathway
      a. Ascending pathways: transmit impulses to the brain
         (1) Posterior columns; conscious muscle sense, pressure and touch
         (2) Spinocerebellar tracts; unconscious muscle sense in reflex adjustments of posture and muscle tone

(3) Spinothalamic tracts; pain and temperature (lateral tract), crude touch and pressure (ventral tract)
b. Descending pathways: transmit impulses from the brain
(1) Pyramidal or corticospinal tracts concerned with voluntary movements
(2) Extrapyramidal tracts concerned with involuntary skeletal muscle coordination and possibly with some gross voluntary movements
C. Injury to spinal cord
a. Transection of cord results in complete paralysis of skeletal muscle and loss of sensation below level of injury
b. Reflex activity will return but leads to spasms of flexor and extensor muscles with one group eventually predominating

PRACTICAL APPLICATIONS AND QUESTIONS

(Encircle the letter of the *best* answer to each of the following questions.)

While visiting neurology clinic you may have an opportunity to observe the following cases.

A. *Tommy, a victim of poliomyelitis, has extensive destruction of lower motor neurons.*

1. Destruction of lower motor neurons results in
   a. loss of conscious muscle sense
   b. flaccid paralysis
   c. loss of unconscious muscle sense
   d. spastic paralysis
2. The cell bodies of spinal cord neurons which supply skeletal muscles are located in the
   a. ventral columns of white matter
   b. dorsal root ganglion
   c. ventral horns of gray matter
   d. anterior root

B. *One of the clinic patients submits to a spinal tap for diagnostic purposes and is then admitted to the hospital.*

1. At what level is the needle usually introduced in spinal tap?
   a. between the 1st and the 2nd thoracic vertebrae
   b. between the 3rd and the 4th lumbar vertebrae
   c. between the 1st and the 2nd sacral segment
   d. below the last lumbar vertebra
2. Cerebrospinal fluid is withdrawn from the
   a. epidural space
   b. subdural space
   c. central canal of the cord
   d. subarachnoid space

C. *A. C. is suffering from a disease which has destroyed the posterior columns of white matter in the spinal cord.*

1. This patient has difficulty in walking because
   a. he is unaware of the location of his body parts
   b. he is partially paralyzed from the waist down
   c. he is blind
   d. upper motor neurons have been damaged
2. Nerve impulses which normally travel over the posterior columns are originated by receptors in the
   a. brain
   b. spinal cord
   c. skeletal muscles
   d. heart

8

*"Our purses shall be proud, our garments poor:
For 'tiz the mind that makes the body rich."*

THE TAMING OF THE SHREW ● WILLIAM SHAKESPEARE

THE BRAIN AND THE CRANIAL NERVES

Just as the executive offices of many large corporations are located on the uppermost floors of the building, so is the human brain positioned in the body. Enclosed in a snug bony box on top of the vertebral column, the brain receives a constant stream of information which has been relayed upward through the spinal cord and the cranial nerves. "Junior executives" in the lower brain divisions are capable of handling routine problems and dispatching orders to various parts of the body, but "command decisions" based on associative memory and processes of evaluation are made only by a "board of directors" located in the topmost executive suites (the cerebral cortex). It is the amazing development of this upper brain division that truly distinguishes man from lower animals. For example, the chimpanzee (most intelligent of the apes) is unable to carry on a conversation, to read a book or to dress himself and go to school, no matter how much training he may receive. On the other hand, human beings quickly acquire these skills and then proceed to even more complicated mental activities. Man, possessing the ability to think, to reason and to exercise judgment, has the most elaborate brain of any living creature.

The average adult human brain, or **encephalon**, weighs approximately 3 pounds, but its size varies with the age, the sex and the size of the individual. For example, men generally have larger brains than women, due to the fact that they have larger heads, but this does not mean that they are necessarily any smarter, since size normally is not indicative of intelligence. Housed in the cranial cavity, the brain is the largest and most complex mass of nervous tissue in the body, and it attains its full growth by the 18th or the 20th year of life. However, it should be noted that although physical growth ceases, there is an unlimited number of neural pathways to be developed so long as we *use* our brains. In other words, mental exercise is just as important to brain development as physical exercise is to the development of sturdy muscles.

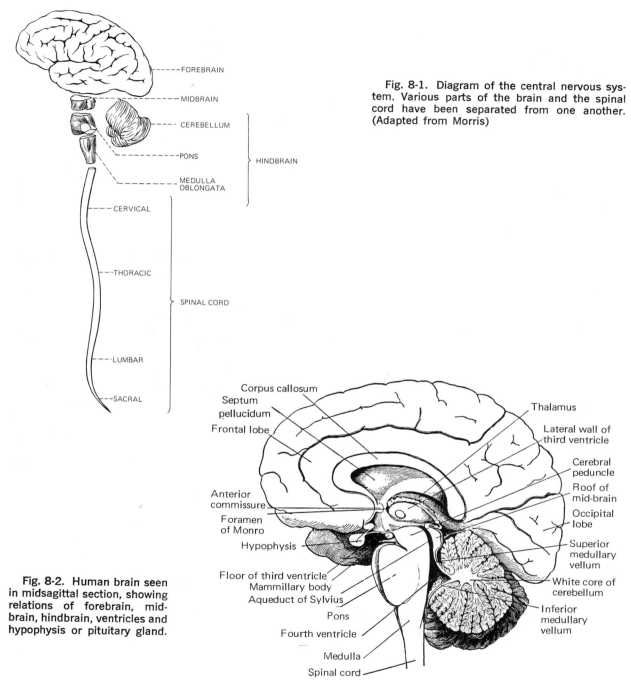

FOREBRAIN

MIDBRAIN

CEREBELLUM

PONS

MEDULLA
OBLONGATA

HINDBRAIN

CERVICAL

THORACIC

SPINAL CORD

LUMBAR

SACRAL

Fig. 8-1. Diagram of the central nervous system. Various parts of the brain and the spinal cord have been separated from one another. (Adapted from Morris)

Fig. 8-2. Human brain seen in midsagittal section, showing relations of forebrain, midbrain, hindbrain, ventricles and hypophysis or pituitary gland.

Corpus callosum
Septum pellucidum
Frontal lobe

Thalamus

Lateral wall of third ventricle

Cerebral peduncle

Roof of mid-brain

Occipital lobe

Anterior commissure

Foramen of Monro

Hypophysis

Superior medullary vellum

White core of cerebellum

Floor of third ventricle
Mammillary body
Aqueduct of Sylvius

Pons

Fourth ventricle

Inferior medullary vellum

Medulla

Spinal cord

221

Divisions of the brain

Based on embryologic development, there are 3 primary divisions of the brain: the forebrain, the midbrain and the hindbrain (Fig. 8-1). Within these divisions are spaces (ventricles) which are concerned with the formation and the circulation of cerebrospinal fluid (Fig. 8-12). Each primary division is then subdivided into various parts, a few of which are listed in the following outline:

1. Forebrain (prosencephalon)
   A. Cerebral hemispheres (telencephalon)
      a. cerebral cortex
      b. basal ganglia (cerebral nuclei)
      c. lateral ventricles
   B. Diencephalon
      a. thalamus
      b. hypothalamus
      c. third ventricle
2. Midbrain (mesencephalon)
   A. Cerebral peduncles
   B. Corpora quadrigemina
   C. Cerebral aqueduct
3. Hindbrain (rhombencephalon)
   A. Cerebellum
   B. Pons
   C. Medulla oblongata
   D. Fourth ventricle

Study of various animal brains shows that, generally speaking, there is a marked correlation between the size of any given part and the importance of that part in the life of the animal. For example, in lower vertebrates (such as the fish and the frog) the cerebrum is extremely small, but in man this all-important part of the brain fills most of the cranial cavity.

Much like a large flower, the human **cerebrum** is attached to the lower portions of the brain which are referred to as the **brain stem.** Following our pattern of proceeding from lower to higher levels of nervous system activity we shall first describe the brain stem and the cerebellum, the diencephalon, and finally the illustrious cerebral hemispheres. A discussion of the meninges, the cerebrospinal fluid and the cranial nerves will complete this chapter.

THE BRAIN STEM AND CEREBELLUM

The brain stem serves not only as a conduction pathway to and from the cerebrum but also as an important reflex center. It consists of the medulla oblongata, the pons and the midbrain. The cerebellum is attached to the medulla and pons.

Medulla oblongata

The medulla oblongata, or *bulb* of the brain, is an expanded continuation of the spinal cord, extending slightly forward and upward from the level of the foramen magnum to the pons (Fig. 8-2). It is composed of white fiber tracts that conduct impulses to and from the spinal cord and the brain; as previously noted, many of these tracts cross to the opposite side as they pass through the medulla. Scattered throughout the white matter are small nuclei (controlling centers) of gray matter. Cranial nerves 9, 10, 11 and 12 have their nuclei of origin in the medulla.

In addition to being a *conduction pathway* and *decussation* (crossing) *center,* the medulla contains many of the *vital centers,* so called because they are essential to one's very life. These centers are the (1) *cardiac,* to speed or slow the heart rate, (2) *vasomotor,* to constrict or dilate the blood vessels, and (3) *respiratory,* to change the rate and the depth of breathing. Afferent impulses from various parts of the body reach these centers and are integrated with impulses from higher levels of the brain; from these centers efferent impulses are then sent to appropriate organs to coordinate their activities for the good of the body as a whole. For this reason, injury to the medulla, as in basal skull fracture or by a disease such as bulbar poliomyelitis, frequently is fatal.

Other reflex centers located in the medulla are those of coughing, sneezing, vomiting and swallowing. Afferent impulses may be started by various changes in the external environment or by changes within the body itself. For example, the swallowing reflex is initiated when a mass of food touches the mucous membrane lining of the throat. Afferent impulses are sent to the medulla and shunted to the swallowing center; in a fraction of a second, efferent impulses are dispatched to all effectors concerned with the act of swallowing. This means not only contraction of the throat muscles but also inhibition of breathing while food passes through the throat to the esophagus; elevation of the soft palate closes the upper respiratory passages, and elevation of the larynx closes the opening into the trachea below. Place your fingers on the upper part of your throat (pharynx) and swallow; note the various movements. These are just a few of the things which occur during swallowing, yet even a newborn babe can perform this complicated reflex act if something is placed in his mouth.

The pons

The term *pons* means "bridge," a word that is quite descriptive of its functions. The pons lies between the medulla and the midbrain, in front of the fourth ventricle and the cerebellum (Fig. 8-2). It consists of longitudinal and transverse white fiber tracts, the former connecting the medulla with the cerebrum, and the latter connecting the two halves of the cerebellum with the pons. In addition to its role as a *conduction pathway*, the pons also contains the motor and the sensory nuclei of cranial nerves 5, 6, 7 and 8.

The cerebellum

The term cerebellum means "little brain," in contrast to the larger cerebrum which overlaps it from above. The cerebellum lies in the lower, back part of the cranial cavity overlapping the pons and the medulla. Its outer portion is composed of a mantle of gray matter, the cerebellar cortex, which is thrown into slender folds and furrows; beneath the gray matter are white matter tracts which resemble branches of a tree as they extend to all parts of the cortex. Deep within the white matter are masses of gray matter which are called the cerebellar nuclei. In midsagittal section, this arrangement of gray and white matter in the cerebellum presents such a treelike appearance that it is called the *arbor vitae,* or "tree of life" (Fig. 8-2).

The cerebellum is somewhat oval in form, consisting of a constricted central portion and two lateral masses, the cerebellar hemispheres. It is attached to the brain stem by 3 paired bundles of nerve fibers, the *cerebellar peduncles.* The inferior peduncles connect the cerebellum with the medulla and the spinal cord. The middle peduncles, largest of the 3 paired bundles, transmit impulses between the cerebellar cortex and the cerebral cortex by way of the pons. The superior peduncles connect the cerebellum with the midbrain, from which fibers course upward to the cerebrum and downward to the pons, the medulla and the spinal cord. Over these various pathways the cerebellum transmits and receives messages to and from other levels of the nervous system.

Functionally, the cerebellum is primarily concerned with the *coordination of muscular activity;* consequently, its connections with proprioceptor endings in skeletal muscles, tendons, joints and the inner ear (vestibular sense organ, p. 291) are of major importance. However, the cerebellum is not concerned with sensation, nor does it initiate voluntary acts as does the cerebrum. It is primarily involved with reflexes for the regulation of muscle tone, the maintenance of equilibrium and posture, and the smooth performance of voluntary movements. For example, impulses from the cerebrum initiate our voluntary movements, but impulses from the cerebellum also are needed to coordinate the contraction of prime movers and the relaxation of antagonists if we are to have accurate voluntary movements.

The disturbances that follow injury to the cerebellum vary with the severity of the lesion. If all parts of the cerebellum are involved, there will be a loss of equilibrium, a reeling walk (*cerebellar ataxia*), reduced muscle tone (*hypotonia*) and abnormal postural reflexes. Voluntary movements are inaccurate, and there may be tremors in the muscles when one attempts to perform some activity.

The midbrain

The midbrain is a short, narrow segment of nervous tissue that connects the forebrain with the hindbrain; it extends from the pons to the inferior surface of the cerebrum (Fig. 8-2). A narrow canal, the *cerebral aqueduct,* passes through the central gray matter of the midbrain and serves to connect the third ventricle of the diencephalon with the fourth ventricle of the hindbrain for the circulation of cerebrospinal fluid (p. 236).

The ventral portion of the midbrain consists of 2 fiber bundles, the *cerebral peduncles,* which constitute the main conduction pathway between forebrain and hindbrain. Cranial nerves 3 and 4 also originate from this ventral area. The dorsal portion or roof of the midbrain consists of 4 rounded eminences, the *corpora quadrigemina* (2 superior and 2 inferior colliculi), each of which has connections with higher brain centers and with the nuclei of those cranial nerves which supply the muscles of the eyeball (p. 240). The corpora quadrigemina are concerned with *visual and auditory reflexes,* such as movement of the eyeball in accordance with changes in the position of the head, and turning the head to hear sounds which originate at one side of the body.

The midbrain also contains centers for *postural and righting reflexes.* Postural reflexes are concerned with the position of the head in relation to the trunk and with adjustments of the extremities and the eyes to the position of the head. Righting reflexes are concerned with the orientation of the head in space; men and animals are alike in wishing to keep the head right side up.

In summary, it is evident that the midbrain is not only a *conduction pathway* but also a *reflex center* of great importance, as are all the levels of the CNS below it. The more complicated reflexes which occur through activities in the brain stem are sometimes referred to as "second level" reflexes, in contrast to the simpler "first level" reflexes of the spinal cord.

THE DIENCEPHALON

Situated above the midbrain, the diencephalon is almost completely covered by the cerebral hemispheres. It is composed of a larger dorsal portion, the thalamus, and a smaller ventral portion, the hypothalamus; these structures surround the third ventricle, the cleftlike cavity of the diencephalon.

The hypothalamus

The hypothalamus forms the floor and part of the lateral walls of the third ventricle. Within its substance are several masses of cell bodies (nuclei), and it has extensive connections with other parts of the central nervous system (CNS) as well as with the posterior lobe of the pituitary gland. Most of the functions of the hypothalamus are either directly or indirectly related to the fact that it is the chief subcortical center for the *regulation of visceral activities.* Both the sympathetic and the parasympathetic divisions of the autonomic nervous system (Chap. 9) are under the control of the hypothalamus; thus, it is possible to coordinate the responses that maintain optimal internal conditions to meet the changing needs of the body. Some outstanding examples are the control of body temperature, control of the motility and secretions of the gastrointestinal tract, and control of arterial blood pressure.

In the *regulation of body temperature,* one area of the hypothalamus is concerned with the dissipation of heat, while another promotes its conservation and production. For example, if the body temperature begins to rise, the heat loss mechanism is set in motion; this involves vasodilation of blood vessels in the skin (p. 50), as well as profuse perspiration. On the other hand, if the body temperature begins to fall, the cutaneous vessels are ordered to constrict; perspiration ceases, and one may even begin to shiver as the skeletal muscles contract involuntarily to aid in the production of heat.

Behavior and emotional responses. Neurons of the hypothalamus not only have extensive connections with autonomic centers but also with the thalamus and the cerebral cortex; thus it is possible for our emotions to influence visceral effectors on certain occasions. For example, in response to a rising body temperature the hypothalamus orders the dilatation of superficial blood vessels, and the skin appears flushed as heat is dissipated through radiation. However, this dilatation also may occur when the hypothalamus is stimulated by higher brain centers, as when one "blushes" with embarrassment. Extreme anxiety, worry and tension may play a part in bringing about hyperactivity of either the sympathetic or the parasympathetic systems (Chap. 9). For example, such psychosomatic (p. 232) effects as increased heart rate and palpitation of the heart, (awareness of the heartbeat), elevated blood pressure, constipation, hyperacidity of the stomach with resultant development of peptic ulcer, and the like, may be related to excessive activity of one division or the other of the autonomic nervous system. The hypothalamus also is believed to play a central role in the emotional expression of rage.

The regulation of water balance through the control of water excretion by the kidney, is an involuntary activity that does not operate directly through the autonomic nervous system. This important regulatory activity involves special nerve cell bodies within the hypothalamus and thousands of axons that descend into the posterior lobe of the pituitary gland (p. 549). A neurosecretion, called *antidiuretic hormone* or ADH, is produced by the nerve cell bodies and then "flows" down the axons to the posterior pituitary where it is stored until needed. Other neurons in the hypothalamus, known as *osmoreceptors,* are sensitive to changes in the concentration of the extracellular fluid. For example, if the amount of water in the body decreases, there is a relative increase in the osmotic pressure of the extracellular fluid as it becomes more concentrated. It is believed that the increased osmotic pressure pulls water out of the osmoreceptors, thus stimulating them to discharge impulses at a very rapid rate; these impulses promote the release of ADH from the posterior pituitary. This hormone is carried in the blood stream to the kidney tubules, where it greatly accelerates the reabsorption of water (p. 536), thus preventing its loss in the urine. On the other hand, if the amount of water in the body tends to increase, there will be a relative decrease in the osmotic pressure of the extracellular fluid; water will enter the osmoreceptors, thus decreasing their rate of discharge and inhibiting the secretion of ADH. The excess water then will be eliminated in the urine.

Another neurosecretion, *oxytocin* (p. 552), is produced by cells in the hypothalamus and stored in the posterior lobe of the pituitary until needed; oxytocin acts on smooth muscle, particularly the wall of the uterus, where it promotes contraction.

The hypothalamus has control centers for many other involuntary activities of the body that do not operate directly through the autonomic nervous system. These include the regulation of body weight through *appetite control,* an intimate concern with normal *sleeping-waking mechanisms,* and the *regulation of many endocrine glands* through its influence on the secretory activity of the anterior lobe of the pituitary gland (p. 551).

Injury to the hypothalamus may result in a variety of symptoms which include: (1) *diabetes insipidus,* the condition in which a patient passes excessive amounts of dilute, sugar-free urine, (2) loss of temperature control, (3) obesity, and (4) pathologic sleep during which the patient may sleep for abnormally long periods of time.

The thalamus

The right and left thalami are elongated, egg-shaped masses that make up the great bulk of the diencephalon; they form the lateral walls of the third ventricle (Fig. 8-3) and are composed primarily of gray matter which contains many nuclei.

Each thalamus is an important *relay center* for incoming impulses from all parts of the body and a *sensory integrating organ* of great complexity. The relatively simple afferent impulses coming from the periphery are sorted out and rearranged; those having to do with similar functions are grouped together and then relayed to a definite area in the cerebral cortex. It also is believed that the activities of the thalamus are related to consciousness, to a crude sort of awareness such as the recognition of pain and temperature and of the "affective" quality of sensations (i.e., whether pleasant or unpleasant). However, true discrimination (the comparison of stimuli as to intensity, locality, etc.) is a function of the cerebral cortex.

In addition to the peripheral afferent fibers,

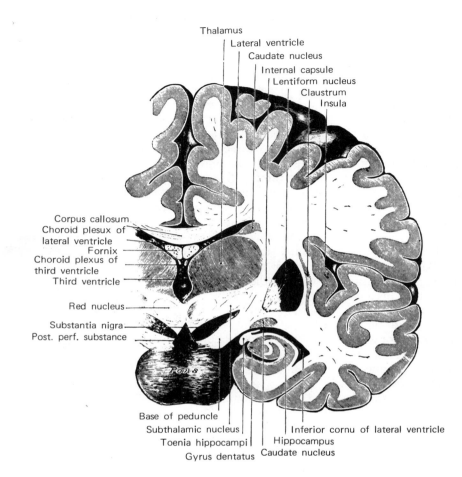

Fig. 8-3. Coronal section of brain immediately in front of pons. Some of the basal ganglia of the cerebral hemisphere, the thalamus of the diencephalon, the red nucleus of the midbrain and the pons are shown. (From Lewis, W. H.: Gray's Anatomy, ed. 26, Philadelphia, Lea & Febiger)

there are also cortical fibers that bring the thalamus under the control of the cerebral cortex. Efferent connections with the hypothalamus and the basal ganglia (p. 228) enable the thalamus to exert its influence on both visceral and somatic effectors.

The pineal body

The pineal body or *epiphysis* is a small, cone-shaped structure that extends posteriorly from the third ventricle and lies just above the roof of the midbrain. It frequently is referred to as an endocrine gland, but investigators have not yet proved that pineal cells secrete functionally significant hormones (p. 553). The pineal body begins to atrophy at about 7 years of age, and in some adults it becomes completely calcified.

THE RETICULAR FORMATION

Somewhat like the core of an apple, the reticular formation lies within the brain stem and the basal part of the diencephalon. It extends from the superior portion of the spinal cord upward and forward through the medulla, the pons, the midbrain, and into the hypothalamus. The reticular formation is composed of small islands of gray matter (cell bodies) separated by fine bundles of nerve fibers that run in various directions. It has widespread afferent connections and, in turn, sends efferent impulses over ascending relays into the cerebral cortex and over descending relays into the spinal cord.

The basic importance of the reticular formation involves its regulation of the background activities of the rest of the nervous system by the excitation of certain activities and the inhibition of others. Caudally, it facilitates both reflex and voluntary movements, thus contributing to optimal motor performance. The cephalic influence of the reticular formation is one of activation and regulation of cortical activities that underlie the state of wakefulness or alertness on which the highest functions of the cerebral cortex depend.

THE CEREBRUM

The cerebrum is the largest part of the human brain, and it fills the entire upper portion of the cranial cavity. This mass of nervous tissue consists of literally billions of neurons and synapses which form a fantastic network of neural pathways.

The cerebrum is almost completely separated into right and left halves, or **hemispheres,** each of which is further subdivided into 4 lobes which are named according to the overlying cranial bones: *frontal, parietal, temporal,* and *occipital* lobes (Fig. 8-5). Both cerebral hemispheres consist of (1) an external layer of gray matter, the **cerebral cortex,** (2) underlying **white matter tracts,** and (3) deeply situated masses of gray matter, the **basal ganglia** (cerebral nuclei). Within each hemisphere is an elongated cavity, or *lateral ventricle,* which is concerned with the formation of cerebrospinal fluid (p. 236).

The cerebral cortex

The surface layer of each cerebral hemisphere consists of an elaborate mantle of gray matter which is called the cerebral cortex. This is the topmost "executive suite" in the nervous system organization, and it has been estimated that there are almost 14 billion neurons in this area. Generally speaking, the amount of cortical gray matter is one indication of *potential* intelligence; however, there are many other factors which are involved in the *realization* of this potential, and individual variations are great.

To provide a maximal amount of this important gray matter, yet keep the size of the brain within reasonable limits, the cortex is arranged in a series of folds or ridges as it dips down into underlying regions. Each fold is called a *convolution* or *gyrus.* Between these folds are grooves or furrows which give the exterior of the brain a wrinkled appearance; a deep groove is called a *fissure,* while a shallow one is referred to as a *sulcus.* Figure 8-3 vividly illustrates the way in which the cortical folds and grooves increase the total surface area of gray matter.

The cerebral hemispheres are separated from each other by the **longitudinal fissure,** a deep groove that extends from front to back in the midline. Anteriorly and posteriorly the separation is complete, but in the middle portion the fissure extends only to the *corpus callosum,* a massive band of white fibers that serves to unite the two hemispheres (Fig. 8-4). Posteriorly the cerebrum is separated from the cerebellum by the deep **transverse fissure** (Fig. 8-2).

In each hemisphere there are 3 fissures which serve as boundary lines between the lobes: (1) the **central fissure** (of Rolando) which separates the frontal and the parietal lobes, (2) the **lateral fissure** (of Sylvius) which lies between the frontal and the parietal lobes above and the temporal lobe below, and (3) a small *parieto-occipital* fissure located between the parietal and the occipital lobes (Fig. 8-6). The insula or island of Reil is a part of the cortex which lies buried in the lateral fissure and can be seen only when the lips of that fissure are drawn apart.

White matter

Beneath the cerebral cortex there are myelinated nerve fibers which are arranged in related bundles or tracts. These fibers travel in 3 principal directions and are considered as 3 groups.

Fig. 8-4. Oblique coronal section through the brain in the direction of the cerebral peduncles and the pyramids, as seen from in front. (After Toldt) (From Schaeffer, J. P.: Morris' Human Anatomy, ed 11, New York, Blakiston Division of McGraw-Hill)

1. **Commissural fibers** are those that transmit impulses from one hemisphere to the other. The largest group of these fibers is the *corpus callosum* as shown in Figures 8-2, 8-3, and 8-4.

2. **Projection fibers** transmit impulses from one level of the CNS to another. For example, the *internal capsule* (Figs. 8-3 and 8-4) is literally a "superhighway" of ascending and descending fibers.

3. **Association fibers** transmit impulses from one part of the cerebral cortex to another on the same side. These fibers do not cross from one hemisphere to another, nor do they pass to lower levels of the CNS.

The basal ganglia

The basal ganglia, or cerebral nuclei, are 4 deep-lying masses of gray matter within the white matter of each hemisphere. Two of these are the *caudate nucleus* and the *lentiform nucleus*, the latter being subdivided into the putamen and the globus pallidus (Figs. 8-3 and 8-4). The internal capsule (a massive bundle of white fibers) passes between these nuclei and continues on to form the cerebral peduncle on its own side (Fig. 8-4). The basal ganglia are important links in the extrapyramidal motor pathway.

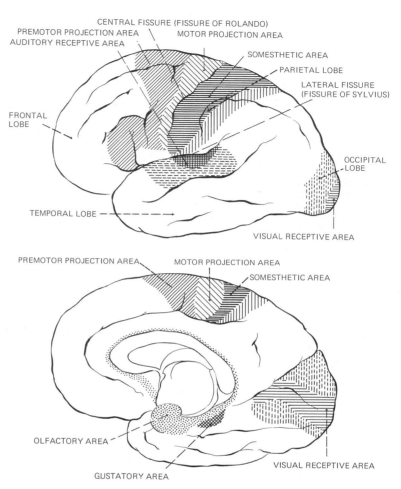

CENTRAL FISSURE (FISSURE OF ROLANDO)
PREMOTOR PROJECTION AREA
MOTOR PROJECTION AREA
AUDITORY RECEPTIVE AREA

SOMESTHETIC AREA

PARIETAL LOBE

LATERAL FISSURE
(FISSURE OF SYLVIUS)

FRONTAL
LOBE

OCCIPITAL
LOBE

TEMPORAL LOBE

VISUAL RECEPTIVE AREA

PREMOTOR PROJECTION AREA
MOTOR PROJECTION AREA
SOMESTHETIC AREA

OLFACTORY AREA

VISUAL RECEPTIVE AREA

GUSTATORY AREA

Fig. 8-5. Diagram of the localization of function in the cerebral hemisphere. The various functional areas are shown in relation to the lobes and the fissures: (top) lateral view; (bottom) medial view.

Functions of the cerebrum

Due to the fantastic activity of his cerebral cortex, man is the most intelligent creature on earth. In a limited way, lower animals can "learn" through experience, but only man has the neural mechanism necessary for the more complex discrimination and correlation of sensory impulses, and for greater utilization of past experiences.

Practically every part of the cerebral cortex is connected with subcortical centers and, strictly speaking, there are no perfectly circumscribed areas in the cortex which are purely motor or purely sensory. However, in a very general way there are regions which are primarily concerned with the *expressive* phase of cortical functioning and other regions which are primarily *receptive* in nature. These generalizations facilitate study of the brain, but one must never lose sight of the fact that the cortex as a whole makes possible the *associative memory* reactions which are so characteristic of man.

The motor area is located in the frontal lobe, immediately anterior to the central fissure (Fig. 8-5). The pyramidal (corticospinal) tract, which transmits impulses for fine, voluntary movements, arises principally in this area. The **pre-motor area** lies immediately in front of the motor area,

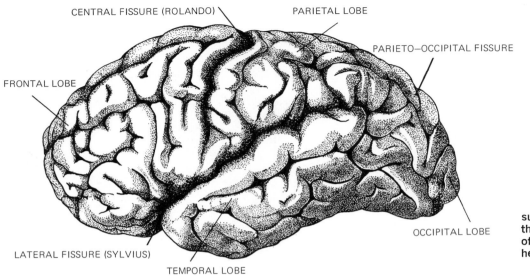

CENTRAL FISSURE (ROLANDO)

PARIETAL LOBE

PARIETO—OCCIPITAL FISSURE

FRONTAL LOBE

OCCIPITAL LOBE

LATERAL FISSURE (SYLVIUS)

TEMPORAL LOBE

Fig. 8-6. Fissures and lobes of the lateral aspect of the left cerebral hemisphere.

and its projection fibers (part of the extrapyramidal pathway) transmit impulses to the thalamus, the basal ganglia and other subcortical centers; these impulses play an important role in coordinating the gross, synergistic muscular activities which are so necessary in all voluntary movement.

In man, the basal ganglia aid the activity of the motor area of the cerebral cortex in many ways. For example, when one "wills" to walk, impulses are sent from the motor cortex to the spinal cord and then are relayed out to the proper skeletal muscles of the lower extremities. Meanwhile, impulses are sent from the premotor cortex to the basal ganglia and then are relayed to the lower levels of the CNS where they eventually bring about the accessory or *associated movements* which accompany voluntary activity. For example, the swinging of the arms as one walks, the changes in facial expression and the gesticulations that accompany speech all are associated movements. The basal ganglia also help to control one's voluntary movements by exerting some sort of inhibitory influence on impulses from the motor area of the cerebral cortex. Figure 8-7 illustrates two anatomic facts which are of considerable

clinical importance: (1) fibers from both the motor and the premotor areas are funneled through the narrow internal capsule as they descend to lower levels of the CNS and (2) due to the crossing of fibers, the cortex of one side of the cerebrum controls the skeletal muscles on the opposite side of the body.

The motor speech area (Broca's area) lies at the base of the motor area and slightly anterior to it. This portion of the cortex is thought to be concerned with the ability to form words both in speaking and in writing. The motor speech area is located in the left hemisphere of right-handed persons and in the right hemisphere of left-handed persons. In fact, most of man's higher cortical functions are vested principally in one hemisphere, an unexplained phenomenon known as "cerebral dominance."

The prefrontal cortex is that which lies anterior to the premotor area and comprises all of the frontal pole of the cerebral cortex. It has extensive connections with the thalamus and the hypothalamus, thus exerting a strong influence on visceral activities (Chap. 9). While the hypothalamus regulates these activities under ordinary conditions, cortical control is of great functional im-

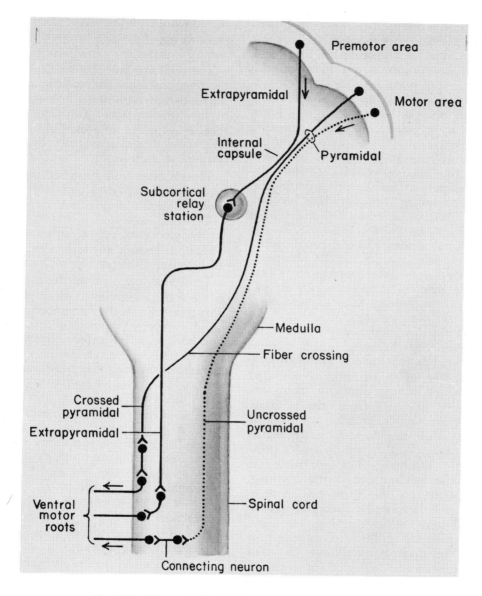

Fig. 8-7. Diagram of principal motor pathways between cerebral cortex, subcortical relay stations and lower motor neurons in spinal cord. Note crossing of fibers in medulla and in spinal cord.

portance in emotional states. For example, anxiety, fear, anger, etc., may cause an increase in heart rate, elevation of blood pressure and interference with the digestion of food. In extreme cases there may even be pathologic changes in the viscera. Such disturbances in body function are sometimes referred to as *psychosomatic disorders* (*psyche* meaning "mind," and *soma* meaning "body").

The prefrontal cortex also has many connections with association areas in other parts of the brain and is thought to be greatly concerned with such complex intellectual functions as abstract thinking and highly creative activities. Much has been learned about the functions of this area since the advent of psychosurgery and an operation known as *prefrontal lobotomy*. This procedure involves the cutting of fibers which connect the prefrontal cortex with underlying parts of the CNS. It was first performed on persons who had certain types of mental illness (e.g., morbid anxiety, obsessive-compulsive states, etc.); later lobotomy was performed for the relief of intractable pain in patients suffering from cancer. After surgery these patients no longer complain of pain nor do they appear to be in any distress; however, when asked they will acknowledge that pain is still present. It is thought that this relief is due to the absence of anxiety and fear which are usually associated with the pain. Following lobotomy, there are varying degrees of intellectual deterioration. These patients are unable to solve complicated problems of an abstract nature, they are unable to analyze situations, and their judgment is poor. They are highly distractible and turn from one activity to another without completing anything. Even more striking are the alterations in emotional behavior; lobotomized patients are easily amused, have lowered ethical standards, are careless in their personal habits and unconcerned with financial or domestic problems. In other words, nothing seems to bother them anymore.

The general sensory area (somesthetic area) is located in the parietal lobe on the postcentral gyrus (Fig. 8-5). While crude sensations of pain, temperature and touch enter consciousness at the level of the thalamus, *true discrimination* is a function of the cerebral cortex. The position of the body in space, the recognition of size, shape and texture of objects, the comparison of stimuli as to intensity and locality, etc., all depend on the activities of this area. The left hemisphere receives impulses from the right side of the body, and vice versa.

The auditory area lies in the superior part of the temporal lobe, and each hemisphere receives impulses from both ears. The **visual area** is located in the occipital lobe. The right occipital cortex receives impulses from the right half of each eye, and the left cortex receives impulses from the left half of each eye.

The olfactory and gustatory areas have not yet been determined with certainty. However, it is thought that one area for the sense of smell (olfactory) is located in the hippocampal gyrus on the medial aspect of the temporal lobe (Fig. 8-5), and the area for taste (gustatory) close by at the base of the postcentral gyrus.

The remaining areas of the cerebral cortex are referred to as **association areas,** and they play an important role in the integration of the receptive and the expressive phases of cortical functioning. For example, when you are taking an examination, the occipital lobe serves as the primary receptive area for visualizing the words in each question, and the frontal lobe directs those activities which are involved in expressing your answers. However, impulses must be relayed back and forth through a complex maze of association areas (probably involving the entire cerebral cortex) before you are able to understand the meaning of the question, to sort out and to organize those facts which are related to the question, and to reach a logical conclusion based on your past experience.

One of the most striking features of the cerebral cortex is its ability to retain, modify and reuse information which has been received through the senses; this is the basis of *associative memory* and is the foundation of all knowledge. Such things as abstract reasoning, judgment and moral sense are made possible by the almost unbelievable activities of the estimated 14 billion neurons in the human cerebral cortex.

Acquired or conditioned reflexes, so prominent in all human behavior, also are dependent on associative memory. These reflexes must be "learned" by each individual, since they are not transmitted from parent to child as are the unconditioned or natural reflexes such as the knee jerk, swallowing, etc. Since acquired reflexes involve the cerebral cortex, they are sometimes referred to as "third level" reflexes in contrast to those which involve only subcortical centers in the brain ("second level") or in the spinal cord ("first level"). Voluntary control of urination is a good example of an acquired reflex. The infant bladder when filled with urine automatically empties itself, and it is only through training and practice that this spinal reflex is brought under control of the cerebral cortex. In fact, most of our daily activities involve behavior patterns which we learned as children. For example, we get dressed every day, giving little or no thought to the shoelace, the button, or the buckle that presented such problems when we were young, and the use of knife, fork and spoon no longer requires our complete attention at the dinner table.

Cerebral lesions

A detailed description of tumors, abscesses, depressed skull fractures, etc., obviously is not within the scope of this textbook, but a few basic principles related to the more common lesions may facilitate future studies.

The blood supply to the brain (p. 354) is of primary importance, and any lesion that interferes

Fig. 8-8. Diagram representing conduction pathways through the mammalian nervous system. An impulse which arises in skin, muscle, tendon or joint has many pathways open to it: it may be transferred to an efferent neuron in the spinal cord, at the same or a slightly higher level; it may reach the medulla, the cerebellum, the thalamus or the cortex of the cerebral hemisphere. Regardless of the pathway taken, the impulse (in this diagram) eventually reaches the nerve cells in the ventral horn of the spinal cord, from which it passes to striated muscular tissue. (Modified from Bayliss)

GENERAL SENSORY AREA (POST–CENTRAL CONVOLUTION)

CEREBRAL CORTEX

MOTOR AREA (PRE–CENTRAL CONVOLUTION)

THALAMUS   RED NUCLEUS   CORPUS STRIATUM

MEDULLA   CEREBELLUM   MEDULLA

CONSCIOUS MUSCLE SENSE (POSTERIOR COLUMNS)

PAIN, TOUCH, HEAT, COLD (SPINOTHALAMIC TRACT)

SPINAL   CORD

VOLUNTARY MOTOR (CORTICOSPINAL TRACT)

INVOLUNTARY COORDINATION OF STRIATED MUSCLE (RUBROSPINAL TRACT)

UNCONSCIOUS MUSCLE SENSE (SPINOCEREBELLAR TRACT)

STRIATED MUSCLE

SKIN, MUSCLE, TENDON, OR JOINT

with its normal distribution may cause irreparable damage to nerve cells. For example, a clot may form within a vessel (*cerebral thrombosis*) and block the flow of blood to a particular area, or there may be bleeding into the brain substance (*cerebral hemorrhage*) from a ruptured blood vessel. Such lesions are called **cerebral vascular accidents** ("stroke" or apoplexy).

The location of these injuries determines the symptoms that will be presented by the patient. For example, let us consider a small lesion which is localized in part of the motor cortex. Since the pyramidal tract is widely spread out here in the frontal area, such cortical lesions involve only part of the fibers, thus producing a contralateral muscular paralysis of a single extremity (*monoplegia*) or possibly paralysis of facial muscles depending on which portion of the cortex is injured. A similar lesion in the sensory cortex would result in a contralateral loss of sensation. On the other hand, if the lesion is in the area of the internal capsule and the basal ganglia, all of the fibers that supply the opposite side of the body may be involved, and a complete *hemiplegia* (one-sided paralysis) will be the end-result. If this lesion is in the dominant hemisphere there may be speech defects in addition to the contralateral motor and sensory losses. Headache, dizziness, mental confusion and coma usually are present during the acute phase. If the patient survives the initial attack, he may be rehabilitated to an amazing degree, but it is a long slow process requiring persistence and patience on the part of all concerned.

Special nursing problems accompany the care of patients who are paralyzed, who have sensory disturbances or are unconscious (in coma). Paralyzed patients cannot perform the voluntary movements necessary for daily care. The nurse has to do a great many things for them. It requires skill and tact on her part to keep them from feeling useless and depressed. Patients with sensory disturbances need special protection, since their warning signals are absent; harmful stimuli arouse no impulses which bring about responses of self-preservation. Unconscious patients are even more helpless than newborn babies; the latter can cry when something disturbs them, but the unconscious patient is quite unaware of everything. Such patients must be fed, given fluids and kept warm, and the emptying of the bladder and bowel must be taken care of.

Epilepsy is one of the most important of the convulsive states, and it is characterized by sudden, transient alterations of brain function. In many cases the attacks are the result of abnormally active brain tissue caused by injury, infection or unknown agents. In *grand mal seizures*, the patient usually has a specific warning (aura) before the attack; this may be a visual image, an odor, a sound or a tingling in some region of the body. Loss of consciousness follows, and the patient falls to the floor. Strong contractions of the jaw muscles during the ensuing convulsions may injure the tongue, and there frequently is involuntary emptying of the bladder and the bowel. A variable period of sleep and stupor follows the attack. Drugs that depress the excitability of the nervous system may be administered to epileptic patients in an attempt to prevent attacks.

Destructive lesions localized in the basal ganglia may lead to one of several conditions, depending on the site of injury. One of these is called paralysis agitans or **Parkinson's disease.** This condition is characterized by muscular rigidity and tremor which result in disturbances of posture and voluntary movement. Tremor of the hands results in a characteristic rubbing together of the thumb and the fingertips which is called the "pill rolling" movement. These patients have no change in facial expression (masklike appearance), the arms do not swing when walking, and the body is bent forward to such an extent that they walk with a peculiar running gait.

Sydenham's chorea (St. Vitus' Dance) and *athetosis* are other conditions which are due in part to lesions in the basal ganglia.

PROTECTION OF THE BRAIN

The outer covering of the brain is osseous connective tissue which forms the cranial bones. The inner covering is membranous and consists of the 3 meninges. Cerebrospinal fluid fills the brain cavities and the surrounding subarachnoid space.

PIA MATER
ARACHNOID
DURA MATER
SUPERIOR SAGITTAL SINUS
ARACHNOID VILLI
CRANIUM
BRAIN SUBSTANCE

Fig. 8-9. The cranial meninges. Arachnoid villi shown within superior sagittal sinus; one site of passage of the cerebrospinal fluid into the blood. (After Weed)

The cranial bones

Housed in its snug bony box, the brain is well protected from ordinary bumps and jolts. As described in Chapter 3, the frontal, the parietal, the occipital, the temporal, the sphenoid and the ethmoid bones all contribute to the formation of the walls of the cranial cavity wherein lies the brain.

The meninges

The membranes that cover the brain are continuous with those of the spinal cord and have the same names, but a few anatomic variations should be noted.

The cranial portion of the *dura mater* consists of 2 layers. It not only covers the brain but also lines the interior of the skull and serves as the internal periosteum of the cranial bones. The two layers of the dura mater are in contact with each other in some places, and in other places they are separated as the inner layer dips inward to form protective partitions between parts of the brain. The spaces or channels which are formed by this separation of dural layers (Fig. 8-9) are filled with blood which is flowing out of the brain; thus they are an important part of the circulatory system. These blood-filled channels are called the *cranial venous sinuses* (not to be confused with the air sinuses of the cranial bones as described on p. 79).

The projection of dura mater which dips into the longitudinal fissure and separates right and left halves of the brain is called the *falx cerebri* (Fig. 8-10); the superior sagittal venous sinus lies in its upper margin (Fig. 8-9). A second projection of dura mater dips into the transverse fissure and separates the cerebrum from the cerebellum; this projection is called the *tentorium cerebelli* (Fig. 8-10). All of the cranial venous sinuses formed by these extensions of the dura are described in Chapter 13.

The cranial portion of the **arachnoid membrane** sends little tuftlike extensions through the inner layer of dura mater and into the cranial venous sinuses. These tiny fingers, called *arachnoid villi*, are most numerous along the superior sagittal sinus, but they also are found along the other venous sinuses of the brain. The arachnoid villi help in the return of cerebrospinal fluid to the blood stream.

The inner layer of the meninges or **pia mater** covers the brain very closely and follows all of the "hills and valleys" of the brain surface. The larger blood vessels of the brain lie in the subarachnoid space, and branches from these pass through the pia mater and enter the brain substance, as shown in Figure 8-11. In certain places the pia mater is caught in the folds of the developing brain, and bits of it remain there and become part of the *choroid plexuses* of the ventricles. The pia mater and the arachnoid are connected by a

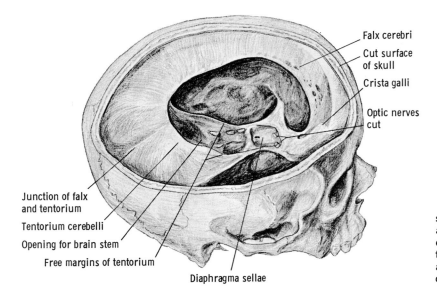

Falx cerebri
Cut surface
of skull
Crista galli
Optic nerves
cut
Junction of falx
and tentorium
Tentorium cerebelli
Opening for brain stem
Free margins of tentorium
Diaphragma sellae

Fig. 8-10. Dura mater. Side of skull removed, showing falx cerebri and tentorium cerebelli. These are extensions of the dura mater between the two cerebral hemispheres, and between the cerebrum and the cerebellum, respectively.

network of fine, threadlike structures (trabeculae); in some areas over the brain it is difficult to separate them.

Inflammation of the meninges is called **meningitis.** It may involve the dura only, or it may involve the arachnoid and the pia mater. It may be due to a variety of infectious agents, such as the tubercle bacillus, meningococcus, streptococcus or staphylococcus.

The cerebrospinal fluid

The cerebrospinal fluid is a clear, colorless, watery fluid that fills the ventricles of the brain, the subarachnoid spaces around the brain and the spinal cord, and the perivascular spaces related to those blood vessels that penetrate the brain substance (Fig. 8-11). Some of this fluid is formed by filtration through capillary walls, just as is tissue fluid in other parts of the body, but the major portion is formed by the choroid plexuses (networks of blood vessels) in the ventricles of the brain. In the latter case, as fluid filters through the walls of the choroid plexuses it is modified slightly by the secretory activities of the epithelial cells; for this reason, cerebrospinal fluid is referred to as *modified tissue fluid.* Some of its constituents are water, sodium chloride, potassium, glucose, traces of protein, and a few white blood cells (3-8/cu. mm.); it has a specific gravity of 1.004 to 1.008. The quantity of cerebrospinal fluid is subject to individual variation, but the average range is from 100 to 200 cc. in the adult.

Functionally, cerebrospinal fluid protects the brain and the spinal cord from mechanical injury by acting as a watery shock absorber. It serves also as a "middleman" in the exchange of nutrients and wastes between the blood stream and the busy cells of the CNS.

Because most of the cerebrospinal fluid is formed from the blood that passes through the choroid plexuses in the ventricles of the brain, one should be familiar with the pathway that it follows while seeping downward to the subarachnoid space for distribution to all parts of the CNS. The following structures are of great clinical importance in the circulation of cerebrospinal fluid.

1. **The first and second ventricles, or lateral ventricles,** are elongated cavities that lie within the cerebral hemispheres, as illustrated in Figure 8-12. Each contains a large choroid plexus.

2. From each lateral ventricle cerebrospinal

Fig. 8-11. Schematic diagram to show the relations of the pia mater, the arachnoid, the blood vessels and the brain. The perivascular spaces are in communication with the subarachnoid space. (Weed, L. H.: Am. J. Anat. 31:202)

Arachnoid trabecula

Cortex cerebri

Arachnoid membrane

Cerebral vein

Pia mater

Perivascular space

Lining cells of perivascular space

Fig. 8-12. Encephalogram, showing the ventricles of the brain and their connecting channels. (From Dr. Kuhlenbeck)

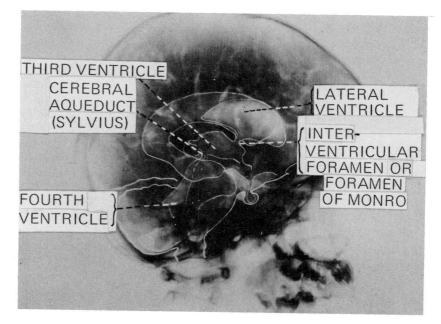

THIRD VENTRICLE

CEREBRAL AQUEDUCT (SYLVIUS)

LATERAL VENTRICLE

INTER-VENTRICULAR FORAMEN OR FORAMEN OF MONRO

FOURTH VENTRICLE

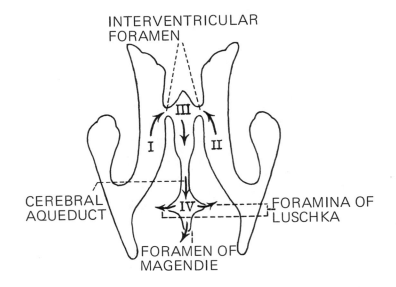

Fig. 8-13. Outline of the ventricles of the brain. Arrows indicate direction of flow of cerebrospinal fluid.

fluid passes through a narrow, oval opening, the **interventricular foramen** (of Monro) into the third ventricle.

3. **The third ventricle** is merely a slitlike cavity located between the right and the left thalami, but it too contains a choroid plexus.

4. **The cerebral aqueduct** (of Sylvius), which passes through the midbrain, is the connecting link between the third and the fourth ventricles.

5. **The fourth ventricle** is a diamond-shaped cavity located between the medulla and the pons anteriorly, and the cerebellum posteriorly. The *central canal* of the spinal cord opens into this cavity from below.

6. From the fourth ventricle there are 3 openings into the cranial subarachnoid space: 2 lateral openings, called the **foramina of Luschka,** and a medial opening called the **foramen of Magendie.** Figures 8-12 and 8-13 illustrate various features of the ventricular portion of the cerebrospinal fluid pathway.

In the subarachnoid space, cerebrospinal fluid ebbs and flows around the spinal cord and the brain. It seeps into the sheaths of all cranial and spinal nerves, and into the perivascular spaces (Fig. 8-11) where it mingles with ordinary tissue fluid. Inasmuch as cerebrospinal fluid is being formed constantly, it must be removed at a comparable rate or a marked increase in intracranial pressure will result. The bulk of this fluid is absorbed from the cranial subarachnoid space into the blood stream by way of the arachnoid villi that project into certain of the cranial venous sinuses (Fig. 8-9); it is believed that processes of filtration and osmosis are largely responsible for this absorption of fluid. Because the blood in the venous sinuses has a low hydrostatic pressure and a high osmotic pressure (owing to its protein content), conditions are ideal for the movement of cerebrospinal fluid (with its low protein content) from the arachnoid villi into the blood stream. The relatively small amount of fluid that passes outward along the sheaths of the cranial and spinal nerves probably enters blood and lymph capillaries as does tissue fluid in other parts of the body.

Brain lesions which interfere with the passage of cerebrospinal fluid from the ventricles to the subarachnoid space may result in a condition known as **internal hydrocephalus** or "water in the brain" (Fig. 8-14). For example, if a tumor presses on the midbrain and compresses the cerebral aqueduct, cerebrospinal fluid will accumulate in the lateral and the third ventricles of the brain,

Fig. 8-14. Hydrocephalus. This child was 11 years of age at the time the photograph was taken. (From Minnesota School for the Feeble Minded)

greatly distending them and exerting pressure on the brain substance.

Examination of the cerebrospinal fluid is almost a routine procedure in clinical neurology, as both the composition and the pressure of this fluid may provide valuable diagnostic information. Samples of fluid usually are withdrawn through a long spinal needle which taps the large subarachnoid space below the level of the spinal cord (*lumbar puncture* or *spinal tap,* as described on p. 207). Various laboratory tests may then be ordered; for example, cell counts, chemical analysis, presence of bacteria, etc.

Lumbar puncture usually is performed with the patient lying on his side; in this position the cerebrospinal fluid pressure ranges from 70 to 200 mm. of water (average 125 mm. of water). The *Queckenstedt test* is performed by compressing large veins in the neck and temporarily stopping the

Olfactory
Optic
Optic chiasma
Optic tract
Oculomotor
Trochlear
Trigeminal
Abducens
Facial
Acoustic
Glossopharyngeal
Vagus
Accessory
Hypoglossal

Fig. 8-15. Base of brain showing entrance or exit of cranial nerves.

flow of blood from the cranial venous sinuses. As blood "backs up" in the brain, its pressure rises, interfering with the drainage of cerebrospinal fluid; as a result there normally is a prompt rise in cerebrospinal fluid pressure which is maintained until the neck veins are released from compression. If the pressure fails to rise and fall promptly, the doctor presumes that there is a block in the system somewhere between the site of puncture and the site of compression. Further definitive studies then must be carried out to locate the lesion.

A pneumoencephalogram (Fig. 8-12) is an x-ray picture of the skull following replacement of the cerebrospinal fluid with air by means of a lumbar puncture. The ventricles and the subarachnoid spaces usually can be visualized by this method, a valuable tool in localizing intracranial pathology. The air will be absorbed and fluid replaced within 24 to 72 hours. A more rapid and less traumatic diagnostic study is the echoencephalogram. The use of ultrasound echoes to locate the position of midline structures (e.g., falx cerebri, third ventricle, and so on) is of particular value in the diagnosis of expanding intracranial lesions that cause distortion of the aforementioned structures.

THE CRANIAL NERVES

There are 12 pairs of cranial nerves originating from the undersurface of the brain (Fig. 8-15) and passing through small foramina in the skull to reach their destination. The cranial nerves are numbered according to the order in which they arise from the brain (front to back), and their names are descriptive of their distribution or of their function. Most are classified as mixed nerves, having both motor and sensory fibers, but 3 pairs contain only sensory components (olfactory, optic and acoustic). Cell bodies of the primary afferent neurons are located in ganglia which lie outside the brain, while the motor or efferent fibers arise from cell bodies within the brain (nuclei of origin). Some cranial nerves contain only somatic fibers, others contain both somatic and visceral components. Details of the origin and the distribution of visceral fibers are presented in Chapter 9.

1. **The olfactory nerves** are those that conduct impulses related to the sense of smell. They are composed of axons that pass from cell bodies in the olfactory portion of the nasal mucosa upward through the olfactory foramina of the ethmoid bone to reach the brain. Injury results in loss of the sense of smell (anosmia).

2. **The optic nerves** are the nerves of vision. Each arises from cell bodies in the retina of the eye and passes through the optic foramen to reach the base of the brain. Injury to the optic nerve results in blindness. (The optic chiasma and the optic tract are described on p. 278.)

3. **The oculomotor nerves,** as indicated by the name, are concerned with eye movements. Arising from the midbrain, each nerve supplies motor fibers to the levator palpebrae superioris and to all the extrinsic muscles of the eyeball *except* the superior oblique and the lateral rectus. Visceral efferent fibers supply the constrictor muscle (sphincter pupillae) of the iris and the muscle for accommodation of the lens (ciliaris). Afferent fibers transmit impulses concerned with muscle sense from proprioceptors in the eye muscles to the brain. Signs of oculomotor nerve damage are drooping (ptosis) of the upper eyelid, turning of the eyeball downward and outward, and dilatation of the pupil.

4. **The trochlear nerves** are the smallest of the cranial nerves. Each supplies motor and sensory fibers to the superior oblique muscle of the eye on its own side.

5. **The trigeminal nerves,** arising from the pons, are the largest of the cranial nerves. Although they are often referred to as the "great sensory nerves" of the head and the face, they actually are mixed nerves. The afferent or sensory portion of each consists of 3 large divisions—*ophthalmic, maxillary* and *mandibular branches.* Sensory fibers are supplied to the front part of the head, the orbit, the face, the nose, the mouth, the tongue, the teeth and the upper part of the throat (nasopharynx). Motor fibers are supplied to the muscles of mastication by way of the mandibular branch. The distribution of the trigeminal nerve is shown in Figures 8-16 and 8-17.

Fig. 8-16. Dissection of the lateral side of cranium and face. Ramus of mandible is removed. Shown are the divisions of the trigeminal nerve, and the optic, facial, glossopharyngeal, vagus, accessory and hypoglossal nerves. Internal pterygoid and external pterygoid (cut) muscles are shown. Opening of auditory tube to middle ear and the connection of middle ear with mastoid air cells also are shown.

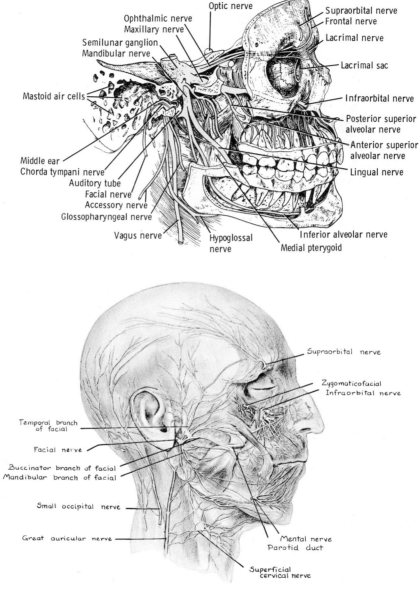

Fig. 8-17. Superficial dissection of head and neck, showing facial nerve branches, terminal branches of the trigeminal nerve and branches of the cervical plexus.

Fig. 8-18. Left-sided facial paralysis of the central type. (Minneapolis General Hospital)

with facial expression (Fig. 8-17). Afferent fibers transmit impulses concerned with muscle sense from proprioceptors in those muscles to the brain. The facial nerves also supply sensory fibers for taste on the anterior two thirds of the tongue. Visceral efferent (secretory) fibers are supplied to the submaxillary and the sublingual salivary glands.

Injury to the facial nerve produces a paralysis of the muscles of facial expression (*Bell's palsy*). Figure 8-18 illustrates the resulting masklike expression on the affected side; note the drooping of the corner of the mouth and the inability to close the eye or to wrinkle the forehead. There is also loss of taste in the anterior portion of the tongue and interference with the secretion of saliva.

8. **The acoustic nerves** are concerned with hearing and with equilibrium. Each consists of 2 distinct fiber divisions, both of which are purely sensory. The *cochlear* division arises from cell bodies in the cochlea of the internal ear (p. 290) and transmits impulses related to the sense of hearing. The *vestibular* division arises from cell bodies in a ganglion near the vestibule and the semicircular canals of the inner ear (p. 291); it transmits impulses which are initiated by changes in the position of the head and by the movement of the body through space. Injury to the cochlear portion of the acoustic nerve results in deafness; injury to the vestibular portion results in disorientation accompanied by dizziness and nystagmus.

9. **The glossopharyngeal nerves,** as indicated by the name, are distributed to the tongue and the pharynx (Figs. 8-16 and 8-19); they arise from the medulla oblongata. These nerves are very important in the act of swallowing, since they supply sensory fibers to the lining of the pharynx and motor fibers to some of the underlying constrictor muscles; they also supply sensory fibers for taste on the posterior third of the tongue. Special visceral afferent fibers conduct impulses from the large artery (internal carotid) in each side of the neck, keeping vital centers in the medulla informed about the pressure and the oxygen tension of the blood. Visceral efferent (secretory) fibers are supplied to the parotid salivary glands. Injury to the glossopharyngeal nerve results in loss

Tic douloureux, a paroxysmal neuralgia of the trigeminal nerve, is an extremely painful condition. Cutting the nerve at its origin, or injecting it with alcohol, may relieve the pain, but the patient also will lose all other sensations in the areas served by the nerve; thus he might burn his tongue with hot coffee, be unaware of a decayed tooth that should be treated by the dentist, or fail to realize that a cinder is injuring the delicate cornea of his eye. He also would experience difficulty in chewing his food.

6. **The abducens nerves** are small nerves that arise from the pons. Each supplies both motor and sensory fibers to the lateral rectus muscle of the eye on its own side. Injury to the abducens nerve results in the eyeball being turned inward.

7. **The facial nerves,** arising from the pons, are mixed nerves; however, they are often referred to as the "great motor nerves" of the face, as they supply efferent fibers to all the muscles concerned

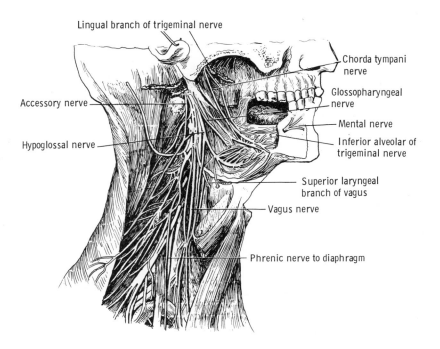

Lingual branch of trigeminal nerve

Chorda tympani nerve

Accessory nerve

Glossopharyngeal nerve

Mental nerve

Hypoglossal nerve

Inferior alveolar of trigeminal nerve

Superior laryngeal branch of vagus

Vagus nerve

Phrenic nerve to diaphragm

Fig. 8-19. Deep dissection of neck, showing branches of trigeminal, facial, glossopharyngeal, vagus, accessory and hypoglossal nerves.

of the gag reflex, loss of sensation in the throat and the base of the tongue, difficulty in swallowing and disturbance of the carotid sinus and carotid body reflexes (p. 405 and p. 409).

10. **The vagus nerves,** after arising from the medulla, live up to their name which means "wanderer." In other words, these are the only cranial nerves that extend beyond the region of the head and the neck. Each vagus nerve contains both somatic and visceral fibers, but the latter have by far the most extensive distribution as they supply most of the organs in the neck, the thorax and the abdomen. Figure 9-3 illustrates the fiber pathways of the vagus nerve as it makes an outstanding contribution to the craniosacral division of the autonomic system; functions of this system are described in Chapter 9. In addition to its thoracic and abdominal distribution, the vagus also helps with the action of swallowing by sending motor fibers to skeletal muscle in the soft palate and the pharynx. A very important branch of the vagus (recurrent laryngeal nerve)

supplies motor fibers to the muscles in the larynx enabling one to speak. Complete bilateral vagal paralysis is rapidly fatal, but if only one nerve is involved, there will be such things as impairment of voice, difficulty in swallowing, dilatation of the stomach and other visceral disturbances.

11. **The accessory nerves** arise from both the medulla and the spinal cord (cervical segments); they were formerly called "spinal accessory" because of the cord component. Each supplies somatic motor and sensory fibers to the sternocleidomastoid and part of the trapezius muscles. They also share some of the functions of the vagus nerves. Following injury to the accessory nerve there is difficulty in rotating the head and in raising the shoulder on the affected side.

12. **The hypoglossal nerves** supply motor and sensory fibers to the muscles of the tongue (Fig. 8-19). Injury results in difficulty in speaking, chewing and swallowing.

Functions of the cranial nerves are summarized in the table on p. 246–247.

SUMMARY

1. Brain, or encephalon, in bony box atop vertebral column
   A. Size varies with individual
      a. Physical growth ends by 18th or 20th year
      b. Development depends on mental exercise
   B. Divisions of the brain
      a. Forebrain: cerebral hemispheres and diencephalon
      b. Midbrain
      c. Hindbrain
2. Brain stem and cerebellum
   A. Medulla oblongata
      a. Bulb of brain; conduction pathway and decussation center
      b. Contains vital centers
      c. Centers for higher reflexes
   B. Pons
      a. Between medulla and midbrain
      b. Part of conduction pathway to cerebrum
      c. Connects halves of cerebellum
   C. Cerebellum
      a. Attached to brain stem by peduncles
      b. Concerned with coordination of muscular activity
      c. Functions not on conscious level
      d. Reflexes for regulation of muscle tone, maintenance of equilibrium and posture, smooth performance of voluntary movements
   D. Midbrain
      a. Cerebral peduncles—main conduction pathway to and from forebrain
      b. Centers for visual and auditory reflexes, postural and righting reflexes
3. The diencephalon
   A. Hypothalamus (in floor of third ventricle)
      a. Regulation of visceral activities
      b. Many connections with thalamus and cerebral cortex: emotions may influence visceral effectors
   B. Thalamus (in lateral walls of third ventricle)

a. Relay center of incoming impulses and sensory integrating organ
      b. Crude recognition of unlocalized pain and temperature
   C. Pineal body
      a. Outgrowth of third ventricle
      b. Function unknown
4. Reticular formation
   A. "Core" of brain stem
   B. Regulates background activities of nervous system
   C. Concerned with alertness or wakefulness
5. The cerebrum
   A. Description
      a. Largest part of brain
      b. Divided into two hemispheres
      c. Each hemisphere consists of four lobes
   B. Cerebral cortex
      a. Surface layer of gray matter; highest level of the nervous system
      b. Thrown into folds (convolutions) and grooves (fissures)
      c. Major fissures:
         (1) Longitudinal
         (2) Transverse
         (3) Central (Rolando)
         (4) Lateral (Sylvius)
   C. White matter tracts
      a. Commissural fibers
      b. Projection fibers
      c. Association fibers
   D. Basal ganglia
      a. Four deep masses of gray matter
      b. Links in the extrapyramidal motor pathway
   E. Functions of cerebrum
      a. Expressive phase
         (1) Motor area
         (2) Premotor area
         (3) Basal ganglia
         (4) Motor speech area (Broca's)
         (5) Prefrontal cortex
      b. Receptive phase
         (1) General sensory area
         (2) Auditory area
         (3) Visual area

(4) Olfactory area

(5) Gustatory area

   c. Association areas: role in integrating receptive and expressive phases

   d. Associative memory: ability to retain, modify and reuse information received through senses; basis of all knowledge

   e. Acquired or conditioned reflexes: learned through experience rather than inherited

F. Cerebral lesions

   a. Interference with blood supply to brain: cerebral vascular accident

   b. Epilepsy: abnormally active brain tissue

   c. Injury to basal ganglia: paralysis agitans or Parkinson's disease

6. Protection of the brain

A. Cranial bones

B. Meninges

   a. Dura mater

   b. Arachnoid

   c. Pia mater

C. Cerebrospinal fluid

   a. Clear, colorless, watery cushion to absorb shock: aids in exchange of nutrients and wastes; formed and drained continuously

   b. Circulation pathway: lateral ventricles, interventricular foramina, third ventricle, cerebral aqueduct, fourth ventricle, foramina of Luschka and Magendie, subarachnoid space, arachnoid villi, cranial venous sinuses

   c. Examination of fluid for constituents and for pressure valuable diagnostic tool

7. Cranial nerves

A. Twelve pairs arising from base of brain; numbered from front to back

B. See table for review of functions

PRACTICAL APPLICATIONS AND QUESTIONS

(Encircle the letter of the *best* answer to each of the following questions.)

A. *Students in neurology clinic attempted to determine the location of destructive lesions of the nervous system by observing the symptoms which were presented by various patients.*

1. A patient with visual disturbances may have pressure on the

   a. temporal lobe

   b. frontal lobe

   c. parietal lobe

   d. occipital lobe

2. Mr. R. walked with a reeling gait and had trouble maintaining his equilibrium. His postural reflexes were highly abnormal, and he was unable to execute accurate voluntary movements because of a lesion involving the

   a. midbrain

   b. pons

   c. cerebellum

   d. medulla

3. Mr. Y. walked without swinging his arms, and other associated movements were lacking. The students suspected that the lesion was in the region of the

   a. basal ganglia

   b. motor cortex

   c. cerebellum

   d. thalamus

4. Death would result most quickly from a lesion of the

   a. medulla

   b. cerebellum

   c. cerebral cortex

   d. midbrain

5. Following a cerebral vascular accident, one patient suffered damage to the left pyramidal (corticospinal) tract. Which of the following symptoms would be observed on the affected side?

   a. loss of muscle sense

   b. loss of muscle tone

   c. loss of fine, voluntary movements

   d. loss of temperature, touch and pain sensations

B. *Identify the cranial nerve which is primarily involved in each of the following:*

1. Inability to smile or to whistle
   a. facial
   b. accessory
   c. trigeminal
   d. hypoglossal

2. Loss of sensation in the face
   a. abducens
   b. trigeminal
   c. vagus
   d. accessory

3. Drooping of the eyelid, dilated pupil, eyeball turned downward and outward
   a. optic
   b. olfactory
   c. facial
   d. oculomotor

4. Inability to shrug the shoulders
   a. vagus
   b. accessory
   c. facial
   d. glossopharyngeal

5. Blindness
   a. oculomotor
   b. olfactory
   c. optic
   d. trochlear

FUNCTIONS OF CRANIAL NERVES

Number	Name	Structures Innervated by Efferent Components	Structures Innervated by Afferent Components	Functions
I	Olfactory	None	Olfactory mucous membrane	Nerve of smell
II	Optic	None	Retina of eye	Nerve of vision
III	Oculomotor	Superior, medial, inferior recti; inferior oblique; levator palpebrae superioris; ciliary; sphincter of iris	Same muscles (muscle sense)	Motor and muscle sense to various muscles listed; accommodation to different distances; regulates the amount of light reaching retina. Most important nerve in eye movements
IV	Trochlear	Superior oblique	Same	Motor and muscle sense to superior oblique. Eye movements
V	Trigeminal	Muscles of mastication	Skin and mucous membranes in head; teeth. Same muscles	Nerve of pain, touch, heat, cold to skin and mucous membranes listed; same for teeth; movements of mastication and muscle sense

FUNCTIONS OF CRANIAL NERVES Continued

Number	Name	Structures Innervated by Efferent Components	Structures Innervated by Afferent Components	Functions
VI	Abducens	Lateral rectus	Same	Motor and muscle sense to lateral rectus. Eye movements
VII	Facial	Submaxillary and sublingual glands; muscles of face, scalp and a few others	Same muscles; taste buds of anterior two thirds of tongue	Taste to anterior two thirds of tongue; secretory and vasodilator to two salivary glands; motor and muscle sense to facial and a few other muscles. Nerve of facial expression
VIII	Acoustic (cochlear and vestibular portions)	None	Cochlear-organ of Corti. Vestibular-semicircular canals, utricle and saccule	Cochlear division is nerve of hearing. Vestibular division is concerned with registering movement of the body through space and with the position of the head
IX	Glossopharyngeal	Superior pharyngeal constrictor; stylopharyngeus muscle; parotid gland	Taste buds of posterior one third of tongue; parts of pharynx; carotid sinus and body; stylopharyngeus muscle	Taste to posterior one third of tongue and adjacent regions; secretory and vasodilator to parotid gland; motor and muscle sense to stylopharyngeus; pain, touch, heat and cold to pharynx; afferent in circulatory and respiratory reflexes
X	Vagus	Muscles of pharynx, larynx, esophagus, thoracic and abdominal viscera; coronary arteries; walls of bronchi; pancreas; gastric glands	Same muscles; skin of external ear; mucous membranes of larynx, trachea, esophagus; thoracic and abdominal viscera; arch of aorta; atria; great veins	Secretory to gastric glands and pancreas; inhibitory to heart; motor to alimentary tract; motor and muscle sense to muscles of larynx and pharynx; constrictor to coronaries; motor to muscle in walls of bronchi; important in respiratory, cardiac and circulatory reflexes
XI	Accessory	Sternocleidomastoid and trapezius muscles; with vagus	Distributed with vagus	Motor and muscle sense to muscles listed; shares certain function of vagus
XII	Hypoglossal	Muscles of tongue	Same	Motor and muscle sense to muscles of tongue; important in speech, mastication and deglutition

9

"What a piece of work is man!"

HAMLET ● WILLIAM SHAKESPEARE

THE AUTONOMIC DIVISION OF THE NERVOUS SYSTEM

The autonomic division of the nervous system consists of those neural pathways which are primarily concerned with the regulation of visceral activities, such as the beating of the heart, the secretion of glands and the movement of food through the digestive tract. As the term "autonomic" implies, this portion of the nervous system has a certain degree of functional independence; it is not under direct voluntary control as is the somatic division which innervates skeletal muscles. Although visceral structures are less dependent on nerve impulses than are the skeletal muscles, their activities are constantly being monitored and regulated by the central nervous system (CNS).

This division of the nervous system into "visceral" and "somatic" portions is convenient from a physiologic standpoint, but it does not mean that we are dealing with two anatomically distinct systems. For example, the higher centers of the brain regulate *both* somatic and visceral activities, and, peripherally, all spinal nerves and many of the cranial nerves contain *both* somatic and visceral fibers. Moreover, most body responses to changes in the environment (both internal and external) usually involve skeletal muscle activity on the one hand and simultaneous changes in smooth muscle, cardiac muscle and glands on the other. Such coordination of somatic and visceral activity is basic to the maintenance of homeostasis. In the light of these facts it is apparent that the autonomic division is only one aspect of an integrated nervous system, but, in accordance with custom, it will be given special consideration in this text.

GENERAL ORGANIZATION

The innervation of visceral structures is fundamentally similar to that of somatic structures in that spinal reflex arcs and higher brain centers are involved. Although *visceral afferent* components are of importance in initiating certain reflexes, major emphasis will be placed on the *visceral efferent* pathways over which "orders" are transmitted from the CNS to visceral effectors (smooth muscle, cardiac muscle and glands).

Visceral afferent fibers

Various visceral and viscerosomatic reflexes are initiated by nerve impulses which originate in the viscera and are transmitted over afferent fibers to the spinal cord and the brain stem. These fibers

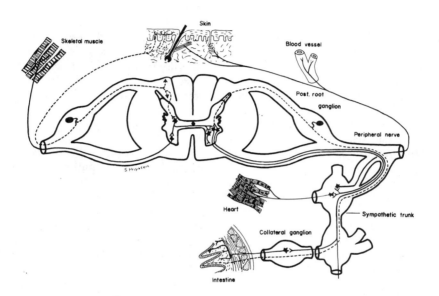

Fig. 9-1. Diagram showing four functional components of a peripheral nerve. On the left, a somatic afferent neuron is shown (broken lines), bringing impulses from receptors in the skin and around a hair follicle. The impulses may travel to ipsilateral and contralateral anterior horn cells in the same segment, and they may ascend or descend to other segments. A somatic efferent neuron is shown (solid lines) conducting impulses from the anterior horn to skeletal muscle fibers.

On the right a visceral afferent neuron is shown (broken lines), bringing impulses from receptors in the small intestine. The impulses may travel to cells in the lateral horn, as indicated; they may travel to ipsilateral and contralateral anterior horn cells and may ascend or descend to other segments, although the paths are not indicated. Two visceral efferent neurons are shown (solid lines), with cell bodies in the lateral horn. Both travel through a white ramus to an autonomic ganglion. One collateral is in contact with a neuron in a lateral ganglion, the axon of which travels in a gray ramus to a spinal nerve, to be distributed to smooth muscle in a blood vessel, a pilomotor muscle and a sweat gland. Another collateral is in contact with a neuron in the ganglion, the axon of which supplies cardiac muscle. The other visceral efferent neuron shows an axon which travels without synapse through the sympathetic trunk into a collateral ganglion, in which it comes in contact with a neuron whose axon travels to supply smooth muscle in the wall of the intestine.

are contained in cranial and spinal nerves, thereby traveling with somatic afferent fibers but completely independent of them. The cell bodies of visceral afferent neurons are located in the dorsal root ganglia of spinal nerves or in comparable ganglia of cranial nerves. Visceral afferent impulses are primarily concerned with the reflex control of those activities concerned with the maintenance of life (e.g., metabolism, nutrition, and so on), but they also may give rise to organic sensations and visceral pain (p. 268).

Visceral efferent fibers

Visceral efferent fibers are those that transmit impulses from the CNS to smooth muscle, cardiac muscle and glands. These fibers differ from somatic efferent fibers in that there are 2 neurons in the pathway from the CNS to the visceral effector. (The somatic efferent pathway to skeletal muscle consists of only 1 neuron.) *Visceral efferent neuron No. 1* has its cell body in the brainstem or in the spinal cord, from which the axon extends to a ganglion of the autonomic group; such axons are called **preganglionic fibers.**

Within the autonomic ganglion lie the dendrites and the cell body of *visceral efferent neuron No. 2.* The preganglionic fiber (axon No. 1) synapses with the dendrites or the cell body of neuron No. 2; the axon of this second neuron, called a **postganglionic fiber,** transmits impulses from the ganglion to the visceral effector. Figure 9-1 illustrates the general arrangement of these visceral efferent fibers.

Preganglionic fibers have a less extensive origin than somatic efferent fibers. The former are limited to 3 regions of outflow from the CNS.

The first region is cranial. Preganglionic fibers accompany somatic efferent fibers in the oculomotor (3rd), facial (7th), glossopharyngeal (9th) and vagus (10th) cranial nerves and are called the *cranial autonomics.*

The second outflow of autonomic fibers is from the thoracic and upper lumbar regions of the spinal cord. These preganglionic fibers, which form part of the anterior roots of the spinal nerves

from the 8th cervical to the 2nd lumbar, are called the *thoracolumbar autonomics.* This group of fibers passes through the intervertebral foramina as part of the respective spinal nerves, then leaves each spinal nerve as a white ramus (p. 209) and continues on to an autonomic ganglion, as shown in Figure 9-1. Of particular interest in this group are those preganglionic fibers which enter into the formation of the **splanchnic nerves;** fibers from the 5th to the 9th thoracic spinal nerves form the *greater splanchnic* nerve, and those from the 9th and the 10th thoracic nerves form the *lesser splanchnic* nerve. These important nerves pierce the diaphragm and enter the celiac plexus (p. 252).

The third outflow is in the sacral region. Preganglionic fibers, which are present in the anterior roots of the 2nd, the 3rd and the 4th sacral spinal nerves, are called *sacral autonomics.*

The autonomic ganglia

Synaptic connections between neurons in the visceral efferent pathway occur in autonomic ganglia which are divided into 3 groups—lateral, collateral and terminal. The **lateral** or **vertebral ganglia** are beadlike structures which are united by "threads" of nervous tissue (axons and dendrites), forming two distinct chains. Each chain lies close to the bodies of the vertebrae on its own side of the vertebral column, extending downward through the neck, the thorax and the abdomen to the coccyx (Fig. 9-2). There are usually 22 ganglia in each chain (3 cervical, 11 thoracic, 4 lumbar and 4 sacral), but individual variations are common.

The lateral ganglia receive preganglionic fibers from the thoracolumbar region of the spinal cord; some of these fibers terminate here, either in the ganglion which they entered first, or they may pass up or down the chain and terminate in a ganglion which is above or below their level of entrance. Of the postganglionic fibers leaving the lateral ganglia, some pass directly to visceral structures in the head, the neck, the chest, etc., while others join the spinal nerves (as a gray ramus) and supply peripheral structures such as the sweat glands and smooth muscle in the walls

Fig. 9-2. (Left) Schematic representation of craniosacral pathways (blue lines). (Right) Schematic representation of thoracolumbar pathways (red lines). (Modified from Maxson; Pitkin's Conduction Anesthesia, ed. 2, Philadelphia, Lippincott)

of blood vessels and around hair follicles (Fig. 9-1). However, some of the thoracolumbar preganglionic fibers do not terminate in the lateral ganglia but merely pass through them and emerge as the splanchnic nerves which make their synaptic connections in the collateral ganglia of the abdomen.

The collateral or prevertebral ganglia lie in front of the vertebral column, and close to the large abdominal arteries from which their names are derived. For example, the two *celiac* ganglia lie one on either side of the celiac artery as it arises from the abdominal aorta; the *superior* and *inferior mesenteric* ganglia lie near the roots of their respective arteries, etc. The collateral ganglia receive preganglionic fibers from the thoracolumbar region of the spinal cord. Postganglionic fibers follow the course of various arteries as they extend from the ganglia to visceral effectors in the abdomen and pelvis. An exception to this pattern concerns those preganglionic fibers, conveyed by the splanchnic nerves, that are destined for the adrenal medullae (p. 561); these fibers pass through the collateral ganglia, without synapses, to the adrenal medullae, which serve as "ganglia" in this particular instance, the cells of which correspond to postganglionic fibers.

Terminal ganglia constitute the third group of autonomic ganglia and, as their name implies, are located near the end of the visceral efferent pathway. These ganglia lie close to or within the walls of the visceral effectors which their postganglionic fibers supply; they receive preganglionic fibers from the cranial and the sacral regions of the CNS.

Divisions of the autonomic system

Structurally and functionally, the autonomic portion of the nervous system can be divided into two distinct parts: (1) the thoracolumbar or sympathetic division, and (2) the craniosacral or parasympathetic division.

The thoracolumbar or sympathetic division consists of the *thoracic* and *lumbar* outflow of visceral efferent fibers. The term *sympathetic* pertains to a mutual relation between parts, whereby a change

in one has an effect on the other. Preganglionic fibers of this division make their synaptic connections with many neurons in various *lateral* or *collateral* ganglia. For example, fibers entering the sympathetic chains may establish connections with as many as 9 lateral ganglia, and the branches of a single axon may synapse with 30 or more ganglionic neurons. This arrangement makes possible a widespread radiation of impulses and an extensive distribution of postganglionic fibers.

The craniosacral or parasympathetic division consists of the *cranial* and *sacral* outflow of visceral efferent fibers. The term *parasympathetic* means "beside" or "near" the sympathetic yet having an opposite effect on individual organs. The preganglionic fibers of this division make their synaptic connections only in *terminal* ganglia, and individual fibers synapse with only a few ganglionic neurons (in contrast to the multisynaptic connections of the sympathetic division). Consequently, there is no widespread radiation of impulses and a relatively limited distribution of parasympathetic postganglionic fibers.

The great autonomic plexuses

The autonomic plexuses are complicated networks of fibers found in the thoracic, the abdominal and the pelvic cavities. They serve as areas of redistribution for both the sympathetic and the parasympathetic fibers which enter into their formation. The cardiac, the celiac and the hypogastric plexuses are of greatest prominence.

The cardiac plexus is located at the base of the heart, overlying the roots of the great blood vessels. From this plexus, and smaller subplexuses, sympathetic and parasympathetic fibers are routed to the heart, the lungs and other visceral effectors in the thorax.

The celiac plexus (solar plexus) is located behind the stomach, overlying the abdominal aorta and the celiac artery. In addition to the sympathetic splanchnic nerves, the celiac ganglia and related postganglionic fibers, this great plexus also consists of parasympathetic preganglionic fibers which pass through on their way to terminal

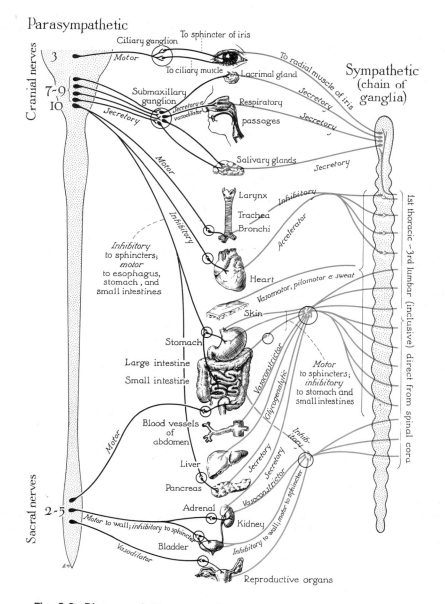

Fig. 9-3. Diagram of the autonomic nervous system (visceral efferent). The craniosacral (parasympathetic) division is shown in black; the origin, relay station and functions are indicated. The thoracolumbar (sympathetic) division is shown in red; the origin in the spinal cord is not shown; the fibers as they emerge from the spinal cord and enter the chain of lateral ganglia are indicated, together with the relay stations and the functions.

ganglia. From the celiac plexus (and smaller sub-plexuses) fibers are routed to most of the abdominal viscera.

The hypogastric plexus is located in front of the 5th lumbar vertebra and the sacral promontory. It receives fibers from both of the autonomic divisions and distributes them to the pelvic viscera.

Although it is evident that the autonomic plexuses consist of intermixtures of both sympathetic and parasympathetic fibers, it must be emphasized that the sympathetic fibers may be preganglionic, postganglionic, or both, due to the anatomic location of their ganglia. On the other hand, the parasympathetic fibers are preganglionics which are merely passing through the plexus en route to their terminal ganglia.

PHYSIOLOGIC CONSIDERATIONS

The sympathetic and the parasympathetic divisions of the autonomic nervous system are primarily concerned with the regulation of visceral activities; thus they play an important role in the maintenance of homeostasis. Most of the visceral effectors in the body have a double autonomic nerve supply, one from the sympathetic and one from the parasympathetic division. These divisions are usually antagonistic in their effect on individual organs or structures, one serving to initiate or increase activity, the other to inhibit or decrease the activity. For example, stimulation of sympathetic fibers which supply the heart will speed its action, but stimulation of parasympathetic fibers will slow its rate of beat. There are a few visceral effectors which receive only one nerve supply; the sweat glands and the smooth muscle bundles (pilomotor muscles) around hair follicles are supplied with sympathetic fibers only.

The parasympathetic (craniosacral) division

The parasympathetic division is primarily concerned with those activities which deal with the restoration and the conservation of bodily energy and with the elimination of body wastes. To a large extent, such activities are initiated by internal changes in the viscera themselves, changes which act on the interoceptors of visceral afferent neurons. These activities are almost entirely involuntary and unconscious; the few visceral afferent impulses that do reach the conscious level are poorly localized and vague. However, muscular spasms or the distention of the walls of visceral structures may result in sensations of pain. Due to the limited distribution of efferent fibers, parasympathetic activity may involve only one organ at a time; there is no widespread response as is the case in the sympathetic division.

The functions of the craniosacral division are illustrated in Figure 9-3, in black, on the left side of the diagram. A list of these functions follows:

1. **Motor or Augmentative Functions.** This division causes *contraction* of the sphincter muscle of the iris, which makes the pupil of the eye smaller; of the ciliary muscle of the eye, which adjusts the lens system for vision at different distances; of the smooth muscle of the bronchioles, which makes them smaller, and air is moved in and out of the lungs with more difficulty; of the smooth muscle of the walls of the stomach, the intestine and the urinary bladder, which causes these organs to become more active.

2. **Inhibitory Functions.** The impulses that reach certain effectors by way of this division lead to a decrease in the activity or the *relaxation* of smooth muscle. The smooth muscle in the walls of blood vessels of the salivary glands and the external genitalia is relaxed, which means that these blood vessels dilate. Impulses that reach the heart cause it to beat more slowly and weakly. The sphincters of the gastrointestinal tract and the urinary bladder are relaxed by this division.

3. **Secretory Functions.** Impulses that reach the stomach and the pancreas stimulate them to produce more secretions. Impulses that reach the salivary glands lead to the production of a thin, watery saliva.

In summary, the functions of the parasympathetic division are *conservative* and *restorative*. For example, by narrowing the pupil of the eye, the retina is shielded from excessive light; by promoting the digestive processes, energy-giving foods can be taken into the body and stored for future use; by slowing the heart rate, cardiac muscle has more opportunity to rest; by emptying the bladder and the bowel, waste products are removed from the body.

The sympathetic (thoracolumbar) division

The sympathetic division is greatly influenced by changes in the external environment, changes that stimulate the exteroceptors of somatic afferent neurons. Although constantly involved in the routine day-to-day maintenance of homeostasis, this division probably is best known for the widespread response which results from stimulation of the unit as a whole. Fear, anger, severe pain, loss of blood, asphyxia and other forms of physical danger will strongly stimulate the sympathetic system. At such times this division is primarily concerned with the mobilization of bodily reserves. For this reason the sympathetic division might be called the "emergency system," since it prepares us for the intense muscular activity that may be involved in meeting a stress situation. Whether we stand our ground and "fight it out" or take to our heels in flight, there are certain visceral changes that take place as we prepare for action.

The functions of the thoracolumbar division of the autonomic system are illustrated in Figure 9-3, in red, on the right side of the diagram. A list of these functions follows:

1. **Motor or Augmentative Functions.** This division causes *contraction* of the following: the radial muscle of the iris, which means dilatation of the pupil of the eye; the pilomotor muscles, which make the hair stand on end or cause "gooseflesh"; and the smooth muscle in the sphincters of the gastrointestinal tract and the urinary bladder for retention of contents. When the sympathetic fibers to the heart are stimulated, they cause it to beat faster and more forcibly. When impulses reach the smooth muscle of the blood vessels in the skin and the viscera, they cause the muscle to contract to a greater extent; this is called *vasoconstriction*, since the blood vessels become constricted or smaller.

Fig. 9-4.
Appearance of
a cat in an
emotional crisis.

2. **Inhibitory Functions.** This means that when impulses reach certain effectors by way of the sympathetic autonomic fibers, the smooth muscle *relaxes*. The smooth muscle which is so affected is that in the blood vessels of skeletal and cardiac muscle (leading to dilatation of these vessels), the muscle in the walls of the gastrointestinal tract (which stops contracting), the wall of the urinary bladder, and the walls of the bronchioles (which makes it easier for air to get into and out of the lungs).

3. **Secretory Functions.** Sympathetic fibers carry impulses that increase the activity of sweat glands and promote the secretion of epinephrine (Adrenalin) by the adrenal glands. Impulses to the salivary glands result in the production of a thick, viscid saliva, which leads to a feeling of dryness in the mouth.

4. **Glycogenolytic Function.** When impulses reach the cells of the liver, glycogen is broken down to glucose which then is released to the bloodstream, adding to the available sources of energy.

In summary, the sympathetic division not only counterbalances routine parasympathetic effects but also prepares the body for *"fight or flight"* in times of physical danger or in emotional crises. For example, let us consider the chain of events that occur in a cat when a dog approaches. Afferent impulses from the eyes and the nose reach the cat's cortex and in some way affect the centers for vision and smell, and the prefrontal area. Outgoing impulses are sent to the hypothalamus and are relayed on to the lower levels, which prepare the cat to meet the emergency.

The whole sympathetic division goes into action. As a result, there is dilatation of the pupils and contraction of the pilomotor muscles to make the hair stand on end (causing the cat to appear larger and possibly frightening the dog) (Fig. 9-4). The heart beats faster, and the blood vessels of the viscera and the skin are constricted, thus raising blood pressure and shunting blood into the dilated vessels of skeletal muscle, heart muscle, lungs and brain. Breathing becomes more rapid, and the bronchioles dilate to facilitate the movement of air into and out of the lungs. The blood sugar level rises as liver glycogen is changed to glucose and put into circulation where it will be available to supply the increasing energy needs of the body. The secretion of epinephrine (Adrenalin) intensifies and prolongs the activity of the entire sympathetic division. Since the cat is going to fight or to take flight, the above changes in the body are primarily concerned with supplying the skeletal muscles and the vital organs with increased amounts of blood that is rich in oxygen and glucose. Peaceful activities, such as the various digestive processes, are slowed down or even stopped as the cat prepares for offensive or defensive action.

We can recognize many of these same responses in our own bodies during some emotional upheaval or when in actual physical danger; therefore, it would behoove all of us to avoid such situations whenever possible. It also stands to reason that doctors and nurses should attempt to shield their patients from unnecessary pain, anger, fear or worry, since overactivity of the sympathetic system not only puts an extra strain on the heart but markedly interferes with those restorative processes which are so essential for full recovery from any illness. The systemic effects of parasympathetic and sympathetic activity are summarized in tabular form on page 259.

Coordination of visceral activity

As stated previously, visceral structures have a certain degree of functional independence in that one cannot voluntarily alter their activity, but they are continuously monitored and regulated by cortical and subcortical centers. Microscopic "sentries," the receptor end organs, are constantly dispatching reports to headquarters, keeping it informed of tissue activities and needs in all parts of the body; consequently, it is imperative that these reports be sorted out and correlated if appropriate visceral responses are to be ordered.

The *cerebral cortex* is apparently the master switchboard for all incoming calls after they have undergone preliminary sorting and grouping in the *thalamus*. However, the cortex shunts most of its calls to the *hypothalamus* which then assumes the responsibility for coordinating the appropriate visceral activities. In this way the cerebral cortex is relieved of the burden of dealing with the constant demands for routine visceral adjustments but can exert its influence whenever necessary.

Chemical mediators

Chemical substances liberated by nerve fibers are of fundamental importance in the transmission of impulses at synapses (p. 198) and at neuroeffector junctions (i.e., neuromuscular or neuroglandular junctions). Two very important chemical mediators are acetylcholine and norepinephrine.

Acetylcholine is released by all "incoming" or preganglionic fibers (both sympathetic and parasympathetic) at their endings in the autonomic ganglia; this mediator then serves to excite the "outgoing" or postganglionic fibers. Those postganglionic fibers related to the parasympathetic division in turn release acetylcholine at their endings at neuroeffector junctions, and the transmission process is completed. All fibers that liberate acetylcholine are referred to as *cholinergic fibers*. As previously noted in the description of neuromuscular transmission in skeletal muscle (p. 120) acetylcholine is destroyed very rapidly by the enzyme cholinesterase; thus, the duration of its activity is limited.

Norepinephrine (sympathin) is the chemical mediator that is released at most (but not all) postganglionic fiber endings of the sympathetic division. One such exception is at the neuroeffector junctions in sweat glands; these fibers liberate acetylcholine. Because norepinephrine closely resembles epinephrine (Adrenalin) in its effects, the fibers that release it are called *adrenergic fibers*. In general, the effect of these substances is more widespread, because they are augmented by the secretions of the adrenal medullae (p. 561) and are removed somewhat more slowly from the tissues.

The action of drugs

Atropine inhibits the activities of the parasympathetic division. The pupils are dilated, the bronchioles dilated, secretion of glands along the respiratory passages inhibited and movements of stomach and intestine inhibited. The most common uses of atropine are in eye examinations (to dilate the pupils) and before the administration of a general anesthetic (to reduce secretions in the respiratory passages).

Pilocarpine has the same effects as normal stimulation of the parasympathetic division. One of the chief effects is to constrict the pupils. Consequently, this drug is used in the treatment of glaucoma (p. 278).

Epinephrine has the same effects as normal stimulation of the sympathetic division. The effects of epinephrine are: relaxation of bronchioles in asthma, stimulation of the heart in cardiac collapse and constriction of blood vessels with a rise in blood pressure.

SUMMARY

1. Autonomics regulate visceral activity; only one aspect of nervous system
2. General organization
   A. Visceral afferent fibers
      a. Reflex control of activities concerned with maintenance of life
   B. Visceral efferent fibers
      a. Preganglionic fibers from CNS to autonomic ganglia
      b. Postganglionic fibers from ganglia to effectors
      c. Preganglionics limited to 3 regions of outflow from CNS
         (1) Cranial autonomics
         (2) Thoracolumbar autonomics
         (3) Sacral autonomics
   C. Autonomic ganglia
      a. Lateral or vertebral: beaded chains along vertebral column
      b. Collateral or prevertebral: lie in front of vertebral column in relation to abdominal arteries
      c. Terminal ganglia: lie close to or within walls of effector
   D. Divisions of autonomic system
      a. Thoracolumbar or sympathetic; synaptic connections in lateral and collateral ganglia
      b. Craniosacral or parasympathetic; synaptic connections in terminal ganglia
   E. Autonomic plexuses
      a. Areas of redistribution of fibers
      b. Cardiac: visceral effectors in thorax
      c. Celiac: visceral effectors in abdomen
      d. Hypogastric: visceral effectors in pelvis
3. Physiologic considerations
   A. Parasympathetic or craniosacral division
      a. Conservation and restoration of bodily energy
      b. Review table on p. 259
   B. Sympathetic or thoracolumbar division
      a. Counter-balance for parasympathetic effects
      b. "Emergency system" prepares for "fight or flight"
      c. Review table on p. 259
   C. Coordination of visceral activity
      a. Receptor end organs dispatch reports on environmental change
      b. Reports undergo preliminary grouping in thalamus
      c. Cerebral cortex is master switchboard; shunts most calls to hypothalamus which coordinates visceral responses
   D. Chemical mediators
      a. Acetylcholine released at all preganglionic fiber endings and at parasympathetic neuro-effector junctions; cholinesterase inactivates it; fibers called cholinergic

    b. Norepinephrine released at sympathetic neuro-effector junctions (except sweat glands); fibers called adrenergic

E. Action of drugs
    a. Atropine inhibits activities of parasympathetic division
    b. Pilocarpine mimics effect of parasympathetic stimulation
    c. Epinephrine (Adrenalin) has same effect as stimulation of sympathetic division

PRACTICAL APPLICATIONS AND QUESTIONS

(Encircle the letter of the *best* answer to each of the following questions.)

A. *Mrs. H. M. was walking down a dark street late in the evening, when she was suddenly accosted by an armed robber.*

1. Which of the following would be most active in the above situation?
    a. cranial nerves
    b. spinal nerves
    c. parasympathetic nerves
    d. sympathetic nerves

2. Mrs. H. M.'s response might include
    a. rapid breathing, rapid heart beat and constricted pupils
    b. increased perspiration, lowered blood pressure and low blood sugar

    c. dilated pupils, rapid heart beat and rapid breathing
    d. rapid heart beat, constricted bronchioles and elevated blood pressure

3. The autonomic system
    a. responds only during emotional crises
    b. innervates visceral effectors
    c. is completely separate from the cerebrospinal system
    d. consists primarily of afferent fibers

4. Which one of the following is *not* controlled by the autonomic system?
    a. making a decision
    b. emptying of the bladder
    c. the distribution of blood
    d. the secretion of saliva

B. *The enzyme cholinesterase may be destroyed by a poison gas used in chemical warfare.*

1. The action of cholinesterase involves the
    a. destruction of norepinephrine
    b. inactivation of acetylcholine
    c. stimulation of sympathetic fibers
    d. formation of epinephrine

2. Destruction of cholinesterase would result in muscle spasm and death because of the
    a. prolonged action of acetylcholine
    b. destruction of epinephrine
    c. inhibition of adrenergic fibers
    d. formation of norepinephrine

TABLE OF AUTONOMIC EFFECTS

Structure or Activity	Parasympathetic Effects	Sympathetic Effects
Pupil of the eye	Constricted	Dilated
The circulatory system		
Rate and force of heart beat	Decreased	Increased
Blood vessels in heart muscle and in skeletal muscles	Constricted	Dilated
Blood vessels in abdominal viscera and the skin		Constricted
Blood pressure	Decreased	Increased
The respiratory system		
Bronchioles of the lungs	Constricted	Dilated
Rate of breathing	Decreased	Increased
The digestive system		
Peristaltic movements of the digestive tube	Increased	Decreased
Muscular sphincters of the digestive tube	Relaxed	Contracted
Secretion of the salivary glands	Thin, watery saliva	Thick, viscid saliva
Digestive secretions of the stomach, intestine and pancreas	Increased	
Conversion of liver glycogen to blood sugar (glucose)		Increased
The genito-urinary system		
Urinary bladder	(Elimination of urine)	(Retention of urine)
Muscular walls	Contracted	Relaxed
Sphincters	Relaxed	Contracted
Muscle of the uterus	Relaxed; variable	Contracted under some conditions; varies with menstrual cycle and pregnancy
Blood vessels of external genitalia	Dilated	
The integument		
Secretion of sweat		Increased
Pilomotor muscles		Contracted ("gooseflesh")
Medullae of the adrenal glands		Secretion of epinephrine (Adrenalin) and norepinephrine

10

"I have heard of thee by the hearing of the ear; but now my eye seeth thee."

JOB 42:5

THE SENSE ORGANS

Man's internal and external environments constitute ever-changing worlds of beauty and of danger. However, were it not for millions of receptor end organs (aided by other components of the nervous system) he would be unable to appreciate the lovely things in life or to recognize danger in time to execute proper withdrawal responses. Needless to say, without his sense organs man would be completely helpless and unable to survive for any appreciable length of time.

Sensations may be classified as cutaneous, visceral, olfactory (smell), gustatory (taste), visual, auditory and position sense.

Sensory mechanisms

A sensory mechanism is a group of structures by means of which a change in the environment gives rise to a sensation. The 3 components of such a mechanism are: a sense organ or receptor, which is like a special receiving instrument; a pathway to the brain; and a sensory area in the cerebral cortex which is definite for each sense. The parts of a sensory mechanism are shown by diagram in Figure 10-1.

Sense organs or **receptors** are the peripheral endings of dendrites of afferent neurons. In these endings the property of excitability (p. 195) reaches its peak of development. The threshold or minimal stimulus (least change necessary to affect the receptor) is very low. Each receptor, except those for pain, is specialized for the reception of a particular type of stimulus which is called its *adequate stimulus*. For example, light is the adequate stimulus for the receptors of vision, and sound waves for those of hearing.

The afferent pathway to the brain consists of those neurons that conduct nerve impulses from the periphery to appropriate sensory areas in the cerebral cortex. The first neuron in the pathway is the afferent neuron whose dendrites are specialized to serve as receptors; these fibers travel in various cranial and spinal nerves. From the axons of the latter neurons, impulses travel over one or more additional neurons before reaching the cerebral cortex.

Sensory areas in the cerebral cortex are well defined for most of our sensations (p. 232). For example, the sensory areas for touch, temperature and muscle sense are in the postcentral region of the parietal lobe, the visual area is in the occipital lobe, and the auditory area is in the temporal lobe.

Each sensory unit ends in a sensory area in the cerebral cortex, and the end-result of the stimulus applied to a receptor is a sensation aroused in consciousness. However, activity does not stop here. Sensations are interpreted, analyzed, combined with sensations from other sensory units and synthesized into perceptions. As sensations take on meaning, there may be voluntary or reflex movements, visceral reflexes or storing of sensations in memory to be used in the future. Thus, various sensations contribute to the general fund of information about the outside world and to the knowledge of normal or pathologic activities within the body itself.

All parts of a particular sensory unit must be functioning in order to give rise to its characteristic sensations. If one sense is lost, other senses may be developed more highly. Such a condition exists in blindness, in which the patient learns to read and write through touch and muscle sense by the Braille method. Children who are deaf cannot learn to speak by hearing others speak; they learn through sight, by watching others speak, and by touch, as they feel the throat, the tongue and the lips. Helen Keller, who was both blind and deaf, learned to speak through touch and muscle sense, by noting the position of tongue, cheeks, lips and larynx when her teacher was speaking.

Characteristics of sensations

Projection. Although the brain is the seat of sensation we can scarcely realize that this is the case, since we have the habit of projecting the sensation to the source of stimulation. For example, we say "Sugar is sweet," when we really mean that it arouses in our brains a sensation which we call "sweetness." We say that a light is bright, but the sensation of brightness is in the brain. This habit of projection accounts for the fact that if an afferent nerve is stimulated anywhere along its course other than at its end (receptor), the impulses that reach the brain set up the sensation as usual, and it is projected to the receptor as usual. There is nothing in consciousness to differentiate impulses aroused by stimulation along the course of afferent nerves from those aroused by stimulation at the ends of afferent fibers or receptors.

Fig. 10-1. Parts of a sensory mechanism: receptor or sense organ, afferent (lower) and internuncial (intermediate and higher) neurons, center or sensory area in brain. The neuron in the sensory area of the brain leads to an association area (not shown) where the sensation may be interpreted and given added meaning.

RECEPTOR   AFFERENT NEURON   FIRST RELAY IN CENTRAL NERVOUS SYSTEM   SECOND RELAY IN CENTRAL NERVOUS SYSTEM   SENSORY AREA IN BRAIN (CENTER)

Fig. 10-2. Variations in sensitivity in two-point or spatial discrimination. The distance between the compass points indicates the sensitivity in different regions. The tip of the tongue is most sensitive, the back of the neck least sensitive. These are the actual averages found on a group of 25 medical students.

After-images. Sensations tend to persist in consciousness after the cessation of stimulation. This lingering sensation is called an *after-image*. For example, if we look at a bright light for a few seconds and then close our eyes we shall still "see" the light for a variable period of time.

Adaptation. Prolonged application of certain stimuli may result in a temporary loss of irritability of the receptor end organs. This phenomenon is called adaptation. For example, when we first walk into a room we may be very aware of a stuffy odor, but within a few minutes the olfactory end organs in the nose become adapted, and we are no longer conscious of that odor. The speed with which adaptation occurs varies with different receptors; fortunately for us, it is exceedingly slow or absent in those end organs which are responsible for alerting us to dangerous conditions in our environment.

Intensity. Sensations are more intense on some occasions than others. The intensity depends on the number of receptors stimulated and on the number of impulses that each afferent fiber transmits per second. With a stronger stimulus more receptors are stimulated, and the afferent fiber of each carries a greater number of impulses per second than when a weaker stimulus is applied.

CUTANEOUS SENSES

Touch, pressure, heat, cold and pain comprise the cutaneous senses. The receptors for these senses are widely distributed in the skin and the connective tissues, but the number of each type varies. For example, pain receptors are the most numerous, while those for heat are least numerous. Due to such variations in the number of receptors, not all parts of the body are equally sensitive. An area that has few receptors is relatively insensitive, while sensitive areas have large numbers of receptors. The variation in sensitivity to touch can be shown by the two-point discrimination test. A compass is used, and the distance between its points is varied. The subject tells whether he feels the compass points separately or as one. The more sensitive the area, the closer together the points of the compass may be and still be felt as 2

Fig. 10-3. Free nerve endings in epithelial tissue of a rabbit. Expanded ends (not to be confused with nuclei) can be made out between epithelial cells.

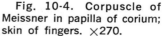

Fig. 10-4. Corpuscle of Meissner in papilla of corium; skin of fingers. ×270.

receptor of touch — "corpuscles of Meissner" found in papillary layer of sk
receptor of pressure — "corpuscles of Vater-Pacini" — are
264 found in skin, membranes, near tendons & joints.

THE SENSE ORGANS

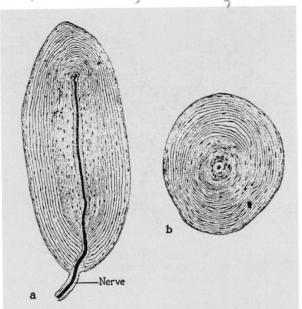

Fig. 10-5. Corpuscles of Vater-Pacini (lamellated) from skin of finger: (A) longitudinal and (B) cross section. ×145.

—Nerve

a

b

Fig. 10-6. End-bulbs of Krause from conjunctiva.

separate points. Figure 10-2 shows the tip of the tongue to be the most sensitive and the back of the neck the least sensitive of the many areas tested. In other words, the points can be very close together on the tongue and be felt separately, since the receptors are so numerous in this area. The scarcity of the receptors on the back of the neck requires that the distance between the points be great in order to feel them as separate.

The sense of touch and pressure

Receptors for touch include free nerve endings around hair follicles (Fig. 10-3) and the corpuscles of Meissner in the papillary layer of the skin (Fig. 10-4). Receptors for pressure are the corpuscles of Vater-Pacini deep in the tissues beneath skin, mucous and serous membranes, and near tendons and joints (Fig. 10-5). The adequate stimulus for these receptors is anything that moves a hair or dents or deforms the tissue in which the receptors are located.

The afferent pathway for impulses concerned with touch and pressure begins with the aforementioned receptors which are excited by adequate stimuli (superficial or deep pressure). The resulting nerve impulses travel from the receptors over large myelinated dendrites, in spinal and cranial nerves, to cell bodies in dorsal root ganglia of spinal nerves and corresponding ganglia on cranial nerves, and then on over axons into the CNS. Those impulses that reach the spinal cord travel in ascending tracts to the thalamus and are relayed to the cerebral cortex. The pathways for touch impulses in the spinal cord (posterior columns and anterior spinothalamic) are shown in Figure 7-5. The impulses that travel over cranial nerves likewise reach the thalamus before they are relayed to the cerebral cortex.

The sensory area for touch is in the general sensory area of the parietal lobe of the cerebral cortex, just posterior to the central fissure (Fig. 8-5). The ability to recognize the point of stimulation (local sign) is very well developed for the sense of touch, but after-images are short. Adaptation is rapid, and we get used to clothes very quickly

the receptor for cold called Krause (lie in surface of skin,
the receptor for heat are corpuscles of "Ruffini" (lie deep in the skin)

Cutaneous Senses 265

unless they cause pain or discomfort. We soon become accustomed to the pressure of a seat against the skin of the buttocks and only realize that the seat is hard if we sit still for a long time.

The sense of touch is exceedingly important in acquiring information about the outside world; children and adults alike desire to take objects in their hands when observing them for the first time.

Temperature sense

The receptors for cold are the endbulbs of *Krause,* which lie near the surface of the skin (Fig. 10-6). The receptors for heat are the corpuscles of *Ruffini,* which lie deep in the skin.

The afferent pathway consists of small myelinated fibers in cranial and spinal nerves which conduct impulses from temperature receptors to the CNS. These impulses are relayed on by other neurons to the thalamus, and from here to the cerebral cortex. The ascending tracts (lateral spinothalamic) over which temperature impulses travel in the spinal cord are illustrated in Figure 7-5.

The sensory area for temperature is in the general sensory area of the parietal lobe of the cerebral cortex, just posterior to the central fissure. Temperature sensations are particularly affected by events which have just preceded them, as shown by the following experiment. Place one hand in a basin of hot water and the other in a basin of cold water, for 30 seconds. Then place both hands in a basin of tepid water; it will feel cold to the one which has been in hot water and hot to the one which has been in cold water previously. In other words, the sensation of temperature aroused in each hand when placed in tepid water is greatly influenced by preceding events. After-images are long in the temperature sense, as can be shown by the following trick. If you blindfold a person and press a cold coin on his forehead and tell him to shake his head until the coin falls off he will shake his head about 3 times if he does not hear the coin fall the first time he shakes his head. He continues to shake his head until the after-image disappears.

The skin of the face and the hands is less sensitive to temperature changes than the parts of the body covered by clothing. In general, the mucous membranes, except in the mouth and the rectum, are insensitive to temperature. One can drink a hot liquid at a temperature that would be painful to the hands. If hot food burns the mouth, the person usually swallows it quickly since he cannot feel it burn the esophagus and the stomach. However, it may damage the mucous membrane, even if he is unaware of it.

eg. mucous membrane of esophagus not sensitive

Somatic pain

There are two general types of pain: (1) somatic and (2) visceral. Visceral pain is described on page 268. Somatic pain may be subdivided into superficial, or cutaneous pain, and deep pain from muscles, tendons and joints.

The receptors for pain are free nerve endings. They are scattered throughout the body, and it is estimated that there are several million of them. These receptors respond to more than one variety of stimulus. An intense stimulus of any type, such as a hot object, can affect them, especially if it threatens harm to the body. Since pain is important in protecting us, it is the harmful nature of the stimulus that is noted rather than its specific quality.

The afferent pathway for somatic pain consists of fine myelinated and unmyelinated fibers in cranial and spinal nerves. The ascending tracts (lateral spinothalamic) in the spinal cord are shown in Figure 7-5. By various relays, pain impulses reach the thalamus.

The sensory area for the discrimination of somatic pain is thought to be in the parietal lobe of the cerebral cortex, although when this region is stimulated in conscious patients during brain operations they do not report a sensation of pain as one of the results. As previously noted (p. 225), crude sensations of unlocalized pain and temperature may be experienced in the thalamus; the fear and anxiety, usually associated with pain, probably are experienced in the prefrontal cortex.

Adaptation does not exist in the sense of pain. This is especially important, since pain is a warning signal of danger, and if we became used to it and ignored it, damage to the body would follow.

Fig. 10-8. Receptors in smooth muscle of bronchi.

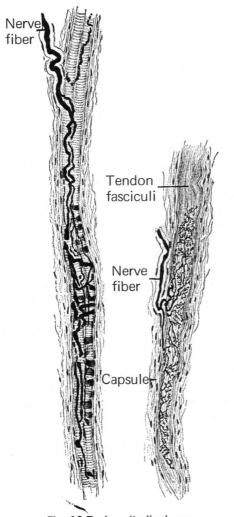

Fig. 10-7. Longitudinal section of receptor in muscular tissue (neuromuscular spindle, left) and in tendon (neurotendinous organ, right).

Muscle sense

Because conscious muscle sense impulses inform us of the degree to which the skeletal muscles are contracted and the tendons tensed, it is possible for us to adjust our muscular efforts to the work to be done. This sense also is called the *proprioceptive* or *kinesthetic* sense and it enables us to know the position of various parts of the body without the aid of vision. It is indispensable for the proper control of voluntary movements and for the correlation of various muscle groups, as in walking. There must be coordination in both time and space. When this sense is lacking the movements become ataxic.

Muscle sense and touch combined enable us to judge the texture of cloth, the weight of objects and the shape of objects even if we are blindfolded. The ability to judge the above properties is called *stereognosis* (meaning "solid knowledge"). A lack of this ability is called *astereognosis*.

Some examples of skills in which muscle sense is all-important are typing, piano playing and violin playing.

The receptors for skeletal muscle may be localized in muscular tissue, in tendons or at the junctions of muscle and tendon. The receptors may be simple or complex endings, such as muscle spindles. Receptors in skeletal muscle and in a tendon are illustrated in Figure 10-7. The receptors for smooth muscle may be located between muscle bundles or in the fibers; a receptor for smooth muscle is shown in Figure 10-8.

The afferent pathway for muscle sense impulses consists of large myelinated fibers in cranial and spinal nerves. Those impulses destined to reach consciousness travel in ascending tracts (posterior columns) to the medulla where they then are relayed onward to the thalamus and cerebral cortex; those impulses destined for reflex adjustments travel to the cerebellum over spinocerebellar tracts (Fig. 7-5).

The sensory area for conscious muscle sense impressions is in the general sensory area in the parietal lobe of the cerebral cortex, just posterior to the central fissure (Fig. 8-5).

THE VISCERAL AFFERENT SYSTEM

Stimuli and pathways

Adequate stimuli for visceral receptors fall into 3 groups: (1) dilatation or distention of a viscus, (2) spasms or strong contractions (such as colic), and (3) chemical irritants.

Impulses from visceral receptors travel over one of the following pathways: (1) afferent fibers which travel in company with parasympathetic nerves but are quite independent of them, (2) afferent fibers which travel in company with sympathetic nerves but are quite independent of them, and (3) afferent fibers which travel with somatic afferent nerves from the body walls and the diaphragm.

The dendrites that make up all 3 pathways belong to cell bodies in dorsal root ganglia of spinal nerves or comparable ganglia of cranial nerves. Visceral afferent fibers have no cell bodies or synapses in autonomic ganglia and must not be confused with visceral efferent fibers in whose company they travel for a part of their journey to the CNS. For example, one might compare the visceral afferent and visceral efferent fibers with a two-lane highway, as the nerve impulse "traffic" moves in opposite directions. However, the visceral afferent fibers leave this highway at the first possible exit and join the somatic afferent route to the CNS.

Reflex control

Visceral afferent impulses which are concerned with the reflex control of vital visceral phenomena are conducted by afferent fibers which travel in the company of parasympathetic (craniosacral) autonomic fibers, and they do not reach consciousness. These impulses are concerned with such activities as the reflex control of the heart, the size of blood vessels, emptying of the urinary bladder, etc. They are regulatory in function and active at all times.

Organic sensations

Visceral afferent impulses concerned with organic sensations, like those of reflex control, are conducted by afferent fibers which travel in the company of parasympathetic autonomic fibers. They give rise to the so-called organic sensations of hunger, thirst, nausea, distention of the bladder and the bowel, etc. The sensory areas in the brain have not yet been identified.

The sensation of hunger is projected to the stomach and is associated with powerful rhythmic contractions of the stomach musculature. Hunger occurs periodically, if food is not eaten. You can be very hungry, and after a little while you forget that you are hungry. Then contractions begin again and you feel hungry again, and so it goes until the next meal is eaten.

Hunger is a disagreeable sensation. In some persons it is accompanied by a feeling of weakness, trembling, nausea and headache. The nervous system seems to be hyperexcitable, and one feels more and more miserable. When you have a particularly difficult or trying task to perform, tackle it with a comfortably filled stomach. Make no important decisions when you are hungry. If you have favors to ask you may receive a more impartial reply from the donor after he has had a good dinner.

The receptors that are stimulated during hunger contractions have not been located. Perhaps the spindles in the stomach musculature serve this function.

Appetite is an agreeable desire for food and pleasure in thinking about it, seeing it or smelling it. The senses of taste and smell contribute to one's appetite. You can have an appetite for your favorite dessert even at the end of a full meal. When a person is mentally depressed or ill there is "no appetite," or if one has an unpleasant experience just before a meal the appetite disappears.

The sensation of thirst is projected to the pharynx. It is a protective signal and warns of the need for the intake of fluid. It may be unquenchable after vomiting, diarrhea or hemorrhage in which large amounts of fluid are lost. Thirst may be extreme in untreated diabetes mellitus (p. 563) and in diabetes insipidus (p. 553), because large amounts of urine are excreted and the patients are dehydrated.

If fluid is not available when one desires it, thirst becomes more and more acute and leads to mental anguish. In fact, prisoners and suspected criminals used to be tortured by depriving them of water and letting them hear the sound of dripping or running water. Insanity may develop under such conditions.

Visceral pain

Visceral afferent impulses concerned with pain are conducted by afferent fibers which travel in the company of sympathetic (thoracolumbar) autonomic fibers. They reach the brain and give rise to somatic reflexes which involve skeletal muscle, visceral reflexes or sensations of pain. An example of the first is the reflex muscular rigidity of the abdominal wall which accompanies appendicitis. An example of the second is the reflex secretion of mucus when the large intestine is distended. An example of the third is pain due to an irritating substance in the stomach.

The impulses that give rise to the sensation of pain require further consideration. The afferent neurons that conduct such impulses from receptors in the viscera to the spinal cord come in contact with central neurons in the spinal cord whose axons form the lateral spinothalamic tracts. Some of these impulses (such as those from serous membranes) have a private pathway to the brain, somewhat like a private telephone line. Other impulses are not so fortunate; being on a "party telephone line," they must share the central neurons with impulses from cutaneous areas. Thus the axons of the central neurons do double duty by conducting impulses from visceral pain receptors and from cutaneous pain receptors to the same areas in the thalamus and the cerebral cortex. This arrangement is called convergence, and sometimes it can lead to confusion as you will see.

In the first case, in which there is a private wire to the cerebral cortex, the pain can be localized accurately as it is projected to the point of stimulation with ease. As an example of this, the patient with pleurisy can point to a certain spot where he experiences a sensation of pain on the chest, and the physician will hear a "friction rub" over this area, which means that the pleural membrane is inflamed in this particular spot.

In the second case, in which there is a party line, the sensation of pain is aroused in the brain as usual. However, it is projected to the cutaneous area from which impulses come to the same area in the brain. This happens since cutaneous pain is of more frequent occurrence than visceral pain, and the brain projects over the well-trod path. This phenomenon is called *referred pain*, which means that pain from a viscus is referred to a related cutaneous area.

The cutaneous areas to which visceral pains are referred are of great diagnostic importance. In angina pectoris (due to lack of oxygen in the heart muscle) the pain is referred to the left shoulder and down the left arm, instead of to the heart, in which the difficulty really lies. In pneumonia the pain often is referred to the abdomen, and in some cases may be confused with appendicitis. Figures 10-9 and 10-10 illustrate the cutaneous areas to which pain from the various viscera is referred.

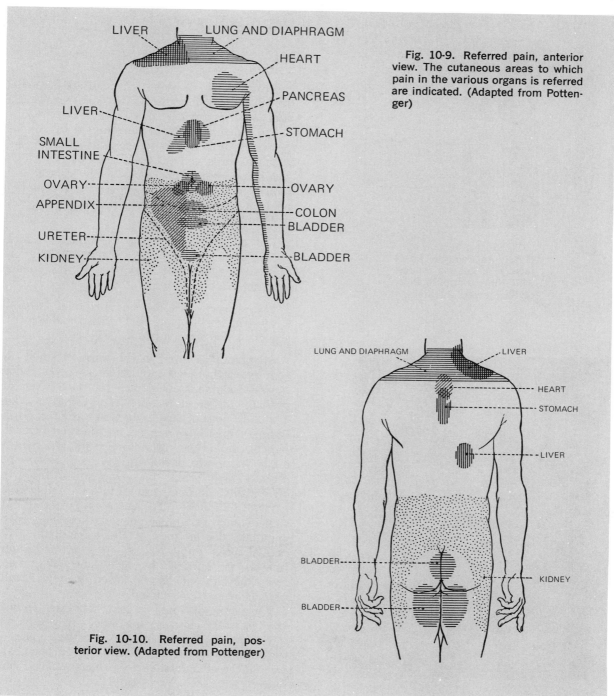

Fig. 10-9. Referred pain, anterior view. The cutaneous areas to which pain in the various organs is referred are indicated. (Adapted from Pottenger)

Fig. 10-10. Referred pain, posterior view. (Adapted from Pottenger) olfactory - smell - in temporal lobe.

SMELL AND TASTE

The sense of smell

Fig. 10-11. Section of olfactory epithelium. Two olfactory cells are shown,
with the axon of one ex-
tending toward the brain.

Receptors for the sense of smell are located in the mucous membrane lining (olfactory epithelium) of the upper part of the nasal cavity.

The olfactory cells are surrounded by supporting cells and glands. The latter secrete fluid which absorbs and dissolves gaseous particles of volatile, odorous substances. Only volatile substances in solution can stimulate the receptors of smell. A section of olfactory epithelium is shown in Figure 10-11.

The afferent pathway is the olfactory or 1st cranial nerve (Fig. 8-15), fibers of which pass through the olfactory foramina of the ethmoid bone to reach the brain.

The sensory area for smell is thought to be located in the hippocampal gyrus on the medial aspect of the temporal lobe (Fig. 8-5).

Adaptation is rapid in the sense of smell. Receptors are fatigued rapidly by persistent odors, but new odors may be detected at once. There are probably different receptors for different odors. The sensations of smell which are aroused during ordinary breathing depend on diffusion from the moving air in the respiratory path into the still air of the upper portion of the nasal cavity. For a really good "whiff," one must sniff to bring the air with its odorous particles into the upper nasal cavity to stimulate the receptors. Irritating substances, such as ammonium salts (smelling salts), stimulate the endings of the trigeminal or 5th cranial nerve and give rise to pain. Respiratory reflexes are initiated by such substances; therefore, they frequently are used to revive individuals who have fainted.

The sense of smell is less important in man than in lower animals, but it does play a part in initiating the flow of certain digestive juices at mealtime. Memory for odors is very keen, and we can recall odors that we have smelled only once.

Olfactory hallucinations (vivid sensations of

Fig. 10-12. Taste buds.

Receptors for taste are the taste buds

smell when no stimulus is present) are a fairly common occurrence in persons who are mentally ill.

The sense of taste

Receptors for the sense of taste are the taste buds, which are located chiefly in papillae on the tongue; there may be a large number of receptors in one papilla. At the top of each bud there is an opening called the taste pore through which solutions enter in order to stimulate the receptors. Taste buds are illustrated in Figure 10-12.

The afferent pathway is the glossopharyngeal or 9th cranial nerve for the posterior third of the tongue, and a branch of the facial or 7th cranial nerve for the anterior two thirds of the tongue.

The sensory area for taste is thought to be located in the area that receives other sensory impulses from the mouth, at the base of the post-central gyrus near the lateral fissure. *where?*

Substances must be in solution to be tasted, and one of the functions of saliva is to dissolve substances so that they may enter the taste pores and stimulate the receptors. Just as the smell of food serves as a stimulus for the secretion of certain digestive juices, so do taste sensations.

There are four primary tastes: sweet, sour, salt, and bitter. The tongue is not equally sensitive to all 4 tastes in all areas. The back of the tongue is more sensitive to bitter, the tip to sweet, the sides to sour and both the tip and the sides to salt. The regions most sensitive to each of the primary tastes are shown in Figure 10-13.

The property which we call the "taste" of certain substances is really the odor; the sense of taste is greatly influenced by the sense of smell. If one has a cold "foods taste differently," since they cannot be smelled.

It has been found, from animal experiments, that taste is important in nutrition, as animals deprived of taste suffer from malnutrition even when all the requirements of an adequate diet are available to them and they choose what they wish. Persons who suffer from diseases of the tongue, injury to the 7th or the 9th cranial nerves or to the sensory area for taste lose this sense.

Fig. 10-13. Regions of the tongue which are most sensitive to the various tastes.

S S S B

odour (so cold food has no odour) influences taste.

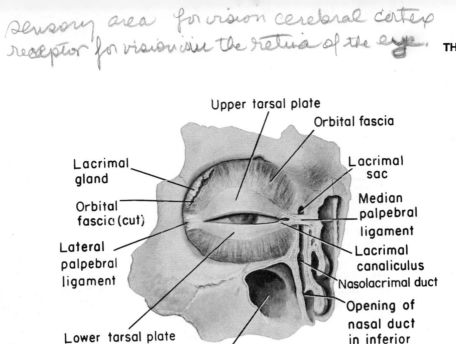

Fig. 10-14. Eyelids and adjacent structures, showing lacrimal gland, sac, canal, nasolacrimal duct and tarsal plates.

VISION

14 Pages

The receptors for vision lie in the retina of the eyeball, the afferent pathway is the optic or 2nd cranial nerve, and the sensory area for vision is located in the occipital lobe of the cerebral cortex. In addition to these basic units, it is imperative to consider the associated structures which make possible the total functioning of the sensory mechanism for vision.

Protection of the eye

The orbit is a cone-shaped cavity whose protective walls are formed by the union of 7 cranial and facial bones: frontal, maxillary, zygomatic, lacrimal, sphenoid, ethmoid and palatine (Fig. 3-10). The eyeball occupies only the anterior one fifth of the orbital cavity, the posterior four fifths of the space being filled with muscles, nerves, blood vessels, the lacrimal gland and a proportionately large amount of adipose tissue which

eyeball 1/5

serves as a protective cushion. Loss of this orbital fat causes the eyeball to present a "sunken" appearance (enophthalmus) as seen in persons who have suffered a severe weight loss during prolonged illness. The posterior three fourths of the eyeball is covered by fascia called the *capsule of Tenon;* the smooth inner surface of this capsule forms a socket in which the eyeball moves.

The palpebrae or eyelids are protective, movable curtains located in front of the eyeball. The space between them is called the *palpebral fissure.* The upper and the lower lids meet at the medial and the lateral angles of the eye; these meeting places are called the inner and the outer canthi. In each lid there is a *tarsus* or plate of dense connective tissue which gives shape to the lid. Modified sebaceous glands, called *meibomian glands,* are associated with the tarsal plate; a *chalazion* is a small tumor of the eyelid, formed by the distention of a meibomian gland with accumulated secretions. The *eyelashes* are hairs which are located at the margins of the eyelids.

[handwritten: Sclera = white of eye]

Sebaceous glands are associated with the follicles of the eyelashes; hordeolum, or sty, is an inflammation of one or more of these glands.

The conjunctiva is the mucous membrane which lines each eyelid and is reflected over a portion of the front part of the eyeball. It is a thin, transparent membrane, containing goblet cells which secrete mucus. When the conjunctiva becomes infected, the condition is called *conjunctivitis* or pink-eye. Drops of silver nitrate are placed in the eyes of new born babies; this is done to prevent the possibility of infection by the gonococcus during delivery through the birth canal of the mother. This treatment is required by law, since blindness follows such infection at birth (ophthalmia neonatorum), and it is essential to prevent such a disaster.

The lacrimal apparatus consists of the lacrimal gland, its ducts and passages. The lacrimal gland resembles an almond in size and shape. A portion of a lacrimal gland is shown in Figure 10-14. The lacrimal gland secretes tears, which are carried to the conjunctival sac through about a dozen short ducts. Tears bathe the anterior surface of the eyeball and keep it moist at all times. They protect the cornea (the transparent structure at the front of the eyeball) which would become cornified like the epidermis of the skin, if exposed to air. The tears also wash away any particles that enter the conjunctival sac. A bactericidal enzyme, lysozyme, in the tears offers protection against certain microorganisms.

Tears normally drain off through the lacrimal canals which begin as small openings, called the lacrimal *punctae,* at the inner canthus. Tears flow into the lacrimal sac and then into the *nasolacrimal duct* which passes downward through a bony canal to open into the lower portion of the nasal cavity (Fig. 10-14). Inflammation and swelling of the nasal mucosa, as when one has a cold, causes obstruction of the nasolacrimal ducts and interferes with the normal drainage of tears; this accounts for the "watering" eyes which accompany a cold. During emotional crises and during irritation of the conjunctiva, tears are produced in such abundance that they overflow and run down the cheeks.

Extrinsic muscles of the eye

Each eye is equipped with 6 tiny muscles which arise from bones of the orbit and insert into the outer coat of the eyeball. Four straight, or rectus muscles rotate the eyeball in the direction indicated by their names (superior, inferior, medial and lateral); 2 oblique muscles, called superior and inferior, serve to rotate the eyeball on its axis. The extrinsic muscles of the eye are described fully on page 143 and illustrated in Figure 5-7.

The levator palpebrae superioris (meaning "lifter of the upper lid") arises from the back of the orbit and passes forward to be inserted into the tarsal plate as shown in Figure 5-7. This muscle draws the upper lid upward and backward.

Coats of the eyeball

[handwritten: Sclera outer]

The eyeball consists of 3 coats or layers of tissue which surround the transparent internal structures. There is an external fibrous layer, a middle vascular layer and an inner layer of nervous tissue. **The fibrous coat** of the eyeball consists of the sclera and the cornea. The sclera, also called the *white of the eye,* is composed of dense fibrous tissue. It is the outer, protective and supporting layer of the eyeball. The location of the sclera is shown in Figure 10-15. Anteriorly, the sclera is modified from a white, opaque membrane to the transparent cornea; the point at which this transition of sclera to cornea occurs is called the *limbus* (meaning "a border"). The cornea is composed of a special kind of dense connective tissue, and no blood vessels are present. The transparent cornea refracts light rays and allows them to enter the eyeball where they ultimately reach the retina.

The vascular coat of the eyeball is heavily pigmented and contains many blood vessels which help to nourish other tissues of the eye. This layer is subdivided into 3 belts or zones. (1) The **choroid** portion lies immediately under the sclera to which it is attached. Anteriorly, the choroid is thickened and modified to form (2) the **ciliary body,** the main mass of which is made up of the *ciliary muscle.* This muscle arises from the sclera

[handwritten margin notes: middle is outer; vascular; liver is nervous.]

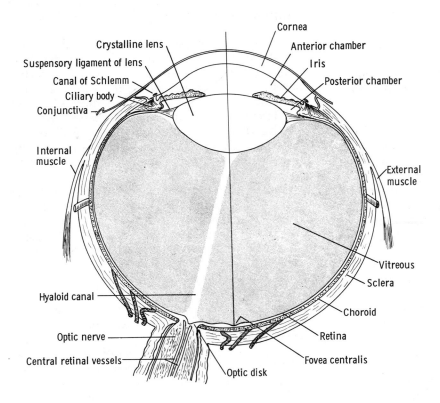

Crystalline lens
Suspensory ligament of lens
Canal of Schlemm
Ciliary body
Conjunctiva
Cornea
Anterior chamber
Iris
Posterior chamber
Internal muscle
External muscle
Vitreous
Sclera
Hyaloid canal
Choroid
Optic nerve
Retina
Central retinal vessels
Fovea centralis
Optic disk

Fig. 10-15. Diagrammatic transverse section of right eyeball. The lateral rectus muscle is labeled "external muscle," and the medial rectus muscle is labeled "internal muscle."

at its junction with the cornea and is inserted into the choroid layer; contraction of the ciliary muscle aids in the adjustment of the eye for vision of near objects. (3) The **iris** is a circular curtain attached at its outer circumference to the ciliary body and suspended between the cornea and the lens; its color varies in different individuals. The round hole in the center of the iris permits the entrance of light rays and is called the *pupil*.

The iris is made up of 2 sheets of smooth muscle, a circular one, called the *sphincter* muscle, and a radial one, called the *dilator* muscle. The function of the iris is to regulate the amount of light entering the eye. The ciliary muscle, the sphincter and the dilator muscles of the iris are called the *intrinsic muscles* of the eye. The ciliary and the sphincter muscles are supplied by the parasympathetic fibers of the oculomotor or 3rd

cranial nerve, and the dilator is supplied by fibers of the sympathetic division of the autonomic nervous system.

The pupil becomes smaller (contraction of sphincter muscle) as the light becomes brighter (light reflex) and as one looks at a near object (accommodation reflex). The latter response is associated with a contraction of the ciliary muscle, which increases the ability of the eye to refract or bend rays of light. The pupil becomes larger (contraction of dilator muscle) in dim light and when looking at a distant object. The latter response is associated with a relaxation of the ciliary muscle.

Around the circumference of the cornea, where it meets the anterior surface of the iris, there is a sort of groove or recess in which the *canal of Schlemm* lies (Fig. 10-15). This is a drainage canal through which the aqueous humor leaves the eyeball and enters the blood.

The nervous coat, or **retina,** is the third and innermost layer of the eyeball. Posteriorly, the retina is continuous with the optic nerve; and anteriorly, it ends a short distance behind the ciliary body in a wavy border called the ora serrata. The retina is composed of two parts, the outer being pigmented and attached to the choroid layer, and the inner consisting of nervous tissue.

The nervous part of the retina is made up of 3 layers of neurons: (1) ganglion cells, (2) bipolar cells and (3) cones and rods. The most sensitive to light are the *cones* and the *rods*, and these are the *receptors* for the sense of sight (Fig. 10-16). There are about 7 million cones and 100 million rods in each human retina. The 2 types of receptors in the retina have different functions to perform. The cones are used for daylight vision, during which we see detail and color of objects. The rods, plus the pigment *visual purple* or rhodopsin associated with them, are used in twilight vision when we see outlines of objects, but no color or detail. The rods are very sensitive to movements of objects in the field of vision. Vitamin A (p. 456) is essential for the synthesis of visual purple in the rods; a deficiency of this vitamin may result in poor vision in dim light (night blindness). A more serious impairment of vision may follow a separation of the retinal layer from the choroid; this condition is known as *detached retina.*

AFTER-IMAGES are long in vision. There are 2 types: (1) After-images which appear in the same color as the original stimulus are called *positive* after-images. A positive after-image can be brought to the attention by fixing the gaze on an electric light bulb for a few seconds and then closing the eyes, the after-image of the bulb appears in the same color as the stimulus. (2) *Negative* after-images are those which appear in a color complementary to the original stimulus. To produce a negative after-image, fix the gaze on a colored object for about 20 seconds and then look at a white surface. The after-image appears in the complementary color.

Fig. 10-16. Cone and rod cells of human retina; the receptors for vision.

In the eye the term "adaptation" refers to the changes which occur in the retina when going from a lighted into a darkened room, or vice versa. You have all noted the difficulty in vision when you first step out into the sunlight when the ground is covered with snow, or when you first enter a dark movie theater after passing through a brightly lighted lobby. The sensitivity of the retina can be adjusted to correspond to the intensity of illumination, but it requires a little time. Adaptation is a very remarkable property of the retina; the range of adaptation, with the corresponding change in sensitivity of the retina, is far beyond that of any physical instrument. A dark-adapted retina is 10 billion times as sensitive to light as a light-adapted retina.

As yet, there is no completely satisfactory theory of color vision, but the Young-Helmholtz theory probably is the most widely accepted by physiologists. According to this theory, there are 3 fundamental color sensations: red, green and violet. It is assumed that there are 3 kinds of cones, each containing a different photochemical substance. Each type of cone gives rise to impulses which travel over specific fibers to definite areas of the visual center in the occipital lobe. When the 3 types of cones are stimulated equally, a sensation of white results. When there is no stimulation a sensation of black is experienced. Other color sensations are due to the combined stimulation of the 3 types of cones to different degrees.

We know that if we pass white light (sunlight) through a prism, it is divided into a band of colors which is called the *spectrum* (red, orange, yellow, green, blue, blue-green and violet). The red rays are the longest, violet the shortest. Spectral colors may be arranged in pairs called *complementary* colors which produce white light when they are blended. Red and blue-green are complementary colors; also yellow and violet.

Some persons are color-blind—they may be blind to one, two or all colors. Color blindness is more common in men than in women. Men who are employed in certain occupations, such as those requiring recognition of signal lights, must be tested for color blindness before receiving their appointments.

Retinal Examination. In order to see the retina, reflected light is essential. The reason we do not see retinae when we look at people's eyes is that we are in our own light. We need a device that will enable us to throw more light into the eye and yet not cut it off as it is reflected to the source. The ophthalmoscope is such an instrument, being a mirror with a hole in it. The mirror enables the observer to throw more light into the eye, and the hole permits rays reflected from the patient's retina to enter the observer's eye. Near the center of the retina, as one looks into the eyeball, there is a small, oval, yellowish spot called the *macula lutea*. The center of the macula lutea is depressed, due to thinning of the retina. This region is called the *fovea centralis* (Fig. 10-15) and is the area of most acute vision or of highest visual acuity in which cones, only, are present.

A short distance to the nasal side of the fovea centralis a pale pink, disklike papilla is seen. This papilla is called the *optic disk* or "blind spot" since there are no receptors in this area. The optic disk is the point of exit of the optic nerve from the eyeball; it is a relatively weak area, since it is not covered by sclera. If the intraocular pressure rises, the disk becomes cup-shaped as it is pushed backward; this condition is called *cupped disk*.

The blood supply for the retina enters the eyeball as the central artery of the retina, a branch of the ophthalmic, which in turn is a branch of the internal carotid artery (p. 354). The central artery enters the eyeball in the center of the optic disk and divides into many branches. The appearance of the central artery and its branches also contributes valuable information to the examiner of the retina. Such pathologic conditions as high blood pressure and diabetes mellitus are accompanied by typical changes in the retinal vessels. A rise in the intracranial pressure (as with a brain tumor) may obstruct the flow of blood away from the eyeball through the central vein, causing a reddening and swelling of the optic disks; this condition is referred to as *papilledema* or *choked disk*. The appearance of a normal retina is shown in Figure 10-17 and of a pathologic retina in Figure 10-18.

Fig. 10-17. Normal fundus, as seen in retinal examination with an ophthalmoscope.

Fig. 10-18. Pathologic fundus, as seen in retinal examination. Chronic glomerulonephritis. Choked disk, macula not evident, edema, "cotton wool" patches, petechial and flame-shaped hemorrhages and interrupted arteriovenous crossings. (Minneapolis General Hospital)

Transparent internal structures of the eye

Before reaching the retina, a light ray must pass through the cornea, the aqueous humor, the crystalline lens and the vitreous body.

The crystalline lens is suspended from the inner surface of the ciliary body by circular ligaments called the *suspensory ligaments* (or zonule of Zinn). The function of the lens is to bend rays of light in order to focus an image on the retina. As one ages the crystalline lens loses water, becomes denser and less elastic and is less able to bend rays of light.

A *cataract* is an opacity of the lens or its capsule; light rays cannot pass through the lens to reach the retina, and consequently, the lens must be removed. After the lens is removed, corrective lenses must be used in order to see objects clearly. Opacity of the cornea likewise prevents light rays from reaching the retina, but this cannot be aided by use of lenses.

The space bounded by the lens and the iris, behind, and the cornea, in front is called the *anterior chamber*. The space back of the iris is called the *posterior chamber* and is bounded in front by the iris, on the sides by the ciliary body and toward the center and the back by the lens and the suspensory ligaments (Fig. 10-15). Both the anterior and the posterior chambers are filled with a fluid called **aqueous humor**. The aqueous humor is formed constantly by filtration from the capillaries in part of the ciliary body and is drained off into the blood through the canal of Schlemm. The amount must be constant to maintain a constant pressure inside the eyeball (intraocular pressure). So long as the amount of aqueous humor and the intraocular pressure remain normal, the proper shape of the eyeball is maintained. Intraocular pressure is between 20 and 25 mm. Hg. If there is interference with the drainage of aqueous humor, excess fluid accumulates within the eyeball and increases intraocular pressure, causing pain and interference with vision. This condition is called *glaucoma*.

The space posterior to the lens is filled with the **vitreous body**, which has the consistency of jelly; it helps to support the retina and to maintain the shape of the eyeball. Loss of vitreous is a serious complication of eye surgery, since it may result in detached retina; unlike aqueous humor, vitreous cannot be reproduced by the person.

Comparison of the eye with a camera

The human eye and a camera have many features in common (Fig. 10-19). Each has a *lens* which brings rays of light to a focus and produces an image of external objects. Each has a surface which is sensitive to light; this is the *retina* in the human eye and the *film* or plate in the camera. The *eyelids* and the *shutter* are comparable. The *iris* and the adjustable *diaphragm* are comparable; by these devices the amount of light that reaches the sensitive surface may be regulated. In the camera there is a mechanism for changing the distance between the lens and the film for taking pictures of objects at different distances from the camera. Since there is no such mechanism in the human eye, the shape of the lens must be changed for clear vision of objects at different distances from the eye.

Sensory pathway for vision

Nerve impulses initiated by the rods and the cones are transmitted to the bipolar cells and thence to the deep-lying ganglion cells, the axons of which form the **optic nerve**. On entering the cranial cavity the optic nerves meet to form the **optic chiasma**, beyond which they are continued as the **optic tracts**. Visual impulses are ultimately transmitted to the occipital lobe of the cerebral cortex.

The optic nerve fibers from the medial halves of the retinae cross to the opposite side of the brain in the optic chiasma, while those from the lateral halves of the retinae remain uncrossed. As a result of this the fibers from the right half of each eye carry impulses to the right occipital lobe, and fibers from the left half of each eye carry impulses to the left occipital lobe. The optic chiasma is shown by diagram in Figure 10-20.

Injury to one optic nerve produces total blindness in the corresponding eye. Lesions of the optic

LENS HOLDER
(SUSPENSORY LIGAMENT)

DIAPHRAGM
(IRIS)

APERTURE
(PUPIL)

LENS
(CRYSTALLINE LENS)

PLATE
(RETINA)

Fig. 10-19. Comparable parts
of camera and eye.

SUSPENSORY LIGAMENT

IRIS

PUPIL

CRYSTALLINE LENS

RETINA

RETINA

OPTIC NERVE

OPTIC CHIASMA

HYPOPHYSIS

OPTIC TRACT
LATER
GENICULATE
BODY
PULVINAR OF
THALAMUS

SUPERIOR COLLICULUS

OCCIPITAL CORTEX

Fig. 10-20. Diagram of optic
pathways. The crossing of the
fibers from the medial half of
each retina is shown.

Fig. 10-21. Path of a ray of light passing from air into water. To construct the path, S is taken as the center, and two arcs with radii of 4 and 3 are drawn. A line is drawn from the point at which the ray crosses the inner arc, to the outer arc, parallel to the perpendicular, i to o. The line which connects o and S is projected into the water; this is the path of the ray after refraction. It is bent toward the perpendicular as it enters the denser medium.

Fig. 10-22. Path of a ray of light passing from water into air. Arcs are drawn as in Fig. 10-21. A line is drawn from the point at which the ray crosses the outer arc to the inner, parallel to the perpendicular, o to i. The line which is projected through i and S indicates the path of the ray after refraction. It is bent away from the perpendicular as it enters the less dense medium.

chiasma (e.g., pressure from an enlarged pituitary gland) most commonly involve the central area of fiber crossing and result in "tunnel vision" (bitemporal hemianopsia) as the two temporal visual fields are lost.

Binocular vision

Binocular vision refers to vision with 2 eyes. The advantages of binocular vision are (1) a larger visual field and (2) a perception of depth or "stereoscopic" vision. There is a slight difference in the images on the 2 retinae; there is a right-eyed picture on the right retina and a left-eyed picture on the left retina. It is as if the same landscape were photographed twice, with the camera in 2 positions a slight distance apart. The 2 images blend in consciousness and give us an impression of depth or solidity. In order to experience stereoscopic vision the images must fall on "corresponding or identical" points in the 2 retinae. Only under this condition is there blending in consciousness. Otherwise, one sees 2 views or dissimilar pictures, a condition which is called *diplopia* or double vision.

If images are to be brought to identical points on the 2 retinae, the movements of the 2 eyes must be perfectly coordinated, the pupils of equal size and the lenses of the same thickness so that there may be uniform bending and focusing of light rays on the retinae.

The convergence of visual axes occurs as the eyeballs turn slightly toward one another and enable us to focus on objects which are close at hand. For distant vision the eyeballs are perfectly parallel. *Strabismus* is a deviation of one of the eyes from its proper direction due to a muscle defect or a lack of coordination in the movements of the 2 eyes. Sometimes it is corrected by prismatic lenses; otherwise operative procedures are performed to correct the muscle at fault.

The size of the pupil regulates the amount of light that can enter the eye. For near vision the sphincter muscle of the iris contracts, decreasing the size of the pupil and reducing the amount of light that enters the eye. When looking at distant objects the radial muscle fibers of the iris cause

bent = refracted

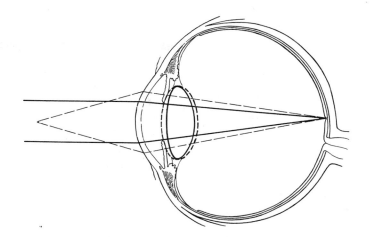

Fig. 10-23. Accommodation. The solid lines represent rays of light from a distant object, and the dotted lines represent rays from a near object. The lens is flatter for the former and more convex for the latter. In each case the rays of light are brought to a focus on the retina.

a dilatation of the pupil and permit the entry of more light.

The refraction of light rays enables them to be focused on the retinae. When a ray of light passes from a medium of one density into a medium of a different density, such as from air to glass, the ray is bent or refracted. If the ray passes into a denser medium it is bent toward the perpendicular, as shown in Figure 10-21. If it passes into a less dense medium it is bent away from the perpendicular as shown in Figure 10-22.

Accommodation is the process by which the strength of the lens is changed for viewing objects close at hand or far away. This is brought about by contraction of the ciliary muscle, by which the choroid coat is pulled forward and the tension on the suspensory ligaments of the lens is lessened. As a result of this, the tension on the capsule of the crystalline lens is lessened, and, since the lens is elastic, it bulges or becomes more convex, thus giving it more bending power when we are looking at near objects. Conversely, for distant vision the ciliary muscle is relaxed, the suspensory ligaments are taut, and the capsule flattens the lens (thereby decreasing its bending power). The change in the lens for distant and near vision is indicated in Figure 10-23.

Failure of any of the aforementioned processes may result in defective vision. Since so many of us need glass lenses to correct defects in our eyes and to enable us to see objects near at hand when we grow older, we should understand a few fundamental facts about glass lenses. The principal types are: (1) convex or positive lenses, which converge or bring together rays of light *bend.* and add to the refractive power of the human eye; (2) concave or negative lenses, which diverge or spread apart rays of light and decrease the refractive power of the human eye; and (3) cylindrical lenses, which equalize refractive power in both the vertical and the horizontal planes, if we happen to have a spoon-shaped cornea instead of a spherical one, as is the case in *astigmatism.* A convex lens is shown in Figure 10-24 and a concave lens in Figure 10-25. The change that occurs in the size and the position of an image when the distance of the object from the lens is changed is illustrated in Figure 10-26. You will note that the image is inverted; images on the retina are inverted likewise, and it is by experience that we see them right side up.

If the refractive power of the eye is too great or the eyeball too long, the images fall in front of the retina; this condition is called *myopia* or near-

BICONVEX LENS

OBJECT

SECONDARY RAY

REAL
IMAGE

PARALLEL RAY AFTER REFRACTION

Fig. 10-24. Formation of an image by a biconvex lens.

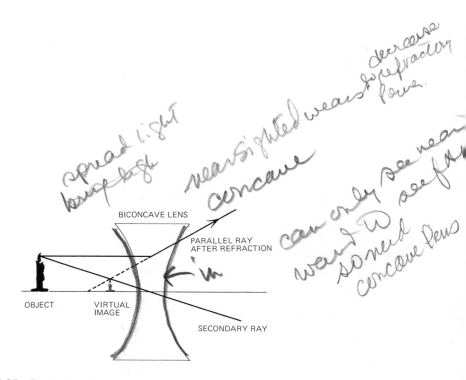

BICONCAVE LENS

PARALLEL RAY
AFTER REFRACTION

OBJECT

VIRTUAL
IMAGE

SECONDARY RAY

Fig. 10-25. Formation of an image by a biconcave lens.

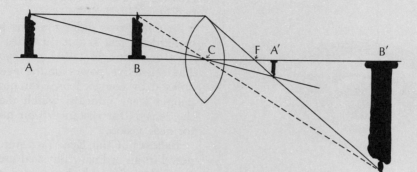

Fig. 10-26. Change in position and size of the image with change in position of the object. When the object is at A, the image is at A'; when the object is moved to B, the position of the image shifts to B'. $1/A + IA' = 1/F$, or 1/distance of object from the lens plus 1/distance of image from the lens equals 1/focal distance of the lens.

Fig. 10-27. (A) Hyperopia and correction. (B) Myopia and correction.

sightedness. The refractive power must be decreased by a concave or negative lens, as illustrated in Figure 10-27.

If the refractive power of the eye is too weak or the eyeball too short, the images fall back of the retina; this condition is called *hyperopia* (farsightedness). The refractive power must be increased by a convex or positive lens, as illustrated in Figure 10-27.

As one grows older the lens loses its elasticity or hardens, just as one's arteries harden with age. This condition is called *presbyopia* or old-sight. The refractive power of the eye needs to be increased by convex lenses for near vision. Elderly people wear bifocals, which means that part of the lens is for distant vision and the remainder for near vision.

Reflexes of the Eye. Two pupillary reflexes are noted in an ordinary physical examination. One is the *light reflex,* which is tested by flashing a light into the eye and determining if the pupil becomes smaller. The second is the *accommodation reflex,* which is tested by having the patient shift the gaze from a distant to a near object, during which the pupil should become smaller. Figure 10-28 illustrates these reflexes. In syphilis of the CNS the light reflex may be lost, and the accommodation reflex retained; such a condition is called an *Argyll Robertson pupil.* The corneal and conjunctival reflexes are tested by touching these surfaces; the response is a blinking of the eye.

Effects of Drugs on the Size of the Pupil. *Homatropine,* which is used in eye examinations, makes the pupil larger by inhibiting the passage of impulses over the visceral efferent fibers of the oculomotor nerve. This means that the sphincter muscle of the iris and the ciliary muscle are paralyzed temporarily. *Epinephrine* and *cocaine* both lead to a dilatation of the pupil also, but through stimulation of the dilator or radial muscle of the iris. *Pilocarpine* leads to a constriction of the pupil by stimulation of the sphincter muscle of the iris. *Morphine* causes the pupil to become exceedingly small; it is called a "pin-point" pupil. The effects of various drugs on the pupils are illustrated in Figure 10-29. Drugs that dilate the pupils are

Fig. 10-28. Light and accommodation reflexes. The pupil above is constricted, as when exposed to light or in looking at a near object; the one below is dilated, as when light is withdrawn or in looking at a distant object.

NORMAL

MORPHINE

PILOCARPINE

ADRENALIN
ATROPINE
COCAINE

Fig. 10-29. Reaction of pupil to drugs. In chronic morphinism, the pupil approaches a pinpoint; it is moderately constricted after pilocarpine; epinephrine (Adrenalin), atropine and cocaine lead to a dilatation.

called "mydriatics," and those that constrict the pupils are called "miotics."

Optical Judgments. Judgments of size and distance depend mainly on the size of the retinal images, the amount of detail seen, the color, the clearness of the outlines and the relative positions of the 2 eyes.

Optical illusions are common experiences. An illusion is a false interpretation of a sensation. Examples of optical illusions are: (1) objects appear larger on a foggy night, since the outlines are hazy, and the objects appear to be farther away than they really are; (2) lines with obtuse angles at the ends appear longer than equally long lines with acute angles at the ends. Some optical illusions are illustrated in Figure 10-30.

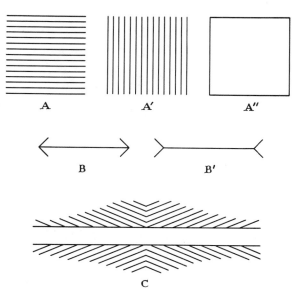

Fig. 10-30. Optical illusions. A, A' and A" are equal squares; A appears taller than A', and A" appears smaller than A or A'. Lines B and B' are of equal length; B' seems longer than B, because of the obtuse angle. (Muller-Lyer) In C, the horizontal lines are parallel, but they do not appear so. (Hering)

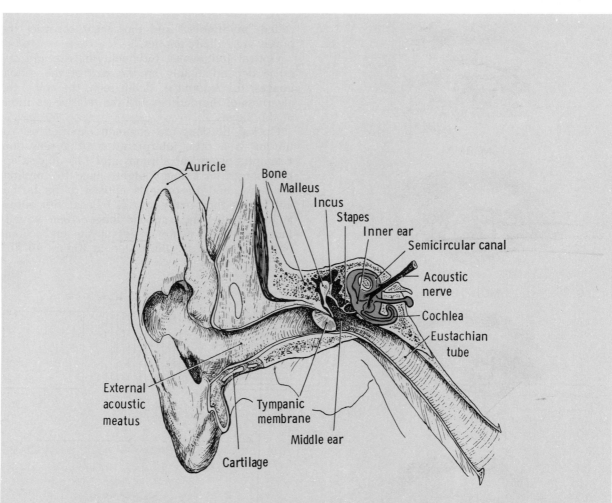

Fig. 10-31. Diagram of the ear, showing the external, middle and internal subdivisions. The perilymph is shown in blue, and the endolymph in red.

HEARING AND POSITION SENSE

Hearing is the sense by which sounds are appreciated; position sense refers to the orientation of the head in space and the movement of the body through space, its balance and equilibrium.

Hearing is called the "watchdog" of the senses; it is the last to disappear when one falls asleep and the first to return when one awakens. Medical personnel should remember this fact and guard their remarks when a patient is going to sleep or when he is "going under" or "coming out" of anesthesia.

There are two sets of receptors in the ear: one set is concerned with hearing and the other with position sense. The 8th cranial or acoustic nerve serves as the sensory pathway to the temporal lobe of the cerebral cortex. Each ear consists of 3 distinct divisions: the external, middle and inner "ears" as illustrated in Figure 10-31.

The external ear

The external portion of the ear, which receives sound waves, consists of the auricle and the external acoustic meatus. The **auricle** or *pinna* is composed of cartilage, covered with skin. To some extent it serves to collect sound waves and direct them into the external meatus, but this function is of limited, if any, value in man. It is of greater importance in some of the lower animals.

The external acoustic meatus (auditory canal) extends inward, forward and downward, from the auricle to the tympanic membrane (ear drum), a distance of approximately 1½ inches. This is an important fact for one to remember when using a stethoscope, since the ear pieces of that instrument are shaped to fit the normal curvatures of the cylindrical ear canal. The external acoustic meatus is formed partly by bone and partly by cartilage and is lined with skin. Ceruminous glands in the area secrete the brown ear wax or *cerumen* which normally serves as a protective agent. However, excessive amounts of this wax may block the ear canal and exert pressure on the tympanic membrane; this pressure is a common cause of earache and may even result in tempo-

rary deafness. In such cases, the removal of cerumen should be done by a doctor who gently syringes the canal with warm water.

The middle ear

The middle ear or tympanic cavity transmits sound waves from the external to the inner ear. Its lateral wall is formed mainly by the **tympanic or drum membrane** (ear drum) that lies at the end of the external acoustic meatus. This thin, fibrous membrane is covered with skin on its lateral aspect, but medially it is covered with mucous membrane which is continuous with that lining the entire middle ear. The tympanic membrane is so attached that it can vibrate freely with all audible sound waves that enter the meatus.

The middle ear is a tiny, irregular cavity in the temporal bone. It is filled with air which reaches it from the upper part of the throat (nasopharynx) by way of the **auditory** or **eustachian tube.** Posteriorly, the middle ear communicates with the *mastoid air cells* of the temporal bone. The mucous membrane which lines the middle ear is continuous with that of the pharynx and the mastoid air cells; thus it is possible for infection to travel along the mucous membrane from the nose or the throat to the middle ear (otitis media) and to the mastoid air cells (mastoiditis). When pus forms in the middle ear, the membrane should be lanced (myringotomy) to allow drainage and prevent the backing up of pus into the mastoid air cells. Early treatment is advisable for any middle-ear infection. If the membrane is not lanced it will rupture spontaneously, and when it heals the scar will be large and irregular instead of small and regular as occurs after lancing. The danger of permitting the infection to spread to the mastoid air cells lies in the nearness of these cells to the venous sinuses and the meninges of the brain.

The auditory tube serves to equalize the pressure in the middle ear with atmospheric pressure. It opens during swallowing and yawning. It tends to remain closed when the pressure is greater outside, as during rapid descent in an airplane. In some persons, after frequent infection, the tube is closed permanently by adhesions, and the hear-

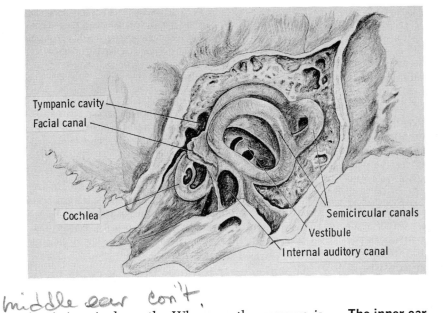

Tympanic cavity
Facial canal

Cochlea

Semicircular canals
Vestibule
Internal auditory canal

Fig. 10-32. Right temporal bone. Upper part of petrous portion has been removed to show bony labyrinth.

[handwritten: middle ear con't,]

ing is impaired greatly. Whenever the pressure is unequal on the 2 sides of the tympanic membrane it is not free to vibrate with sound waves. Sometimes air is forced into the middle ear, by means of a bulb, to break down adhesions.

A chain of 3 tiny, movable bones extends across the cavity of the middle ear. Named according to their shape, these bones are the **malleus** (hammer), **incus** (anvil) and **stapes** (stirrup); their function is to transmit sound waves from the tympanic membrane to the inner ear. The malleus is attached by its handle to the tympanic membrane, and its head articulates with the incus which in turn joins the stapes. The footpiece of the stapes fits into the **oval** or **vestibular window**, a small opening in the wall between the middle and the inner ears. Freely movable joints between these bones contribute to an ingenious little lever system which converts the vibrations of the tympanic membrane to intensified thrusts of the stapes against the fluid of the inner ear. However, the inner ear is protected from loud noise by two small muscles. The *tensor tympani* tightens the tympanic membrane, thus restricting its ability to vibrate; and the *stapedius* tends to pull the stapes away from the oval window, thus reducing the intensity of its thrusts into the inner ear.

[handwritten margin note: Anvil bigger than a hammer.]

The inner ear

The inner ear, or fluid-filled *labyrinth,* contains the receptors for hearing and for position sense. It consists of a bony labyrinth which contains a membranous labyrinth.

The bony labyrinth consists of a series of tiny canals and cavities which have been hollowed out of the petrous portion of the temporal bone. They contain a watery fluid which is called *perilymph.* There are 3 bony divisions: the *cochlea,* the *vestibule* and the *semicircular canals.*

Within the bony labyrinth lies the **membranous labyrinth,** a series of fluid-filled sacs and tubes which have approximately the same shape as the surrounding bony walls. There are 4 membranous structures: the *cochlear duct* (in the cochlea), the *utricle* and the *saccule* (in the vestibule) and the *semicircular ducts* (in the semicircular canals). The fluid which fills these membranous structures is called *endolymph.* The general structure of the inner ear might roughly be compared to an automobile tire and its tube. The tough outer casing of the tire is comparable to the bony labyrinth and the rubber inner tube to the membranous labyrinth. For the position of the bony labyrinth in the temporal bone, see Figure 10-32.

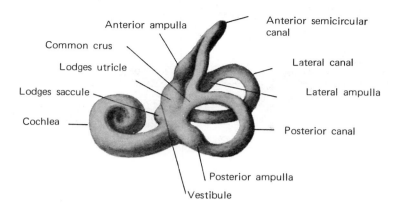

Fig. 10-33. Cast of right bony labyrinth, medial aspect. ×2.

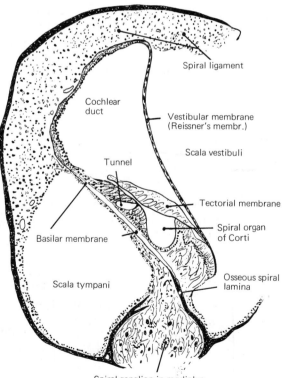

Fig. 10-34. Drawing of a portion of the bony cochlea. The relation of the cochlear duct to scalae vestibuli and tympani is shown. The basilar, tectorial and Reissner's membranes are shown. (Modified from Ham, A. W.: Histology, ed. 2, Philadelphia, Lippincott)

receptor end of organ for hearing—spiral organ of Corti, in cochlea in inner ear.

Labels on figure: Outer hair-cells · Inner hair-cells · Membrana tectoria · Basilar membrane · Outer pillar · Nerve fibers · Tunnel · Inner pillar · Spiral ganglion

Fig. 10-35. Section of organ of Corti from human cochlea. ×375.

The **cochlea** is shaped like a snail shell, as shown in Figure 10-33. It is a bony tube which winds spirally around a central pillar of bone called the modiolus. The membranous **cochlear duct** resembles a lopsided triangle as it lies within the bony cochlea (Fig. 10-34). It extends like a shelf across the bony canal to the sides of which it is attached. The portion of the bony canal above the cochlear duct is called the *scala* (meaning "stairway") *vestibuli,* and the portion below is called the *scala tympani.*

The cochlear duct connects with the inner wall of the bony canal by the osseous spiral lamina, and with the outer wall by the spiral ligament. The roof of the cochlear duct is thin and is called *Reissner's membrane.* The floor is composed of the *basilar membrane.* Resting on this basilar membrane is the **spiral organ of Corti,** the essential receptor end organ for hearing (Fig. 10-35). It is a very complicated structure, consisting of a supporting framework on which rest the important *hair cells,* so called because each one of them bears about 20 fine hairs on its free border. The *tectorial membrane* extends from the osseous spiral lamina and rests like a lid on the aforementioned hairs; vibration of the organ of Corti results in the hairs being bent against the fixed tectorial membrane. Nerve impulses initiated by the stimulated hair cells pass over dendrites whose cell bodies are located in the spiral ganglion in the modiolus (Fig. 10-34). Axons extending from this ganglion unite to form the *cochlear branch* of the 8th cranial or acoustic nerve.

In summary, sound waves which enter the ex-ternal acoustic meatus cause the tympanic membrane to vibrate. These vibrations are transferred across the middle ear by the malleus, the incus and the stapes. Since the stapes fits into the oval window like a piston it can move in and out with each vibration. In the transfer across the middle ear, sound waves are reduced in amplitude but increased in *force* by the lever system of bones. This makes possible the effective transmission of vibrations from air to fluid. However, as the stapes bulges into the fluid-filled vestibule of the inner ear, there must be a corresponding outward bulge, since fluids cannot be compressed; this protective function is assumed by the *round* or *cochlear window,* a small membrane-covered opening in the bony wall just below the oval window.

Each pistonlike thrust of the stapes into the vestibule sends a rippling wave through the perilymph of the inner ear. This sets into motion the basilar membrane and the organ of Corti. The resulting stimulation of hair cells arouses nerve impulses which are transmitted to the center for hearing in the temporal lobe of the cerebral cortex (Fig. 8-5). It is thought that analysis of sound takes place in the cochlea. This means that a certain portion of the basilar membrane and certain hair cells are affected by sound waves of one frequency. Waves of a different frequency set up vibrations in another portion of the basilar membrane.

Sounds differ in pitch (number of vibrations per second), in loudness (amplitude) and in timbre (quality, which is dependent on overtones). Figure

10-36 illustrates 3 sound waves; 2 pitches and 3 degrees of loudness are represented.

An impairment of the sense of hearing is called *deafness.* There are 3 types of deafness: conduction, nerve, and central deafness.

Conduction deafness is caused by interference with the transmission of sound waves through the external or middle ear. For example, excessive amounts of cerumen (p. 50) may block the external acoustic meatus; there may be injury to the tympanic membrane; there may be ankylosis (stiffness of joints) of the bones of the middle ear; the stapes may be bound at the oval window by new growths of bone; or the auditory tube may be closed by adhesions, thus preventing equalization of pressure on the two sides of the tympanic membrane. However, sound waves can be transmitted through the cranial bones to the fluid in the inner ear, and various hearing aids are so constructed as to take advantage of this fact.

Nerve deafness may follow degeneration of the sensory cells in the cochlear duct, tumors involving the cochlear branch of the acoustic nerve, and so on. The hearing of high tones usually is the most impaired.

Central deafness may follow interference with the pathway of nerve impulses to the cerebral cortex, or it may be a manifestation of aphasia. This type of deafness is rare.

The instrument designed to measure one's ability to hear is called the *audiometer.* It is useful in testing hearing in relation to occupational fitness or disability, in school children, in workmen who are subjected to excessive noise in their jobs and in fitting hearing aids.

The sense of hearing is important in learning to speak and in modulating the voice; deaf persons cannot modulate their voices, since they cannot hear them. Children who are born deaf will be mute (unable to speak) unless speech is taught by some channel other than the ear. The sense of sight may be used, by watching the position of the lips and the tongue. It is quite unnecessary and cruel indeed for a child to be compelled to remain mute if his intelligence is sufficient to enable him to speak. Schools for the deaf and training in lip reading are important in preparing deaf persons for occupations in which their handicap does not prevent them from being able to support themselves.

The vestibule is a disklike cave in which float 2 membranous sacs, the utricle and the saccule, each of which is filled with endolymph. On the floor of the *utricle* is a patch of hair cells which constitute the vestibular receptors or maculae acustica. Entangled in the brushlike hairs are tiny particles of calcium carbonate that are called otoliths. Nerve impulses are initiated when the otoliths push or pull on the hairs and bend them in the direction of the pull of gravity. The *vestibular branch* of the acoustic nerve transmits impulses to the cerebral cortex, and we recognize the position of the head in space as it relates to the pull of gravity. The *saccule* has a similar patch of sensory epithelium, but its functions are not yet fully understood.

There are 3 **semicircular canals** in each ear; they are so arranged at right angles to one another that all 3 planes of space are represented (Fig. 10-33). Lying within these bony tunnels are

Fig. 10-36. Three sound waves. Waves A and B have the same pitch, but A has a greater intensity than B. Wave C has a different pitch and is least intense of the three.

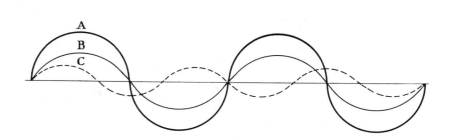

the membranous **semicircular ducts** which loop through semicircles, beginning and ending at the utricle. At one end each duct has a dilatation, the *ampulla*, which contains a patch of hair cells or receptor end organs known as the *cristae acustica*. Movement of the endolymph bends the hairs and sets up impulses in the *vestibular branch* of the acoustic nerve. The cristae are stimulated by sudden movements, or by a change in rate or direction of movement. In other words, whenever movement begins or ends, accelerates or decelerates, or changes in direction, impulses are set up in dendrites of the vestibular nerve.

If a person is rotated in a chair, the endolymph in the semicircular canals is set into motion and stimulates the hair cells. A sense of movement either of self or surroundings (vertigo) occurs, together with a peculiar movement of the eyes called *nystagmus*. Nystagmus consists of a rapid movement of the eyes in one direction and a slow movement in the opposite direction; they appear to oscillate. Nausea may occur. We speak of these sensations which are set up by rotation as motion sickness. Many somatic reflexes accompany rotation; these involve the muscles of the neck, the trunk and the extremities. Visceral reflexes occur, also. There is a fall in blood pressure and a change in heart rate, and the skin becomes pale, all of which involve visceral efferent nerves.

In summary, it may be stated that the semicircular canals are dynamic sense organs; they rouse sensations of starting and stopping movement, changing its speed (either acceleration or deceleration) and direction. They also originate many reflexes which involve skeletal, smooth and cardiac muscles. The utricle is a static sense organ; it gives information regarding the orientation of the head in space, in relation to gravity and sets into action postural and righting reflexes. Injury to the semicircular canals or utricle leads to disturbances in maintaining one's orientation and balance. Vertigo is the most common symptom. Nystagmus is also a common sign of vestibular pathology.

Impulses from the semicircular canals and the utricle are considered to be less important in man than in lower animals, since man uses his eyes to help him maintain equilibrium. However, if he is blind, or even blindfolded, impulses from the vestibular portion of the inner ear assume great importance in orientation in space and in maintaining equilibrium.

Menière's syndrome is a condition in which a person hears buzzing noises in the ears and also has severe attacks of vertigo. During an attack he cannot stand up and may even show rolling movements when lying down. It is caused by disturbances in the inner ear. Various surgical and medical procedures may relieve the distress. The hearing of subjective buzzing, high-pitched noises is called *tinnitus*.

SUMMARY

1. Introduction
   A. Sensory mechanisms
      a. Sense organs or receptors
      b. Afferent pathway to brain
      c. Sensory area in cerebral cortex
      d. All parts must function to give rise to sensation
   B. Characteristics of sensations: Projection, after-image, adaptation, intensity
2. Cutaneous senses
   A. Sense of touch and pressure
      a. Receptors: free nerve endings; corpuscles of Meissner and Vater-Pacini
      b. Pathway: cranial and spinal nerves
      c. Cortex: parietal lobe of cerebrum
   B. Temperature sense
      a. Receptors: cold — Krause; heat — Ruffini
      b. Pathway: cranial and spinal nerves
      c. Cortex: parietal lobe of cerebrum
   C. Somatic pain
      a. Receptors: free nerve endings
      b. Pathway: cranial and spinal nerves
      c. Cortex: parietal lobe of cerebrum (true discrimination of pain)
3. Muscle sense
   A. Proprioceptive or kinesthetic sense; awareness of position of body
   B. Sensory mechanisms

a. Proprioceptors in muscle and tendon
b. Afferent pathway: cranial and spinal nerves
c. Cortex: parietal lobe of cerebrum
4. Visceral afferent system
  A. Stimuli and pathways: distention, spasm, chemical irritants. Fibers travel in cranial and spinal nerves
  B. Reflex control of visceral activity: e.g., heart rate, etc.
  C. Organic sensations: hunger, thirst, nausea, etc.
  D. Visceral pain
    a. Receptors in viscera: afferent fibers travel with sympathetic nerves
    b. Impulses reaching brain may result in somatic or visceral reflexes or pain
    c. Localized pain: neurons have "direct line" to brain
    d. Referred pain: impulses must share relay neurons with somatic areas
5. Sense of smell
  A. Receptors: olfactory epithelium in nasal cavity
  B. Pathway: olfactory or 1st cranial nerve
  C. Cortex: hippocampal gyrus, temporal lobe
6. Sense of taste
  A. Receptors: taste buds on tongue
  B. Pathway: glossopharyngeal (posterior third) and facial (anterior two thirds) nerves
  C. Cortex: at base of postcentral gyrus near lateral fissure of cerebrum
  D. Primary tastes; salt, sweet, sour, and bitter
7. Vision
  A. Protection of eyeball: orbit, palpebrae, tarsus, meibomian glands, eyelashes, conjunctiva, lacrimal apparatus
  B. Extrinsic muscles of eye
    a. Movement of eyeball: recti and obliques
    b. Movement of eyelids: orbicularis oculi and levator palpebrae superioris
  C. Coats of the eyeball
    a. Fibrous: sclera and cornea
    b. Vascular: choroid, ciliary body and iris
    c. Nervous: the retina
      (1) Rods: receptors concerned with twilight vision
      (2) Cones: receptors concerned with daylight and color vision
      (3) Retinal examination with ophthalmoscope reveals: macula lutea, fovea centralis, optic disk and blood vessels
  D. Transparent internal structures of eye: aqueous humor, crystalline lens and vitreous body
  E. Sensory pathway for vision
    a. Rod and cone receptors sensitive to light, initiate impulses which travel over optic nerves
    b. Optic chiasma: crossing point for fibers from medial halves of retinae
    c. Optic tracts: from chiasma to cerebrum
    d. Right occipital cortex receives impulses from right half of each eye, and left cortex receives from left halves
  F. Binocular vision: that with two eyes
    a. Provides larger visual field and depth perception
    b. Images must be brought to identical points on the two retinae
    c. Processes necessary
      (1) Convergence of visual axes
      (2) Regulating size of pupil
      (3) Refraction of light rays
      (4) Accommodation
    d. Defective vision may be corrected by use of glass lenses
      (1) Convex lenses add to refractive power of eye
      (2) Concave lenses decrease refractive power of eye
      (3) Cylindrical lenses equalize refractive power in both vertical and horizontal planes
      (4) Myopia or near-sightedness: eyeball too long or refractive power of eye too great; images fall in front of retina
      (5) Hyperopia or far-sightedness: eyeball too short or refractive power

of eye too weak; images fall back of retina
   (6) Presbyopia: loss of elasticity of lens
   G. Reflexes of eye
      a. Light reflex: pupil becomes smaller when light is flashed in the eye
      b. Accommodation reflex: pupil becomes smaller when gaze is shifted from distant to near object
   H. Effects of drugs on size of pupil
      a. Atropine, epinephrine and cocaine—dilatation of pupil
      b. Pilocarpine and morphine—constriction of pupil
8. Hearing and position sense
   A. External ear
      a. Auricle and external acoustic meatus
      b. Directs sound waves to tympanic membrane
   B. Middle ear
      a. Lateral wall formed by tympanic membrane which vibrates with sound waves
      b. Mucosal lining continuous with that of nasopharynx via eustachian tube
      c. Communicates posteriorly with mastoid air cells
      d. Malleus, incus and stapes transmit sound waves from tympanum to oval window of inner ear; bony lever system
   C. Inner ear or labyrinth
      a. Bony labyrinth consists of cochlea, vestibule and semicircular canals
      b. Membranous labyrinth within bony consists of cochlear duct, utricle, saccule and semicircular ducts
      c. Fluid in bony canals—perilymph; in membranous structures—endolymph
      d. Spiral organ of Corti, within cochlear duct, receptor end organ for hearing
         (1) Hair cells stimulated by movements of perilymph as stapes moves like piston in oval window
         (2) Nerve impulses transmitted over cochlear branch of acoustic nerve to auditory area in temporal lobe of cerebral cortex

      e. Deafness: difficulty in external or middle ear (conduction type), in inner ear (cochlea) or acoustic nerve (nerve type) in cerebrum (central type)
      f. Maculae acustica: vestibular receptors for position of head as it relates to pull of gravity
      g. Cristae acustica: receptor end organs in ampullae of semicircular ducts, stimulated by movement of endolymph during changes in rate or direction of movement
      h. Menière's syndrome due to disturbance in inner ear

PRACTICAL APPLICATIONS AND QUESTIONS

(Encircle the letter of the *best* answer to each of the following questions.)

A. *Mrs. M. M. had an ophthalmologist examine her eyes as a part of her regular yearly physical checkup. This year the doctor told her that she would need to wear glasses because of presbyopia.*

1. Presbyopia occurs in older individuals because
   a. the aging optic nerve no longer can conduct impulses rapidly
   b. there is a loss of elasticity of the lens
   c. there is a lack of coordination of the extrinsic eye muscles
   d. the lens becomes opaque and light cannot pass through it

2. Mrs. M. M. did not object too strenuously to the wearing of glasses. She was thankful to have had good vision thus far. Many of our youngsters have impaired vision. Some of these common defects are:
Strabismus, which is a defect of the
   a. lens
   b. cornea
   c. extrinsic eye muscles
   d. ciliary muscles
Astigmatism, which is a defect of the
   a. optic nerve
   b. occipital lobe of cerebral cortex

c. cornea
d. choroid layer

When light rays are focused behind the retina because an eyeball may be too short, the condition is referred to as *in front*
a. myopia
b. hyperopia
c. diplopia
d. blindness

B. *Mrs. M. M. also had a small amount of cerumen removed from her external ear during her physical checkup. The doctor very gently irrigated the ear as he did not want to injure the tympanic membrane.*

1. The tympanic membrane
a. separates the middle and the internal ears
b. is set into vibration when sound waves enter the external ear
c. is composed mostly of cartilage
d. amplifies sound as it is transmitted through the auditory pathways

2. Deafness that cannot be relieved by the use of a hearing aid would result from
a. damage to the organ of Corti
b. perforation of the tympanic membrane
c. immobility of the joints between the ossicles of the middle ear
d. failure of the stapes to move in the oval window

Auditory pathway is for pressure.

11

BLOOD, TISSUE FLUID AND LYMPH

Each system of the human body plays an important part in maintaining homeostasis in the internal cellular environment, but the movement of blood through the circulatory "subway" system is of fundamental importance. Although blood as a whole normally does not leave the vessels in which it is contained (with the exception of certain female reproductive functions), it still provides an efficient "pick up" and "delivery" service for "customer" cells in every organ of the body. As was stressed in Chapter 2 (pp. 31–37), blood renders this service only while passing through the tiniest vessels of the circuit, the microscopic capillaries. Water and other diffusible substances are able to pass freely back and forth through the capillary walls, thus contributing to the formation of tissue fluid which serves as the "middleman" between capillary "depots" and the neighboring customer cells.

In summary, the maintenance, of homeostasis in the internal cellular environment depends on both blood and tissue fluid for the prompt delivery of supplies and the equally prompt removal of "end products" which result from the metabolic activities of all living cells.

BLOOD

Blood is classified as one of the connective tissues. However, its intercellular substance is a liquid, called plasma, and its cells or corpuscles are not in a fixed position as is the case in other tissues. Blood is circulating constantly through a closed circuit of tubes; it is pumped from the heart into arteries, from the arteries into capillaries, and from the capillaries it flows into veins for return to the heart.

Functions of the blood

The chief function of the blood is to keep the internal cellular environment of body tissues in that state of dynamic equilibrium which is called homeostasis. Various metabolic processes going on at all times within the body tend to change the chemical composition of the internal environment, such as the chemical changes that accompany contraction of muscles, conduction of nerve impulses and the secretion of glands. All of these forms of metabolism use food and oxygen and produce waste products. The circulating blood makes it possible for the various organs to "take these changes in their stride" and yet remain normal.

The blood transports oxygen, from the lungs to the tissues, and carbon dioxide, from the tissues to the lungs to be eliminated. It carries food materials from the intestine to all parts of the body and returns waste to the kidneys to be excreted. The blood distributes the heat produced in active muscles and thus aids in the regulation of body temperature. It transports internal secretions from the glands in which they are produced to the tissues on which each exerts its effects. The buffers (p. 298) in the blood help to maintain acid-base balance. The blood also is concerned with immunity to disease and in protecting the body against invading bacteria.

Characteristics of blood

The color of whole blood (plasma and cells) is perhaps its most striking characteristic. With only one exception, arterial blood is a bright scarlet color due to its high oxygen content, and venous blood is a very dark red due to a lower oxygen content; the exception to this statement involves the pulmonary arteries and veins (in which the colors are reversed), since they carry blood to and from the lung capillaries for the elimination of carbon dioxide and the pick-up of oxygen.

The quantity of circulating blood varies with the size of the person, the total volume being approximately 7 per cent of the body weight. For example, if you weigh 100 lbs. you have about 7 lbs. of blood or 2.6 quarts (1 lb. of blood being equal to about 0.37 qt.).

The viscosity of blood refers to its resistance to flow. It is thick and sticky, and it normally flows with difficulty. It has been found that the viscosity of whole blood is about 5 times as great as that of water. Part of the viscosity is due to the cells and part to the proteins of the plasma. When either of these factors is altered, the viscosity changes. For example, in certain diseases, such as malaria, red cells tend to stick together and to form clumps in the vessels. These clumps make it much more difficult for the blood to

Fig. 11-1. Wintrobe tube. When blood is prevented from coagulating and allowed to stand undisturbed in this tube for 1 hour, the corpuscles begin to settle out, and a clear layer of plasma may be seen above the corpuscles. The depth of the plasma is read on the scale at the left, in millimeters (1 cm. = 10 mm.); this is called the sedimentation index. Then the tube is centrifuged; this packs the corpuscles. The height of the corpuscle layer is read on the scale at the right; this is called the cell volume. As drawn, the cell volume (hematocrit) is 45 per cent. The Wintrobe tube thus serves a double function as a sedimentation tube and as a hematocrit tube.

circulate; therefore, its speed of circulation is slow. This thick, highly viscous blood with its clumped cells is called *sludged blood*. Human beings are examined for the presence of sludge by looking at the capillaries of the conjunctiva with a special microscope.

Specific gravity refers to the weight of blood compared with that of water. The specific gravity of water is taken as 1.00 (1 cc. of water weighing 1 Gm. at 4° C). The specific gravity of whole blood is between 1.055 and 1.065, with an average of 1.060 which means that 1 cc. of whole blood weighs 1.060 Gm.

The specific gravity of plasma is between 1.028

and 1.032. The cells are much heavier than the plasma. If clotting of blood is prevented, the cells tend to settle out, or sink to the bottom of a tube, as blood stands. They have no opportunity to settle out in the body, as the blood is kept moving in the vessels due to the pumping action of the heart.

The speed with which cells sink to the bottom of a tube is called the *sedimentation rate* or *index* (Fig. 11-1). Expressed in millimeters per hour, the sedimentation rate normally ranges from 4 to 10 mm. per hour (Wintrobe); it depends on the condition of the blood and the general state of health of the individual. For example, the sedimentation rate is increased in acute infectious processes.

The reaction or pH of blood is slightly alkaline,

the average figure being 7.4 under normal conditions. This pH is maintained within a remarkably narrow range (7.35 to 7.45) despite great fluctuations in the quantities of acid and base which are ingested in food, and equally great fluctuations in the amount of acid produced during metabolic activities in the tissues. The maintenance of optimal pH, or *acid-base balance,* is greatly facilitated by the presence of buffer systems in the blood.

Buffers are chemical substances that resist changes in the pH of a solution when an acid or a base is added to it. In the body most buffers occur in pairs, consisting of substances that are weakly acid and salts of those substances. These chemical "partners" can react with relatively strong acids, or bases, and replace them with less

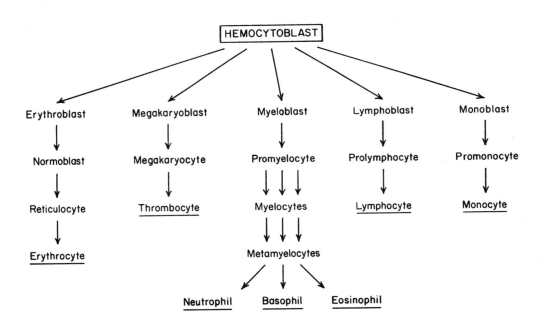

Fig. 11-2. Diagrammatic summary illustrating orderly development of erythrocytes, thrombocytes and leukocytes from primary cell or "forefather" called hemocytoblast (stem cell).

harmful substances, which in turn can be eliminated more easily by the body. Since variable amounts of both acids and bases are constantly entering the blood stream, buffers are of primary importance in maintaining the proper ratio of hydrogen (H^+) and hydroxyl (OH^-) ions in the body. For example, a buffer of great importance is basic *sodium bicarbonate* ($NaHCO_3$) and its weakly acid partner *carbonic acid* (H_2CO_3). To illustrate the principle of buffer action, let us add hydrochloric acid (HCl) and sodium hydroxide ($NaOH$) to a solution that contains the aforementioned buffer pair:

$$\frac{H_2CO_3}{NaHCO_3}$$

(1) $NaHCO_3 + HCl \rightarrow NaCl + H_2CO_3$. Note that the chloride ion (Cl^-) of the HCl is replaced by the bicarbonate ion (HCO_3^-). In this way the relatively strong hydrochloric acid is buffered to form ordinary table salt ($NaCl$) and weak carbonic acid (H_2CO_3).

(2) $H_2CO_3 + NaOH \rightarrow NaHCO_3 + H_2O$. In this case, a strong base is converted to harmless sodium bicarbonate and water.

This particular buffer pair is just one of many in the body fluids, and they all play a vital role in preserving homeostasis.

In addition to the blood buffer systems, maintenance of optimal pH in the body fluids requires also the specialized services of the lungs and the kidneys; the role of these organs in the maintenance of acid-base balance is described on pages 446 and 535, respectively.

Blood structure and formation

Whole blood consists of the liquid *plasma* in which are suspended the microscopic *formed elements*. Plasma constitutes a little more than half of the blood (53 to 58%); it is made up of approximately 90 per cent water and 10 per cent dissolved solids. The formed elements are the erythrocytes or red blood cells, the leukocytes or white blood cells, and the thrombocytes or blood platelets; these elements constitute a little less than half of the blood (42 to 47%).

Fig. 11-3. Human blood corpuscles. Two leukocytes are noted among the red corpuscles; most of the latter are grouped in rouleaux (resembling a roll of coins). × 625.

Hemopoietic tissue is a kind of connective tissue that is highly specialized for both the production of new blood cells and the removal of those which are old and worn out. To keep the total number of cells fairly constant, new ones must be added to the blood each day to replace the old ones which are removed. Hemopoietic tissue is found in red bone marrow and in organs of the lymphatic system (p. 379). The primary cell or "forefather" of all types of formed elements is the *hemocytoblast;* for example, this cell is able to develop into the precursor of a red cell, a white cell or a blood platelet according to the needs of the body (Fig. 11-2).

The erythrocytes

The red cells of the blood are called erythrocytes, a term derived from the Greek words *erythros* (red) and *kytos* (cell). They are also referred to as red corpuscles (meaning "little bodies"), a term that is technically preferable to "cells," since mature erythrocytes do not have nuclei. However, all of these terms (red blood cell, red blood corpuscle and erythrocyte) are in common use, and students in the health professions should be familiar with each of them.

Description. Red blood cells are shaped like bi-

Fig. 11-4. Normal blood smear. Erythrocytes, platelets and various types of leukocytes are noted.

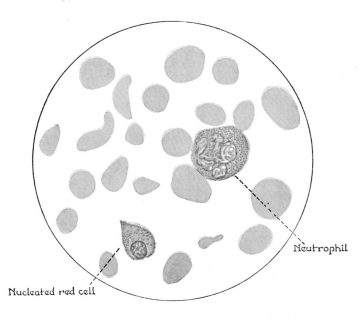

Fig. 11-5. Blood smear in pernicious anemia. Changes are evident in the erythrocytes and in the neutrophil.

concave disks (Fig. 11-3), which means that they are thinner in the center than around the edges. These tiny disks are very flexible, a feature that makes it possible for them to bend and twist when squeezing through the narrowest of capillaries and then to regain their original shape when they enter larger vessels.

The diameter of normal red cells varies from 6 to 9 microns, with an average of 7.5 (one micron is one one-thousandth of a mm. or 1/25,000 inch). In normal blood, the red cells in a blood "smear" are all about the same size, as illustrated in Figure 11-4. If there is great variation in size, the condition is called *anisocytosis* (meaning "a condition of unequal cells"). If there is great variation in shape, it is called *poikilocytosis* (meaning "condition of varied cells"). The shape and the size of red cells is important in the diagnosis of various blood diseases.

Each red blood cell consists of an inner framework that contains hemoglobin, and an outer limiting membrane. **Hemoglobin** is a conjugated protein, which means that it consists of a simple protein (globin) to which is attached an iron-containing pigment (hematin). By virtue of its iron, hemoglobin can combine with oxygen to form *oxyhemoglobin*, a compound that gives the bright scarlet color to oxygenated blood in the arteries. We might note also that it is the presence of oxyhemoglobin in red blood cells passing through capillaries near the body surface that gives pinkness to the skin and varying degrees of redness to mucous membranes and to the lips.

Hemoglobin that has given up its oxygen is called *reduced hemoglobin*, and it is blue in color rather than red. Under normal conditions not enough reduced hemoglobin is formed for the blue color to be visible, and blood in the systemic veins merely appears dark red in color. However, various diseases or abnormalities related to the cardiovascular and respiratory systems may result in the presence of such large quantities of reduced hemoglobin in the capillaries that the skin and mucous membranes have a distinctly blue color; this condition is called **cyanosis**. There must be at least 5 gm. of reduced hemoglobin per 100 ml. of arterial blood to cause frank cyanosis.

The formation of oxyhemoglobin occurs while blood is passing through the pulmonary capillaries that surround the microscopic air sacs (alveoli) in the lungs. When this blood eventually reaches systemic capillaries in all parts of the body, oxygen leaves the hemoglobin, diffuses out of the blood stream and through the tissue fluid to satisfy the needs of active cells. On the return trip to the lungs, hemoglobin does not travel "empty handed." In fact, one might even think of hemoglobin as being fickle, since as it gives up its oxygen it immediately combines with a small amount of carbon dioxide, the gas that diffuses into the blood after being formed during oxidative processes in the tissue cells. In the lung capillaries, hemoglobin gives up carbon dioxide which then diffuses into the alveoli to be exhaled and eliminated from the body. At the same time, it picks up another supply of oxygen, and the entire process is repeated. The transport of respiratory gases is considered in greater detail on pages 441–444.

Hemoglobin also can unite with carbon monoxide gas, which is very unfortunate. In fact, if hemoglobin has a choice, it will select carbon monoxide as its partner in preference to oxygen, and the resulting union is a firm one. Since hemoglobin that is bound to carbon monoxide is unable to carry oxygen, it is really oxygen starvation that causes death in cases of carbon monoxide poisoning (e.g., following prolonged inhalation of automobile exhaust fumes).

Estimation of the *hemoglobin content* of the blood is an important part of every physical examination. In women the average is 14 gm. per 100 cc. of blood (range 12-16 gm.); in men the average is 16 gm. per 100 cc. of blood (range 14-18 gm.).

The limiting membrane of a red blood cell is much like that of a nucleated cell, the important properties of which were described on page 22. Normally, the plasma and the red cells are isotonic; that is, they have the same osmotic pressure. If red cells are exposed to hypotonic solutions, water enters the cells more rapidly than it leaves, causing them to swell (Fig. 2-15). If

hematin = iRon

Isotonic, hypo & hypertonic refer to osmotic pressure

this swelling progresses to the point where the membrane ruptures, then the cell will lose its hemoglobin; such a sequence of events is known as *hemolysis* or laking. Red cells which have lost their hemoglobin can no longer transport oxygen and carbon dioxide. In the clinical situation, the *fragility test* is based on the behavior of red blood cells when placed in hypotonic sodium chloride solutions of varying strengths. Blood is drawn from the patient's vein (venipuncture), and one drop is placed in each of a series of tubes containing sodium chloride solutions ranging from 0.7 to 0.3 per cent. The cells swell to some extent in each solution, but the aim of the fragility test is to see at which concentration actual hemolysis begins and at which it is complete; these results then are compared with those of normal individuals. The fragility test is often helpful in the differential diagnosis of anemias, that is in determining the exact type of blood deficiency that is causing the patient's trouble.

Hemolysis may be brought about not only by hypotonic salt solutions but also by (1) the products of bacterial activity, (2) a transfusion of blood that is the "wrong type" (p. 313), (3) some snake venoms, and other agents.

Formation of Erythrocytes. The red blood cells have their origin in red bone marrow. In infancy and childhood every bone in the body contains active marrow to meet the intense needs that accompany normal growth processes. As the bones grow larger there is more than enough red marrow to meet the demands of the body, and much of it is gradually replaced by fatty yellow marrow. In the adult, active red marrow is found only in the thoracic bones, the vertebrae, the cranial bones and in the proximal ends of the femurs and the humeri. Microscopic examination of this marrow, usually obtained by sternal puncture, often is a valuable tool in the diagnosis of certain blood diseases.

Although millions of red blood cells are formed every second of every day of your life, their development proceeds in an orderly fashion through the following stages: from hemocytoblasts to erythroblasts, to normoblasts, to reticulocytes, to erythrocytes or mature red blood cells

(Fig. 11-2). Since reticulocytes are nearly mature red cells, it is normal to find a small number of them in the circulating blood (0.5 to 1.5% of the total red cells). However, an increase in the reticulocyte count is one of the first indications that the production of red cells has been accelerated, usually to meet an increasing need on the part of body tissues. The presence of normoblasts in the circulating blood is distinctly abnormal and indicates such an urgent demand for erythrocytes that cells are being released from the red marrow before they are mature.

If red blood cells are to mature normally, one needs not only normal bone marrow but also the presence of a special *maturation* or *antianemic factor*—vitamin B_{12}. This important vitamin sometimes is referred to as the "*extrinsic factor*" in blood formation, since it is ingested in the food which one eats. However, the absorption of vitamin B_{12} from the intestinal tract seems to depend on a special component of the gastric juice; this substance is called the "*intrinsic factor*," since it is produced within the body by cells in the lining of the stomach. After its absorption from the intestine, vitamin B_{12} is carried in the blood stream to the liver where it is stored until needed in the bone marrow (Fig. 11-6). Failure of the stomach lining cells to produce sufficient quantities of the intrinsic factor may result in a disease called *pernicious anemia* (Fig. 11-5), one symptom of which is a marked reduction in the number of circulating red cells due to inadequate absorption of vitamin B_{12}.

Other essentials for the formation of normal red blood cells are found in a well-balanced diet. These include iron, copper, riboflavin, nicotinic acid, vitamin C and plenty of protein, all of which serve as important "raw materials" in the red blood cell "factories."

Functions. The chief function of red blood cells is to carry oxygen from the lungs to the tissues, and carbon dioxide back from the tissues to the lungs. The amount of oxygen that is dissolved in the plasma is small, and it would be impossible to supply the demands of the tissues if this were the only means of transport. The hemoglobin in the red cells, by means of its iron, makes it possible

ANTIANEMIC FACTOR STORED IN LIVER
CARRIED BY BLOOD

LIVER

STOMACH

EXTRINSIC FACTOR IN
FOOD (VITAMIN B 12

INTRINSIC FACTOR IN
GASTRIC JUICE

CARRIED BY BLOOD

STIMULATES ERYTHROPOIESIS IN
RED BONE MARROW

Fig. 11-6. Factors important in normal erythropoiesis. The extrinsic factor is vitamin B_{12}; the intrinsic factor (a mucoprotein is involved in facilitating the absorption of vitamin B_{12} from the small intestine.

to carry an abundance of oxygen to tissues for ordinary requirements.

Life Span. After red blood cells leave the bone marrow they circulate in the blood stream for about 120 days, a figure based on studies of red cells which were "tagged" with radioactive iron. Each cell works very hard during its 4 month life span, loading and unloading oxygen about twice a minute and traveling an estimated 700 miles before wearing out. Worn-out red cells are destroyed by phagocytes (macrophages) in the spleen, the liver and the red bone marrow (*reticuloendothelial system*). During the breakdown, iron is salvaged and returned to the bone marrow where it is used over again in making new hemoglobin. The remainder of the hemoglobin mole-

cule is converted into bile pigments which are excreted by the liver into the bile and eventually eliminated through the intestinal tract.

Number of Erythrocytes. Every second of every day, millions of red blood cells are destroyed, and other millions are formed to take their place. However, the body has an amazing capacity for maintaining a dynamic balance between these two processes, and the healthy adult has a relatively constant number of red cells circulating in his blood stream at all times. The average "red cell count" falls within the range of 4½ to 5½ million per cu. mm. of blood; thus the total number for the entire body would be a staggering figure somewhere in the trillions. Women generally have a lower red cell count than do men. Determina-

Erythrocytes (R.B.C.)

tion of the *cell volume* or *hematocrit* (Fig. 11-1) also gives certain information regarding the number of red blood cells, since they constitute approximately 42 to 47 per cent of the total blood volume.

Normally, the rate of destruction of red blood cells equals the rate of production. However, if the number of red cells in the blood is reduced by hemorrhage or by an increased rate of destruction, the bone marrow can greatly increase its rate of production. The stimulus for such an increase is related to the reduced oxygen-carrying capacity of the blood and to the resultant tissue *hypoxia* (low oxygen content). It is believed that a lack of oxygen causes an increase in the formation of *erythropoietin,* a substance that directly stimulates red cell production; relatively large quantities of erythropoietin are formed in the kidney during hypoxia; lesser amounts are formed in the liver and possibly in other tissues.

Anemia is the term that refers to a blood deficiency in which the red cells are reduced in number, or are deficient in hemoglobin, or both. In any case, there is a decrease in the oxygen carrying capacity of the blood. With reduced amounts of oxygen being supplied to the tissues there is impairment of oxidative processes in the tissue cells, inadequate liberation of energy and interference with normal cellular functions. In severe cases of anemia, a person may be bedridden and have only enough energy to maintain vital activities such as respiration, heart beat, etc. If the disease continues unchecked, death will be the end-result.

The leukocytes *WBC*

The white blood cells are called leukocytes, a term derived from the Greek words leukos (white) and kytos (cell). They are less numerous than red blood cells but are easily recognized by their greater size (10-15 microns) and by the presence of nuclei. Although the red cells do their work in the blood, the chief functions of most white blood cells are performed only when they leave the blood and enter neighboring tissues; thus they use the blood stream as a transport sys-

tem, much as one might take a bus or subway to work.

The classification of white blood cells is based upon the presence or absence of granules in the cytoplasm. Thus we have two groups: granular leukocytes and nongranular leukocytes.

The Granular Leukocytes. In addition to granules in their cytoplasm, these white blood cells have distinctive nuclei that consist of a variable number of lobes. Because of such nuclear variations the members of this group may be referred to as *polymorphonuclear* leukocytes or "polymorphs"; however, in clinical practice this term most frequently is used in reference to one specific subgroup, the neutrophils. There are 3 subgroups of granular leukocytes, each being named according to the acid or basic staining characteristics of the cytoplasmic granules: neutrophils are those that do not stain well at the point of neutrality with either acid or basic dyes; eosinophils stain well with acid dye (eosin), and basophils stain well with basic dye.

1. *Neutrophils* have nuclei that are divided into 3 to 5 lobes; thus the term polymorphonuclear is particularly well-suited to them. They are the most numerous of all the white blood cells, constituting from 60 to 70 per cent of the total number. Neutrophils serve as a mobile defense force against infection (as described under functions); thus, their numbers may be greatly increased on certain occasions. At such times, when there is a great need for neutrophils, immature forms may appear in the blood; these cells are called *band* or *stab neutrophils* because their nuclei are horseshoe-shaped.

2. *Eosinophils* have nuclei made up of 2 oval lobes, and their cytoplasmic granules stain with acid dye (eosin). They form only 1 to 3 per cent of the total number of white cells.

3. *Basophils* have nuclei that are bent into an S-shape, and their large cytoplasmic granules stain with basic dyes. They are the least numerous of the white cells, constituting approximately 0.3 to 0.5 per cent of the total number.

The Nongranular Leukocytes. These white cells have no granules in their cytoplasm. There are only 2 subgroups of nongranular leukocytes.

1. *Lymphocytes* have very large nuclei surrounded by a relatively thin layer of cytoplasm. They comprise from 20 to 35 per cent of the total number of white cells. Most lymphocytes are smaller than the other kinds of white blood cells.

2. *Monocytes* are the largest of all blood cells. They have large nuclei which may be oval or kidney-shaped, and there is an abundance of cytoplasm. Monocytes constitute only 3 to 8 per cent of the total number of white cells.

The various subgroups of leukocytes are illustrated in Figure 11-4.

Formation of Leukocytes. Leukocytes are formed in both types of hemopoietic tissue—red bone marrow (myeloid tissue) and lymphatic tissue. All 3 types of granular leukocytes originate in red bone marrow, but the lymphocytes are formed in lymphatic tissue (p. 384) which is found in such organs as the spleen, lymph nodes, and thymus. The origin of monocytes is uncertain, but one widely held view is that they are formed particularly in the spleen and in the bone marrow. In a manner quite similar to that of the red blood cells, leukocytes develop in orderly stages as illustrated in Figure 11-2.

Functions. The broad, general function of the leukocytes is to protect the body against infection. For example, let us consider the case of a person who receives a cut through the skin of his finger. This is just like opening a door to admit the bacteria that are always present on the skin. Once inside, the bacteria begin to multiply and to damage tissue cells. A chemical substance (necrosin) is liberated by the injured cells, causing dilatation of the neighboring blood vessels and increasing the permeability of capillary walls. As a result, the skin *reddens* and feels *hot* as dilatation of the vessels brings more blood to the area. *Swelling* occurs as large quantities of fluid and protein escape from the highly permeable capillaries, and the pressure of these swollen tissues causes *pain*. This sequence of events constitutes the classic picture of *inflammation*.

From the very beginning of the inflammatory process, white blood cells are attracted to the area that is involved. Granulocytes and monocytes are particularly notable for their ability to leave the blood vessels and migrate to sites of inflammation or infection. Much like the amoeba, their protoplasm streams out into pseudopodia ("false feet") enabling them to squeeze through the tiny openings in capillary walls and out into the neighboring tissues (diapedesis). This type of locomotion is slow indeed, but it enables the white cells to leave the blood stream and enter into mortal combat with the bacterial invaders.

The major weapon of the leukocytes is **phagocytosis (p. 26)**, a process whereby they engulf and actually digest bacteria, fragmented cells and foreign particles. Granulocytes, the neutrophils in particular, seem to concentrate on the ingestion of bacteria, hence they are called microphagocytes. On the other hand, monocytes are especially good at the removal of larger particles such as broken-down tissue cells; thus they are called macrophagocytes. The ingested bacteria usually are killed and digested quickly, but occasionally the leukocytes themselves are destroyed by strong bacterial poisons. Therefore, following unusually severe battles, the combat area will be full of pus, which is a thick, semiliquid mass of living and dead leukocytes and bacteria, as well as battered tissue cell fragments. If the leukocytes defeat the bacterial invaders, they remove the debris from the "battlefield," and healing begins. At this time, monocytes may become fibroblasts and aid in the repair of tissue. But if the bacteria overwhelm the leukocytes and continue to multiply, eventually they may get into the blood stream and cause *septicemia* or "blood poisoning."

The small lymphocytes also play an important role in defense of the body against disease. It is believed that these cells are capable of multiplying and forming certain precursor cells, which in turn give rise to *plasma cells* (plasmacytes); as previously described on page 43, plasma cells are the primary producers of antibodies (gamma globulins) in the presence of antigens (i.e., foreign substances such as bacteria). Antibodies, in turn, combine with the antigen and lead to its inactivation.

The function of eosinophils is not yet certain, but it has been suggested that they detoxify foreign protein that may gain entry to the body.

Antigen = foreign substance.

Eosinophils increase in number in the circulating blood during allergic reactions (such as asthma) and when certain animal parasites invade the body (e.g., *Trichina*, the organism that may be ingested if one eats infected pork that is poorly cooked). Basophils, like eosinophils, also seem to be involved in allergic and stress reactions. Their granules are very similar to those in mast cells (p. 43), and it is believed that they, too, are a source of histamine and heparin.

Life Span. Because leukocytes do their work outside of the blood stream, they remain in the circulation for a variable period of time; to some extent this is determined by the need for their "services" in neighboring tissues. Granular leukocytes remain in the blood for an average of about 10 hours before migrating into neighboring tissues. Lymphocytes circulate back and forth between the blood and the lymph streams for 90 to 100 days, depending on the need for them in other tissues. The length of time that monocytes remain in the blood is unknown.

The ultimate fate of the leukocytes is variable. Some of these cells die in combat with bacteria; others may migrate into the intestine, where they are lost in the feces; and some probably are destroyed by cells of the reticulo-endothelial system.

Number of Leukocytes. During the course of each day there may be marked variations in the number of circulating leukocytes. For this reason the *absolute count* or total number of white blood cells may be anywhere from 5,000 to 10,000 per cu. mm. of blood in the healthy adult.

A *differential count* is an estimation of the number or percentage of each variety of leukocyte in the blood. It is made on a film of blood stained with Wright's stain. Each leukocyte seen is tabulated, until 100, or even 200, are counted, and then the percentage of each type is noted. For example, if a total of 200 have been counted and 140 of them are neutrophils, this means that 70 per cent of the leukocytes are neutrophils, and if 6 eosinophils are found, it means that 3 per cent of the total leukocytes are eosinophils. Variations in the percentage of certain types of leukocytes are characteristic of some diseases.

An increase in the number of leukocytes (above the upper limit of 10,000) is called *leukocytosis;* this occurs in most systemic and localized infectious processes, such as appendicitis, abscesses, etc. It is a normal response to infection. On the other hand, a decrease in the number of leukocytes (below the lower limit of 5,000) is called *leukopenia;* this may occur in certain acute and chronic diseases, such as typhoid fever, tuberculosis, etc. Leukopenia also is a constant finding in *radiation sickness,* the clinical result of excessive exposure to gamma rays. For example, victims of the atomic bomb explosions were exposed to intensive radiation and as a result suffered a marked depression of bone marrow function; the absolute white count in the more severe cases ranged from 1,500 to zero per cu. mm. of blood. There also was anemia due to interference with the formation of red blood cells.

Leukemia is a disease which is characterized by a rapid and uncontrolled proliferation of leukocytes in the blood-forming organs; for this reason it is sometimes called "cancer of the blood." The white cell count is greatly elevated, and large numbers of immature cells are found in the circulating blood. Chronic forms of this disease can be controlled for some time by the use of drugs that depress the activity of bone marrow and lymphatic tissue, but it usually terminates fatally within a few years. Acute leukemia is more rapidly fatal.

Infectious mononucleosis is an acute infectious disease that is probably caused by a virus. Commonly seen in young adults, it is characterized by fever, sore throat and swollen cervical lymph nodes. As the white count rises, there is a decrease in the percentage of polymorphonuclear cells and an increase in the mononuclear series.

Agranulocytosis refers to a condition in which there is a deficiency of granulocytes (granular leukocytes). It is characterized by fever, prostration, ulcerative lesions in the mucous membranes of the mouth and the pharynx and by a very low granulocyte count. It may occur in patients who have been taking thiouracil (for overactive thyroid gland) or sulfonamide drugs or in individuals who become sensitized to various other drugs or chemical substances.

The thrombocytes

The thrombocytes, or blood platelets, are the smallest of the formed elements (Fig. 11-4). These oval, granular bodies do not possess nuclei, since they are merely fragments of large cells (megakaryocytes) that are found in red bone marrow.

Functions. Platelets perform 3 important functions in the control of bleeding:

1. They clump together and stick to the inner surface of blood vessels wherever there is damage. This helps to plug up leaks and prevent a prolonged loss of blood.

2. As platelets come in contact with injured tissues they disintegrate and release a substance ("platelet-factor") which is essential for the clotting of blood.

3. Once a blood clot has formed at the site of injury, platelets cause it to shrink, or retract. During this process, the clot is changed from a soft mass to a firm one which further helps to stop bleeding.

Life Span. Those platelets that escape disintegration at the site of injured tissues probably are destroyed in the reticuloendothelial system, particularly the spleen. Their survival time is thought to be about 5 to 9 days.

Number. It is difficult to make an accurate platelet count, but the average range is probably somewhere between 250,000 and 350,000 per cu. mm. of blood. A marked reduction in the number of blood platelets is called *thrombocytopenia,* and a marked increase is called *thrombocytosis.*

The plasma

Plasma is the liquid portion of circulating blood, and its numerous constituents play an important part in the maintenance of homeostasis. In a healthy, fasting individual the plasma is clear and straw-colored, but it is milky white following the ingestion of meals that contain fat. A few of the normal constituents of plasma will be described.

Water. The most abundant of all constituents is water, comprising from 91 to 92 per cent of the plasma. The functions of water are described on page 15.

Proteins. Plasma consists of 6 to 8 per cent proteins. Most of the plasma proteins are formed in the liver, but some are produced by plasma cells, the spleen and the bone marrow, while others are released by disintegrating erythrocytes, leukocytes and general tissue cells. Regardless of their location in the body, all the proteins serve to form a large, dynamic pool or "bank" which may be drawn on by any tissue that needs protein. Proteins are dynamic in the sense that a particular molecule may be synthesized in the liver, travel in the blood as part of the plasma pool, make up part of an enzyme in some cell, and eventually be incorporated into the hemoglobin of an erythrocyte. When this erythrocyte wears out and is broken down, the protein molecule then may be available for use elsewhere in the body.

Plasma proteins have many functional and clinical uses, only a few of which will be mentioned at this time.

Albumin, the most abundant protein in plasma, is formed primarily by the liver. It is especially important because of its osmotic relationships, since it is the protein mostly responsible for the "colloid osmotic pressure" of the plasma. It helps to regulate the volume of plasma within the blood vessels by pulling in water from tissue fluid. When whole blood and plasma are not available, an albumin solution may be given intravenously to increase the blood volume following hemorrhage. Albumin also is of value in treating a patient who has lost large amounts of protein following extensive burns.

There are 3 major *globulin* fractions in the plasma: alpha, beta, and gamma. Alpha and beta globulins are formed primarily in the liver; they aid in the transport of other substances (by combining with them), and in the transport of protein itself from one part of the body to another. The gamma globulins (antibodies) are produced by the plasma cells (p. 43). They resist infection, thus providing the body with immunity to certain diseases.

Fibrinogen also is made in the liver; it is in a liquid or "sol" form in circulating blood. When blood clots, fibrinogen changes from a liquid state to a solid state, or from a sol to a "gel" called *fibrin.* Fibrin films and fibrin foams are useful clinically to stop bleeding during general surgery, in making skin grafts, in surgical operations on blood vessels and in neurosurgery (surgery of the CNS).

Prothrombin, which plays a part in the clotting of blood, is made in the liver. However, its production is governed by the availability of vitamin K; if this vitamin is lacking, the liver will be unable to produce sufficient amounts of prothrombin, and the blood clotting mechanism will be disturbed.

Nutrients. Carbohydrate is present in the blood chiefly in the form of glucose, a simple sugar, which is referred to as "blood sugar." Glucose is carried to all tissues where it is used as a source of energy or stored as reserve food until needed. Amino acids, the end products of protein digestion, likewise are carried to all tissues where they are used in the processes of building and repair. Lipids are present in plasma primarily as neutral fats, cholesterol and phospholipids. They are carried to the tissues where they may be used to supply energy or stored as fat.

Inorganic Salts. Forming about 0.9 per cent of the plasma, inorganic salts occur primarily as chlorides, carbonates and sulfates and phosphates of sodium, potassium, calcium and magnesium. Iron, copper, iodine and traces of many other elements also play a role in the preservation of homeostasis. The proper concentration and distribution of various salts is referred to as *electrolyte balance.*

Gases. Oxygen, carbon dioxide and nitrogen are found in solution in the plasma, but only small amounts are transported in this manner.

Waste Products. Urea, uric acid, lactic acid and creatinine are the most important of the metabolic waste products that are carried in the plasma to organs of elimination.

Special Substances. The endocrine glands, or glands of internal secretion, produce chemical substances called hormones; these substances are transported in the plasma to tissues in all parts of the body.

Composition of Plasma in Disease. Laboratory tests which determine the quantities of various plasma constituents are valuable diagnostic tools. For example, in uncontrolled diabetes mellitus the blood sugar (glucose) is well above the average of 80 to 110 mg. per 100 cc. of blood, but if an overdose of insulin is given, the blood sugar may fall to dangerously low levels. In nephritis, one type of kidney disease, the nitrogenous waste products accumulate in excessive amounts in the blood. Functional disturbances in the endocrine glands also cause changes in the quantity of plasma constituents. For example, in overactivity of the parathyroid glands (hyperparathyroidism) the amount of calcium is greatly increased, but in cases of underactivity (hypoparathyroidism), the calcium level is low.

The table on page 310 summarizes the normal and the pathologic values of a few of the blood constituents. However, due to variations in laboratory technics, the figures which are presented here may differ slightly from those quoted elsewhere.

Coagulation of blood

The coagulation or *clotting* of blood is a protective mechanism that guards against excessive loss of the body's life-sustaining fluid. During the clotting process blood loses its liquid quality and forms a jellylike mass which helps to plug up leaks in the wall of an injured vessel. There are many theories regarding the specific chemical reactions which are involved in the clotting process, but such details are beyond the scope of this textbook. Consequently, the following discussion is limited to a brief consideration of the three general phases or steps in the clotting of blood as illustrated in Figure 11-7.

The first phase of coagulation involves the formation of *thromboplastin,* a substance that "triggers" the clotting mechanism. For example, let us suppose that your finger has been cut with a knife. As blood flows from severed vessels it passes over rough or "foreign" surfaces where the platelets tend to accumulate and to disintegrate with the release of a substance known as "platelet factor." In the presence of calcium ions (Ca^{++}) and certain accessory substances, the platelet factor reacts with an antihemophilic factor to form thromboplastin. Neighboring tissue cells which were injured by the knife also will liberate thromboplastic substances.

The second phase of coagulation involves the conversion of prothrombin to *thrombin*. Prothrombin, one of the normal plasma proteins, is formed in the liver in the presence of vitamin K; a deficiency of this vitamin may result in a bleeding tendency due to inadequate prothrombin formation. The thromboplastin formed in phase one serves to initiate the conversion of prothrombin, but the presence of calcium ions (Ca^{++}) and certain "accelerator" factors are necessary for rapid completion of the reaction.

The third phase of coagulation involves the action of thrombin in converting soluble fibrinogen to insoluble *fibrin*. Fibrinogen is another protein which is produced in the liver and found circulating in the plasma. Fibrin first appears as a fine network of threads that gradually becomes denser, forming the structural substance of the clot. Erythrocytes are trapped in the fibrin mesh, but these red cells have nothing to do with actual coagula-

tion, since clotting will occur in plasma after the blood cells have been removed. The clotting process draws to a close as blood platelets cause a retraction or shrinking of the clot, thus producing a firm but fairly elastic plug. As the clot shrinks, a clear yellow liquid is squeezed out; this liquid, called *serum*, is similar to plasma except for the absence of fibrinogen and certain other clotting elements that have been used in the coagulation process.

Limitation of Coagulation. Although the coagulation of blood is a life-preserving mechanism, nature provides certain inhibitory substances which circulate in the blood stream and help to limit clot formation to areas of injury. One such substance is *heparin* and another is *antithrombin*; it is believed that these inhibitory agents either interfere with the formation of thrombin or in some way neutralize it so that it cannot accumulate in healthy vessels. However, there is not enough inhibitory substance to prevent clotting when platelets disintegrate in large numbers, as is the case when vessels are injured.

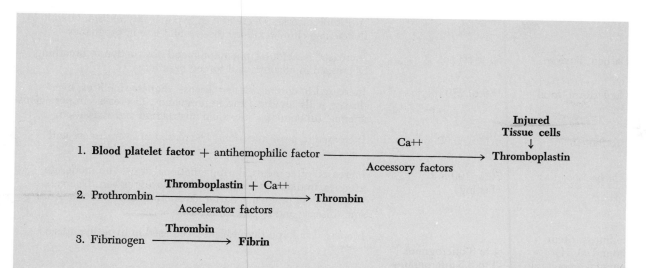

Fig. 11-7. Schematic representation of the three phases of blood coagulation. Those substances which normally are not present in significant amounts in the circulating blood are shown in **boldface type**.

Coagulation Time. Blood taken from a normal person will clot within a predictable length of time, depending on the method that is used. For example, blood drawn into a capillary tube will clot in 3 to 6 minutes, but in a larger tube the range is from 5 to 15 minutes (Lee & White method).

Bleeding Time. This test is performed to determine the time required for a small sharp incision to cease bleeding. The normal bleeding time is from 1 to 3 minutes. It is greatly prolonged in such conditions as thrombocytopenia, pernicious anemia and acute leukemias.

Blood Preservation. Chemical agents that prevent the clotting of blood play an important role in hospital laboratories. The addition of citrate or oxalate solutions to blood samples will prevent clotting by combining with calcium ions, thus interfering with the formation of thrombin. However, when blood is to be used for transfusions (p. 312) and must be stored in "banks" until needed, the best preservative is an acid-citrate-dextrose solution (A.C.D.); this anticoagulant delays the breakdown of red cells and preserves blood for as long as 3 weeks.

Abnormal Coagulation of Blood. Intravascular coagulation, or *thrombosis*, refers to the abnormal clotting of blood within the vessels of a living

BLOOD CONSTITUENTS (ADULT) IN NORMAL AND PATHOLOGIC CONDITIONS

Constituent	Normal Level*	Pathologic Changes
Bilirubin, total direct indirect	0.7 mg. 0.4 mg. 0.3 mg.	Increased in liver disease, pernicious anemia and hemolysis after transfusion. Decreased in carcinoma and chronic kidney disease
Calcium	9 to 11 mg.	Increased in hyperparathyroidism, malignant bone tumors and Addison's disease. Decreased in hypoparathyroidism, vitamin D deficiency, chronic kidney disease and late in pregnancy
Carbon dioxide	55 to 65 vol. %	Increased in acidosis, pneumonia and obstruction to breathing. Decreased in alkalosis and forced breathing
Cholesterol, total	150 to 280 mg.	Increased in chronic kidney disease, diabetes mellitus, liver disease with jaundice, and in pregnancy. Decreased in pernicious anemia, tuberculosis, intestinal obstruction and starvation
Fibrinogen	0.15 to 0.30 gm.	Increased in most infections. Decreased in liver disease and severe malnutrition
Glucose	70 to 100 mg. (fasting)	Increased after meals, during emotional stress and moderate exercise, in diabetes mellitus and hyperthyroidism. Decreased in starvation, pregnancy, after severe muscular exercise, Addison's disease and hyperinsulinism
Iodine, protein bound (PBI) butanol extractable (BEI)	4 to 8 micrograms 3 to 6.5 micrograms	Increased in hyperthyroidism. Decreased in hypothyroidism
Nonprotein nitrogen (NPN)	25 to 35 mg.	(Includes urea, uric acid, creatinine, ammonia and amino acids) Increased in kidney disease, intestinal obstruction and severe heart failure. Decreased on low protein diet

person. A stationary blood clot is called a **thrombus,** and it may partially or completely block the vessel in which it is formed. Occasionally one of these clots may break loose from its place of formation and be swept away in the rapidly moving blood stream until it plugs up a vessel elsewhere in the body; such a "wandering" clot is called an **embolus.**

One cause of thrombosis may be a "roughening" of the normally smooth endothelial lining of a blood vessel due to infection or to fatty degeneration (atherosclerosis) of the vessel wall. For example, *thrombophlebitis* is a term that means inflammation of a vein associated with the formation of a clot. Other conditions that favor thrombosis are stasis or sluggish flow of blood through the vessels and the presence of foreign material in the blood. The great danger associated with thrombosis and with embolism is that the blood flow to a vital organ may be shut off if clots plug up its vessels. For example, *coronary thrombosis* may be rapidly fatal if one of the vital arteries leading to the heart muscle is occluded. Another serious problem is *pulmonary embolism,* or an obstruction of one or both of the great arteries leading to the lungs. This may occur as a complication of prolonged bed rest when there is stasis of blood in the veins of the extremities. Such

BLOOD CONSTITUENTS (ADULT) IN NORMAL AND PATHOLOGIC CONDITIONS (Continued)

Constituent	Normal Level*	Pathologic Changes
Phosphatase acid	0.1 to 1 Bodansky units	Increased in carcinoma of prostate and bony metastases
alkaline	1.5 to 4 Bodansky units	Increased in pregnancy, infancy, childhood, certain bone diseases and in healing fractures
Phosphate, inorganic	3 to 4.5 mg.	Increased in certain kidney and bone diseases, in hypoparathyroidism and Addison's disease. Decreased in vitamin D deficiency causing rickets, diabetes mellitus and hyperparathyroidism
Potassium	3.5 to 5 mEq./L.	Increased in Addison's disease, bronchial asthma, tissue breakdown and kidney disease. Decreased in vomiting, diarrhea, following surgery and administration of adrenal cortical hormones
Protein total "A-G" ratio	6 to 8 gm. 1.5 to 2.5:1	Albumin averages 4.5 to 5.5 Gm. and globulin 1.5 to 3.4 Gm. Total protein increased in certain infections. Decreased in diseases of kidney, liver and intestinal tract, and in malnutrition
Sodium Chloride	136 to 145 mEq./L. 98 to 106 mEq./L.	Increased in kidney and heart disease. Decreased in vomiting, diarrhea, Addison's disease, diabetes mellitus and pneumonia
Urea nitrogen (BUN)	10 to 15 mg.	Increase parallels that of NPN. Decreased in liver disease, eclampsia and low-protein diet
Uric acid	2 to 4 mg.	Increased in liver and kidney disease, in gout, leukemia and pneumonia

*The values given are per 100 ml., unless otherwise stated.

periods of sluggish blood flow favor the formation of clots which are only loosely attached to the vessel walls. When such a person gets out of bed, the contraction of his leg muscles may cause the clots to break loose and be swept onward to the pulmonary arteries. Fortunately, such complications are rare when early ambulation is possible.

Anticoagulant drugs are agents that retard or prolong the clotting process. They are of particular value in disease conditions that involve abnormal coagulation of the blood, such as thrombosis. However, great care must be exercised in the use of anticoagulants, since an overdose may result in fatal hemorrhage.

Commercial preparations of heparin are used when a rapid depression of blood coagulability is desired; injected intravenously, its effect is immediate but short-lived. On the other hand, drugs of the dicumarin group (e.g., Dicumarol) are anticoagulants that can be taken orally, but they do not take effect for about 48 hours; Dicumarol retards blood clotting by interfering with the formation by the liver of prothrombin and one of the accelerator factors, both of which are needed for coagulation. The dosage of Dicumarol is subject to individual variations, and for this reason frequent blood tests of prothrombin activity are advisable so that the dosage may be adjusted.

An estimation of prothrombin activity may be made in the laboratory by mixing a citrated sample of the patient's plasma with standardized amounts of thromboplastin and calcium ions; the time required for this plasma to clot is reported as the *prothrombin time*. If there is a normal amount of prothrombin and accelerator factor in the plasma, clotting will occur in 12 to 20 seconds. During treatment with Dicumarol, however, prothrombin activity may be only 15 to 25 per cent of normal, and the prothrombin time increased to 35 seconds or more.

Excessive bleeding

The escape of blood from the vessels in which it is contained is referred to as *hemorrhage*. The control of excessive bleeding may be accomplished by direct pressure at the site of injury, by hemo-

stats (surgical clamps), by ligatures (ties), and by the application of tourniquets. Sometimes gauze applied over the bleeding surface will help to stop the flow by favoring the breakdown of platelets and hastening coagulation. Following the loss of a relatively small amount of blood (e.g., a blood donation of 500 cc.), the plasma volume is regained within a few hours as tissue fluid is pulled in by osmosis from the tissue spaces, but the erythrocytes and the plasma proteins are restored more slowly. It takes about 50 days for a healthy blood donor to regenerate corpuscles and hemoglobin. The signs and symptoms of severe hemorrhage are described on page 410.

Thrombocytopenic purpura is a condition characterized by the formation of purple patches in the skin and the mucous membranes due to subcutaneous extravasation (escape of blood from the vessels into the tissues) of blood. The platelets are reduced in number, and the bleeding time is prolonged greatly.

Hemophilia is the classic hereditary disease in which a sex-linked characteristic is transmitted by females, but in which bleeding difficulties occur exclusively in males. The underlying defect is still obscure, but it is thought to be a congenital absence of the antihemophilic factor (AHF) which plays such an important part in the formation of thromboplastin during the first phase of blood clotting. As a result, hemophilia is characterized by a prolonged coagulation time (up to 2 hours or more) and a tendency toward bleeding in the skin, the muscles and the joints. The bleeding may occur spontaneously or as a result of minor injuries.

A deficiency in one of the accessory factors, which also is needed in phase one of the clotting process, results in a disease that closely resembles hemophilia. However, it differs in that it can occur in either males or females.

Blood transfusions

A transfusion with whole blood is indicated primarily in those cases in which there has been an acute loss of both red cells and plasma, as in severe hemorrhage. Plasma is the next best substance for use in such emergencies, but it is no substitute for whole blood, since the oxygen-carrying red cells have been removed.

The person from whom blood is taken is called a *donor,* and the patient who receives blood is called a *recipient.* The safe transfusion of blood from donor to recipient depends on careful laboratory tests to ensure that the patient receives only *compatible* blood, or that which "agrees" with his own. The administration of unsafe or *incompatible* blood may lead to serious or even fatal "transfusion reactions."

Blood compatibility and the systems of classification are based on the presence or the absence of specific antigens (agglutinogens) in the red blood cells, and the presence or the absence of specific antibodies (agglutinins) in the plasma. Because of these factors, the red blood cells of one person may be *agglutinated* or clumped by the plasma of another person. Clarification of the relationships between compatible and incompatible blood groups won the Nobel prize for Karl Landsteiner and led to the establishment of the international ABO system of classification. According to this system, there are 4 human **blood groups** or types: O, A, B and AB.

There are 2 *antigens* or agglutinable substances, called A and B, that may be present in red blood cells, making it possible for them to be agglutinated. Neither antigen is present in the red cells of group O individuals; A is present in group A, B in group B, and both A and B in group AB.

There are 2 *antibodies* or agglutinins, called *alpha* and *beta,* that may be present in plasma, making it possible for plasma to agglutinate cer- ―CLUMP tain red cells. Both antibodies are present in the plasma of group O, beta in group A, alpha in group B, and neither alpha nor beta in group AB.

If the antigen A in the red cells of a donor comes in contact with the antibody or agglutinin alpha in the plasma of a recipient, or if antigen B in the red cells of a donor comes in contact with beta agglutinin in the plasma of a recipient, agglutination or clumping of cells will occur. This is followed by *hemolysis* or rupture of red cell membranes allowing hemoglobin to escape into the plasma. Such bloods are incompatible and lead to

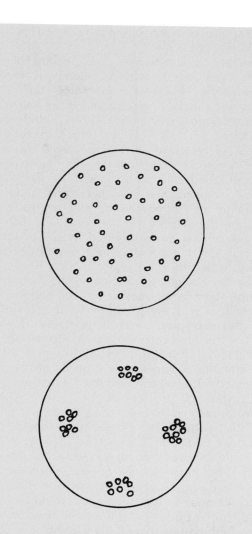

Fig. 11-8. Diagram to show agglutination (clumping) of red blood cells. The normal distribution is shown on the top and agglutination on the bottom. Agglutination is followed by hemolysis.

A, B, AB, O.

Antibodies: ALPHA + BETA
BLOOD   A—has Beta
              B—has alpha
              AB—no alpha or beta
              O—has Alpha + Beta.

a "transfusion reaction." Agglutination is illustrated in Figure 11-8.

The hemoglobin that escapes into the plasma, in the course of a transfusion reaction, is excreted in the urine. Masses of it may block the kidney tubules and make it impossible for the kidneys to function normally. Urticaria (hives), chills, fever and hematuria (blood in the urine) are the indications of incompatible bloods. Thus, the event to be avoided in transfusions is the destruction of the red blood cells of the donor by the plasma of the recipient. We need not worry about the possibility of destruction of the recipient's red cells by the donor's plasma, since the latter is immediately so greatly diluted by the plasma of the recipient that the agglutinins have little opportunity to destroy the recipient's red cells.

The Rh Factor. In addition to the ABO blood groups, there is yet another red cell factor which not only is very much concerned in transfusions but also may play a role in pregnancy as well. This is the Rh Factor, so named because it was first discovered in the blood of Rhesus monkeys. As with the A and the B antigens of the ABO system, the Rh factor is contained in the red blood cells. About 85 per cent of the white population have Rh antigen in their red cells and are said to be *"Rh positive."* The 15 per cent who lack this factor are said to be *"Rh negative."* Human plasma normally does not contain corresponding Rh antibodies, but they may be formed in Rh-negative blood if Rh-positive blood is used for transfusion purposes; such an individual then would be "sensitized" to the Rh factor, and any subsequent injection of Rh-positive blood might result in a severe or even fatal transfusion reaction. Sensitization also may occur during pregnancy in Rh-negative women who are married to Rh-positive men, but we wish to emphasize the fact that the vast majority of such women have no difficulty with their pregnancies. However, it is possible for some Rh-negative women to become so sensitized during their first or second pregnancies that future pregnancies may result in injury to the baby. This sensitization may occur when an Rh-negative woman is carrying an Rh-positive baby in her uterus. Normally the blood streams of mother and child are completely separated by a thin partition of tissue through which only small nutrient and waste particles can pass. However, near the end of pregnancy, a small "leak" may develop in the membranous barrier, permitting Rh-positive red cells to pass from the child's blood stream into the Rh-negative blood stream of the mother; as a result, Rh antibodies are produced, and the mother is sensitized. These Rh antibodies do not harm the mother directly, since they will not attack her Rh-negative red cells, but in a future pregnancy they may harm an Rh-positive baby by diffusing into its blood stream and destroying its red cells. Such a condition in the baby is called *erythroblastosis fetalis.* However, recent investigation indicates that a program of passive immunization can prevent the sensitization of Rh-negative mothers and the subsequent erythroblastosis fetalis. Indeed, in the very near future, this serious medical problem may be completely eliminated.

Laboratory Tests. The safety of blood transfusions first requires determination of the ABO group and the Rh type. However, there are so many subgroups that a final test, the *cross-matching* of the patient's blood with that to be administered, also is required; this is done by mixing some of the donor's red cells with a sample of the recipient's plasma to see if clumping occurs. Figure 11-9 illustrates the results of cross-matching the 4 main blood groups of the ABO system. Blood to be used for transfusion purposes also is subjected to a serologic test for syphilis.

TISSUE FLUID

Definition

Tissue fluid is that fluid which is found in all parts of the body, filling tissue spaces, lying between cells and fibers of connective tissue and between the cells of organs. It fills serous cavities (pleural, pericardial and peritoneal) and synovial sacs and occupies such special spaces as the subarachnoid space, the space between the bony and the membranous labyrinths, the space within the membranous labyrinths and within the cham-

Fig. 11-9. Diagram of results obtained when cross-matching the main human blood groups, both donor and recipient being Rh positive. Even distribution of cells indicates safe or compatible blood for transfusion. Clusters indicate the clumped cells of incompatible blood which may cause transfusion reaction. Individuals in group O are called universal donors; their erythrocytes are not agglutinated by any plasma, since they contain no antigen. Individuals in group AB are called universal recipients; since there is no antibody (agglutinin alpha or beta) in their plasma, erythrocytes from any group will not be agglutinated.

bers of the eyes. The cells of the body live in tissue fluid and are surrounded by it.

Importance

The cells of the body are not in contact with blood, so nutrient materials and oxygen must pass through the walls of the capillaries and through tissue fluid to reach the cells. Wastes must pass from cells through tissue fluid and through the walls of capillaries to be carried by the blood to the organs of excretion. Tissue fluid may be considered as a "middleman" through which exchanges between blood and cells take place continuously.

Formation and composition

Tissue fluid is formed by outward filtration and diffusion of all constituents of plasma except large protein molecules. Blood pressure, which is due to the pumping action of the heart, furnishes the filtering force, and molecular movement makes diffusion possible (pp. 23–24).

The walls of capillaries resemble collodion membranes in permitting everything except large molecules to pass through. There are pores in the capillary walls through which water and crystalloids pass easily, but large protein molecules pass through only with difficulty, so that at least 90 per cent of the protein molecules remain inside the capillary wall and exert osmotic force which opposes filtration. Since crystalloids pass through the capillary walls easily, they exert the same osmotic pressure on both sides of the capillary wall and, therefore, are not responsible for the movement of water. Water leaves the capillary by filtration at the arterial end and is pulled back into the capillary at the venous end by osmosis, as shown in Figure 2-16.

The composition of tissue fluid is practically identical with plasma except for less protein.

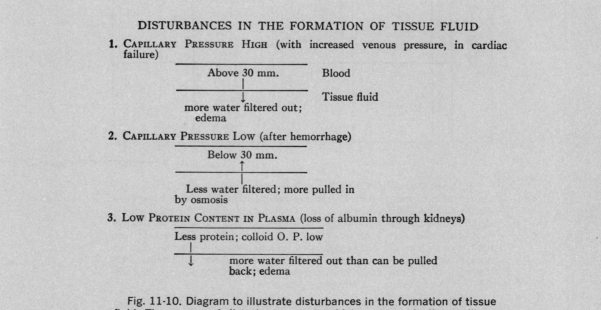

DISTURBANCES IN THE FORMATION OF TISSUE FLUID

1. CAPILLARY PRESSURE HIGH (with increased venous pressure, in cardiac failure)

Above 30 mm.   Blood

          ↓   Tissue fluid
more water filtered out; edema

2. CAPILLARY PRESSURE LOW (after hemorrhage)

Below 30 mm.
          ↑

Less water filtered; more pulled in by osmosis

3. LOW PROTEIN CONTENT IN PLASMA (loss of albumin through kidneys)

Less protein; colloid O. P. low

          ↓   more water filtered out than can be pulled back; edema

Fig. 11-10. Diagram to illustrate disturbances in the formation of tissue fluid. The causes of disturbance are too high pressure in the capillary, too low pressure and a decrease in the protein content of plasma.

Fate

The fluid that filters out at the arterial end of the capillary has several courses available to it. (1) It may be pulled back into the capillary by osmosis at the venous end. (2) It may move on into the cells and become part of the intracellular fluid (Fig. 18-10), p. 541. (3) It may remain in the tissue spaces as part of the tissue fluid reservoir. (4) It may enter the lymphatic capillaries and form lymph, in which case it eventually enters the blood again. Any protein molecules that escape from the vascular capillaries have no choice but the last course.

Tissue fluid disturbances

When the blood pressure in the capillaries is increased, there may be excessive filtration of fluid into the tissue spaces. This happens when the pressure in the veins rises and blood backs up in the capillaries. Such a sequence of events may occur in heart failure, and, as a result, *edema* (meaning "swelling") and *ascites* (meaning "a bag") may appear. In edema the tissue cells are spread apart by the accumulation of tissue fluid between them. Ascites refers to an excessive accumulation of fluid within the abdominal cavity. Edema also may result from too little osmosis at the venous end of the capillary. This is due to low plasma protein content, such as may occur in kidney disease when protein is lost in the urine. Whenever filtration is not balanced by osmosis, edema will occur.

Another disturbance in fluid balance may follow a severe hemorrhage when the blood pressure is low and the driving force for filtration is decreased. This means that the colloidal osmotic pressure is increased (proportionately) and more fluid is pulled into the blood stream than is filtered out; as a result, the tissues become *dehydrated*. Circulatory collapse and death may result unless intravenous fluids are administered immediately; plasma, isotonic saline solution (0.9%), and 5 per cent glucose in water are emergency fluids that may be used while waiting for whole blood to be typed and cross-matched. Disturbances in tissue fluid formation are illustrated in Figure 2-12.

LYMPH

Definition and origin

Lymph is the fluid that is present in vessels of the lymphatic system (p. 379). As described previously, one of the courses open to tissue fluid is drainage into the lymphatic capillaries; once it enters these vessels it is called lymph.

Composition

Since lymph is derived from blood plasma we would expect it to have approximately the same composition as the tissue fluid that filters through the vascular capillary wall. In other words, lymph has almost the same proportions of water and solutes as are found in plasma, but it has considerably less protein (with the exception of lymph that is drained from the liver—the latter having a protein content of about 6%). Lymph that is drained from the intestinal area may contain large amounts of fat after meals; the suspended fat droplets give this lymph a milky white appearance. The cell content of lymph varies from 500 to 40,000 leukocytes per cu. mm. or more, depending on the number of lymph nodes it has traversed; these cells are predominantly lymphocytes which have been formed in the lymphatic tissue.

Fate

Lymph ultimately enters the blood stream after a journey through various lymphatic vessels. The circulation of lymph is described on pages 379–384.

SUMMARY

1. The blood
   A. Functions:
      a. Delivery of vital substances to capillaries
      b. Pick-up of metabolic end products; delivery to organs for use or elimination
      c. Aids in regulation of body temperature

d. Helps to maintain acid-base balance
e. Protects body against bacterial invasion and disease

B. Characteristics
   a. Color: bright red if well oxygenated; dark red if poorly oxygenated
   b. Quantity: approximately 7 per cent of body weight
   c. Viscosity: about 5 times thicker than water
   d. Specific gravity: between 1.055 and 1.065. Sedimentation rate ranges from 4 to 10 mm. per hour
   e. Reaction or pH: slightly alkaline (7.35 to 7.45). Maintenance of acid-base balance facilitated by buffer systems

C. Structure and formation
   a. Hemopoietic tissue found in red bone marrow and lymphatic tissue
   b. Plasma constitutes 53 to 58% of blood; formed elements 42 to 47%

D. Erythrocytes (red blood cells)
   a. Flexible, biconcave disks; framework contains hemoglobin
   b. Hemoglobin aids in transport of oxygen and carbon dioxide. Average hemoglobin content: female 14 gm. and male 16 gm./100 cc. blood
   c. Red cell may rupture in hypotonic solution with loss of hemoglobin (hemolysis); basis of fragility test
   d. Formation: in red bone marrow; millions formed every second. Requires vitamin B_{12} (extrinsic factor); gastric juice component (intrinsic factor) essential for B_{12} absorption
   e. Destruction occurs in reticuloendothelial system: average life span 120 days
   f. Average range for number of red cells $4\frac{1}{2}$ to $5\frac{1}{2}$ million/cu. mm. of blood. Hypoxia causes increased formation of erythropoietin, stimulates bone marrow

E. Leukocytes (white blood cells)
   a. Larger than red cells; all are nucleated
   b. Granular leukocytes (polymorphonuclear leukocytes) granules in cytoplasm; nuclei have lobes. Subgroups—neutrophils, eosinophils and basophils. Formed in red bone marrow
   c. Nongranular leukocytes: no granules in cytoplasm. Subgroups — lymphocytes and monocytes. Lymphocytes formed in lymphatic tissue, monocytes in bone marrow
   d. General function: to protect body against infection. Granulocytes and monocytes are active phagocytes. Lymphocytes may be concerned with immunity reactions; give rise to plasma cells
   e. Life span may be 10 hours (granulocytes) to 100 days (lymphocytes); probably destroyed in reticuloendothelial system and in combat
   f. Absolute count falls within range of 5,000 to 10,000/cu. mm. of blood

F. Thrombocytes (blood platelets)
   a. Merely cell fragments
   b. Function: help in control of bleeding
   c. Average count between 250,000 and 350,000

G. Blood plasma (liquid portion of circulating blood)
   a. Composition: water (92%); proteins (6-8%); nutrients; inorganic salts; gases, waste products and special substances
   b. Composition in disease: see table, p. 310

H. Coagulation of blood
   a. Guards against excessive loss of blood
   b. First phase: formation of thromboplastin
   c. Second phase: conversion of prothrombin to thrombin
   d. Third phase: conversion of soluble fibrinogen to insoluble fibrin
   e. Serum is liquid squeezed out of clot as it shrinks
   f. Heparin and antithrombin limit clot formation to areas of injury
   g. Coagulation time: 3 to 6 minutes in capillary tube; 5 to 15 minutes in larger tubes (Lee-White)
   h. Bleeding time: 1 to 3 minutes

i. Blood preserved in blood bank by acid-citrate-dextrose solution (ACD)
j. Intravascular clotting: stationary clot-thrombus; wandering clot — embolus. Anticoagulant drugs: Dicumarol and commercial preparation of heparin. Prothrombin time averages 12 to 20 seconds
I. Excessive bleeding:
a. Small loss tolerated well; severe loss may lead to death
b. Thrombocytopenic purpura and hemophilia
J. Blood transfusions
a. Treatment of severe hemorrhage; replaces red cells as well as fluid
b. Safe transfusion from donor to recipient depends on typing and cross-matching
c. Blood compatibility based on presence or absence of specific antigens and antibodies in red cells and plasma, respectively. ABO system and Rh factor of primary importance

2. Tissue fluid
A. Fills tissue spaces in all parts of body, serous cavities and spaces
B. Serves as "middleman" in exchange between blood and cells
C. Low protein filtrate of plasma; formed constantly; blood pressure provides filtering force
D. May return to capillary by osmosis, enter cells, remain in tissue spaces, enter lymphatic capillaries and form lymph
E. Disturbances may lead to edema, ascites and dehydration

3. Lymph
A. Fluid present in lymphatic vessels; called tissue fluid until it moves into the lymph capillaries
B. Similar to tissue fluid; water and solutes as in plasma, only small amount of protein. Lymph from intestinal area rich in fat after meals. Cell content varies; primarily lymphocytes
C. Ultimately enters blood stream

PRACTICAL APPLICATIONS AND QUESTIONS

(Encircle the letter of the *best* answer to each of the following questions.)

A. *Blood is a vital, life-sustaining fluid, excessive loss of which results in the disturbance of various body processes.*

1. A marked reduction in the number of red blood cells would result in
   a. defective coagulation
   b. reduced oxygen transport
   c. polycythemia
   d. depressed bone marrow function
2. With the loss of white blood cells, there may be a disturbance in
   a. transportation of waste products
   b. absorption of vitamin K
   c. clot retraction
   d. defense against bacterial invasion
3. Loss of plasma proteins could result in
   a. dehydration
   b. hematuria
   c. edema
   d. water balance
4. The plasma protein most concerned with colloidal osmotic pressure is
   a. globulin
   b. albumin
   c. fibrinogen
   d. prothrombin

B. *Blood coagulation prevents excessive loss of blood in case of injury to vessel walls.*

1. The substance that initiates the clotting mechanism is
   a. thromboplastin
   b. vitamin K
   c. fibrinogen
   d. prothrombin
2. Sodium citrate solution prevents clotting by combining with what ions?
   a. iron
   b. chloride
   c. potassium
   d. calcium

3. What insoluble gel forms during coagulation?
   a. thrombin
   b. prothrombin
   c. fibrin
   d. fibrinogen

4. Drugs of the dicumarin group (e.g., Dicumarol) interfere with the formation of
   a. prothrombin
   b. thrombin
   c. fibrinogen
   d. hemoglobin

12

"He fashioned their hearts alike."

PSALMS 33:15

THE HEART

Every minute of every hour of every day, the heart serves as a powerful muscular pump which beats out the steady rhythm of life. Contracting at a rate of 70 to 75 times each minute, the heart generates the all-important pressure necessary for the adequate circulation of blood through the vessels of the body. This amazingly tough muscle pumps over 3,000 gallons of blood every day as it helps to provide the capillaries with quantities of blood sufficient to meet the ever-changing cellular needs. While skeletal muscles can rest for relatively long periods of time, the heart muscle can never indulge in such luxury. For example, if you run up a flight of stairs, the leg muscles can rest as soon as the exercise is completed, but the sturdy heart has only a fraction of a second to rest before it is time for the next contraction.

STRUCTURAL FEATURES

Location and description

The heart is a hollow muscular organ that is slightly larger than your clenched fist. It is located in the *mediastinum*, the space between the lungs, in the thoracic cavity. About two thirds of the heart lies to the left of the midline, and its relation to other organs is illustrated in Figure 1-6. The heart is somewhat cone-shaped, with the base directed upward toward the right and the apex pointing downward to the left where it rests on the diaphragm. If you place your fingers in the space between the 5th and the 6th ribs (about 2 inches below the nipple line of the left breast), you can feel the apex come in contact with the chest wall with each beat of the heart. Nurses occasionally are asked to "take an apical pulse"; this is done by counting the number of heart beats while listening through a stethoscope placed over the apex of the heart.

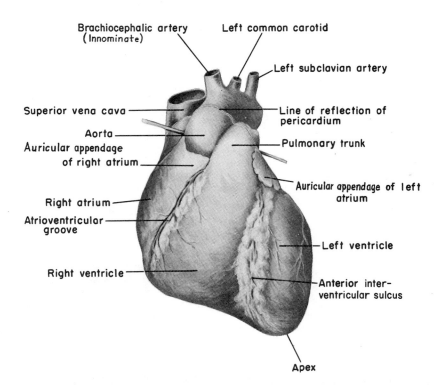

Fig. 12-1. Anterior aspect of heart, showing grooves, beginning of aorta and pulmonary artery, position of right atrium and right and left ventricles. The probe is in the transverse sinus of the pericardium.

Covering of the heart

The heart is covered by a slippery, loose-fitting sac called the **pericardium;** this protective cover consists of 2 parts—an outer fibrous portion and an inner serous portion.

The fibrous pericardium is a tough fibrous membrane; this layer is attached (1) to the large vessels that enter or leave the heart, (2) to the diaphragm, and (3) to the sternum.

The serous pericardium consists of 2 distinct layers: (1) an outer or parietal layer that lines the fibrous pericardium and (2) an inner or visceral layer, the epicardium, which is closely adherent to the heart itself. Between the visceral and the parietal layers of the serous pericardium there is a potential space which contains a small amount of slippery pericardial fluid; this serous fluid serves as a lubricant to reduce friction resulting from movements of the heart as it beats.

An infection of the pericardium is called *pericarditis*. In some persons the inflammatory process may result in the formation of fibrous adhesions between the visceral and the parietal layers; such adhesions tend to constrict the heart and interfere with its activity. In severe cases of constrictive pericarditis it may be necessary to perform a pericardectomy, or removal of the fibrous pericardium with its serous lining.

LEFT COMMON ARTERY
LEFT SUBCLAVIAN ARTERY

BRACHIOCEPHALIC ARTERY
(INNOMINATE)

AORTA

AZYGOS VEIN

SUPERIOR VENA CAVA

LEFT PULMONARY
ARTERY

RIGHT PULMONARY
ARTERY

PULMONARY VEIN

PULMONARY VEIN

PULMONARY VEIN

LEFT ATRIUM

RIGHT ATRIUM

CORONARY SINUS

INFERIOR VENA
CAVA

LEFT VENTRICLE

RIGHT VENTRICLE

APEX

Fig 12-2. Posterior aspect of heart, showing the apex, the coronary sinus, pulmonary veins and venae cavae. The posterior longitudinal sulcus is shown (but not labeled) between the right and the left ventricles. The azygos vein is shown as it empties into the superior vena cava.

Walls of the heart

The walls of the heart are composed of 3 distinct layers. The outer layer is the *epicardium*, or visceral pericardium, as mentioned previously. The middle layer is called the *myocardium*, since it consists of interlacing bundles of cardiac muscle fibers. The arrangement of these muscle bundles is such that their contraction results in a "wringing" or "milking" type of movement that efficiently squeezes blood out of the heart with each beat. Inflammation of the heart muscle is called *myocarditis*.

Lining the inner surface of the myocardial wall is a thin layer of endothelial tissue which is called the *endocardium*. This delicate lining is continu-ous with that of the blood vessels. The endocardium also assists in forming the valves of the heart. Rheumatic fever is a disease that frequently attacks the heart, causing an inflammation of the lining (endocarditis) as well as myocarditis and pericarditis.

Heart chambers and valves

Study of the heart chambers and "one-way" valves is greatly simplified if one thinks of the heart as consisting of 2 separate pumps (right and left) which lie side by side and work in perfect harmony. The right side of the heart is concerned with receiving blood which is low in oxygen and pumping it to capillaries in the lungs. At the same

Handwritten margin notes: "Blood flow sources: superior vena cava + coronary sinus → R ATRIUM", "blood flow valve from lungs → L ATRIUM / MITRAL valve", "R vent / L vent", "up out to caval lungs", "to all parts of body", "interventricular septum"

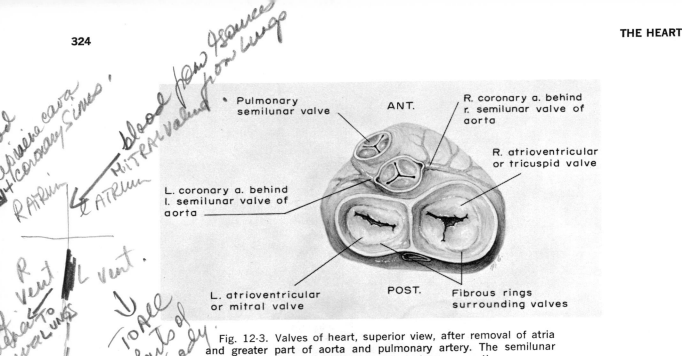

Fig. 12-3. Valves of heart, superior view, after removal of atria and greater part of aorta and pulmonary artery. The semilunar valves are closed; the atrioventricular valves are partly open.

*Diagram labels:*
- Pulmonary semilunar valve
- ANT.
- R. coronary a. behind r. semilunar valve of aorta
- R. atrioventricular or tricuspid valve
- L. coronary a. behind l. semilunar valve of aorta
- L. atrioventricular or mitral valve
- POST.
- Fibrous rings surrounding valves

time, the left side of the heart receives oxygenated blood which has passed through the lung capillaries, and then pumps it into the aorta for distribution to all parts of the body.

The upper or "receiving" chambers of the heart are called the right and left atria. The lower or "dispatching" chambers are called the right and left ventricles. Grooves on the anterior and the posterior surfaces of the heart indicate the underlying dividing lines between chambers (Figs. 12-1 and 12-2). The main branches of the coronary arteries and veins lie in these grooves.

Right Atrium. The right atrium is larger than the left, but its walls are very thin. It receives blood from the upper portion of the body via the superior vena cava and from the lower portion of the body by way of the inferior vena cava. The venae cavae are called the *great veins*. The terminations of the great veins are shown in Figures 12-2 and 12-4. The right atrium also receives blood from the heart muscle itself by way of the coronary sinus (Fig. 12-2).

The right atrium opens into the right ventricle; this opening is surrounded by a fibrous ring that is large enough to admit 3 or 4 fingertips. The 3 leaflets or cusps of the **tricuspid** or **right atrioventricular valve** are attached to the fibrous ring. These leaflets completely close off the atrium from the ventricle during contraction of the latter. The valve as it appears when looking down at it from the atrium is shown in Figure 12-3. The leaflets are composed of folds of endocardium, reinforced with a flat sheet of dense connective tissue.

Left Atrium. The left atrium has thicker walls than the right. It receives blood from the lungs by way of 4 pulmonary veins (Fig. 12-2). The opening between the left atrium and the left ventricle admits only 2 or 3 fingertips, and the 2 leaflets of the **bicuspid**, or **left atrioventricular valve** are attached to the fibrous ring around this opening. Because of its resemblance to a bishop's miter, this valve also is called the **mitral valve**. The purpose of the atrioventricular valves of the heart is to keep the blood flowing in the proper direction. They permit it to flow from atria to ventricles but prevent it from flowing in the reverse direction.

The interatrial septum is the partition that separates the right and left atria. During fetal life there is an opening in this septum, called the *foramen ovale*, which permits a certain amount of blood to flow from right to left atrium, thus by-passing the lung circuit. After birth, when the lungs are functioning, this foramen normally closes; a thin, depressed area, called the fossa ovalis, indicates the site of closure. In some children, the foramen may remain open or patent; this congenital defect is called *patent foramen ovale*.

In addition to the main cavity of each atrium, there is a hollow, external projection that resembles a rooster's comb lying on its side. These protuberances are called the right and left auricular appendages. The internal surface of each appendage is uneven due to the presence of muscular ridges, but the main cavity of the adjacent atrium has a smooth inner surface.

Right Ventricle. The right ventricle receives blood from the right atrium and, following closure of the atrioventricular valve, pumps that blood into the pulmonary artery; this artery arises from the base of the ventricle. Backflow of blood from the artery to the ventricle is prevented by the **pulmonary semilunar valve.** This valve consists of a set of 3 pocketlike flaps that face upward as they arise from the fibrous ring around the orifice of the artery. Blood flows freely out of the heart as the valve flaps are flattened against the arterial wall but is unable to return as the little pockets fill with blood and "balloon out" to block the opening (Fig. 12-3).

In contrast to the thin-walled atrium (which merely empties itself into the adjacent ventricular chamber), the wall of the right ventricle is thicker, since it must generate sufficient pressure to pump blood to the lungs. Also, the inner surface of the ventricle is very uneven due to the presence of a latticework of muscular columns. Some of these columns project like papillae ("nipples") into the ventricular cavity, and for this reason are called *papillary muscles.* From the summits of the papillae you will see slender fibrous strands which extend upward to be attached to the edges of the leaflets of the atrioventricular valve. These

strands are called *chordae tendineae* and are composed of dense fibrous connective tissue covered with endocardium. The function of the chordae tendineae is to keep the valve leaflets from turning inside out as they would do otherwise when the pressure is high in the ventricle. Papillary muscles and chordae tendineae are shown in Figure 12-4.

Left Ventricle. The left ventricle receives blood from the left atrium and, following closure of the atrioventricular valve, pumps it into the aorta. The aorta arises from the base of the left ventricle, and it is the largest artery in the body. Its orifice is guarded by the **aortic semilunar valve,** which has the same pocketlike structural features as does the pulmonary valve.

While the right ventricle pumps blood only to the lungs, the left ventricle must generate sufficient pressure to pump blood to all other parts of the body; consequently, its walls are 3 times as thick and muscular as the right. The lower portion of the left ventricle forms the apex of the heart. The inner surface of the left ventricle is quite similar to that of the right ventricle except that the papillary muscles and chordae tendineae are much larger and stronger to withstand the greater pressure.

The interventricular septum is a thick partition that separates the right and left ventricles. Normally, there is no opening in this septum, but in certain cases of congenital heart disease (p. 378) there may be such a septal defect.

Valvular Disease. Two types of difficulty may arise in connection with heart valves. One type arises when there is narrowing of the fibrous ring to which the leaflets are attached or when the leaflets themselves become thick and stiff and fail to open widely. This condition is called *stenosis,* and when it exists there is difficulty in pumping the blood through the narrowed opening as rapidly as it should be going through. In the second type of difficulty, the edges of the valve leaflets are eroded, or the fibrous ring is stretched. This condition is called *insufficiency* or *regurgitation;* when it exists the valve cannot be closed completely, and blood leaks back through the valve when it is supposed to be flowing in the

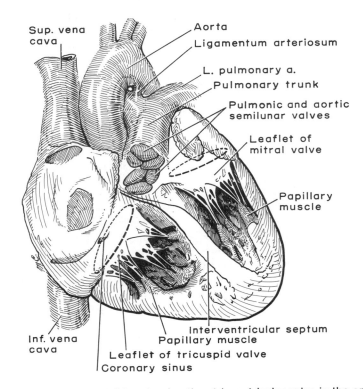

Fig. 12-4. Interior of the ventricles showing the atrioventricular valve in the open position. The dotted circular areas indicate in a highly diagrammatic way the general region of the fibrous ring to which the valve leaflets are attached. The origins of the aorta and pulmonary arteries are also exposed, and the semilunar valves are shown in the closed position.

forward direction. These valvular difficulties are of frequent occurrence in bacterial endocarditis; some persons may have mitral stenosis, mitral regurgitation, aortic stenosis, aortic regurgitation or tricuspid or pulmonary valve impairments. In some persons one valve may exhibit both types of difficulty; the leaflets may be thickened and stiff, and their edges may be eroded by the same disease process.

Modified cardiac muscle tissue

In certain areas of the myocardium the muscle cells are modified and specialized to form the excitatory and conductive system of the heart; this system enables the atria and the ventricles to contract in orderly sequence.

As will be described later in this chapter, one very important property of cardiac muscle is its automaticity, or its inherent ability to contract rhythmically in the absence of external stimuli. Those cells that have the most rapid inherent rhythm are found in the **S-A node** (sinoatrial node) of the conduction system; this knot of modified myocardium is located in the wall of the right atrium near the entrance of the superior vena cava. Since the heart beat normally begins in this area, the S-A node is called the *"pacemaker"* of the heart.

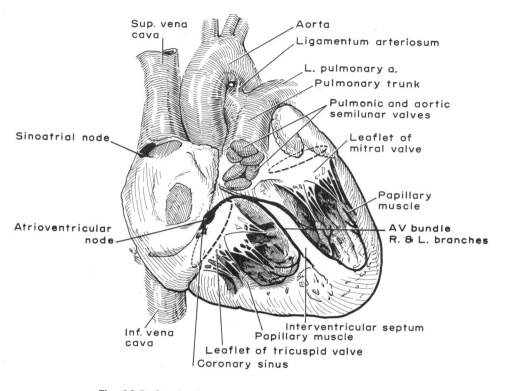

Fig. 12-5. Conducting system. Diagram showing relations of the sinoatrial node, the atrioventricular node, the atrioventricular bundle and its branches.

A second knot of modified myocardium is the **A-V node** (atrioventricular node) which is located in the lower part of the interatrial septum near the opening of the coronary sinus. The A-V node is continuous with the **A-V bundle** (atrioventricular bundle) which serves as the connecting link between the atria and the ventricles; this modified myocardium also is known as the *bundle of His*, after its discoverer. The A-V bundle divides into branches which extend downward into the interventricular septum where they become continuous with the Purkinje fibers; these fibers form a widespread network which penetrates both right and left ventricular muscle masses.

The importance of the A-V node and the A-V bundle becomes apparent when one considers the fact that the muscle mass of the two atria is completely separate and distinct from the muscle mass of the two ventricles; the rings of fibrous tissue which encircle the openings of the atrioventricular valves interrupt the continuity of muscle between the upper and the lower chambers. However, the A-V bundle serves as a bridge whereby the rhythmic "beat" is transmitted from atria to ventricles. Figure 12-5 illustrates the conduction system of the heart. The relation of this system to the cardiac cycle is described on page 332.

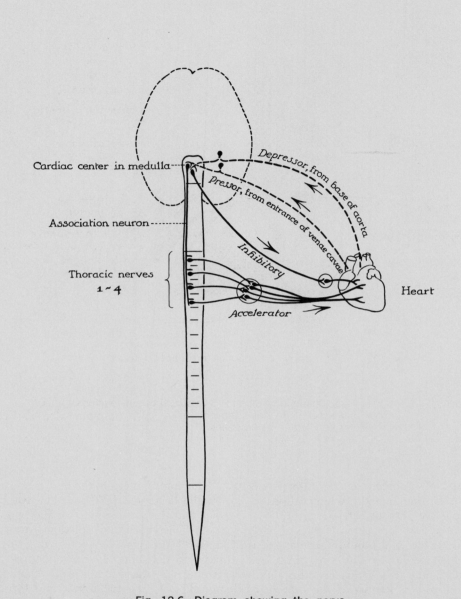

Fig. 12-6. Diagram showing the nerve supply of the heart. Both afferent and efferent supplies are indicated.

Nerve supply

Although cardiac muscle possesses the property of automaticity, it also has an efferent and an afferent nerve supply (Fig. 12-6). These nerves play an important part in adjusting the rate of heart beat to meet the ever-changing needs of the body.

Efferent Fibers. There is a double efferent nerve supply that transmits "orders" from cardiac centers in the medulla oblongata to the heart. These fibers are derived from both divisions of the autonomic system (pp. 248–257).

1. *Parasympathetic* or inhibitory fibers, traveling in the vagus nerves, conduct impulses that slow and weaken the beat of the heart. Slowing of the heart rate provides longer periods of rest for the cardiac muscle cells. The vagus nerves to the heart are in tonic activity, which means that impulses are passing continuously to the heart from the center in the medulla. If the vagus nerves, which maintain a slow rate, are cut, the heart beats much faster than when the nerves are intact.

2. *Sympathetic* or accelerator fibers, arising from the upper thoracic region of the spinal cord and traveling in cervical cardiac nerves, conduct impulses that speed and strengthen the heart beat. Such acceleration is particularly important during times of physical or emotional stress. For example, note the change in your heart beat the next time you run up a flight of stairs, or when the teacher unexpectedly asks you a question in class.

Afferent Fibers. The only sensation that may be aroused by impulses from the heart is that of pain. Whenever there is interference with the blood flow through the arteries of the heart, the resultant lack of oxygen in the myocardium serves to stimulate the receptors of certain visceral afferent fibers. These fibers then conduct impulses to the CNS, and the individual experiences a sensation of pain.

Other visceral afferent fibers conduct impulses that are initiated by pressure-sensitive receptors in the walls of the right atrium and adjacent portions of the venae cavae. These impulses figure prominently in a reflex which causes acceleration of the heart during exercise (p. 332).

Blood supply to the myocardium

One might think that since blood is flowing through the heart almost constantly no other blood supply is needed, but the blood in the cardiac chambers comes in contact only with the endocardium and does not reach the myocardium. Consequently, the thick myocardium needs its own blood supply, like any other mass of muscular tissue.

The arteries that supply the myocardium are called the right and left *coronary arteries*. These two important blood vessels are the very first branches of the aorta, and their orifices may be seen in the aortic wall near the semilunar valve (Fig. 12-3). The coronary arteries encircle the heart, and their many branches convey blood to capillaries in all parts of the myocardium. After delivering oxygen and nutrients to the cardiac muscle cells and picking up waste products, the blood flows into the coronary veins. The principal coronary veins empty into the coronary sinus which in turn conveys blood to the right atrium to be recirculated through the lungs, etc. However, a few small coronary veins empty directly into both sides of the heart. The larger coronary vessels are illustrated in Figure 12-7.

The efficient contraction of heart muscle is dependent on a good blood supply, and any interference with the normal flow of blood through the coronary vessels may result in impaired cardiac function. For example, in some persons the smooth muscle in the walls of the coronary arteries may undergo spasmodic contractions; this in turn causes such a narrowing of the vessels that blood flow is temporarily shut off. In others, the walls of the coronary arteries undergo hardening (arteriosclerosis) or fatty degeneration (atherosclerosis); these conditions also interfere with the proper supply of oxygen and nutrients to the massive heart muscle. A cardinal symptom of oxygen-lack in the myocardium is *angina pectoris*, or paroxysmal pain that may be referred to the left shoulder and then radiate down the left arm; this pain may occur during physical exertion or severe emotional stress. The mechanism of referred pain is described on page 268. Certain drugs, such as

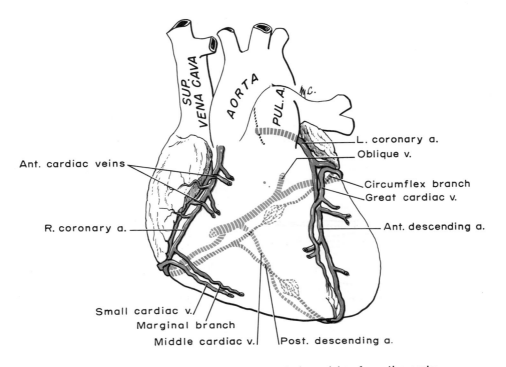

Fig. 12-7. Diagram of the coronary arteries arising from the aorta
and encircling the heart. Some of the coronary veins are also shown.

nitroglycerine and amyl nitrite, help to dispel an-
ginal pain by causing a dilatation of the coronary
arteries and thus improving blood flow to the
myocardium.

When there is a complete and prolonged lack
of blood supply to any area of heart muscle there
may be actual death of tissue. For example, in
coronary thrombosis a blood clot plugs up an artery and prevents blood from reaching the tissues
that lie beyond the point of obstruction. This area
which has been cut off from its blood supply is
known medically as an "infarct" or an area of
myocardial infarction. The pain associated with
myocardial infarction usually is more severe than
that of angina pectoris and is not relieved by
nitroglycerin. This clinical picture commonly is
referred to as a "heart attack" or a "coronary."
Occlusion of a coronary artery may result in sudden death if a large area of myocardium is deprived of its blood supply.

If the victim survives the initial attack, the
physician will attempt to assess the amount of
damage, if any, to the myocardium. One test that
may prove helpful is a laboratory determination
of the amount of glutamic oxalacetic transaminase
in the serum (SGOT). Normally, this enzyme is
present in the blood in the amount of 10 to 40
units per cc., but when cardiac muscle cells are
injured they release additional quantities of enzyme into the bloodstream. Thus a mild heart
attack may elevate the SGOT to 90 or 100 units,
and a severe attack to as high as 500 units. Inasmuch as the rise is proportional to the severity
of myocardial damage, it serves as a guide to the
physician in prescribing treatment.

THE WORK OF THE HEART

The function of the heart is to pump into the
arterial system that blood which returns to it

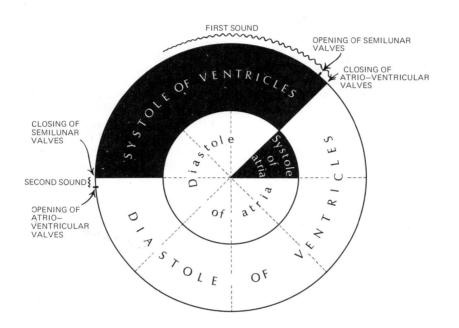

Fig. 12-8. Cardiac cycle. The heart rate represented in the diagram is 75 beats per minute; each cycle lasts 8/10 of a second; each sector represents 1/10 second. The inner circle represents the atria; atrial systole lasts 1/10 second, and atrial diastole, 7/10 second. The outer circle represents the ventricles; ventricular systole lasts 3/10 second, and diastole, 5/10 second. The atrioventricular valves close at the beginning of ventricular systole; the semilunar valves open shortly thereafter. The latter valves close at the beginning of ventricular diastole, and the atrioventricular valves open shortly thereafter. The first sound is due to the closing of the atrioventricular valves and systole of the ventricle; the second sound is due to the closing of the semilunar valves; it is of shorter duration than the first.

from the venous system. The right side of the heart receives poorly oxygenated blood from the venae cavae and pumps it into the pulmonary artery for a trip to the lungs; the left side of the heart receives richly oxygenated blood from the pulmonary veins and pumps it into the aorta for a trip to all other tissues in the body. The pressure necessary for this vital task is generated by powerful contractions of the cardiac musculature. However, the rate and the force of these contractions, as well as the amount of blood ejected from the heart with each beat, will vary according to the changing needs of the body. The cardiac control mechanisms are described in Chapter 14.

The cardiac cycle

One cardiac cycle means one complete heartbeat, consisting of contraction (*systole*) and relaxation (*diastole*) of the muscular heart walls. The heartbeat is initiated by the "pacemaker cells" of the S-A node in the right atrium. These specialized cells generate an impulse that sweeps through the muscle mass of both atria, much like the ripple pattern produced when a pebble is dropped into a pool of still water; this impulse causes both atria to contract simultaneously.

When the atrial impulse reaches the A-V node and the related A-V bundle, conduction is slowed somewhat. However, once the impulse reaches the mass of ventricular muscle it spreads rapidly from fiber to fiber throughout both ventricles, causing them to contract simultaneously. The slight delay in conduction over the node and the bundle branches provides sufficient time for the atria to complete their work before ventricular contraction begins.

The duration of one cardiac cycle is 0.8 of a second when the heart is beating at a rate of 75 times per minute. As illustrated in Figure 12-8, atrial systole lasts 0.1 of a second, and diastole 0.7 of a second. In other words, the atria work 0.1 and rest 0.7 of each second. Ventricular systole lasts 0.3 of a second, and diastole 0.5, which means that the ventricles work 0.3 and rest 0.5 of each second. The entire heart rests 0.4 of a

second, and the period during which both atria and ventricles are relaxed is called *diastasis*.

If the heart is to function efficiently, the events of the cardiac cycle must follow each other in orderly sequence, and the conduction system of the heart must be in good working order. Impairment of myocardial function is the causative factor in *heart failure*, a broad term which means that the heart is unable to maintain an adequate output of blood in relation to the needs of the body.

Cardiac output

Under average conditions, each ventricle pumps out about 70 ml. of blood with each contraction; this is called the *stroke volume*. If the stroke volume is multiplied by the number of heartbeats per minute, one arrives at the "minute volume" or *cardiac output*. For example, if the stroke volume is 70 ml. and the heart is beating at a rate of 72 times per minute, the cardiac output is 5,040 ml. In other words, each ventricle is pumping about 5 L., or quarts, of blood every minute. During strenuous exercise the heart pumps more rapidly, and the cardiac output may be increased to 15 or 20 L. per minute, thus helping to meet the needs of the hard-working muscles. Cardiac output varies during many physiologic activities and in disease.

There are various methods whereby cardiac output may be estimated, but the most accurate figures are obtained during *cardiac catheterization* (p. 337) when the oxygen content of blood samples taken directly from the right side of the heart can be compared with the oxygen content of blood which has passed through the lungs.

Variations in heart rate

There are many factors which influence the heart rate, but **exercise** probably is the best known. Busy muscles require increased delivery of oxygen and swift removal of waste products if they are to function at peak efficiency; consequently, the heart beats rapidly to pump more blood through the "muscle circuits."

The **size** of an individual tends to influence

heart rate; generally speaking, the larger the size, the slower the heartbeat. This is true also of lower animals, as shown by the following examples: elephants, about 20; rabbits, 150; and mice, 700 beats per minute.

Age is another factor in determining heart rate. In a fetus the rate is between 120 and 160; in an infant, 110 to 130; in a child, 72 to 92; and in adults, 65 to 80 beats per minute.

Sex has an influence on heart rate in that women have rates between 70 and 80, while the range for men is between 65 and 70 beats per minute.

Certain **hormones** have a definite effect on heart rate. Epinephrine (Adrenalin), a secretion of the adrenal glands, causes an increase in both the rate and the strength of heartbeat. An increase in the amount of thyroid hormone (thyroxine) in the blood also speeds up the heart rate.

When the body **temperature** rises, as during fever, the heart rate is faster; when the temperature is low, as during hypothermia, the heart beats very slowly.

Blood pressure changes have a marked influence on heart rate. This factor is described in detail in Chapter 14.

Properties of cardiac muscle

Extensibility. This property of heart muscle makes it possible for the heart to dilate enough to receive the blood as it enters from the veins. As the heart fills with blood its fibers are stretched, and, as was found in both skeletal and smooth muscle, when muscle fibers are stretched the contraction is more forceful. The better the heart fills, which means the greater the diastolic volume of the ventricle, the more forceful is the beat. This occurs so consistently that it is called *Starling's "law of the heart"* (so called because it was first described by Dr. Starling).

Automaticity. The term "automatic" is used in reference to the ability of a tissue to generate spontaneous and rhythmic impulses. As noted in Chapter 4, (p. 120), cardiac muscle possesses such ability and can execute rhythmic contractions even though its extrinsic nerve supply has been severed. This property of automaticity, or *rhythmic contractility,* is so highly developed in cardiac muscle, that if a heart is kept under proper conditions it will continue to beat after removal from the body. In an embryo, the heart begins to beat long before any nerves have grown out to it, which is additional proof that the beat is independent of nerves. A third proof of the "myogenic" origin of the heartbeat is the fact that fragments of heart muscle that are growing in tissue cultures beat rhythmically.

In order to keep a heart beating in the laboratory, it must be bathed by a "balanced" solution of sodium, potassium and calcium chlorides. If the solution is not balanced properly, the heart will soon stop beating; likewise, if the salts in one's plasma are not in proper balance, the activity of the heart is altered and may even cease.

Fig. 12-9. Frog's heart. The heart was stimulated at the time indicated by the arrow. A premature systole (contraction) followed; the next diastole (relaxation) was of longer duration than usual. This long rest period is called the compensatory pause.

Refractory Periods. The *absolute* refractory period is the time during which an excitable tissue will not respond to any stimulus, no matter how strong the latter is. The absolute refractory period is very long for heart muscle, since it lasts throughout systole. Because of the long absolute refractory period, no summation or tetanic contractions are possible in heart muscle. This is an excellent protection, since the heart would be worthless as a pump if it went into a tetanic or sustained contraction.

When the absolute refractory period is over, the *relative* refractory period begins, and the heart gradually recovers its excitability. The relative refractory period coincides with the early diastolic period of the ventricle. A strong stimulus given at this time can cause a contraction before the next rhythmic contraction is due. The early beat is smaller in amplitude than a regular beat and is called a *premature systole*. Thus, it is possible to make a beat appear ahead of time, by applying a strong stimulus early in diastole.

A premature systole is followed by a longer diastole, to compensate for its lack of rest after the previous beat. The long diastole is called a *compensatory pause*. Such a pause, following a premature beat is illustrated in Figure 12-9.

An occasional premature beat is of frequent occurrence in the human heart. The cause is not known, but it is some stimulus within the heart muscle itself. The premature beat is small and passes unnoticed, but the person may be conscious of the compensatory pause and say, "My heart has just skipped a beat." The heart does not skip a beat, but the premature contraction is not recognized, and only the compensatory pause comes to the attention.

The All-or-None Law. This refers to the fact that if a heart beats, it gives the strongest contraction that is possible under the conditions existing at that moment. There is no such thing as "gradation" in heartbeats, as is possible in skeletal muscle contractions. In skeletal muscle it is possible to have different numbers of motor units active, but in the heart the muscle mass of the atria is one unit and that of the ventricles is a second unit, due to the branching and the interlacing of the muscle fibers.

In order to illustrate the above fundamental fact about heart muscle in the laboratory, it is necessary to have a quiescent ventricle. This means that only the lower portion of the ventricle of a frog's heart is retained and arranged for stimulation and recording. The strength of the stimu-

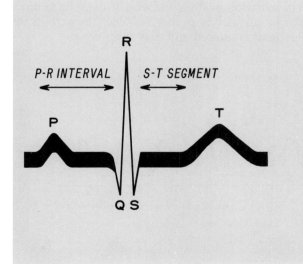

Fig. 12-10. Diagram of the electrical pattern of one cardiac cycle. The P wave represents activity related to atrial contraction; the QRS complex is related to ventricular contraction, and the T wave represents recovery phase. See text for description.

P (Q R S) S,

lus is increased, and the resulting contractions are recorded. No matter how greatly the stimulus is increased, the height of contraction always is the same (Fig. 4-19). This is in striking contrast to skeletal muscle, in which an increase in the strength of the stimulus brings more motor units into activity and a greater contraction follows.

Electrical Activity. Every beat of the heart is accompanied by an electrical change or *action current* (p. 119). Electrolytes in the body fluids and tissues act as conductors to the skin surface; metal leads applied to the skin then conduct the current to an instrument (electrocardiograph) that makes a graphic tracing of the activity. This tracing, called an *electrocardiogram* (ECG), is a valuable diagnostic tool in various types of heart disease.

As illustrated in Figure 12-10, the electrical activity during each cardiac cycle is characterized by 5 wave deflections that are arbitrarily designated as P, Q, R, S and T. Any pathologic process that disturbs the electrical activity of the heart will produce characteristic changes in one or more of the waves.

1. The P wave represents the electrical activity associated with depolarization of the atria. Normal P waves indicate that the impulse originated in the S-A node and then spread through the atria; if the P waves are missing or wandering it suggests that the impulse originated outside the S-A node.

2. The P-R interval is that period of time from the start of the P wave to the beginning of the QRS complex; it indicates the time required for the original impulse to reach the ventricles. If this interval is prolonged, it suggests that there is a conduction delay in the A-V node.

3. The QRS waves represent the activity associated with depolarization of the ventricles; it reflects the time required for the impulse to spread through the A-V bundle and its branches. If the duration of this impulse is increased, it shows that the ventricles have been stimulated in a delayed, abnormal manner, such as might occur in a bundle branch block.

4. The S-T segment represents the period between completion of ventricular depolarization and the start of repolarization. If there is some injury to the muscle, as in acute myocardial infarction, the S-T segment may be elevated or depressed.

5. The T wave represents the recovery phase following contraction. If there is tissue injury or ischemia, repolarization is abnormal and the T wave may be inverted.

Fig. 12-11. Normal electrocardiogram showing the electrical pattern of several cardiac cycles. The Q, S, and T waves are not labeled.

The electrocardiogram provides information regarding the electrical activity of the heart, but it does not reflect the actual physical state or pumping function of this vital organ. One should keep in mind the fact that the electrocardiogram may be perfectly normal in the presence of severe heart disease unless the pathologic process disturbs the heart's electrical activity.

In some persons the atria do not beat normally but show a pathologic type of contraction called *fibrillation;* such contractions are extremely rapid, fluttery and ineffective. The electrocardiogram in atrial fibrillation shows no P waves at all, and the R waves appear at a rapid and irregular rate. While atrial fibrillation is compatible with life, ventricular fibrillation generally is a terminal event, since the chaotic contractions do not pump blood into the great arteries; this is one of the major hazards of cardiac surgery, particularly when the operation is conducted under hypothermia, since severe cooling tends to increase the incidence of fibrillation.

Digitalis is a drug that frequently is used to improve myocardial function in atrial fibrillation and other forms of heart disease. It not only increases the force of each beat but also reduces the rate by slowing impulse conduction between the atria and the ventricles. However, excessive amounts of digitalis may completely stop A-V conduction; this condition, called *heart block,* also may be caused by disease or injury to the conduction system of the heart. Ventricles which are thus "isolated" or functionally separated from the atria will beat at their own slow rate instead of following the atrial beat. For this reason, the electrocardiogram in heart block is characterized by R waves which appear about 20 times per minute, and the P waves about 72 times per minute.

Pressure changes within the heart

The amount of blood and the pressure which it exerts in the heart chambers varies during each phase of the cardiac cycle. Knowledge of such pressure differences is essential to a full understanding of valve action. The valves of the heart are inert structures that are opened and closed only because of differences in pressure exerted by the blood on their two surfaces.

Let us begin with the moment at the end of ventricular systole, when the atria are relatively full of blood and the atrioventricular or A-V valves are still closed, and trace the events step by step. As the blood continues to enter the atria from the veins, the pressure in the atria soon exceeds that in the relaxed ventricles, and the A-V valves open due to the greater pressure on the atrial surface of the leaflets.

When the A-V valves open, blood flows rapidly into the ventricles, and the valve leaflets float in midstream. The two atria contract simultaneously and pump the blood remaining in them into the ventricles, and ventricular systole begins.

As soon as the ventricles begin to contract, the A-V valves close, due to the increasing pressure on the ventricular surface of their leaflets. The leaflets are kept from being pushed up into the atria, like an umbrella being prevented from turning inside out, by the contraction of the papillary muscles, which hold the chordae tendineae taut.

Ventricular systole continues with a very sharp rise in intraventricular pressure, until it becomes great enough to force the semilunar valves open. The extent to which the pressure rises to accomplish this varies in the two ventricles. The pressure in the right ventricle rises to only about one sixth that of the left ventricle, and the pressure in the pulmonary artery is only about one sixth that in the aorta, but the valves open simultaneously as soon as the pressure in the corresponding artery is exceeded.

As soon as the semilunar valves are open, the ventricles begin to empty, the right into the pulmonary artery and the left into the aorta. Ventricular systole continues for about 0.3 of a second, during which time most of the blood is pumped out. With the onset of ventricular diastole, the intraventricular pressure falls rapidly.

As soon as the pressure in the right ventricle falls below that in the pulmonary artery and that in the left ventricle falls below the pressure in the aorta, the blood tends to come back into the ventricles as well as to go forward. The backward flow closes the semilunar valves. The elasticity of the large arteries then comes into play and forces the blood onward.

Meanwhile, the atria have been filling with blood coming in from the veins. As the ventricular diastole continues, the pressure within the ventricles falls below that of the atria, the A-V valves open, and the cardiac cycle begins again. The above events are repeated over and over with each beat, as long as you live.

The opening and the closing of the valves are indicated in Figure 12-8. One should study valvular action in connection with pressure changes in order to understand it clearly. The sole function of the valves it to keep blood flowing in an onward direction. When the A-V valves close at the beginning of ventricular systole, they prevent the passage of blood from the ventricles, back into the atria. When the semilunar valves are forced open early in ventricular systole, they allow blood to flow from the left ventricle into the aorta and from the right ventricle into the pulmonary artery. When ventricular systole is completed, the semilunar valves are closed because the elasticity of the large arteries tends to force blood in both directions, and that which flows back toward the heart closes the semilunar valves. Blood enters both atria from the related veins throughout ventricular systole and diastasis. When ventricular diastole occurs, the ventricular pressure falls, the weight of blood in the atria forces the A-V valves to open, and blood enters the ventricles.

Heart sounds

If you listen (auscultate) with a stethoscope over the heart you will hear two sounds with each heartbeat. The first is longer and louder than the second and sounds like *lubb;* it is due to the closure of the A-V valves and contraction of the mass of ventricular muscle. The second sound is shorter and softer and is due to the closure of the semilunar valves; it sounds like *dup.* The time in the cycle in which each sound is heard is indicated in Figure 12-8.

Since valve closure is the major contributor to heart sounds, one would expect to hear abnormal sounds if the valves failed to function properly. For example, pathologic *heart murmurs* are abnormal sounds which frequently accompany rheumatic heart disease and congenital anomalies of the heart (p. 378). If valves fail to close tightly (insufficiency) and blood leaks back (regurgitation), or if a valve orifice is narrowed and constricted (stenosis), the resulting turbulence in blood flow will be heard through the stethoscope as murmurs.

In *mitral insufficiency* the first heart sound is altered as blood leaks back into the left atrium during contraction of the ventricle; this regurgitation of blood results in a systolic murmur. However, in *mitral stenosis* a murmur is heard just prior to ventricular contraction, when the atrium is pumping blood through the constricted valve, and is called a presystolic murmur. In *aortic insufficiency* blood leaks back into the left ventricle from the aorta during ventricular diastole and is responsible for a diastolic murmur. In *aortic stenosis* a systolic murmur is heard as blood is forced through the constricted semilunar valve. The tricuspid and the pulmonary valves may be similarly involved, but the valves of the left side of the heart are the ones most commonly affected by pathologic changes in adult life.

In the diagnosis of pathologic heart conditions the physician makes use of electrocardiograms, x-ray pictures of the chest, fluoroscopic examinations, heart sounds and other findings of the physical examination. Figure 12-12 is an x-ray picture of a normal heart, and Figure 12-13 illustrates left ventricular enlargement or hypertrophy. Hypertrophy of the left ventricle occurs in such conditions as aortic regurgitation and high blood pressure (hypertension).

Cardiac catheterization

The insertion of a long thin tube, or catheter, into the heart is referred to as cardiac catheterization. The catheter is passed into the venous system through one of the superficial veins (basilic or cephalic) of the left forearm near the bend of the elbow; veins in the right forearm may be used, but those on the left permit entry into the heart

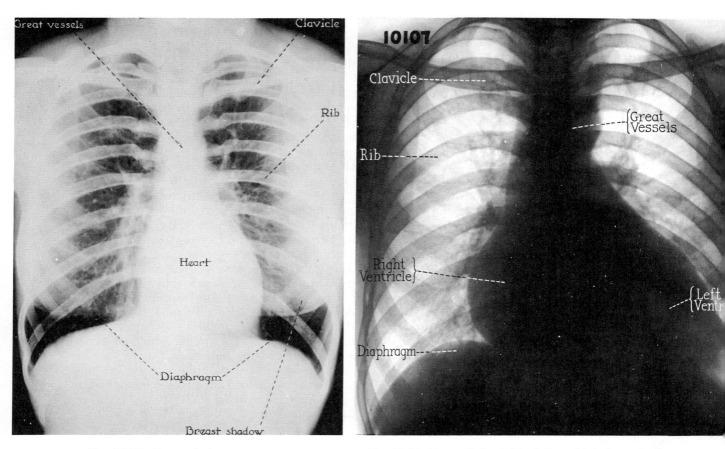

Fig. 12-12. X-ray of chest; normal heart shadow.

Fig. 12-13. X-ray of chest. The left ventricle is markedly enlarged; the right ventricle is moderately enlarged. The great vessels are moderately dilated. (From Dr. Vastine, Woman's Medical College Hospital)

from a better angle. While looking throught a fluoroscope, the doctor gradually advances the catheter until its tip enters the right atrium, passes through the tricuspid valve into the right ventricle and then into the pulmonary artery (Fig. 12-14). Blood samples for chemical analysis are taken from each chamber and from the pulmonary artery. In addition, by measuring pressures in the different chambers, the presence of defective valves can be detected. This is a painless procedure, and general anesthesia usually is not required for mature patients.

The importance of cardiac catheterization in the diagnosis of various types of congenital heart disorders has been well established, and it is a routine procedure in many hospitals. In addition to its value in clinical medicine, cardiac catheterization has become equally important in the study of cardiovascular physiology in experimental laboratories. For example, chemical analysis of blood samples taken from the pulmonary artery is an essential step in the process of calculating cardiac output.

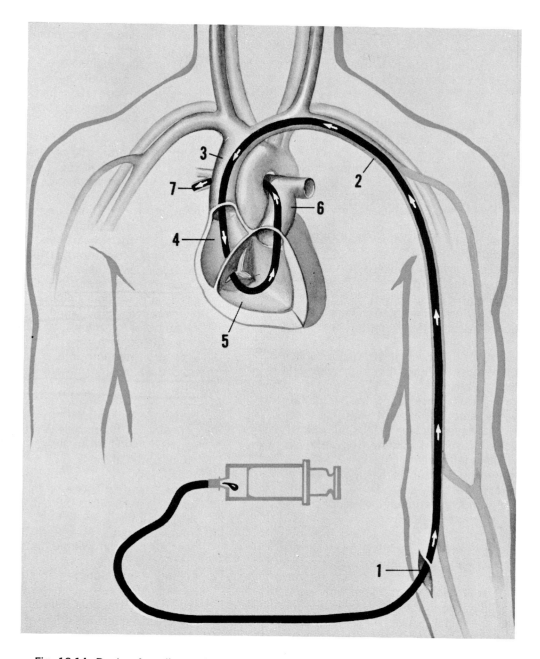

Fig. 12-14. Route of cardiac catheter. Catheter is introduced through cutdown, into the basilic vein (1); thence into the subclavian vein (2); into the superior vena cava (3); into the right atrium (4); into the right ventricle (5); into the main pulmonary trunk (6); and into the right pulmonary artery (7). (Adapted from R.N., February 1958)

SUMMARY

1. Structural features
   A. Hollow, muscular organ in mediastinum; base directed upward to right, apex downward to left
   B. Covering
      a. Pericardial sac, loose-fitting
      b. Outer fibrous portion lined with serous, parietal pericardium
      c. Serous, visceral pericardium closely covers heart
      d. Pericardial space between parietal and visceral layers contains slippery fluid
   C. Walls of heart
      a. Outer layer—epicardium (visceral pericardium)
      b. Muscular layer—myocardium
      c. Lining—endocardium
   D. Heart chambers and valves
      a. Right atrium receives from venae cavae and coronary sinus; empties into right ventricle
      b. Right atrioventricular (tricuspid) valve prevents backflow from right ventricle to right atrium
      c. Left atrium receives from pulmonary veins; empties into left ventricle
      d. Left atrioventricular (bicuspid, mitral) valve prevents backflow from left ventricle to left atrium
      e. Interatrial septum is partition between atria
      f. Right and left auricular appendages lie on top of atria
      g. Right ventricle pumps blood into pulmonary artery; backflow from artery prevented by pulmonary semilunar valve
      h. Left ventricle pumps blood into aorta; backflow from aorta prevented by aortic semilunar valve. Left ventricular walls thicker than right, must generate more pressure to pump blood into larger circuit
      i. Interventricular septum is partition between ventricles
   E. Modified cardiac muscle tissue
      a. Forms conduction system of heart
      b. S-A node called "pacemaker"; heartbeat normally begins here
      c. A-V node and bundle serve as connecting link between atria and ventricles; transmit beat across gap in muscular continuity
   F. Nerve supply
      a. Efferent fibers: parasympathetic in vagus nerve, slow the heart; sympathetic in cardiac nerves speed the heart
      b. Afferent fibers stimulated by lack of oxygen in myocardium; pain
   G. Blood supply to myocardium
      a. Right and left coronary arteries branch to capillaries in heart wall
      b. Coronary veins drain capillaries; most empty into coronary sinus
      c. Interference with blood supply may cause "heart attack" or "coronary"
2. Work of the heart
   A. Sole function to pump into arterial system that blood which returns to it from venous system
      a. Right side of heart receives poorly oxygenated blood, pumps to lungs
      b. Left side of heart receives highly oxygenated blood from lungs, pumps to other parts of body
   B. Cardiac cycle
      a. Systole and diastole (one complete heartbeat); requires 0.8 sec. with heart rate of 75 beats per minute
      b. Impulse begins at S-A node, sweeps over atria; atrial systole lasts 0.1 sec., diastole 0.7 sec.
      c. A-V node and bundle conduct impulse to ventricles as atria contract; ventricular contraction follows, lasts 0.3 sec.; ventricular diastole 0.5 sec.
   C. Cardiac output
      a. About 70 cc. of blood with each beat; called stroke volume
      b. At 72 beats/minute, minute volume or cardiac output is about 5 L. May be

increased to 15 or 20 L. during exercise

D. Factors causing variations in heart rate
   a. Size
   b. Age
   c. Sex
   d. Hormones
   e. Body temperature
   f. Blood pressure

E. Properties of cardiac muscle
   a. Extensibility: stretches when filled with blood; more forceful beat
   b. Automaticity: ability to generate spontaneous and rhythmic beat
   c. Refractory periods: absolute, will not respond to stimulus; relative, gradually recovers excitability, strong stimulus at this time may cause premature systole followed by compensatory pause
   d. All-or-none law: gives strongest contraction possible under existing conditions; beats as one unit
   e. Electrical change: action currents accompany contractions; can be recorded; electrocardiogram

F. Pressure changes within heart
   a. Blood moves from area of greater pressure to area of lower pressure
   b. Contraction of atria forces blood into empty ventricles; A-V valves open
   c. Contraction of ventricles raises pressure so that blood flows into arteries; semilunar valves open and A-V valves close to prevent backflow into atria
   d. After ventricles empty, semilunar valves close as pressure higher in arteries; elasticity of arteries forces blood onward to capillaries

G. Heart sounds
   a. First sound "lubb," due to contraction of ventricles and closure of A-V valves
   b. Second sound "dup," due to closure of semilunar valves
   c. Valvular disease leads to abnormal sounds called murmurs

H. Cardiac catheterization
   a. Insertion of catheter into chambers of heart
   b. Blood samples and blood pressure measurement facilitates diagnosis of heart defects

PRACTICAL APPLICATIONS AND QUESTIONS

(Encircle the letter of the *best* answer to each of the following questions.)

A. *While working on the medical wards of the hospital, one may expect to care for patients with the following cardiac pathology:*

1. Mitral stenosis. Narrowing of the mitral valve prevents the easy flow of blood
   a. from right atrium to right ventricle
   b. from left atrium to left ventricle
   c. from right ventricle through the pulmonary artery
   d. from left ventricle through the aorta

2. Bacterial endocarditis. This refers to an inflammation of the
   a. heart muscle
   b. covering of the heart
   c. nodes and bundle
   d. lining of the heart

3. Coronary thrombosis. Thrombus formation in one of the coronary arteries may result in the death of tissue that is cut off from its blood supply. Such a condition is referred to as
   a. rheumatic heart disease
   b. mitral insufficiency
   c. myocardial infarction
   d. constrictive pericarditis

4. Heart block. Injury to the A-V node means that
   a. the efferent nerves to the heart must control the beat
   b. the ventricles will contract at a slow rate
   c. the atria will no longer be able to function
   d. the S-A node will speed ventricular contraction

B. *Jimmy was admitted to the hospital for a series of diagnostic studies after his family physician suspected the presence of a patent foramen ovale.*

1. The foramen ovale normally closes soon after birth; thus, one that remains open would be a congenital
    a. atrial septal defect
    b. ventricular septal defect
    c. myocardial defect
    d. valvular defect

2. A record of the action currents which accompany each heart beat is called
    a. an encephalogram
    b. a ventriculogram
    c. an electrocardiogram
    d. an angiocardiogram

3. While listening to Jimmy's heart through a stethoscope the doctor heard distinctive sounds which gave him information concerning the
    a. cardiac output
    b. efficiency of heart valves
    c. conduction system
    d. myocardial automaticity

THE MAJOR BLOOD VESSELS AND LYMPHATICS

The circulatory system also is known as the **cardiovascular system,** since it consists of the heart and the blood vessels. As described in Chapter 12, the muscular heart serves as a "pump" which ejects into the arterial portion of the system that blood which returns to it from the venous system. The blood vessels (arteries, capillaries and veins) sometimes are referred to as the "plumbing" of the circulatory system, since they are tubular structures that transport the life-sustaining blood to and from all parts of the body.

The lymphatic circulatory system is structurally and functionally related to the blood circulatory system. Lymph vessels, like blood vessels, are widely distributed throughout the body, but they are concerned with the transport of lymph rather than blood.

The arteries

Arteries are elastic, muscular tubes through which blood flows from the heart to the capillaries. The great arteries which arise from the ventricles give off branches that divide and subdivide, on and on, becoming smaller and smaller as they extend to various parts of the body. The smallest arteries, called *arterioles,* end in the microscopic capillary networks which permeate every organ of the body.

With each ventricular contraction, blood is pumped under pressure into the pulmonary artery and the aorta, causing them to become stretched or distended with blood. Between beats of the heart these elastic tubes recoil, forcing the blood onward in a pulsating wave that sweeps through the entire arterial system; consequently, when an artery is cut, the blood flows in spurts which reflect the ventricular beat of the heart. Obviously, such vessels need strong walls to withstand the pressure of the blood that surges within them.

Fig. 13-1. Cross sections of medium-sized artery and vein, showing the tunica intima, tunica media and tunica externa (adventitia) × 250.

Coats. The thickness of arterial walls varies with the caliber of the vessel. As large arteries branch into smaller ones, the walls become progressively thinner, but in any case there are 3 coats or layers of tissue in the wall (Fig. 13-1).

1. The inner layer, or *tunica intima*, consists of endothelium which rests on an elastic membrane.

2. The middle layer, or *tunica media*, constitutes the bulk of the arterial wall. It is composed primarily of elastic connective tissue in large arteries, such as the aorta, but in smaller arteries, smooth muscle predominates; contraction or relaxation of this muscle makes possible the constriction or the dilatation of the vessel.

3. The outer layer, or *tunica externa* (adventitia), consists largely of fibrous connective tissue which gives strength to the wall. Although this layer has some "give" to it as blood surges through the vessel, it resists rupture even when the blood pressure is elevated. The thickness of arterial walls prevents them from collapsing when cut; consequently, arterial bleeding may be difficult to control by simple pressure if a large vessel is cut.

As you might expect, there can be abnormal changes in the walls of the arteries. Sometimes there is such a change in structure that the wall becomes weak and undergoes a marked dilatation in some portion. The dilated sac which results is called an *aneurysm*. The most frequent site of aneurysm formation is in the ascending portion of the aorta, but it may occur elsewhere. Aneurysms pulsate with each beat of the heart, and one great danger is the possibility that the weakened wall will rupture, causing a fatal hemorrhage. In aortic aneurysm there also is the danger of suffocation if the mass exerts sufficient pressure on the neighboring trachea.

Arteriosclerosis, hardening of the arteries, is a more common affliction of the vessels, and one that most of us will experience as we grow older. Degenerative changes in the arterial walls result in a decrease in elastic tissue and, in some cases, excessive deposits of calcium. These changes also may be accompanied by *atherosclerosis,* a fatty degeneration and lipid infiltration of the vessel walls. Many disturbing changes in function may follow such structural alterations.

Blood Supply. Nourishment of tissue cells in the aforementioned layers depends on tiny blood vessel networks which permeate the walls of all but the smallest of arteries; these nutrient blood vessels are called the *vasa vasorum* (meaning "vessels of the vessels").

Nerve Supply. Arteries are well supplied with nerve fibers. *Afferent nerves* are found which carry impulses to the CNS and lead to reflex changes in heart rate and size of blood vessels; sometimes this arrangement is called the *intrinsic control* of the cardiovascular system. In other words, when there is a change in pressure in the blood vessels in one part of the body, messages are sent to the CNS which immediately set into operation reflexes to compensate for the original change. These reflexes tend to maintain normal conditions or a steady state (homeostasis) throughout the vascular system.

Efferent nerves, or *vasomotor nerves,* of the autonomic division of the nervous system supply the smooth muscle in the walls of small arteries and arterioles. Contraction of this muscle results in *vasoconstriction,* a decrease in the caliber of the vessel as its lumen becomes smaller; as a result of vasoconstriction there is a reduction in the amount of blood flowing through the vessel. On the other hand, relaxation of the muscle results in *vasodilatation,* an increase in the caliber of the vessel as its lumen becomes larger, permitting an increased flow of blood through the vessel. These opposing responses play a vital role in shunting blood from inactive or resting tissues to areas where there is a greater need for "service." The vasomotor control mechanism is described in Chapter 14.

Anastomoses. In many regions of the body there are communications, or anastomoses, between adjacent arteries, so that if the blood supply from one source is cut off, another source is immediately available. Knowledge of this fact enables one to understand why gangrene (death of tissue) does not follow the ligation (tying off) of arteries during surgical operations. In certain parts of the body such anastomoses are not present; the arteries in these areas are called *end arteries,* and if they are obstructed, gangrene will occur.

The veins

Veins conduct blood from the capillaries to the heart. In general, veins tend to follow a course that is more or less parallel with the artery which supplies the area to be drained. However, there are many more veins than arteries, and anastomoses between veins are common. The smallest veins, called *venules,* receive blood from the capillaries and convey it to slightly larger veins, which in turn empty into veins that increase progressively in size from the tissues to the heart.

Coats. Like the arteries, the veins have 3 coats or layers of tissue in their walls (tunica intima, tunica media and tunica externa), but the tunica media consists only of a thin layer of smooth muscle and a few elastic fibers. Consequently, veins have thinner walls than do the arteries, a fact that is correlated with the relatively lower pressure of the blood that flows within them. When veins are cut, their thin walls tend to collapse, and blood escapes in a steady stream. A section of a medium-sized vein is shown in Figure 13-1.

Another structural feature of many veins is the presence of *valves* which help to prevent the backflow of blood. Each valve consists of a pocketlike fold of endothelium that is strengthened by connective tissue; there are usually 2 such semilunar folds placed opposite one another on the vein wall (Fig. 13-2). These valves are so attached that blood can flow freely toward the heart, but any backflow causes the pockets to "balloon out" as they fill with blood, thus temporarily blocking the venous channel and prevent-

Fig. 13-2. Portion of femoral vein opened, to show valves.

ing blood from returning to the capillaries. Valves are most abundant in the veins of the extremities, particularly the lower extremities, since these vessels must conduct blood upward against the powerful forces of gravity. Some veins, such as the venae cavae, have no valves at all; others may have only one or two.

In persons who stand a great deal of the time, such as teachers and salesladies, the valves of the leg veins seem to wear out and, eventually, are unable to resist the pressure of the long column of blood which they are called upon to support. In these instances, the superficial veins become tortuous and dilated, and we speak of them as *varicose veins*. Varicose veins may appear during pregnancy, due to the pressure in the pelvis which offers some interference with the return of blood from the lower extremities.

Arteriole

Precapillary sphincters

Thoroughfare channel

True capillaries

Endothelial cells

Intercellular cement

Venule

Fig. 13-3. Schematic diagram of a capillary bed. Smooth muscle distribution is indicated by heavier wall thickness. Precapillary sphincters are relaxed, thus permitting flow of blood through true capillary network. A greatly magnified portion of capillary wall is shown in the inset.

The blood and nerve supply to the walls of veins is similar to that of the arteries. Networks of tiny blood vessels, the vasa vasorum, permeate the venous walls and nourish the cells therein. Nerve fibers also are distributed to the veins as to the arteries, but they are somewhat less abundant.

The capillaries

Capillaries are microscopic vessels through which blood flows from the arterioles to the venules (Fig. 13-3). Their walls are only one endothelial cell in thickness, or, in other words, they are tubular continuations of the innermost lining cells of the arteries and the veins. Although these endothelial cells are held together by a cement substance, there remain tiny openings or intercellular spaces through which exchanges take place between the circulating blood in the capillary and the tissue fluid which bathes the neighboring tissue cells. The maintenance of homeostasis in the liquid cellular environment is described in Chapter 2, pages 31–37.

Another anatomic feature of importance is the diffuse branching of arterioles. One arteriole may branch into a number of capillaries, thus contributing to a fantastic, spreading network that permeates every organ of the body. However, not every capillary in the body is "open" at the same time. The entrances into each capillary network are guarded by tiny rings of smooth muscle which are called *precapillary sphincters;* by contracting or relaxing, these muscular "gatekeepers" can regulate the flow of blood through their individual capillaries according to tissue needs in the immediate area. This is indeed a fortunate arrangement for us, since there is insufficient blood to fill every vessel in the body at the same time. The distribution of blood according to body needs is discussed in Chapter 14.

In summary, we wish to emphasize this cardinal principle: *The capillaries are the focal point of the entire cardiovascular system!* The heart is merely a "pump" which serves to keep blood moving through the arterial expressways that lead to the all-important capillaries, and the veins merely collect blood from the capillaries and return it to the heart. The whole system is geared to the task of supplying the capillaries with sufficient quantities of blood to meet the constantly changing needs of the cells. The mechanics of the circulatory system are illustrated in Figure 14-2.

Sinusoids are microscopic, capillary-like blood vessels found in such organs as the liver, the spleen and bone marrow. They differ from true capillaries in that their walls are formed by irregularly placed cells, some of which are phagocytic; the walls of the sinusoids also are more permeable; thus large particles (such as blood cells and proteins) readily pass through them to enter or leave the blood stream.

Arteriovenous anastomoses are found in the distal parts of the extremities. When they are open a large amount of blood flows through the skin directly from small arteries to small veins, without going through capillaries. This arrangement is important in connection with the regulation of body temperature (p. 514).

THE PULMONARY CIRCULATION

The blood from all parts of the body and from the walls of the heart itself enters the right atrium, passes through the right A-V valve into the right ventricle, then through the pulmonary semilunar valve into the pulmonary trunk, into the right and left pulmonary arteries and their branches, into the pulmonary capillaries where it picks up a fresh load of oxygen and gives off some carbon dioxide. The oxygenated blood then enters the pulmonary veins and flows to the left atrium. This short path through the lungs is called the pulmonary circulation and is illustrated in Figure 13-4.

The pulmonary trunk arises from the right ventricle, passes upward, backward and to the left, then divides into the right and the left pulmonary arteries as shown in Figure 13-8.

The right pulmonary artery passes transversely toward the base of the right lung; it divides into 3 branches at the root (hilus) of the lung, and one branch goes to each lobe of the right lung. The left pulmonary artery is shorter than the right; it passes to the root of the left lung, divides

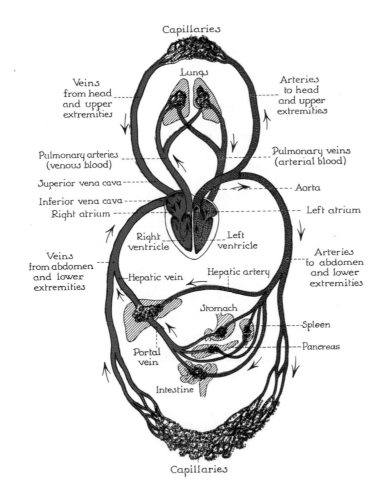

Fig. 13-4. Diagram of the pulmonary and systemic circulations. The pulmonary circulation includes the pulmonary artery, capillaries of the lungs and pulmonary veins. The systemic circulation includes all the other arteries, capillaries and veins of the body. The portal circuit also is shown.

into 2 branches and sends one branch to each of the 2 lobes of the left lung.

From the arteries the blood enters the **pulmonary capillaries,** where it takes up oxygen and gives up carbon dioxide and then is collected into the 4 **pulmonary veins** (Fig. 12-2). Two pulmonary veins arise from the root of each lung. They pass to the posterior surface of the left atrium, into which they open.

THE SYSTEMIC CIRCULATION

From the left atrium blood passes through the left A-V valve into the left ventricle; then it is pumped through the aortic semilunar valve into the aorta. It is distributed to all the systemic arteries of the body, then to the systemic capillaries where oxygen and nutritive materials are delivered to the tissues and carbon dioxide and waste materials are picked up. From the capillaries the blood passes to the veins and eventually returns to the right atrium to begin its circuit all over again. This longer path through all parts of the body (except the air sacs of the lungs) is called the *systemic circulation;* it is illustrated in Figures 13-4 and 13-5.

Arteries of the systemic circuit

The arteries which arise from the aorta may supply one specific organ, or they may give off branches to various structures as they extend to distant regions. Only the major systemic arteries and the most important branches will be mentioned in this text. However, one should keep in mind the fact that these are only the main "highways," and each has many "side roads" which also lead to capillary networks. Most of the arteries are named according to the regions through which they pass or for the structures that they

supply with blood. In any case, you will find that frequent reference to the diagrams will be most helpful in locating the various arterial trunks.

The aorta arises from the base of the left ventricle, arches over to the left side of the vertebral column and passes downward along the vertebral column to the level of the fourth lumbar vertebra. At this level it terminates by dividing into the common iliac arteries. The aorta is shown in Figures 13-6 and 13-7.

For convenience the aorta may be divided into the ascending aorta; the aortic arch, which extends to the left side of the 4th thoracic vertebra;

Fig. 13-5. Scheme of the human circulation. (Modified from Winton and Bayliss).

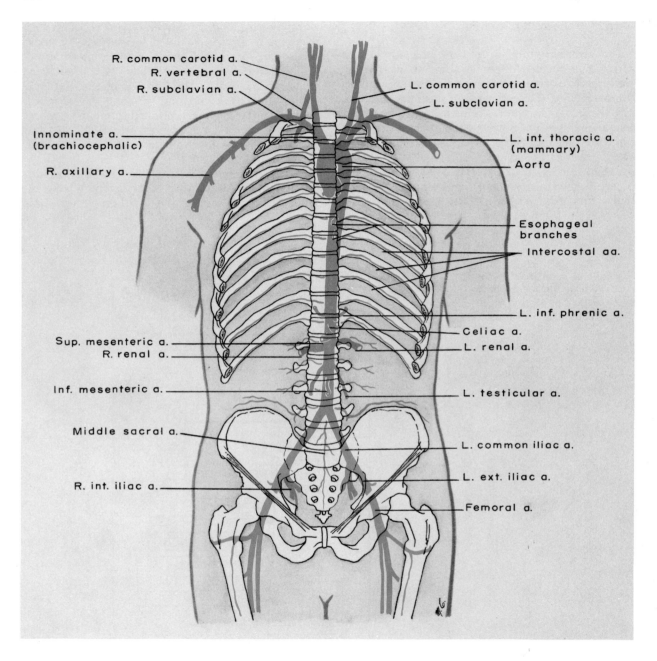

Fig. 13-6. Aorta and its branches. The aortic arch, thoracic aorta, abdominal aorta and terminal branches are shown.

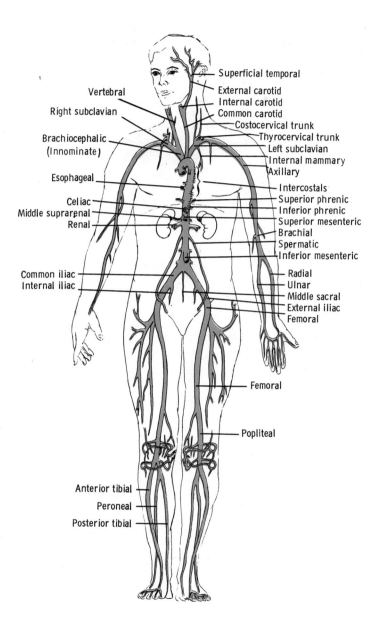

Fig. 13-7. Schematic drawing of the arterial system.

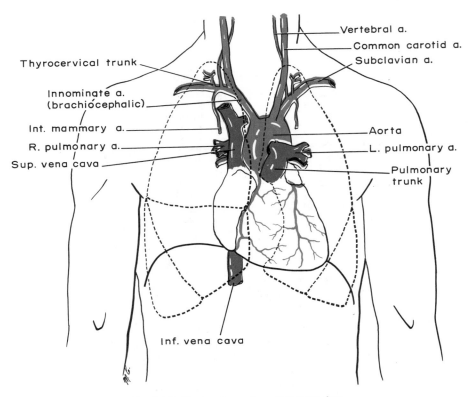

Thyrocervical trunk

Innominate a.
(brachiocephalic)

Int. mammary a.

R. pulmonary a.

Sup. vena cava

Vertebral a.

Common carotid a.

Subclavian a.

Aorta

L. pulmonary a.

Pulmonary
trunk

Inf. vena cava

Fig. 13-8. The aortic arch and its branches.

the thoracic aorta, which extends from the arch to the diaphragm; and the abdominal aorta, which extends from the diaphragm to the 4th lumbar vertebra.

The Ascending Aorta. The only branches of the ascending aorta are the right and the left *coronary arteries*. These arteries arise just above the origin of the aorta, and their orifices can be seen immediately above the leaflets of the aortic semilunar valve. The coronary arteries and their branches conduct blood to capillaries in the myocardium. Figure 12-3 illustrates the origin and Figure 12-7 the distribution of these important arteries.

The Aortic Arch. The arch of the aorta curves to the left and slightly backward (Fig. 13-8) before turning downward to the level of the 4th thoracic

vertebra where it becomes continuous with the thoracic aorta. A short cord, called the ligamentum arteriosum (Fig. 12-4), extends from the upper border of the pulmonary artery to the undersurface of the aortic arch. This is the remains of the *ductus arteriosus,* a fetal vessel that permitted blood to flow from the pulmonary artery into the aorta, thus bypassing the pulmonary circuit. The arteries which arise from the arch of the aorta supply structures in the head, the neck and the upper extremities. These vessels are the innominate, the left common carotid and the left subclavian arteries. The **innominate artery** (*brachiocephalic trunk*) is the largest of the aforementioned branches, but it has a relatively short course. Ascending obliquely upward to the level

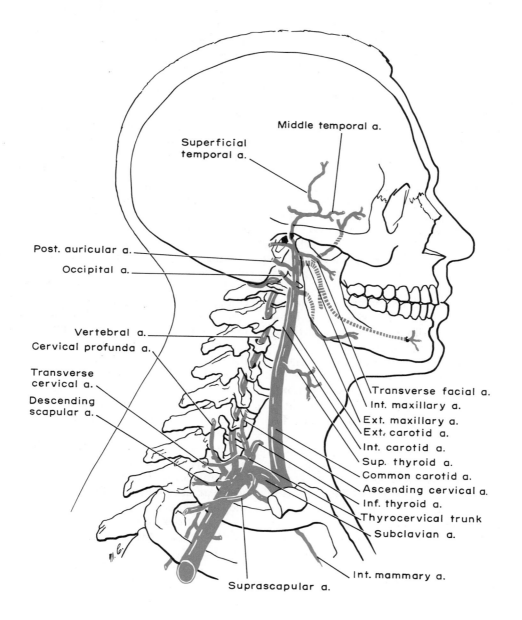

Fig. 13-9. The right common carotid artery and its branches.
The right vertebral artery also is shown as it ascends through
the transverse foramina of the cervical vertebrae.

of the right sternoclavicular joint, this unpaired trunk divides into the right common carotid and the right subclavian arteries.

The **common carotid arteries** conduct blood to capillaries in the head and the neck. The left common carotid artery arises from the aortic arch, but its counterpart on the right side is a branch of the innominate or brachiocephalic trunk (Fig. 13-6). These arteries course upward in the neck along either side of the trachea, and by pressing gently in this area you can feel them pulsating under your finger tips. At the upper border of the thyroid cartilage (Adam's apple), each common carotid bifurcates (divides) into an external and an internal carotid artery. Near this point of bifurcation there is a slight dilatation in the internal carotid artery called the *carotid sinus;* specialized nerve endings in this area respond to changes in the arterial blood pressure. The functions of the carotid sinus are described on page 405. Figure 13-9 shows the right common carotid artery and its branches.

1. The **external carotid artery** gives off many branches as it ascends on its own side to the level of the neck of the mandible; the names of these branches are generally indicative of the areas which they supply (e.g., thyroid, pharyngeal, lingual, etc.). The terminal branches of the external carotid artery are the *superficial temporal* and the *internal maxillary* arteries. The superficial temporal artery (Fig. 13-7) is one of the arteries in which you can feel the pulse easily. Place your finger tips immediately in front of the ear at the level of the eye and note the pulsation of this vessel. The internal maxillary artery is the larger of the two terminal branches; it supplies the deep structures of the face and sends a large branch (the middle meningeal artery) to the dura mater of the brain.

Some of the structures supplied by the external carotid artery and its many branches are the thyroid gland and the muscles of the neck, the pharynx, the tongue, the teeth and the salivary glands, the muscles of facial expression and mastication, part of the nose and the ear and most of the dura mater. Figure 13-9 shows a few of the branches of the external carotid artery.

2. The **internal carotid artery** is shown in Figure 13-10 as it ascends perpendicularly upward to enter the cranial cavity by way of a canal in the temporal bone. Its main branches are: (a) the *ophthalmic* artery, supplying the eyeball and other structures in the orbital cavity and sending branches to the nose and the forehead; (b) the *posterior communicating* artery, forming part of the circle of Willis (see below) as it courses backward to anastomose with the posterior cerebral artery; (c) the *anterior cerebral* artery, supplying part of the frontal and the parietal lobes of the cerebrum; and (d) the *middle cerebral* artery, supplying the basal ganglia, the internal capsule and most of the lateral surface of the brain.

The circle of Willis is an arterial anastomosis at the base of the brain. The two internal carotid arteries conduct blood to the anterior portion of the circle, and the two vertebral arteries (branches of the subclavians) conduct blood to the basilar artery which leads to the rear of the circle. The anterior and the posterior communicating arteries serve as connecting links. Careful study of Figure 13-11 will show that the circle is formed by the anterior communicating artery, the proximal portions of the anterior cerebrals, the internal carotids, the posterior communicating arteries and the proximal portions of the posterior cerebral arteries. The blood supply of the brain is derived mainly from the three pairs of cerebral arteries which may be considered as branches of the circle of Willis.

Cerebral Vascular Accident (CVA). Of all the affections of the brain, cerebral thrombosis and cerebral hemorrhage are the most frequent. Such vascular accidents usually are the result of pathologic changes in the walls of cerebral blood vessels. For example, hemorrhage within the brain substance usually is related to an underlying arteriosclerosis; a sudden strain with a rise in blood pressure may rupture a weakened vessel that has no "give" to it. Cerebral vascular accident, also called *stroke* or *apoplexy,* most frequently occurs in the region of the internal capsule, which is supplied by branches of the middle cerebral artery. Due to the fact that there are only a few, small anastomoses between these branches, there

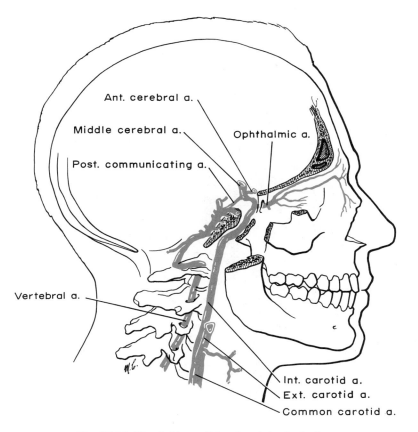

Fig. 13-10. The right carotid and vertebral arteries.

is little chance of a collateral circulation supplying adequate amounts of oxygen and glucose to the affected area. As a result, that part of the brain which is deprived of blood undergoes necrosis or death; paralysis of one side of the body follows such necrosis, if the person survives.

The **subclavian arteries** are shown in Figures 13-6 and 13-7. The left subclavian artery arises directly from the aortic arch, but the right subclavian is a branch of the innominate (brachiocephalic) artery as described previously. One can feel the pulsations in the subclavian artery by pressing inward on the tissues just above the medial third of the clavicle. At the outer border of the first rib the subclavian artery becomes the

axillary artery. Major branches of each subclavian artery and the structures which they supply are as follows:

1. The *vertebral* artery ascends in the neck through the transverse foramina of the cervical vertebrae (Figs. 13-9 and 13-10), enters the skull through the foramen magnum and unites with its counterpart from the opposite side to form the basilar artery at the base of the brain (Fig. 13-11). Branches of the vertebral artery supply the deep muscles in the neck, parts of the spinal cord and the medulla oblongata; the basilar artery supplies the cerebellum and the pons before branching to form the *posterior cerebral* arteries which supply the occipital lobes of the cerebrum.

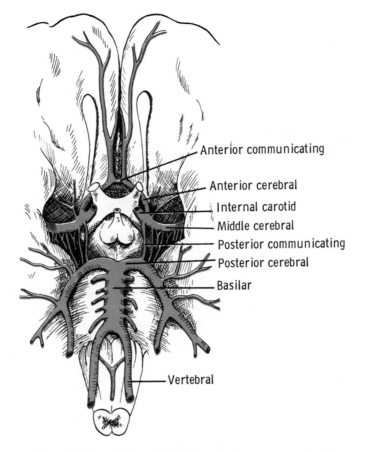

Fig. 13-11. Circle of Willis, showing communicating branches from the basilar and internal carotid arteries.

2. The *thyrocervical trunk* (Fig. 13-8) is short and thick, dividing almost immediately into branches which supply the thyroid gland, the trachea, the larynx and other structures of the neck.

3. The *internal mammary* artery (Fig. 13-7) arises from the undersurface of the subclavian and descends into the thorax. Its branches supply the thymus and the pericardium in the mediastinum, the pectoral muscles, the mammary glands and the skin of the anterior thorax. The *superior epigastric* artery is a terminal branch of the in-

ternal mammary; it supplies the muscles and the skin of the anterolateral abdominal wall.

The **axillary artery** is the continuation of the subclavian into the axillary region (Fig. 13-7). It begins at the outer border of the first rib and courses downward to the lower border of the teres major muscle where it becomes the brachial artery of the arm. While passing through the axillary region, it gives off thoracic, subscapular and humeral branches which supply tissues in the upper part of the thorax, the region of the shoulder and the axilla.

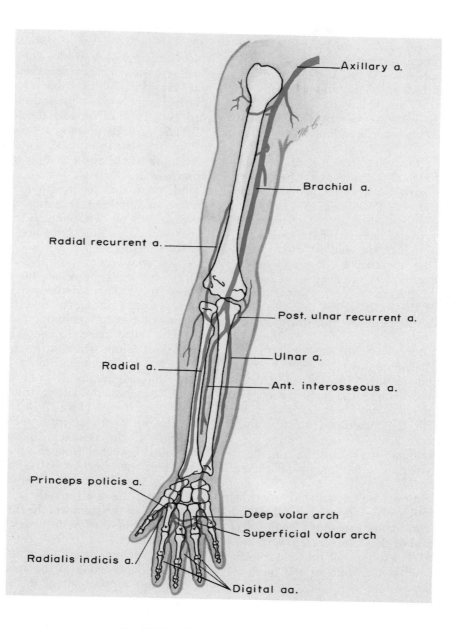

Axillary a.

Brachial a.

Radial recurrent a.

Post. ulnar recurrent a.

Ulnar a.

Radial a.

Ant. interosseous a.

Princeps policis a.

Deep volar arch

Superficial volar arch

Radialis indicis a.

Digital aa.

Fig. 13-12. Major arteries of the upper
right extremity, anterior view.

The **brachial artery** is the continuation of the axillary artery into the upper extremity (Fig. 13-12). It sends branches to the humerus, the muscles and the skin of the arm. At the bend of the elbow the brachial artery lies in front of the humerus, midway between its two epicondyles, where you can feel its pulsations under your fingertips. About 1 cm. below the bend of the elbow, the brachial artery ends by dividing into its two terminal branches, the radial and the ulnar arteries.

1. The **radial artery** (Fig. 13-12) continues the course of the brachial artery down the lateral aspect of the forearm, but it is smaller in caliber than the ulnar artery. Pulsations in the radial artery are easily felt on the thumb side of the wrist where the artery passes in front of the radius. In the palm of the hand, the radial artery turns medially across the metacarpal bones and terminates by anastomosing with the deep volar branch of the ulnar artery to form the *deep volar (palmar) arch*. Branches of the radial artery and the deep volar arch supply tissues in the forearm, the hand and the fingers.

2. The **ulnar artery**, larger of the two terminal brachial branches, courses down the medial aspect of the forearm and the wrist. Crossing the palmar surface of the hand it forms the main component of the *superficial volar arch* and terminates by anastomosing with the superficial volar branch of the radial artery.

Branches of the ulnar artery and the superficial volar arch supply tissues in the forearm, the hand and the fingers.

The thoracic aorta extends downward from the aortic arch, through the posterior mediastinal cavity, to the aortic hiatus (opening) in the diaphragm at the level of the 12th thoracic vertebra. This great arterial trunk gives off branches which supply the viscera and the walls of the thoracic cavity (Fig. 13-6).

A. *Visceral branches* of the thoracic aorta:

1. The **pericardial arteries** are distributed to the posterior pericardium.

2. The **bronchial arteries** are the nutrient arteries of the lungs and are distributed mainly to the walls of the bronchi.

3. The **esophageal arteries**, 4 or 5 in number, form a chain of anastomoses along the esophagus as it passes through the thorax.

B. *Parietal branches* of the thoracic aorta:

1. The **intercostal arteries** (9 or 10 pairs) supply the intercostal muscles, the pleurae, the muscles and the skin of the thoracic wall. Posterior branches supply the vertebral column, the spinal cord and the muscles and the skin of the back.

2. The **superior phrenic arteries** are distributed to the upper surface of the diaphragm.

The abdominal aorta is the continuation of the thoracic aorta through the abdominal cavity. It extends from the diaphragm to the level of the 4th lumbar vertebra where it ends by dividing into the right and the left common iliac arteries. Both visceral and parietal branches arise from this arterial trunk.

A. *Visceral branches* of the abdominal aorta: of these branches the celiac, the superior and the inferior mesenteric arteries are unpaired, while the suprarenal, the renal and the spermatic or ovarian arteries are paired.

1. The **celiac artery** (celiac axis) is a relatively short, thick trunk which arises from the anterior surface of the abdominal aorta a short distance below the diaphragm. It ends by dividing into 3 large branches: the left gastric, the hepatic and the splenic arteries (Fig. 13-13 (Top)).

a. The *left gastric artery* supplies the esophagus and part of the stomach. It anastomoses with esophageal branches from the thoracic aorta.

b. The *hepatic artery* is the nutrient artery of the liver. In addition, it gives rise to the right gastric and the gastroduodenal arteries (which supply part of the stomach, the duodenum and the pancreas), and the cystic artery which supplies the gallbladder.

c. The *splenic artery,* largest branch of the celiac, conducts blood to the spleen. In addition, its branches supply part of the stomach and the pancreas.

2. The **superior mesenteric artery** is an unpaired vessel which arises from the front of the aorta just below the celiac axis (Fig. 13-14); after extensive branching it ends near the junction of the small and the large intestines by anastomosing with one

Fig. 13-13. (Top). The celiac artery and its branches.

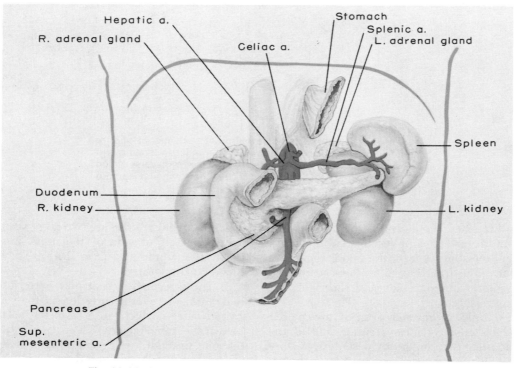

Fig. 13-13. (Bottom). The stomach and liver removed to show pancreas and origin of superior mesenteric artery.

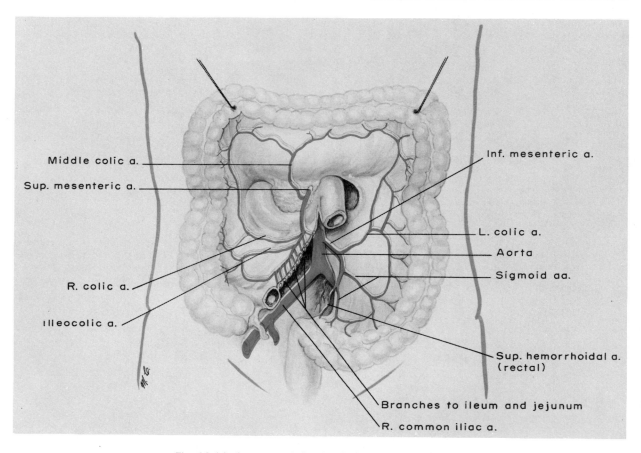

Middle colic a.

Sup. mesenteric a.

R. colic a.

Illeocolic a.

Inf. mesenteric a.

L. colic a.

Aorta

Sigmoid aa.

Sup. hemorrhoidal a. (rectal)

Branches to ileum and jejunum

R. common iliac a.

Fig. 13-14. Course and distribution of the superior and inferior mesenteric arteries, semidiagrammatic. Ascending and descending colons are drawn laterally, the transverse colon superiorly, out of the abdominal cavity. The ileum and jejunum have been removed.

of its own branches, the iliocolic artery. The superior mesenteric artery supplies the entire length of the small intestine (except the duodenum) and part of the large intestine (i.e., the cecum, the appendix, the ascending colon and the right half of the transverse colon).

3. The **middle suprarenal arteries** are paired vessels which arise, one from either side of the aorta, opposite the superior mesenteric artery (Fig. 13-7). They convey blood to the suprarenal (adrenal) glands which are located just above the kidneys.

4. The **renal arteries** are two large vessels which arise from either side of the aorta immediately below the suprarenals (Fig. 13-7). They conduct blood to the kidneys.

5. The **spermatic (testicular) arteries** (in the male) and the **ovarian arteries** (in the female) are paired vessels which arise from the aorta a little below the renal arteries. The spermatic arteries descend through the inguinal canals to supply the testes. The ovarian arteries descend into the pelvis where they supply the ovaries and anastomose with the uterine arteries.

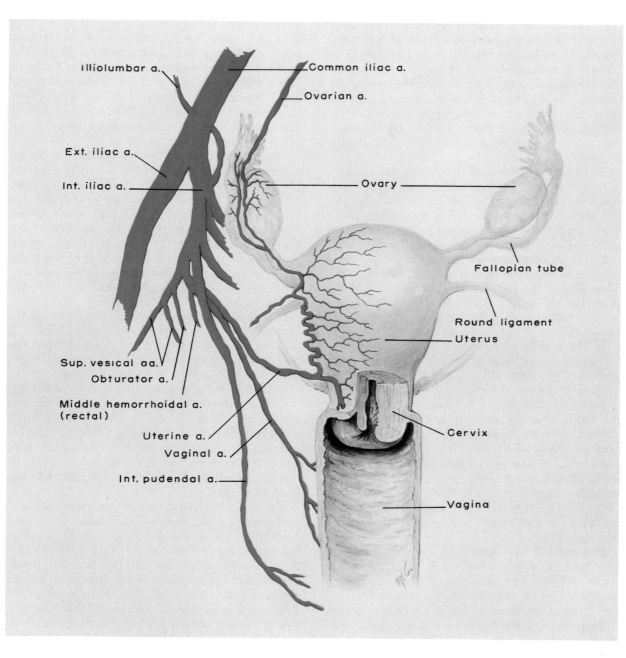

Fig. 13-15. Arterial blood supply to uterus and vagina.
Cut-away section shows interior of cervix and vagina.

6. The **inferior mesenteric artery** is an unpaired vessel which arises from the front of the aorta just above its division into the common iliacs (Fig. 13-14); its terminal branch is the superior hemorrhoidal (rectal) artery which descends along the rectum. The inferior mesenteric artery supplies the remaining portions of the large intestine (i.e., the left half of the transverse colon, the descending colon, the sigmoid colon and most of the rectum).

B. *Parietal branches* of the abdominal aorta:

1. The **inferior phrenic arteries** are 2 small vessels which arise from the first part of the abdominal aorta just above the celiac axis (Fig. 13-6). They supply the undersurface of the diaphragm and send branches to the suprarenal glands.

2. The **lumbar arteries,** usually arranged in 4 pairs, arise from the back of the aorta (Fig. 13-6). They supply the muscles of the anterior and the posterior abdominal walls, the spinal cord, the lumbar vertebrae and the muscles and the skin of the back.

3. The **middle sacral artery** is an unpaired vessel which arises from the back of the terminal portion of the aorta (Fig. 13-6). It descends in the midline to supply the sacrum and the coccyx.

Terminal Branches of the Aorta. At the level of the 4th lumbar vertebra, the aorta terminates by dividing into the right and the left **common iliac arteries.** These vessels pass laterally downward to the level of the sacroiliac joint on their respective sides; at this point each terminates by dividing into the internal and the external iliac arteries (Fig. 13-6). The common iliacs give off small branches to the psoas muscles, the peritoneum and the ureters.

The **internal iliac arteries** (hypogastric arteries) pass into the pelvis where each divides into anterior and posterior divisions (Fig. 13-15). These divisions give off branches to the urinary bladder, the rectum, the internal and the external organs of reproduction, the buttocks and the medial side of the thigh.

The **external iliac arteries** are shown in Figure 13-6. Each courses obliquely downward from the division of the common iliac to a point beneath the inguinal ligament, midway between the anterior superior iliac spine and the symphysis pubis; from this point each continues as the femoral artery of its own side and enters the thigh. The external iliac artery gives off branches to the psoas major muscle and the muscles of the abdominal wall. The *inferior epigastric artery,* a relatively large branch of the external iliac, ascends through the abdominal wall to anastomose with the superior epigastric artery above.

The **femoral artery** is the continuation of the external iliac artery below the inguinal ligament (Fig. 13-16). As it passes in front of the hip joint, you can feel its pulsations under your finger tips by pressing firmly in the groin. This vessel courses downward in the thigh to the popliteal space where it continues as the popliteal artery. Branches of the femoral artery supply the bone, the muscles and the skin of the thigh, and also contribute to anastomoses around the hip and the knee joints.

The **popliteal artery** is the continuation of the femoral artery as shown in Figure 13-17. It courses through the popliteal space behind the knee, giving off muscular, articular and cutaneous branches. This artery ends by dividing into the anterior and the posterior tibial arteries of the leg.

1. The **anterior tibial artery** is one of the terminal branches of the popliteal artery (Fig. 13-16). It courses downward in the leg, between the tibia and the fibula, to the front of the ankle joint where it becomes the dorsalis pedis artery. It supplies muscular and cutaneous branches to the front of the leg.

The *dorsalis pedis artery* is the continuation of the anterior tibial beyond the ankle joint, and pulsations in this vessel may be felt as it passes forward along the top of the foot (Fig. 13-16). Physicians frequently palpate this artery to determine if there is adequate circulation to structures in the leg and the foot. The dorsalis pedis not only supplies superficial tissues in the foot, but one of its branches, the deep plantar artery, descends into the sole of the foot where it unites with a branch of the posterior tibial artery to complete the plantar arch.

2. The **posterior tibial artery** gives off muscular and cutaneous branches as it descends in the

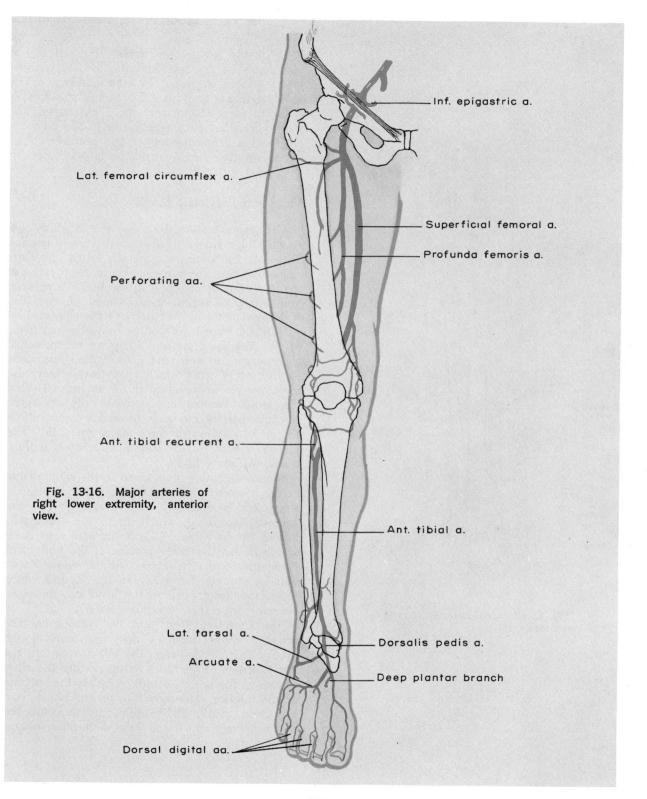

Inf. epigastric a.

Lat. femoral circumflex a.

Superficial femoral a.

Profunda femoris a.

Perforating aa.

Ant. tibial recurrent a.

Fig. 13-16. Major arteries of right lower extremity, anterior view.

Ant. tibial a.

Lat. tarsal a.

Dorsalis pedis a.

Arcuate a.

Deep plantar branch

Dorsal digital aa.

back of the leg to the ankle (Fig. 13-17); it terminates by dividing into the medial and the lateral plantar arteries. The lateral plantar artery unites with the deep plantar branch of the dorsalis pedis to form the plantar arch; metatarsal and digital branches arise from this arch. The *peroneal artery* is a large branch of the posterior tibial which supplies structures in the lateral aspect of the leg.

Veins of the systemic circuit

The systemic veins drain the vast capillary networks which are supplied by the systemic arteries. However, the veins are generally larger and more numerous than the arteries. There are 3 types of systemic venous channels in the body; superficial veins, deep veins and cranial venous sinuses. The *superficial veins* lie just beneath the skin and return blood from it as well as from the superficial fascia. The *deep veins* accompany the principal arteries and, in most cases, have the same name as the artery with which they travel; they also have many connections with the superficial veins. The *cranial venous sinuses,* found only within the skull, consist of channels formed by separations of the two layers of dura mater (p. 235). The general scheme of the venous circulation is illustrated in Figure 13-18.

Blood ultimately is returned to the right atrium of the heart by way of 3 veins: (1) the coronary sinus, which drains the heart muscle; (2) the superior vena cava, which drains the upper portion of the body; and (3) the inferior vena cava, which drains the lower portion of the body. For convenience, the tributaries of the venae cavae will be grouped according to the regions which they drain (e.g., veins of the head and the neck, veins of the upper extremities, etc.).

The Coronary Sinus and Its Tributaries. The coronary sinus occupies the right half of the groove that lies between the left atrium and the left ventricle (Fig. 12-2). It opens into the right atrium on the posterior surface, below the opening of the inferior vena cava. It receives blood from the great, small, and middle cardiac veins, the posterior vein and the oblique vein. Since only a

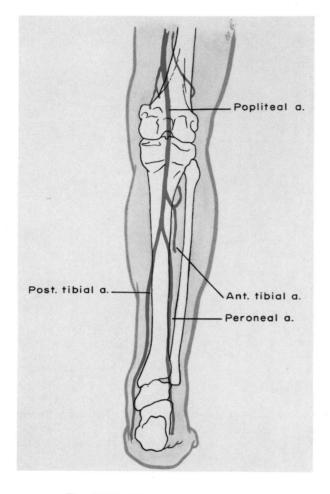

Fig. 13-17. Major arteries of right leg, posterior aspect.

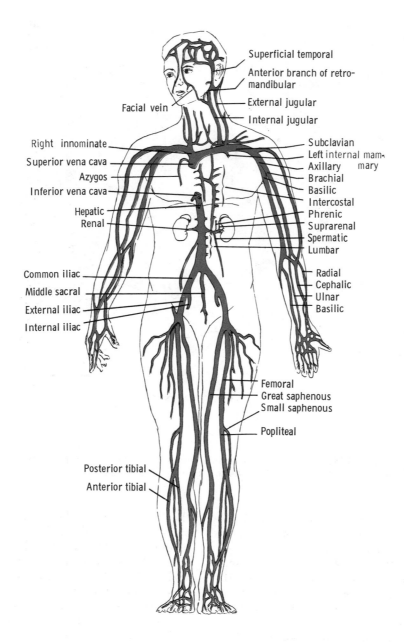

Fig. 13-18. Schematic drawing of the venous system.

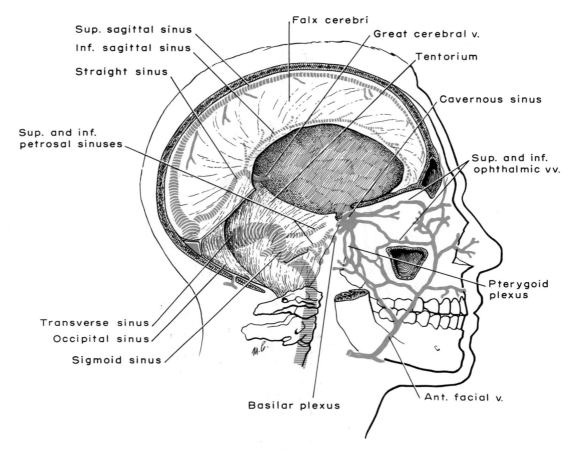

Sup. sagittal sinus
Inf. sagittal sinus
Straight sinus
Sup. and inf. petrosal sinuses
Transverse sinus
Occipital sinus
Sigmoid sinus
Basilar plexus
Falx cerebri
Great cerebral v.
Tentorium
Cavernous sinus
Sup. and inf. ophthalmic vv.
Pterygoid plexus
Ant. facial v.

Fig. 13-19. The cranial venous sinuses. The sigmoid portion of the transverse sinus continues on as the internal jugular vein.

few small veins open directly into the right side of the heart, it is evident that the coronary sinus drains most of the heart muscle.

Veins of the Head and the Neck. The cranial venous sinuses, the internal jugular veins and the external jugular veins are the major systemic venous channels which drain capillary networks in the head and neck.

The **cranial venous sinuses** are a series of channels that lie between the two layers of dura mater; they drain the structures in the orbital and the cranial cavities and communicate with veins outside of the cranium by numerous emissary veins that pass through the cranial wall. The venous sinuses receive blood from the ophthalmic, the cerebral, the cerebellar and the meningeal veins. None of these vascular channels possesses valves, and their walls are extremely thin due to the absence of muscular tissue.

There are many cranial venous sinuses, some of which are median and unpaired, and others which consist of lateral pairs. The major unpaired venous sinuses are: (1) superior sagittal, (2) inferior sagittal, (3) straight, and (4) occipital. The major paired venous sinuses are: (1) transverse (lateral), (2) superior petrosal, (3) inferior petro-

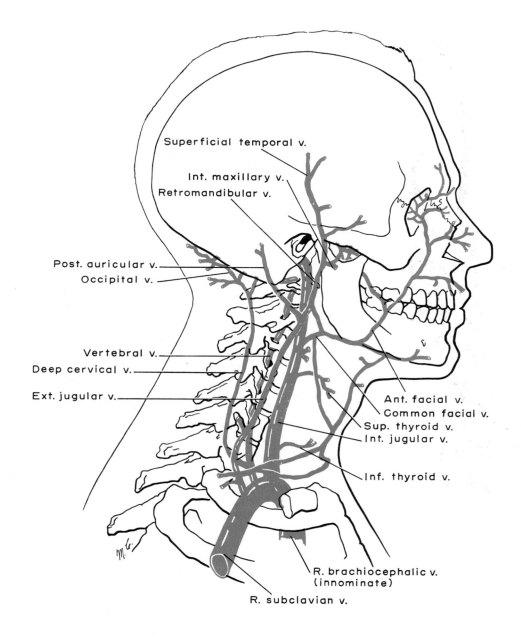

Fig. 13-20. The veins of the head and neck.

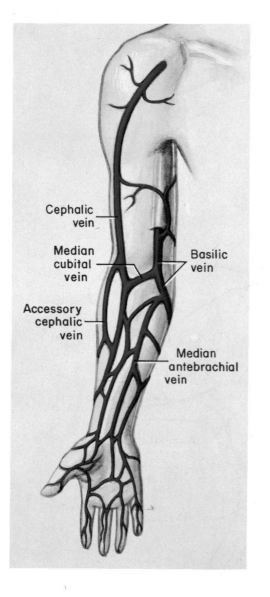

Fig. 13-21. Superficial veins of the anterior aspect of the right upper extremity.

sal, and (4) cavernous. Some of these sinuses are illustrated in Figure 13-19 as they convey blood to one of the internal jugular veins.

The **internal jugular veins** are continuations of the *sigmoid* portions of the two transverse sinuses. They begin at the base of the skull and descend in the neck, just lateral to the common carotid arteries. At the level of the sternoclavicular joint, each unites with the subclavian vein of its own side to form the innominate (brachiocephalic) veins (Fig. 13-20). The internal jugular veins collect blood from the brain, the eyes, the superficial parts of the face and the neck.

The **external jugular veins** are formed near the angle of the mandible, one on either side. Each collects blood from the exterior of the cranium, the deep parts of the face and the neck before ending in the subclavian vein of the same side. Figure 13-30 illustrates the right external jugular vein. When the head is turned to the side, or when one wears a tight collar, this vein will stand out, along the edge of the sternocleidomastoid muscle. Sometimes you will see pulsations, just above the clavicle, in the external jugular vein; these pulsations are called the *central venous pulse* and are reflected changes in pressure from the right atrium, since there are no valves at the entrance of the superior vena cava into the right atrium.

Veins of the Upper Extremity. These veins are subdivided into superficial and deep sets, but there are many anastomoses between the two sets. Valves are present in all of these veins but are more numerous in the deep set than in the superficial.

The **superficial veins** of the upper extremity show considerable individual variation, but the chief ones are the cephalic and the basilic.

1. The **cephalic vein** begins in the dorsal venous network on the thumb side of the hand and ascends along the lateral border of the forearm. In front of the elbow joint (antecubital fossa) it gives rise to the *median cubital vein,* which crosses over to join the basilic vein. The cephalic vein then ascends along the lateral aspect of the arm, passes between the deltoid and the pectoralis major muscles and ends in the axillary vein just

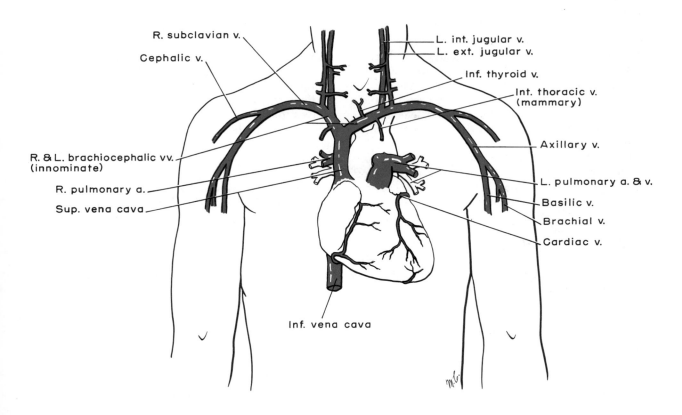

R. subclavian v.

Cephalic v.

L. int. jugular v.

L. ext. jugular v.

Inf. thyroid v.

Int. thoracic v.
(mammary)

Axillary v.

R. & L. brachiocephalic vv.
(innominate)

R. pulmonary a.

Sup. vena cava

L. pulmonary a. & v.

Basilic v.

Brachial v.

Cardiac v.

Inf. vena cava

Fig. 13-22. Diagram showing the termination of veins that
drain the head, neck, and upper extremities.

below the clavicle (Fig. 13-21). It collects blood
from small veins all along its course.

2. The **basilic vein** begins in the dorsal venous
network on the little finger side of the hand and
ascends along the medial side of the forearm
and the arm (Fig. 13-21). It pierces the fascia of
the arm and joins the deep brachial vein to form
the axillary vein of that extremity. It receives
blood from small veins all along its course.

The **deep veins** of the upper extremity follow
the course of the arteries and usually are enclosed
in the same sheath. They also are generally arranged in pairs, called the venae comitantes
(meaning "companion veins"), one lying on either
side of the artery with which they travel. They

receive blood from the deep structures of the
upper extremity.

1. The **radial veins** are the upward continuation
of veins of the deep volar arch.

2. The **ulnar veins** are formed by the union of
veins from both the deep and the superficial volar
arches. They join the radial veins at the elbow.

3. The **brachial veins** are the companion veins
of the brachial artery and are formed at the elbow
joint by the union of the radial and the ulnar
veins. At the level of the lower border of the pectoralis major muscle the brachial and the basilic
veins unite to form the axillary vein.

4. The **axillary vein**, formed by the union of
the brachial venae comitantes and the basilic vein,

becomes the subclavian vein at the outer border of the first rib.

5. The **subclavian vein** (Fig. 13-22) is the end of the venous system of the upper extremity. It extends to the sternal end of the clavicle, where it unites with the internal jugular to form the innominate (brachiocephalic) vein of that side.

Veins of the Thorax. The thoracic vessels which pour their contents into the superior vena cava are the innominate veins and the azygos system of veins.

The **innominate or brachiocephalic veins** are formed by the union of the internal jugular and subclavian veins on either side (Fig. 13-22). These large venous trunks descend to the level of the first right costal cartilage where they unite to form the **superior vena cava.** In addition to the internal jugular and the subclavian veins, the major tributaries of each innominate vein are the vertebral, the internal mammary and the inferior thyroid veins. The left innominate also receives the left highest intercostal veins from the upper 3 or 4 intercostal spaces.

The **azygos system of veins** (Fig. 13-23) not only collects blood from various structures in the thorax but also serves as the connecting link between the superior and the inferior vena caval systems. In cases of obstruction of the inferior vena cava the azygos veins are able to return blood from the lower portion of the body by virtue of their collateral communications with the common iliac, the renal and the lumbar veins.

1. The *azygos vein* lies in front of the vertebral column, slightly to the right of the midline. It usually begins as the continuation of the right ascending lumbar vein, which in turn has connections with the inferior vena cava, the right common iliac and the lumbar veins. The principal tributaries of the azygos vein are the right intercostal veins, the hemiazygos veins, several esophageal, mediastinal and pericardial veins and the right bronchial vein. At the level of the 4th thoracic vertebra the azygos empties into the superior vena cava.

2. The *hemiazygos* and the *accessory hemiazygos veins* also form a channel in front of the vertebral column, but they are slightly to the left of the midline. The hemiazygos begins as the continuation of the left ascending lumbar vein and communicates with the left renal vein instead of with the inferior vena cava; it receives blood from the lower 4 or 5 intercostal veins on the left side and from some of the esophageal and mediastinal veins before crossing the midline to the right side where it joins the azygos. The accessory hemiazygos receives blood from the 3 or 4 intercostal veins above the highest tributary of the hemiazygos, and from the left bronchial vein before crossing the midline to join the azygos vein at the level of the eighth thoracic vertebra.

Veins of the Lower Extremity. These veins are subdivided into superficial and deep sets, as are those of the upper extremity. Valves are present in both sets, but they are more numerous in the deep veins.

The **superficial veins** of each lower extremity are the great and the small saphenous veins and their many tributaries. These vessels are of considerable clinical importance because of the frequency with which they become varicosed.

1. The **great saphenous vein** is the longest vein in the body. It begins at the medial end of the dorsal venous arch of the foot, passes in front of the medial malleolus, and then courses upward along the medial aspect of the leg and the thigh (Fig. 13-24). It receives tributaries from superficial tissues all along its course and has many connections with the deep veins as well. The great saphenous empties into the femoral vein in the region of the groin (Fig. 13-25).

2. The **small saphenous vein** begins at the lateral end of the dorsal venous arch of the foot, passes behind the lateral malleolus and courses upward under the skin in the back of the leg. It receives blood from the foot and from the posterior superficial portion of the leg and then empties into the popliteal vein in back of the knee (Fig. 13-24).

The **deep veins** of the lower extremity accompany the arteries and receive blood from the structures along their course. As in the upper extremity, many of these veins are arranged in pairs, called the venae comitantes.

1. The **posterior tibial veins** are formed behind

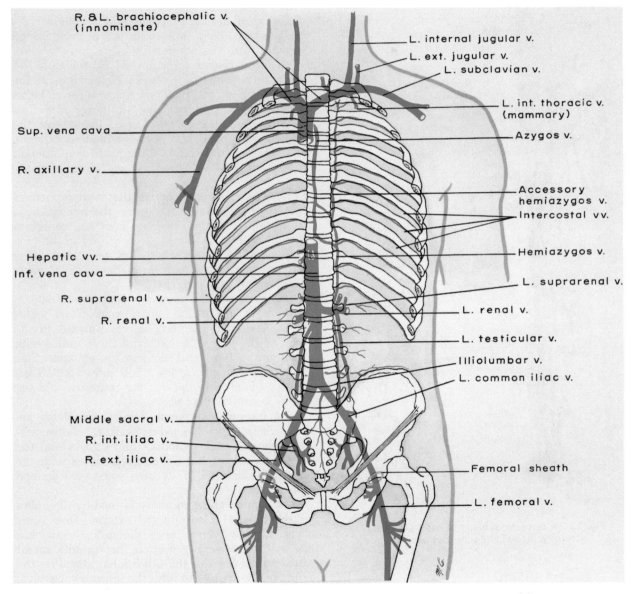

R. & L. brachiocephalic v.
(innominate)

L. internal jugular v.

L. ext. jugular v.

L. subclavian v.

L. int. thoracic v.
(mammary)

Sup. vena cava

Azygos v.

R. axillary v.

Accessory
hemiazygos v.

Intercostal vv.

Hepatic vv.

Hemiazygos v.

Inf. vena cava

L. suprarenal v.

R. suprarenal v.

L. renal v.

R. renal v.

L. testicular v.

Illiolumbar v.

L. common iliac v.

Middle sacral v.

R. int. iliac v.

R. ext. iliac v.

Femoral sheath

L. femoral v.

Fig. 13-23. Diagram of the azygos system of veins. The inferior vena cava and its
tributaries are also shown. (The heart has been removed.)

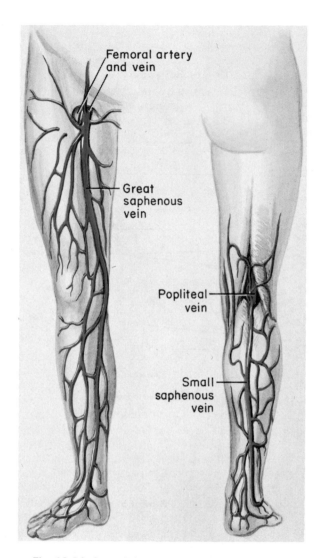

Fig. 13-24. Superficial veins of the right lower extremity, medial and posterior aspects.

the medial malleolus by the union of the medial and the lateral plantar veins. Coursing upward in the leg, they receive the peroneal veins and other tributaries before uniting with the anterior tibial veins just below the knee (Fig. 13-25).

2. The **anterior tibial veins** are the upward continuation of the venae comitantes of the dorsalis pedis artery. They unite with the posterior tibial veins to form the popliteal vein.

3. The **popliteal vein**, formed by the union of the anterior and the posterior tibial veins at the lower border of the popliteal space, receives blood from muscular and articular tributaries as well as from the small saphenous vein. Just above the knee, the popliteal vein becomes the femoral vein.

4. The **femoral vein** is the upward continuation of the popliteal vein, and it receives many tributaries which drain the deep structures of the thigh (Fig. 13-25). After receiving the great saphenous vein in the region of the groin, the femoral vein passes under the inguinal ligament and continues as the external iliac vein.

Veins of the Pelvis. The pelvic veins accompany the pelvic arteries and drain the general areas supplied by those arteries.

The **external iliac veins** are direct continuations of the right and the left femoral veins. Each begins at the inguinal ligament, curves upward to the level of the sacroiliac joint and there unites with the internal iliac vein to form the common iliac vein of its own side (Figs. 13-18 and 13-23). They receive blood from the inferior epigastric and the deep circumflex iliac veins.

The **internal iliac veins** (hypogastric veins) receive blood from the pelvic wall, the pelvic viscera, the external genitalia, the buttocks and the medial aspect of the thigh. Each unites with the external iliac vein of its own side, as described above.

The **common iliac veins** are formed by the union of the internal iliac and the external iliac veins (Fig. 13-23). Each receives iliolumbar veins, and the left receives, in addition, the middle sacral vein. At the level of the 5th lumbar vertebra, the common iliacs unite to form the inferior vena cava.

Veins of the Abdomen. The **inferior vena cava** (Figs. 13-18 and 13-23) is the largest vein in the

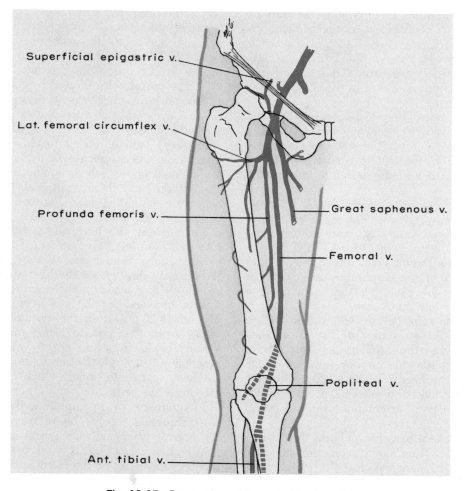

Superficial epigastric v.

Lat. femoral circumflex v.

Profunda femoris v.

Great saphenous v.

Femoral v.

Popliteal v.

Ant. tibial v.

Fig. 13-25. Deep veins of lower right extremity.

body. It is formed by the union of the two common iliac veins and courses upward along the front of the vertebral column, on the right side of the aorta. After passing through a groove on the posterior surface of the liver, this great vein perforates the diaphragm and ascends to enter the lower back part of the right atrium. The inferior vena cava receives blood from the common iliac veins and from the following vessels as well.

1. The **lumbar veins,** 4 in number on each side, arise in the muscles of the posterior abdominal wall (Fig. 13-23). They receive tributaries from the skin and the muscles of the back, the vertebral column and the spinal cord. The lumbar veins are interconnected on either side by an ascending lumbar vein which forms the origin of the corresponding azygos or hemiazygos vein, as previously described.

2. The **spermatic (testicular) veins** (in the male) receive blood from the testes and neighboring

structures. They ascend through the inguinal canal and upward into the abdominal cavity. The right spermatic vein empties directly into the inferior vena cava, but its counterpart on the left empties into the left renal vein (Fig. 13-23). The **ovarian veins** (in the female) receive blood from the ovaries and neighboring structures. They ascend into the abdominal cavity and end in the same way as the spermatic veins.

3. The **renal veins** (Fig. 13-23) empty into the inferior vena cava after receiving blood from the kidneys and the ureters. The left renal vein receives, in addition, the left spermatic or ovarian, the left suprarenal and the left inferior phrenic veins.

4. The **suprarenal veins** receive blood from the suprarenal (adrenal) glands. The right vein empties into the inferior vena cava, and the left empties into the left renal vein (Fig. 13-23).

5. The **inferior phrenic veins** receive blood from the undersurface of the diaphragm and convey it to the inferior vena cava. The left vein sends a tributary to the left renal vein.

6. The **hepatic veins** (Figs. 13-23 and 13-26) are formed within the substance of the liver; they convey blood from the capillarylike sinusoids of this vascular organ to the inferior vena cava. One might think of the hepatic veins as doing "double duty," since the liver sinusoids receive blood not only from the hepatic artery but from the portal system as well.

The **portal system of veins** includes those veins that drain blood from the spleen, the stomach, the intestines, the pancreas and the gallbladder. In general, these veins have the same names as the arteries which supply the aforementioned organs, but instead of emptying their blood directly into the inferior vena cava, they deliver it to the portal vein for a "detour" through the liver. The portal vein itself is formed by the union of the superior mesenteric and the splenic veins.

1. The **superior mesenteric vein** begins in the right iliac fossa and courses upward toward the liver. In general, it drains those structures which were supplied by the superior mesenteric artery (i.e., the small intestine and the first half of the large intestine).

2. The **splenic vein** drains the spleen, and, as it courses from left to right toward the liver, it receives the following tributaries: (a) *gastric veins* from the stomach; (b) *pancreatic veins* from the pancreas; and (c) the *inferior mesenteric vein* from the last half of the large intestine (except the lower portion of the rectum).

3. The **portal vein,** formed by the union of the splenic and the superior mesenteric veins, receives the following additional tributaries before it enters the substance of the liver: (a) the left *gastric (coronary) vein* of the stomach, which receives blood from the esophagus as well; (b) the *paraumbilical veins,* which anastomose with veins of the anterior abdominal wall; and (c) the *cystic vein* from the gallbladder. Figure 13-26 illustrates the portal vein and its tributaries.

On reaching the liver, the portal vein divides into right and left branches which accompany the corresponding branches of the hepatic artery as they ramify throughout the liver substance; these vessels deliver blood to the microscopic sinusoids that lie between the plates of liver cells (Figs. 16-21 and 16-22). Within the sinusoids the arterial blood from the hepatic artery mixes with the venous blood from the portal vein. This mixed blood flows through the sinusoids and eventually reaches the hepatic veins which empty into the inferior vena cava.

In summary, we re-emphasize the fact that the liver sinusoids receive blood from two sources: the hepatic artery and the portal vein. The blood in the hepatic artery is well oxygenated, thus meeting the need of the hard-working liver cells for a constant supply of oxygen. The portal vein, on the other hand, contains blood that is poorly oxygenated, since it has already passed through capillary networks in the digestive organs and the spleen. However, portal blood is rich with substances that have been absorbed from the gastrointestinal tract; this unique arrangement makes it possible for the liver to "inspect" all such materials before they are sent on to other tissues in the body. For example, some substances may be temporarily stored in the liver until needed; others are modified for easier oxidation or disposal in tissues elsewhere in the body, and harmful sub-

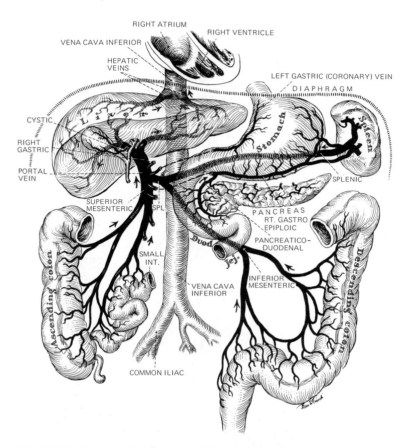

Fig. 13-26. The portal system, semidiagrammatic. The various organs have been moved somewhat out of position to expose the portal vein and its tributaries. The transverse colon and most of the small intestine have been removed. The veins which belong to this system are shown in heavy black. The pancreatic veins, which are shown cut, drain into the splenic vein. The direction of the flow is indicated by arrows. The branching of the portal vein within the liver is indicated. The collection of blood from the liver by the hepatic veins is shown; these enter the inferior vena cava, which passes through the diaphragm to the right atrium.

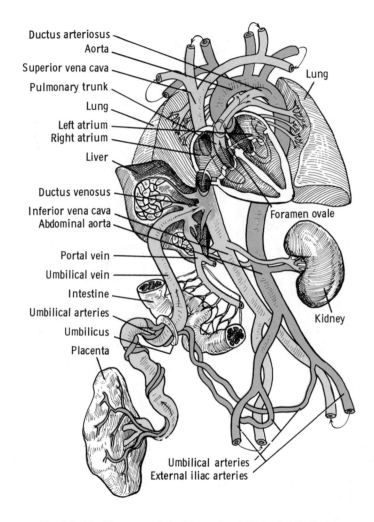

Fig. 13-27. Diagram of the fetal circulation shortly before birth; course of blood is indicated by arrows. Oxygenated, poorly oxygenated and mixed blood indicated by pink, blue and purple, respectively.

stances are detoxified. In other words, the liver "stands guard" by monitoring all absorbed materials before they are allowed to enter the general circulation for dispersal to all parts of the body.

Portal Hypertension. Any interference with the flow of blood through the liver may result in portal hypertension, an abnormal increase in the pressure of the blood within the portal system of veins. Obstruction of the portal system occurs fairly frequently. It may be due to cirrhosis of the liver (an inflammatory process that results in a hardening of liver tissue), various tumors of the liver, or it may be due to back pressure in the inferior vena cava and the hepatic veins in certain types of heart disease. As blood backs up in the portal circuit, its pressure rises, and a collateral circulation is established; this primarily involves communications between the inferior mesenteric and the hemorrhoidal (rectal) veins that empty into the internal iliac veins, and communications between the gastric veins and the esophageal veins that empty into the azygos system. The esophageal veins frequently become dilated and tortuous (*esophageal varices*); rupture of these veins may lead to fatal hemorrhage. Back pressure in the paraumbilical veins may cause the abdominal veins around the umbilicus to dilate, forming a radiating pattern that is called the *caput medusae.*

Surgical intervention in the treatment of portal hypertension may involve a *portacaval shunt.* In this procedure an anastomosis is established between the portal vein and the inferior vena cava so that some of the portal blood can bypass the obstructed liver.

FETAL CIRCULATION

In the fetus the lungs, the gastrointestinal tract and the kidneys do not carry out the functions that they perform after birth. Instead, the fetus derives all of its oxygen and nutritive material from the mother's circulation and depends on her for the elimination of carbon dioxide and other waste products. This exchange of materials between the maternal and the fetal circulation takes place within the *placenta,* a highly vascular structure that is sometimes called the "afterbirth," since

it is cast out of the uterus following the birth of the baby. However, there is no direct connection between the circulatory system of the fetus and that of the mother. Fetal capillaries in the placenta are surrounded by pools of maternal blood, and all exchanges take place across the capillary membrane.

The vessels that connect the fetus with the placenta are the **umbilical arteries** and the **umbilical vein** (Fig. 13-27); these vessels lie in the umbilical cord. Blood leaves the fetus by way of the 2 umbilical arteries, which branch off the internal iliac arteries. After circulating through the capillaries in the placenta, where it picks up nutrients and oxygen and eliminates waste, blood returns by way of the umbilical vein; this vein enters the abdomen of the fetus at the umbilicus and ascends to the liver where it divides into 2 branches. One branch of the umbilical vein joins the portal vein and enters the liver; the other branch, called the *ductus venosus* continues onward to the inferior vena cava, thus permitting a certain amount of blood to bypass the liver. The umbilical vein and the ductus venosus are obliterated within a few days after the baby is born.

Circulation through the lower portion of the body is like that in the postnatal infant. As the blood returns from the lower portion of the body of the fetus, it is mingled with the blood that is returning from the placenta laden with oxygen and nutritive materials. The mixing takes place in the inferior vena cava, and the blood then enters the right atrium.

Circulation through the upper portion of the body also is like that in the postnatal infant. After circulating through the upper portion of the body the blood is returned to the right atrium by the superior vena cava. In the right atrium, blood from the inferior vena cava mixes to some extent with that from the superior vena cava. However, a "valve" in the inferior vena cava guides a steady stream of blood from the right atrium through the *foramen ovale* (p. 325) and into the left atrium, thus bypassing the lungs. That blood which descends into the right ventricle is pumped into the pulmonary artery, but since the fetal lungs are collapsed, only a small amount of blood passes

Fig. 13-28. Diagram of the cardiac and pulmonary circulation before, left, and after, right, the Blalock-Taussig operation: (1) superior vena cava; (2) inferior vena cava; (3) right atrium; (4) right ventricle; (5) pulmonary trunk, dividing into right and left pulmonary arteries; (6) left pulmonary veins; (7) left atrium; (8) left ventricle; (9) aorta; (10) innominate artery; (11) right subclavian artery; (12) defect in interventricular septum; (13) pulmonary stenosis. (Right) The anastomosis between the right subclavian artery and the right pulmonary artery is shown. (Redrawn and greatly simplified from Blalock, A., Hanlon, C. R., and Scott, H. W., Jr.: Surg., Gynec. Obstet. 87:386-387)

through the pulmonary circuit; most of the blood in the pulmonary artery flows through the *ductus arteriosus* (p. 352) which opens into the arch of the aorta. Normally, the foramen ovale and the ductus arteriosus close soon after the baby is born and breathing is established.

The blood in the aorta, a mixture of oxygenated and poorly oxygenated blood, is carried to all parts of the body through its systemic branches. However, on reaching the bifurcation of the common iliac arteries, part of the blood flows into the internal iliac arteries, into the umbilical arteries and back to the placenta for another exchange of nutrients and wastes. Figure 13-27 is a diagram of the fetal circulation; note that the umbilical vein is the only fetal vessel that carries fully oxygenated blood.

Congenital heart disease

Improper or inadequate development of the fetal heart and related blood vessels may result in various congenital defects. For example, there may be atrial or ventricular septal defects, stenosis of the great arteries or of their valves, failure of the ductus arteriosus to close after birth, etc. However, through constantly improving diagnostic and surgical technics many of these defects now can be corrected. In addition to the electrocardiogram and cardiac catheterization, another diagnostic aid in congenital heart disease is *angiocardiography;* this involves the injection of a radiopaque fluid into a vein or into a chamber of the heart and then taking a rapid series of x-ray pictures of the heart and neighboring vessels.

The tetralogy of Fallot was one of the hopeless congenital anomalies of the heart prior to the advent of cardiac surgery, and it usually terminated the patient's life by the age of 12. Today this condition can be corrected, or greatly improved, by surgical intervention. There are four characteristic features of this anomaly: (1) pulmonary stenosis, (2) a high ventricular septal defect, (3) an overriding aorta, and (4) right ventricular hypertrophy. The **pulmonary stenosis** obstructs blood flow to the lungs and results in *hypertrophy of the right ventricle* due to the overload. If the obstruction is severe enough, the pressure of backed-up blood in the right ventricle will become greater than the pressure in the left ventricle, causing unoxygenated blood to flow through the **ventricular septal defect** into the left ventricle and into the *overriding aorta.* Consequently, the blood that is delivered to the systemic capillaries is poorly oxygenated and contains so much reduced hemoglobin that marked cyanosis is present. Because of their cyanotic appearance, these little patients frequently are referred to as "blue babies."

When such youngsters try to run or to play, their oxygen-starved muscles tire very quickly; this causes them to assume a characteristic squatting position on their haunches as they rest and try to "catch their breath."

Tremendous relief of both cyanosis and disability may be obtained by the Blalock-Taussig operation (Fig. 13-28). This surgical procedure consists of joining the end of a systemic artery (usually the right or left subclavian) with the side of the right or the left pulmonary artery. As a result, some of the mixed arterial-venous blood in the aorta flows through the shunt into the pulmonary artery, greatly increasing the volume of blood that reaches the lungs for oxygenation. Although this operation is merely palliative and does nothing to correct the original anatomic de-

fects, it is of great benefit to those patients for whom open-heart surgery is not available.

THE LYMPHATIC SYSTEM

The lymphatic system is anatomically and physiologically interrelated with the cardiovascular system. It not only helps in the removal of tissue fluid from the intercellular spaces but also plays an important role in protecting the body from bacterial invasion. The structures of the lymphatic system include: (1) lymphatic vessels which are concerned with the transportation of lymph, and (2) related lymphatic organs that filter lymph, produce lymphocytes and carry out other specific functions.

The lymphatic vessels

Those vessels that are concerned with the transport of lymph include lymphatic capillaries, collecting vessels and terminal ducts.

The lymphatic capillaries are microscopic, blind tubes which anastomose freely and form vast networks in the intercellular spaces. These networks constitute the beginning of the lymph drainage system and are widely distributed throughout the body; however, they are absent from the CNS, the meninges, the eyeball and orbital fat, the internal ear, cartilage and the epidermis. The walls of lymphatic capillaries consist of a single layer of thin, flat endothelial cells, and they are much more permeable than are the walls of blood capillaries. For this reason, large particles (escaped plasma protein, foreign substances such as soot, dirt, etc.) are able to pass through the lymphatic capillary wall and be carried away in the lymph. Those lymphatic capillaries which are located within the intestinal walls are called *lacteals* because of the milky appearance of their lymph following the absorption of fats. The various lymphatic capillary networks are drained by an elaborate system of collecting vessels.

Lymphatic collecting vessels arise in the capillary networks which they drain. They course through the loose subcutaneous tissues, through

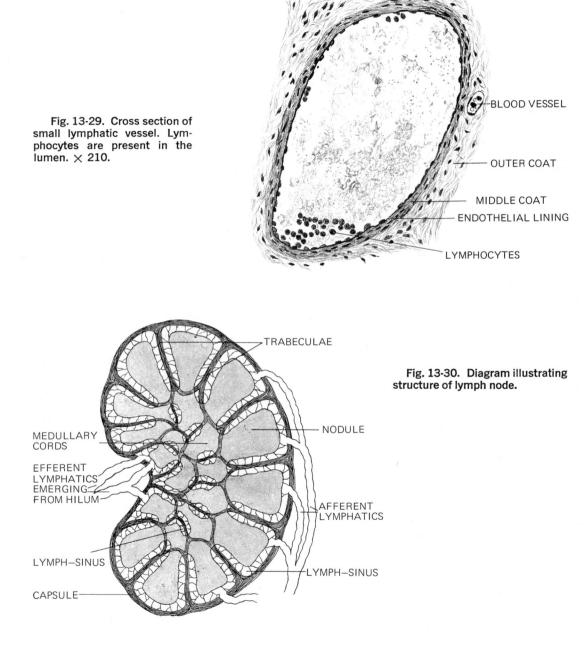

Fig. 13-29. Cross section of small lymphatic vessel. Lymphocytes are present in the lumen. × 210.

BLOOD VESSEL

OUTER COAT

MIDDLE COAT
ENDOTHELIAL LINING

LYMPHOCYTES

TRABECULAE

Fig. 13-30. Diagram illustrating structure of lymph node.

NODULE

MEDULLARY CORDS

EFFERENT LYMPHATICS EMERGING FROM HILUM

AFFERENT LYMPHATICS

LYMPH—SINUS

LYMPH—SINUS

CAPSULE

the connective tissue between muscles and other organs, and often form networks around the blood vessels which they accompany. Lymphatic vessels are extremely delicate, and their walls are so transparent that one can see the lymph within. A cross section of a small lymphatic vessel is illustrated in Figure 13-29. Another feature of these vessels is the presence of numerous valves which prevent the backflow of lymph; these valves occur at such close intervals that the vessel has a knotted or beaded appearance.

Lymph nodes (p. 384) are situated along the course of the lymphatic vessels and serve to filter the lymph before it is returned to the blood stream. A number of *afferent lymphatic vessels* penetrate the capsule of each lymph node and break up into lymphoid sinuses (Fig. 13-30); the sinuses lead into one or two *efferent lymphatic vessels* which carry lymph away from the node. A variable number of nodes may be traversed in a similar manner before the efferent vessels unite to form collecting trunks. Each collecting trunk drains a definite area of the body and eventually empties into one of two terminal vessels; these are the thoracic duct and the right lymphatic duct.

The thoracic duct is the larger of the two terminal vessels. As illustrated by the unshaded areas in Figure 13-31, it receives lymph from all parts of the body below the diaphragm and from the left half of the body above the diaphragm. The thoracic duct begins at the level of the second lumbar vertebra. At its origin there usually is a dilated portion known as the *cisterna chyli;* collecting trunks from the lower extremities, the abdominal and the pelvic viscera and the body wall empty into this structure. Coursing upward along the spinal column, the thoracic duct receives intercostal trunks as it passes through the thorax; at the root of the neck it is joined by collecting trunks from the left upper extremity and the left side of the head, the neck and the upper thorax. The thoracic duct ends by opening into the angle of junction of the left subclavian and the left internal jugular veins; a pair of valves at the terminal end prevents the passage of venous blood into the duct. The thoracic duct is shown in Figures 13-32 and 13-33.

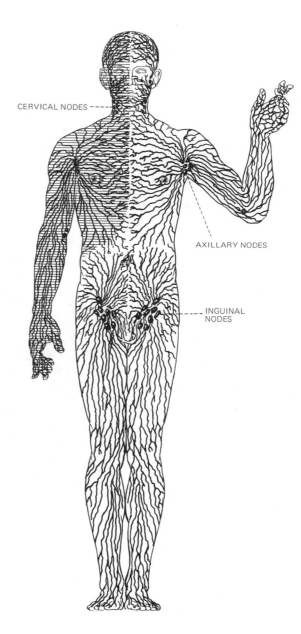

Fig. 13-31. Diagram of superficial lymphatic vessels and cervical, axillary and inguinal nodes. Unshaded area drained by thoracic duct; shaded area drained by right lymphatic duct.

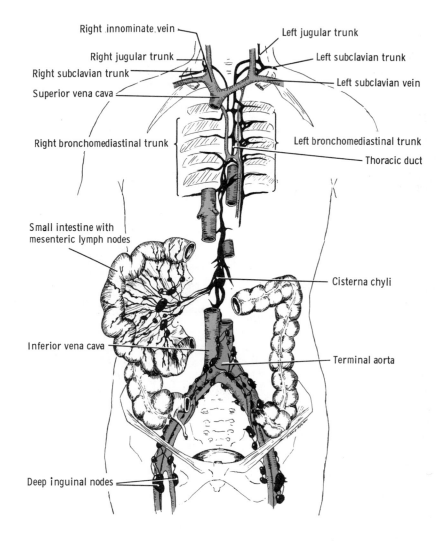

Fig. 13-32. Deep lymphatic vessels and nodes.

The right lymphatic duct (Fig. 13-33) is a short duct that may be formed by the union of trunks from the right upper extremity and the right side of the head, the neck and the upper thorax; it empties into the right innominate or brachiocephalic vein near its origin. However, this terminal duct frequently is missing; when it is, the various collecting trunks empty directly into the right subclavian vein near its junction with the right internal jugular vein. The shaded area in Figure 13-31 illustrates the portions of the body drained by the right lymphatic duct.

In summary, the function of the lymphatic vessels is to return to the blood stream the water, escaped plasma protein, and products of cellular metabolism that cannot be reabsorbed by the blood capillaries; bacteria and other harmful substances generally are filtered out of the lymph stream as it flows through the lymph nodes.

Interference with the drainage of lymph from any part of the body may result in a marked swelling of the tissues; this is called *lymphedema*. Such a condition may occur in the upper extremity following surgical removal of a breast and the axillary lymph nodes in the treatment of cancer; deep x-ray therapy following surgery may damage the remaining lymphatic vessels and further disrupt the flow of lymph.

The flow of lymph

Since there is no pumping mechanism in the lymphatic system, the onward flow of lymph through the vessels depends on forces outside the system. Of primary importance are the contractions of skeletal muscles, the peristaltic movements of the smooth muscle in visceral walls and the pulsating arteries; all of these activities serve to squeeze, to compress or to massage the neighboring lymphatic vessels, thus forcing the lymph onward toward the veins. Backflow of lymph is prevented by the numerous valves that are present in the vessels.

Breathing movements also play a part in the movement of lymph. With each inspiration the pressure within the thoracic cavity is decreased, and the resulting suction causes lymph to flow

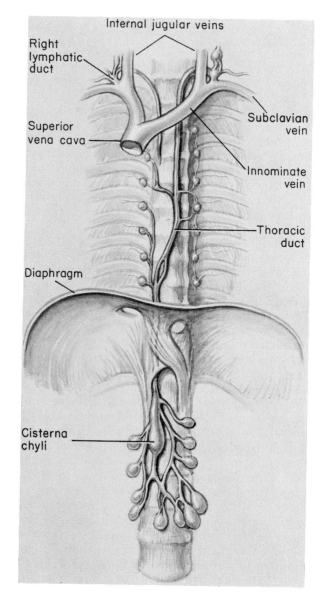

Fig. 13-33. Diagram illustrating course of the thoracic duct and the right lymphatic duct.

upward from the abdominal portion of the thoracic duct.

Lymphatic tissue

Lymphatic tissue is the second type of hemopoietic tissue (p. 299). It consists of a meshwork of reticular fibers in which are found primitive *stem cells* that are capable of mitotic division and of differentiation along two lines: (1) some stem cells differentiate to form *phagocytic cells* of the reticuloendothelial system, (2) others become free *lymphoblasts* that can go on to form *lymphocytes*. As previously described on page 305, lymphocytes can give rise to precursor cells that in turn become *plasma cells,* the important producers of antibodies.

Thus, the very nature of the cells to be found in lymphatic tissue emphasizes its primary function of defending the body against bacteria and other disease-inducing agents that may break through the skin or mucous membrane barriers. The distribution of lymphatic tissue throughout the body is quite logical if one keeps in mind the protective role that it plays.

Lymphatic nodules, designed to filter tissue fluid, are found under wet epithelial surfaces that are exposed to contamination, such as the digestive tract and the respiratory and the genitourinary passages. The simplest forms are merely irregular accumulations of lymphoid cells under the mucous membranes; larger accumulations of these cells produce definite round nodules, which may occur singly (solitary nodules) or in groups (aggregated nodules). *Aggregated nodules,* or *Peyer's patches,* are particularly abundant in the distal portion (ileum) of the small intestine; they may become secondarily infected in cases of typhoid fever and tuberculosis, occasionally contributing to perforation of the intestinal wall. Still larger masses of lymphatic tissue form a protective *tonsillar ring* in the pharynx; the pharyngeal tonsil, the lingual and the palatine tonsils are described on page 419.

Lymph nodes, designed to filter lymph, are small oval or bean-shaped bodies varying in size from that of a pinhead to that of an almond.

Although they may occur singly, most nodes are clustered in groups along the course of lymphatic vessels that drain specific areas of the body; these groups are referred to as regional lymph nodes. Figures 13-31 and 13-32 illustrate some of the superficial and the deep lymphatic vessels and their regional nodes.

Each node consists of a mass of lymphatic tissue that is enclosed in a fibrous capsule; little partitions (trabeculae) extend inward from the capsule and divide the node into compartments. Lymph flows through the node by way of the *lymph sinuses,* a system of microscopic channels that permeate the lymphatic tissue; great numbers of newly formed lymphocytes enter the lymph stream as it passes germinal centers near the periphery of the node. A section of a lymph node is shown in Figure 13-34.

In addition to the production of lymphocytes, lymph nodes also function as "filtration plants." Each lymph sinus is crisscrossed by reticular fibers to which cling numerous phagocytic cells. As lymph flows through these living filters, bacteria and other foreign particles are first trapped by the network of fibers and then destroyed by the phagocytes. This function of the lymph nodes is of particular importance when one has a localized infection; by filtering bacteria from the lymph stream, the nodes prevent the infection from spreading to other parts of the body. However, as the bacteria and the phagocytes engage in mortal combat, the lymph nodes themselves may become inflamed (*lymphadenitis*). One should be aware of the fact that the presence of an infection in almost any part of the body is accompanied by enlargement and tenderness of the lymph nodes which drain that region. Another complication that may follow a severe infection is an inflammation of the lymphatic vessels (*lymphangitis*). When an infection is spreading along the superficial lymphatic vessels its course may be revealed by red streaks in the skin. This is a danger signal, since it indicates that unless the infection is stopped, the invading organisms eventually will reach the blood stream, and *septicemia* (blood poisoning) will follow.

In most instances this vast lymphatic network

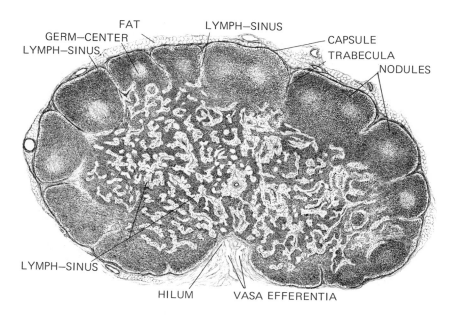

FAT LYMPH—SINUS
GERM—CENTER
LYMPH—SINUS
CAPSULE
TRABECULA
NODULES
LYMPH—SINUS
HILUM VASA EFFERENTIA

Fig. 13-34. Section of small lymph node, through the hilum. × 25.

provides a valuable line of defense against infection and disease, but occasionally it works to the body's disadvantage. In cases of *carcinoma* (cancer), malignant cells frequently break away from the primary, localized tumor and enter the lymph stream; on reaching the regional lymph nodes the cancer cells set up secondary growths or *metastases*. It is for this reason that in treating carcinoma, the surgeon removes not only the original cancerous organ but as many of the surrounding lymph nodes as possible. However, if the disease is not treated in its early stages, it will continue to spread throughout the body until the victim dies.

The spleen, designed to filter blood, is the largest unit of lymphatic tissue in the body. It is located in the left hypochondriac region, just below the diaphragm and posterolateral to the stomach. The shape of the spleen is somewhat variable, since it is accommodated to the surfaces of the adjacent viscera, but it generally is an elongated and ovoid body. It is soft, friable, highly vascular and dark purple.

The spleen is covered by a capsule composed of fibrous and elastic connective tissue, together with a few smooth muscle fibers. At the hilus, a fissure near the medial border, little strands of the tissue of the capsule extend into the substance of the organ; these strands (trabeculae) form a supporting framework for vessels and nerves. To a lesser extent, trabeculae extend inward from the capsule itself, as shown in Figure 13-35. The spaces within the framework are filled with a highly vascular lymphatic tissue called the *splenic pulp*. Two kinds of pulp are readily visible: red and white.

The *white pulp* consists of ordinary lymphatic tissue, some being distributed as tiny islands (nodules) in the soft red pulp that occupies the remaining space. These lymphatic nodules are the major sites for lymphocyte production in the spleen. White pulp also is distributed along the sheaths of arteries as they leave the trabeculae and enter the red pulp. Plasma cells are produced in the white pulp when antigens (e.g., bacteria)

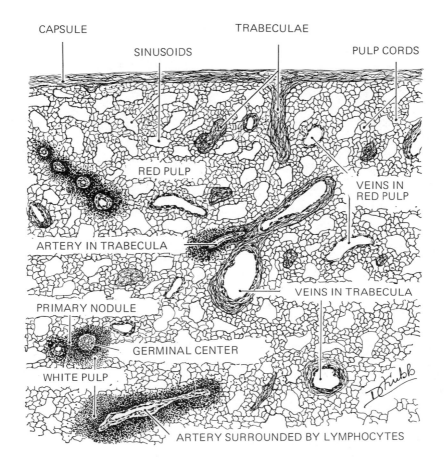

Fig. 13-35. Section of spleen, showing general arrangement of splenic tissue. × 10.

gain entrance to the bloodstream. The *red pulp* consists of a meshwork of reticular fibers containing vast numbers of red blood cells and reticuloendothelial cells (both fixed and free macrophagocytes); many lymphocytes may be seen in this pulp. Monocytes and granular leukocytes also are present, but they are less numerous. It now re-

mains to be seen how blood enters and leaves this living filtering device.

The blood supply of the spleen is derived from the splenic artery, a vessel noted for its large size in proportion to the size of the organ. This large artery divides into 6 or more branches that enter the hilus and diverge in various directions throughout the substance of the spleen. Each branch gives off smaller and smaller branches that ultimately deliver blood to highly permeable capillaries in the red pulp; here the blood trickles slowly through the reticular meshwork and the macrophagocytes can perform their functions (i.e., the removal of old red cells, bacteria, and so forth). The filtered blood then flows through venous sinusoids that empty into veins of the red pulp. The splenic vein ultimately conveys blood from the spleen to the portal vein, as previously described.

Although the spleen is not essential to life, it does perform many important functions. In the fetus it is a major site for the production of red blood cells, but after birth it is limited to the formation of lymphocytes, plasma cells, and some monocytes. The phagocytic reticuloendothelial cells remove most of the old, worn-out red blood cells from the circulation. The iron is extracted from the hemoglobin and liberated into the bloodstream for reuse by the body. The splenic cells also form a pigment, *bilirubin,* from the hemoglobin of the old red cells; bilirubin enters the bloodstream and is carried to the liver for elimination in the bile. Inasmuch as the spleen is able to produce plasma cells, it is a source of antibodies that offer protection against various diseases. The spleen also has a definite capacity to store blood and then to liberate that blood at times when it would be helpful to the body; however, this function is not as important in man as it is in certain lower animals.

Surgical removal of the spleen (splenectomy) ordinarily is tolerated quite well, as other organs in the body can take over splenic functions. For example, other lymphatic tissue will produce lymphocytes in sufficient numbers to meet the body's needs, and phagocytic cells in other parts of the reticuloendothelial system will destroy old red blood cells, bacteria, foreign substances, etc. Blood vessels in the skin, the liver, the lungs and the portal system are more than adequate to provide blood storage space when the body is at rest.

The thymus is a pinkish-gray mass of lymphatic tissue that is situated partly in the root of the neck and partly in the upper thorax beneath the sternum. It is relatively large in children, reaches its maximum size at the age of puberty, and then undergoes involution, slowly becoming smaller as one ages.

The thymus is enclosed in a connective tissue capsule from which trabeculae extend into its substance. It is divided into 2 pyramidal-shaped lobes, which, in turn, are subdivided into numerous lobules. Each lobule displays 2 zones of tissue, an outer cortex and an inner medulla; the cortical portion consists of a meshwork filled with many small lymphocytes, and the medullary portion contains cell nests or *thymic corpuscles.* The blood supply of the thymus is derived from branches of the thyroid and the internal mammary arteries; its nerve supply is derived from both divisions of the autonomic system. Lymphatic vessels from the thymus drain into the anterior mediastinal lymph nodes.

The functions of the thymus are under intensive study in many laboratories. What is accepted today may be proved wrong tomorrow. However, here is a summary of the current state of affairs. At present, it is generally accepted that the thymus is essential for the development of the *immunological competence* of the body—that is, its ability to produce antibodies in the presence of antigens (foreign substances, such as bacteria). It also is generally accepted that the thymus produces lymphocytes (or lymphocytic stem cells) that migrate to other lymphocyte "factories," such as the spleen and the lymph nodes, helping to populate them with immunologically competent cells.

The existence of a thymic secretion that is essential for development of the immune mechanism is not yet generally accepted. However, evidence is mounting that such an internal secretion does exist, and that it is particularly important during the first week of postnatal life. An active secretion, named thymosin, has been isolated from the thymus of a calf; this substance not only stimulates the production of lymphocytes, but also restores immunological competence in mice that have been subjected to whole-body radiation.

SUMMARY

1. Blood vessels
   A. Arteries
      a. Elastic muscular tubes, convey blood to capillaries
      b. Recoil forces blood onward in pulsating waves, reflect ventricular beat
      c. Coats: tunica intima, tunica media, tunica externa
      d. Aneurysm, dilated sac resulting from weakened arterial wall
      e. Arteriosclerosis, decrease in elastic tissue in wall; atherosclerosis, fatty degeneration and lipid infiltration of vessel wall
      f. Blood supply: vasa vasorum
      g. Nerve supply: vasomotor (constrictors and dilators). Afferent fibers related to reflex cardiac and vasomotor control
      h. Anastomoses: communications between adjacent vessels
   B. Veins
      a. Conduct blood from capillaries to heart; more numerous than arteries
      b. Thinner walled than arteries, have same 3 tunics; valves prevent backflow of blood
      c. Blood and nerve supply as in arteries, but less abundant
      d. Varicose veins, dilated and tortuous superficial vessels
   C. Capillaries
      a. Microscopic vessels between arterioles and venules; walls single cell thick
      b. Exchanges between blood and tissue fluid take place through capillary wall; focal point of cardiovascular system
      c. Precapillary sphincters regulate flow of blood through capillaries according to need; not enough blood to fill all vessels at same time
      d. Sinusoids are capillarylike vessels in liver, spleen, bone marrow
      e. Arteriovenous anastomoses, bypass the capillaries
2. Pulmonary circulation
   A. Concerned with oxygenation of blood; relatively short circuit
   B. Pulmonary trunk from right ventricle sends right and left branches to capillaries in each lung; blood oxygenated here, and CO_2 eliminated
   C. Pulmonary veins (2 from each lung) convey blood from capillaries to left atrium
3. Systemic circuit (arterial)
   A. Oxygenated blood pumped into aorta and thence to all parts of body by way of systemic branches which lead to capillaries
   B. Aorta is largest artery in body; arises from left ventricle, arches over to left side of vertebral column, descends to level of 4th lumbar vertebra, bifurcates into common iliac arteries
   C. Ascending aorta: coronary arteries arise just above semilunar valve, extend to capillaries in myocardium
   D. Aortic arch: in adult, connected to pulmonary artery by ligamentum arteriosum; in fetus, connected to pulmonary artery by ductus arteriosus
      a. Branches
         (1) Innominate (brachiocephalic trunk); branches to form right common carotid and right subclavian
         (2) Left common carotid
         (3) Left subclavian
      b. Common carotids supply capillaries in head and neck; branch to form external and internal carotids
      c. Circle of Willis is arterial anastomosis at base of brain; branches (cerebral arteries) supply capillaries in brain
      d. Subclavians supply head, thorax and upper extremities; major branches include vertebrals, thyrocervical trunk and internal mammary arteries. Continue into extremity as axillary, brachial, radial and ulnar arteries
   E. Thoracic aorta: from aortic arch to diaphragm
      a. Visceral branches: pericardial, bronchial and esophageal arteries

b. Parietal branches: intercostal and superior phrenic arteries
F. Abdominal aorta: from diaphragm to 4th lumbar vertebra
   a. Visceral branches: celiac (left gastric, hepatic and splenic), superior mesenteric, middle suprarenal, renal, and spermatic (or ovarian), and inferior mesenteric arteries
   b. Parietal branches: inferior phrenic, lumbar and middle sacral arteries
G. Terminal branches of aorta
   a. Common iliacs—bifurcate to form internal and external iliac arteries; supply pelvic viscera and lower extremities
   b. External iliac continues in thigh as femoral, to popliteal, to anterior and posterior tibial arteries. Dorsalis pedis is continuation of anterior tibial across top of foot
4. Systemic circuit (venous)
   A. Blood returned from capillaries to heart via superficial and deep veins and cranial venous sinuses
   B. Coronary sinus and tributaries return blood from myocardium to right atrium
   C. Veins of head and neck
      a. Cranial venous sinuses drain capillaries of brain, empty into internal jugular veins
      b. Internal jugular veins drain blood from brain, eyes, superficial face and neck
      c. External jugular veins drain deep face and neck
   D. Veins of upper extremity
      a. Superficial: cephalic and basilic
      b. Deep: radial, ulnar, brachial, axillary and subclavian
   E. Veins of thorax
      a. Innominate veins formed by union of internal jugular and subclavian on either side; innominates unite to form superior vena cava after receiving vertebral, internal mammary and inferior thyroid veins
      b. Azygos system of veins collects blood

from intercostal, mediastinal, pericardial and bronchial veins; empty into sup. vena cava
F. Veins of lower extremity
   a. Superficial: great and small saphenous
   b. Deep: anterior and posterior tibials, popliteal and femoral veins
G. Veins of pelvis
   a. External iliacs join internal iliacs to form common iliac veins
   b. Common iliac veins unite to form inferior vena cava
H. Veins of abdomen
   a. Inferior vena cava—largest vein in body; courses upward on right side of aorta, perforates diaphragm and ascends to enter right atrium
   b. Tributaries of inferior vena cava: lumbar, spermatic (or ovarian), renal, suprarenal, inferior phrenic and hepatic veins
   c. Portal system of veins drains gastrointestinal tract, pancreas and spleen; provides "detour" through liver which monitors all absorbed materials; liver drained by hepatic veins which empty into inferior vena cava
   d. Portal hypertension may be caused by cirrhosis and tumors of liver, as well as by heart disease when blood backs up in portal circuit of veins
5. Fetal circulation
   A. Fetus derives oxygen and nutrients from mother's blood; eliminates waste at same time as blood passes through placental capillaries
      a. No direct connection between mother and fetus; each has separate circulatory system
      b. Maternal blood pooled around capillaries in placenta
      c. Umbilical vein conveys blood from placenta to fetus; umbilical arteries convey blood from fetus to placenta
   B. Circulation through upper and lower portions of fetal body like that in postnatal individual

C. Foramen ovale and ductus arteriosus provide bypasses of lung circuit; only small amount of blood passes through lung capillaries since lungs not inflated. Fetal structures close after birth

6. Lymphatic system
   A. Interrelated with cardiovascular system; aids in removal of tissue fluid and in protection against infection and disease
   B. Lymphatic vessels
      a. Lymphatic capillaries: highly permeable, blind tubes in tissue spaces; receive water, escaped protein, foreign particles, etc.
      b. Lymphatic collecting vessels drain capillary networks; valves prevent backflow of lymph
      c. Terminal vessels: thoracic duct drains collecting vessels below diaphragm and on left side of body above diaphragm; right lymphatic duct drains right side of body above diaphragm. Both return lymph to blood stream
   C. Flow of lymph depends on massaging action of contracting muscle tissue and on breathing movements
   D. Lymphatic organs
      a. Lymphatic nodules: found under wet epithelial surfaces exposed to contamination
      b. Lymph nodes: produce lymphocytes, filter foreign particles from lymph
      c. Spleen: produces lymphocytes, filters foreign particles from blood, destroys old red blood cells and saves iron, forms antibodies
      d. Thymus: produces small lymphocytes, may be key to immunity mechanism

PRACTICAL APPLICATIONS AND QUESTIONS

(Encircle the letter of the *best* answer to each of the following questions.)

A. *Miss R. B. works in a store and must stand for long periods of time. As a result the superficial veins in her lower extremities have become varicosed.*

1. Varicose veins are
   a. hardened, due to calcium deposits
   b. dilated and tortuous
   c. narrowed by fatty infiltration
   d. constricted and sclerosed
2. The veins involved in this case are the
   a. femoral veins
   b. basilic veins
   c. cephalic veins
   d. saphenous veins
3. Surgical removal of superficial veins is possible because their work can be taken over by the
   a. superficial arteries
   b. capillaries
   c. deep veins
   d. lymphatic system

B. *Mr. A. A. has portal hypertension. His physician plans to perform a portacaval shunt.*

1. The portal system of veins conveys blood from
   a. the intercostal, the pericardial and the mediastinal spaces
   b. the gastrointestinal tract and the spleen
   c. the reproductive organs
   d. the cranial venous sinuses
2. Portal hypertension is directly related to an obstruction of the blood flow through the
   a. liver
   b. lungs
   c. spleen
   d. brain
3. Portacaval shunt involves the establishment of an anastomosis between the
   a. portal vein and the superior vena cava
   b. inferior vena cava and the portal artery
   c. superior vena cava and the hepatic vein
   d. inferior vena cava and the portal vein

C. *Mrs. A. M. has a severely infected foot and red streaks in the skin of her leg and is complaining of tenderness in her groin.*

1. The pain in her groin is related to the fact that bacteria-laden lymph from the area of infection is first filtered by
   a. regional lymph nodes
   b. lymphatic collecting vessels
   c. the splenic pulp
   d. Peyer's patches

2. The red streaks in the skin of her leg are indicative of spreading infection through
   a. aggregated lymphatic follicles
   b. solitary lymph nodes
   c. lymphatic capillaries
   d. lymphatic collecting vessels

3. The chief danger in cases of lymphangitis is that it may lead to
   a. arteriosclerosis
   b. lymphedema
   c. septicemia
   d. lymphadenitis

14

"And now I see with eye serene
The very pulse of the machine."
"She Was A Phantom of Delight"

WILLIAM WORDSWORTH

THE CIRCULATING BLOOD

Veins - most blood longest

The general function of the cardiovascular system is the transportation of life-sustaining blood from one part of the body to another. In the preceding chapters we have shown that this system consists of a muscular pump (the heart) which is coupled into a closed circuit of tubes (the arteries, capillaries and veins). Although each of the aforementioned structural units plays an important role in the circulation of blood, the capillaries are the focal point of the entire system. In fact, all of the physiologic mechanisms which control heart rate and the internal caliber of blood vessels are geared to the task of supplying the capillaries with adequate amounts of blood to meet the ever-changing needs of the cells.

As the circulating blood flows through the capillary networks, each organ of the body is supplied with the materials it needs for growth, repair, maintenance and its own particular functions. For example, the brain is absolutely dependent on oxygen and glucose; if these are not supplied continuously by the circulating blood, consciousness is lost. Muscles need oxygen, glucose and amino acids, as well as the proper ratio of sodium, calcium and potassium salts in order to contract normally. The glands need sufficient supplies of raw materials from which to manufacture their specific secretions. While these deliveries are being made, the blood picks up the end products of cellular metabolism and carries them to other parts of the body for use or for elimination. All such functions depend on the integration of cardiovascular activities which serve to maintain optimum blood pressure and blood flow through the capillary networks.

BLOOD PRESSURE AND BLOOD FLOW

Blood pressure refers to the force exerted by the blood against the walls of the vessels in which it is contained. Since a liquid will flow only from an area of higher pressure to an area of lower pressure, it necessarily follows that the blood pressure will be higher in some parts of the system than in others. The establishment of this pressure gradient depends on the high head of pressure generated during contraction of the ventricles of the heart.

Blood pressure is expressed in terms of millimeters of mercury *above* the atmospheric pressure, which is 760 mm. Hg. For example, if one's blood pressure is said to be 100 mm. Hg, it really means 860 mm. Hg. Obviously, if the pressure within the blood vessels were not above atmospheric pressure there would be no bleeding from a wound; instead, air would enter the severed vessels.

Kinds of blood pressure

Since there are 3 types of blood vessels in the vascular system, there are 3 "blood pressures" to be considered; these are arterial, capillary and venous pressures. Although arterial pressure is the pressure most frequently determined in clinical situations, one must not overlook the fact that blood also is under pressure in the capillaries and the veins. However, in view of the previously mentioned decreasing pressure gradient that governs the flow of liquids, it naturally follows that capillary pressure is lower than arterial pressure, and venous pressure is lower than capillary pressure. In other words, the farther a liquid flows from its pressure source the lower its pressure becomes.

Arterial blood pressure is the force exerted by the blood against the walls of the arteries. It is much higher in the long systemic arteries than it is in the short pulmonary circuit, but in either locale the pressure varies during the cardiac cycle. With each ventricular contraction a great spurt of blood is pumped into the large arteries, causing their elastic walls to become stretched and distended with blood. In spite of the intermittent delivery

of blood into the arterial tree, the flow is even and steady through the all-important capillaries. This is possible because much of the force of each ventricular contraction is stored as potential energy in the stretched arterial walls. Then, during relaxation of the ventricles, the stored energy is released as the elastic walls recoil and keep the blood flowing onward into the capillaries (backflow is prevented by closure of the semilunar valves). Thus we are dealing with two distinct pressure phases in the arteries: (1) the **systolic pressure,** which is generated during contraction or systole of the ventricles, and (2) the **diastolic pressure,** which is that maintained by the recoil of stretched elastic tissue in arterial walls during ventricular relaxation or diastole.

In healthy young adults at rest, the average systolic pressure range in the *systemic arteries* is 115 to 120 mm. Hg; the diastolic range is slightly lower, or 75 to 80 mm. Hg. However, a systolic pressure of 90 to 140, and a diastolic pressure of 60 to 90 are considered to be within the so-called normal range. When recording a blood pressure, the systolic pressure precedes the diastolic, in this manner: 115/75 or 130/90, whatever the case may be. The difference between the systolic and the diastolic blood pressures is called the *pulse pressure;* it averages about 40 mm. Hg and is generally indicative of the cardiac output, elasticity of arteries and peripheral resistance.

A systolic blood pressure which is consistently above 140 mm. Hg in a person at rest is above the normal range; such a person is said to have **hypertension** or high blood pressure. In many cases, the cause of hypertension is unknown, and the person is said to have *primary* or *essential hypertension;* overweight, nervous tension and heredity are thought to be possible predisposing factors. *Secondary hypertension* is so named because the elevated pressure stems from a known cause; it may accompany kidney disease (nephritis), arteriosclerosis, etc. The accelerated or fulminating form of high blood pressure is called *malignant hypertension;* this is extremely serious, and many pathologic changes occur, often involving the brain and the kidneys. In severe cases of hypertension the systolic pressure may rise to 200 or 300 mm. Hg.

The greatest dangers faced by hypertensive persons are cerebral hemorrhage and heart failure.

Occasionally a systolic pressure is consistently below the normal range, and such a person is said to have **hypotension.** The hypotensive person may complain of fatigue, lack of physical endurance and episodes of fainting due to lack of adequate blood flow to the brain.

The average systolic pressure range in the *pulmonary arteries* is 25 to 30 mm. Hg, and the diastolic range is 5 to 10 mm. Hg. It is essential that the pulmonary pressure be maintained at this relatively low level to insure a correspondingly low pressure value in the pulmonary capillaries, as described below.

Capillary blood pressure is the force exerted by the blood against the walls of the capillaries. It is about 32 mm. Hg at the arterial end of the systemic capillaries and 12 mm. Hg at the venous end. The importance of the capillary blood pressure in the formation of tissue fluid is discussed on page 33. Since this pressure is the driving force in the filtration of liquid through the capillary

walls, the alert student may wonder why the air sacs or alveoli of the lungs are not filled with tissue fluid which has filtered out of the pulmonary capillaries. Normally, there is no fluid in the alveoli due to the very low blood pressure in the pulmonary capillaries. No filtration occurs in these capillaries because there is no driving force. If the pressure is raised, as in failure of the heart, then fluid is formed and it accumulates in the air sacs, giving rise to the condition known as *pulmonary edema.* Another situation which leads to pulmonary edema is damage to the walls of the lung capillaries by inhalation of poisonous gas. As you would expect, if this condition is allowed to progress, death will result, since oxygen cannot enter the lungs to replenish the supply in the blood stream.

Venous blood pressure is the force exerted by the blood against the walls of the veins. At the beginning of the smallest veins this pressure is about 12 mm. Hg, but it gradually decreases to zero (atmospheric pressure) in the great veins near the heart. Thus blood returns to its initial

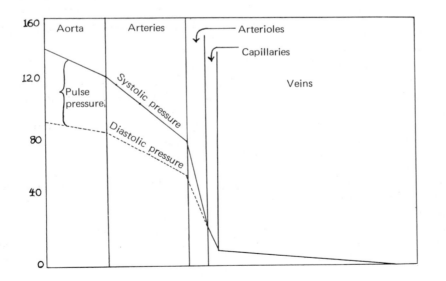

Fig. 14-1. Diagram showing the gradient of pressure in the various parts of the vascular system, between the aorta and the great veins. The gradient is steepest in the arterioles. The pulse pressure disappears as the capillaries are reached.

Fig. 14-2. Diagram illustrating the mechanics of the circulatory system. The ventricle is the pump. The large elastic arteries are distended further with each beat of the heart or stroke of the pump, and their elastic recoil between beats, while the pump refills, keeps arterial pressure high and forces blood onward. Arterioles, which can be regulated by vasomotor nerves, regulate the amount of blood flow to each organ, like reduction valves. The capillary bed receives blood all the time, for the flow of blood is steady in this part of the vascular system. Exchanges between the blood plasma and tissue fluid take place through the capillary walls. The veins return blood to the pump. (From Ham, A. W.: Histology, ed. 2, Philadelphia, Lippincott)

pressure source and is ready to repeat the circulatory cycle. The gradient of pressure in different parts of the vascular system is illustrated diagrammatically in Figure 14-1. It is evident that the most marked decrease in pressure occurs in the smallest arteries or arterioles. The mechanics of the circulatory system are illustrated in Figure 14-2.

An increase in venous blood pressure is a cardinal feature of the clinical syndrome known as "heart failure." Since the failing heart is unable to generate an effective pumping pressure, blood tends to back up in the veins. This results in an abnormally high filtration pressure in the capillary beds, and fluid begins to accumulate in the tissue spaces (edema). On the arterial side, a reduction in blood flow through the kidneys may lead to the retention of sodium and water which further contributes to edema formation. However, if the heart is able to maintain an adequate output of blood to meet the basic needs of the body, it is said to be "compensated." If the heart is unable to maintain an adequate circulation, it is said to be "decompensated." In cardiac decompensation, the symptoms of pulmonary congestion include pulmonary edema, dyspnea (labored breathing) and cough as the air sacs of the lungs fill with tissue fluid; as a result of systemic venous engorgement, there is cyanosis, generalized edema of dependent parts and enlargement of the liver. These symptoms are indicative of "backward failure" of the heart, a condition that is referred to as congestive heart failure. Digitalis is a valuable drug that acts directly on the heart muscle and improves myocardial efficiency by increasing the force of each contraction; as a result, the ventricles empty more completely, and general circulation shows a marked improvement.

The maintenance of arterial blood pressure

Several factors are involved in the maintenance of arterial blood pressure at its usual high level. These are the rate and the force of the heartbeat, the elasticity of large arteries, the peripheral resistance, the quantity of blood in the vascular system in relation to the capacity and the viscosity of the blood.

Rate and Force of Heartbeat. The faster the rate of the beat of the heart and the greater its force of contraction, the higher the arterial pressure will be. The heart is the pump, and if it changes, the pressure in the system is bound to change. A decrease in the rate or force of the beat of the heart leads to a lowering of the arterial blood pressure.

Elasticity of the large arteries is responsible for the maintenance of arterial blood pressure between beats of the heart (diastolic pressure). If the large arteries lose their elasticity the pressure is unusually high during systole and falls to a low level during diastole, which means that the pulse pressure is greater than usual. With rigid arteries, the flow into the capillaries is intermittent, coming in spurts with each ventricular systole and ceasing during diastole.

Figure 14-3 illustrates the steady flow in an elastic system in contrast with the intermittent flow in rigid tubes.

Peripheral resistance refers to the resistance offered by arterioles to the flow of blood. By offering resistance to flow, arterioles maintain a high pressure behind them in the larger arteries and a lower pressure in front of them in the capillaries and the veins. It has been stated by one author that they "act as nozzles that gently spray blood into the capillary beds."

The amount of resistance to flow varies with the size of the lumens of the arterioles. If the lumens are wide there is little resistance to flow. In this case the pressure on the arterial side becomes lower and that on the venous side higher than usual. If the lumens are narrow, the arterioles offer more resistance to the flow of blood, and in this case the pressure on the arterial side becomes higher and that on the venous side lower than before.

The arteriolar region of the vascular system may be thought of as a reducing valve or screw in the outflow tube, as indicated in Figure 14-4. The size of the lumens of the arterioles, which really means the peripheral resistance, is controlled reflexly by vasomotor nerves that supply the smooth muscle in the walls of the arterioles. Peripheral resistance

Fig. 14-3. Diagram to show the effects of elastic vessels. If the vessels were rigid, as in the glass tube, the blood flow would be intermittent. Since the vessels are elastic, the flow is continuous. The recoil of the vessels keeps the blood flowing between beats of the heart. (Adapted from Howell)

is very high in persons who have high blood pressure or hypertension.

By the time the blood enters the venules from the capillaries, it exerts very little pressure on the walls of the veins. This means that the force imparted to it by the heart and the elasticity of the walls of the large arteries is almost spent.

The quantity of blood in the vascular system in relation to the capacity of the system is exceedingly important. If a considerable amount of blood is lost suddenly by hemorrhage, the blood pressure falls. The walls of the arteries are not put on stretch, and the supply to the vital organs, such as the heart and the brain, is not sufficient to maintain homeostasis.

Whenever the quantity of blood is altered, protective mechanisms are brought into action as a result of the attempt to maintain the arterial blood pressure at the usual level. The heart rate is faster, and the arterioles are markedly constricted after blood is lost.

Viscosity of blood is due to the presence of red blood cells and plasma proteins. If the number of red cells is increased, in proportion to the plasma, the viscosity is increased, and the blood pressure is higher. This is noted in polycythemia vera, in which there is a very high red cell count. If the number of red cells is decreased, as in anemia, the viscosity is low, and the arterial blood pressure is below the average.

Fig. 14-4. Diagram of pressure conditions in the vascular system. (a) A steady fall in pressure is noted with increase in distance from the reservoir. (b) The effect of increasing the peripheral resistance (vasoconstriction) is shown. The screw represents the arteriolar area. With vasoconstriction, the pressure rises on the arterial side and falls on the venous side. (Redrawn from Howell)

If the concentration of plasma proteins is low, the blood pressure is low. If albumin solutions are injected, viscosity increases, and blood pressure rises.

Factors influencing arterial blood pressure

There are several physiologic factors, aside from those described above, which influence the arterial blood pressure; these include age, weight, sex, emotions and exercise.

Age. In newborn babies the systolic pressure ranges between 20 and 60 mm. Hg. By the end of the first month the pressure has risen to between 70 and 80 mm. Hg. It continues to rise slowly during childhood and reaches the adult level about the age of puberty. Blood pressure may remain at the same level until a person reaches 50 or 60 years of age, or may rise at any time if changes occur in the walls of large arteries (e.g., arteriosclerosis).

Walls of arteries deteriorate earlier than walls of veins. The arterial walls are under constant tension and are not really well supplied with blood. The capillaries which supply arterial walls collapse when the walls are stretched (which is practically all of the time), and the lymphatic drainage is not efficient. It is often said that a man is "as old as his arteries." This means that if arterial walls are damaged by the age of 30, a man may be 70 so far as his blood pressure is concerned.

Weight. Excess weight is important because often it is associated with the onset of high blood pressure, especially after the age of 40 years.

Sex. After puberty, men have higher average blood pressures than women. However, after the age of 40 or 50 the blood pressure in women tends to be slightly higher than in men.

Emotions have a profound influence on systolic blood pressure, which may increase as much as 40 mm. Hg during fear or anger. If a person is having his blood pressure taken for the first time, the procedure should be explained to him, otherwise the systolic pressure may be elevated due to fear. In emotional crises there is an outpouring of epinephrine (a hormone from the adrenal gland), and

two of its effects serve to increase blood pressure: (1) an increase in the rate and the force of the heartbeat and (2) a constriction of the arterioles. A person with arteriosclerosis may be in serious trouble if he loses his temper, because the sudden, sharp increase in systolic pressure may cause the rupture of an artery in the brain.

Exercise is accompanied by a rise in arterial blood pressure. Systolic blood pressure may rise 60 to 70 mm. Hg (above the resting level) during exercise. There may be great danger in running for a bus or carrying out a vigorous bout of exercise if one has arteriosclerosis, as there may be rupture of one of the diseased arteries when the pressure within them increases.

Method of measuring arterial blood pressure

An important part of any physical examination is a determination of the arterial blood pressure. The instrument used for this purpose is called a *sphygmomanometer;* it consists of a cloth-covered inflatable rubber cuff which communicates with a mercury manometer and a pressure bulb. To measure blood pressure, the cuff is wrapped around the arm above the elbow and fastened snugly in place by an extension of the cloth covering. By means of the bulb, air is pumped into the cuff, thus putting pressure on the arm. Sufficient pressure is applied to compress the brachial artery. This shuts off the blood flow to the portion of the upper extremity distal to the cuff.

The rubber cuff has a second outlet; this leads to a glass tube which contains mercury. The mercury rises in the tube as air is pumped into the cuff. Along the side of the tube in which the mercury rises is a scale ruled in millimeters. The distance to which the mercury rises indicates the amount of pressure necessary to stop the flow of blood in the forearm.

When the brachial artery has been compressed completely, the air is slowly released from the cuff by means of a valve on the bulb. As the air is released, a point is reached (indicated by a tapping sound) at which the pressure of the blood in the artery is just equal to that of the air in the cuff. Below this point the blood pressure

Fig. 14-5. Various methods of estimating the blood pressure. 1. By palpation; the cuff is inflated until the pulse can no longer be felt at the wrist. Air is released from the cuff until the pulse returns. The pressure at which the pulse can first be felt is taken as the systolic pressure. The auscultation method, 2, is described in the text and shown in Fig. 14-6. The palpation method is less satisfactory than the auscultatory method. (After Harris)

exceeds the air pressure in the cuff, and blood begins to flow into the forearm again. The principle is shown by diagram in Figure 14-5.

One listens with a stethoscope for sounds over the course of the brachial artery. The bell is placed just below the bend in the elbow. As air is gradually released from the cuff, the pressure falls to a point where a pulse wave and a spurt of blood can break through the partially compressed artery at the height of ventricular systole. The temporary turbulence in the blood as it passes through this narrow opening results in a distinct tapping sound which can be heard through the stethoscope with each pulse wave. The height of the column of mercury when the sound is first heard corresponds to the *systolic blood pressure*. As additional air is released from the cuff, the tapping sounds first

become progressively louder, then suddenly diminish in intensity and develop a rather muffled quality just before disappearing altogether; the reading on the mercury scale at the time of the sudden muffling of sound corresponds to the *diastolic pressure*. Complete disappearance of the sounds indicates that the cuff pressure has fallen below the diastolic pressure and there is no longer any turbulence in the blood as it flows freely through the decompressed artery. This method of taking the blood pressure is illustrated in Figure 14-6.

Velocity of blood flow

The distance that a particle of blood travels in a given time is called the *velocity* or speed of the

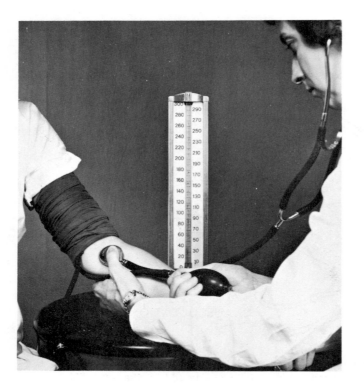

Fig. 14-6. Method of taking blood pressure by auscultation.

blood flow. It is expressed in millimeters per second. Velocity varies in different parts of the vascular system. It is about 300 mm. per second in the aorta, slows down to 0.5 mm. in the capillaries and speeds up to 150 mm. per second in the great veins.

Blood flows most rapidly where the cross-section area of the vascular system is least; in the systemic circuit this is the aorta. Every time an artery branches, the cross-section area of its two branches combined is greater than that of the original vessel. There are countless divisions before the capillaries are reached, and, as a result, the combined cross-section area of the systemic capillaries is about 600 to 800 times as great as the cross-section area of the aorta. Therefore, the blood flows only 1/600 to 1/800 as fast as in the aorta (1/600 × 300 = ½ mm.). The combined cross-section area of the superior and the inferior venae cavae is about twice that of the aorta, and the speed of

blood flow is half as fast. The relationship between cross-section area and velocity in different parts of the vascular system is illustrated in Figure 14-7.

Circulation time depends on velocity of blood flow. It is the time required for a particle of blood to start in the right atrium, go through the pulmonary circuit to the left heart, then through the systemic circuit and back to the right atrium. It takes about 23 seconds for the average round trip. This means that it takes about 27 heartbeats to drive a given unit of blood around the two circuits.

Measurement of the circulation time in part of a vascular circuit may be a helpful diagnostic tool. This is accomplished by the injection of a substance into a peripheral vein and notation of the time it takes for that substance to arrive at another point in the circuit. For example, the doctor may inject a bitter tasting substance (decholin) into the patient's median cubital vein and note the number of seconds that pass before the patient

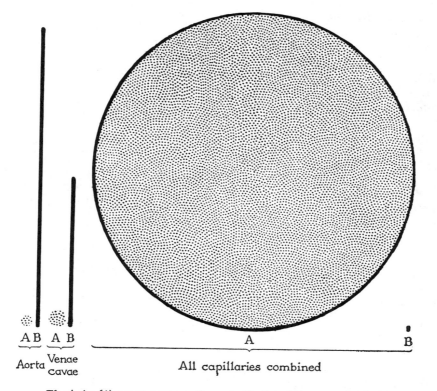

A B A B
Aorta Venae
cavae

A

B

All capillaries combined

The circles (A) represent cross section area; the lines (B) represent velocity

Fig. 14-7. Comparative velocities and cross-section areas in different parts of the vascular system. In the aorta, where the cross-section area (A) is small, the velocity (B) is most rapid. In the venae cavae, the cross-section area is about twice as great as it is in the aorta, and the velocity is about half as rapid. In the capillaries, the combined cross-section area is from 600 to 800 times as great as it is in the aorta, and the velocity is correspondingly slowed.

experiences a bitter taste in his mouth; average circulation time in the *"arm to tongue"* circuit is between 10 and 16 seconds. In a similar manner, the *"arm to lung"* circulation time may be determined by the injection of an aromatic substance such as ether; within 4 to 8 seconds after injection, the patient will smell ether as it diffuses from the blood stream into the air sacs of his lungs and is exhaled through the nose. You will note that the arm to tongue circulation time is slightly greater than that required for the arm to lung circuit; this is to be expected, since the blood must travel completely through the pulmonary circuit and return to the left heart before it can be pumped to capillaries in the tongue. However, in either case the circulation time is increased considerably whenever there is any circulatory obstruction; for example, in cases of congestive heart failure, the circulation time may be increased up to three times the normal.

The arterial pulse

The arterial pulse is a wave of distention or expansion and recoil that sweeps over the arterial system with each systole of the left ventricle. The pulse wave grows weaker as it passes over the arterial system and disappears completely in the capillaries. The pulse wave travels rapidly, at a rate of 6 to 9 м. per second over the large arterial branches. It reaches the periphery before the blood that was pumped from the left ventricle at the same time. In other words, we feel the wave of distention in the wall of the radial artery due to ejection of blood before that blood gets out of the aorta.

Since the arterial pulse generally is indicative of heart action, its rate and characteristics are noted several times a day on hospitalized patients. Most frequently the radial artery is used for this purpose, but the pulse may be felt in any artery

Fig. 14-8. Radial pulse tracings. (Top) Pulse in normal individual; the notch on the descending limb indicates the time of closing of the semilunar valves. (Center) Pulse in hyperthyroidism; the rate is rapid (tachycardia). (Bottom) Pulse in heart block; the rate is very slow.

that lies near the surface of the body and over a bone or other firm tissue. In counting the pulse, place the fingertips over the artery, press lightly and note the waves of distention; the average pulse *rate* is between 70 and 80 waves or "beats" per minute. One also should note the pulse *rhythm* (regular or irregular intervals between beats), *volume* (large or small pulse), and *tension* (compressibility of artery—hard or soft pulse).

Various abnormalities in the pulse wave may be encountered, but only a few of these will be mentioned. If the pulse rate is very rapid, one is said to have *tachycardia;* on the other hand, a very slow rate is called *bradycardia*. Tracings representing normal, rapid and slow pulses are illustrated in Figure 14-8. If the pulse is very weak and rapid with one wave running into the next, it is described as a *thready* or *running pulse*. In *atrial fibrillation* the pulse is totally irregular; this means that in addition to irregular time intervals between each 2 pulses, strong and weak beats are intermingled (Fig. 14-9). Since the ventricles of the heart are contracting at an abnormally rapid rate, they do not always have time to fill with blood; as a result, the pulse rate is slower than the heart rate because some of the systoles do not eject quantities of blood sufficient to distend the arteries and start a pulse wave. In such cases, it is helpful to take an *apical-radial pulse*. To carry out this procedure, one person listens through a stethoscope placed over the cardiac area of the chest and counts the heart rate; at the same time a second person counts the radial pulse at the wrist. If the apical beat is 160 per minute and the radial pulse is only 90 per minute, the patient is said to have a *pulse deficit* of 70. In the normal individual the rate of the heart counted at the apex is the same as the rate counted in a peripheral artery, such as the radial.

The central venous pulse

The arterial pulse dies out in the capillaries, and there are no pulsations in the peripheral veins. However, in the large veins near the heart, a venous pulse is noted. This is called the *central venous pulse,* and it is due to pressure changes which are reflected from the right atrium. By using suitable apparatus, the central venous pulse may be recorded, and it gives the same type of information as the electrocardiogram in some cardiac disorders. You can see the pulse in the external jugular vein of some individuals.

REGULATION OF THE CIRCULATION

The maintenance of optimal blood pressure and blood distribution throughout the body requires that continual adjustments be made in the rate and the force of the heartbeat and in the internal caliber of the blood vessels. Initiation of these activities depends primarily on nerve impulses which are dispatched from cardiac and vasomotor reflex centers within the CNS. These centers are stimulated by various afferent nerve impulses and by chemical substances in the circulating blood stream.

Cardiac reflex centers

There are two cardiac reflex centers in the medulla oblongata of the brain stem. When stimulated, the *cardio-inhibitory* center dispatches impulses over parasympathetic fibers in the vagus nerves and causes the heart to beat more slowly. Located nearby is the *cardio-accelerator* center which dispatches impulses over sympathetic fibers and causes the heart to increase its rate. A very cooperative relationship exists between these centers, as stimulation of one is associated with depression of the other.

Fig. 14-9. Radial pulse tracing in atrial fibrillation. The pulse is totally irregular; it lacks rhythm, and the beats vary in size.

HYPOTHALAMUS

VASOCONSTRICTOR CENTER IN MEDULLA

ASSOCIATION NEURON

LATERAL SPINOTHALAMIC TRACT

COLD NERVE

BLOOD VESSELS OF
SKIN OF ARM

THORACIC NERVES
1–4

V A S O C O N S T R I C T O R

Fig. 14-10. Diagram of pathway of a vasoconstrictor impulse. As the hand is immersed in cold water, the cold nerve endings are stimulated. An impulse travels to the spinal cord and is relayed on to the hypothalamus. An association neuron transmits the impulse to the vasoconstrictor center in the medulla; a second association neuron transmits the impulse from the center to the cells in the upper thoracic region of the spinal cord. The impulse is relayed to a cell in a lateral ganglion, and then it passes to the smooth muscular tissue in the walls of the blood vessels of the skin. The vessels become smaller and thereby decrease the loss of heat from the skin. Thus, reflex vasoconstriction follows exposure to cold.

Vasomotor reflex centers

Since there is great variation in the amount of blood required in different parts of the vascular system during activity and during rest, it naturally follows that there must be some way of regulating the blood flow to meet the need of each organ. This is accomplished primarily by the vasomotor center in the medulla oblongata. Functionally, this center may be subdivided into *vasoconstrictor* and *vasodilator* centers. On stimulation of these centers, impulses are dispatched over efferent nerve pathways that lead to the small blood vessels, causing either contraction or relaxation of their muscular walls; the mechanics of vasoconstriction and vasodilatation are described on page 345.

Vasoconstrictor nerves conduct impulses that lead to a reduction in the internal caliber of blood vessels. They are derived from the sympathetic division of the autonomic system and are controlled by the vasoconstrictor center. Although these nerves are widely distributed throughout the body, they are particularly abundant in the arterioles of the skin and the abdominal viscera. The pathway of an impulse from the center in the medulla to a blood vessel in the skin of the arm is illustrated in Figure 14-10. The constriction of the blood vessel in this illustration is a reflex response to stimulation of cold receptors in the skin of the hand.

The vasoconstrictor center plays an important part in regulating the peripheral resistance to blood flow. This center continuously sends impulses to the muscular walls of the arterioles, keeping them in a state of tonic contraction and thus helping to maintain optimal arterial blood pressure.

If the vasoconstrictor nerves are inhibited, the arterioles relax, and the blood pressure falls due to the reduction in peripheral resistance. When vasoconstrictor activity is increased, there is a rise in blood pressure due to the increase in peripheral resistance.

Vasodilator nerves conduct impulses that lead to an increase in the internal caliber of blood vessels. These fibers are derived from both divisions of the autonomic system and are probably controlled by the vasodilator center. However, this center is not in a state of tonic activity as is the vasoconstrictor center.

Parasympathetic vasodilator nerve fibers travel in the facial, the glossopharyngeal and the vagus nerves; stimulation of these fibers leads to active vasodilatation of arterioles in the nose, the salivary glands, the tongue, the tonsils and the pharynx. Vasodilator fibers in the sacral spinal nerves supply the arterioles of the external genitalia.

Sympathetic vasodilator nerves travel in various peripheral nerve branches. They are distributed to the blood vessels of skeletal muscles and to the coronary arteries. This arrangement is of particular value during exercise, since it provides for a more abundant blood supply to the hard-working skeletal and heart muscle tissues.

Stimulation of the vasodilator fibers leads to an *active* dilatation of the arterioles which they supply. However, *passive* dilatation may be obtained in other areas as well by suppressing the vasoconstrictor center.

Cardiovascular pressoreflexes

Various afferent nerve impulses may stimulate the cardiac and the vasomotor centers, but the most important ones are initiated by specialized receptor end organs in the walls of the great blood vessels and in the carotid sinuses. These end organs are called *pressoreceptors*, since they are highly sensitive to changes in the pressure of the blood against the vessel walls.

Arterial pressoreceptors are located in the walls of the aortic arch and in the carotid sinuses; their afferent fibers travel in the vagus and the glossopharyngeal nerves, respectively (Fig. 14-11). These receptor end organs are discharging nerve impulses continuously, but the *rate of discharge* varies directly with the pressure of the blood within the vessel. If the arterial blood pressure rises above normal levels, the pressoreceptors greatly increase their rate of discharge and the medullary centers are bombarded with nerve impulses; this leads to stimulation of the cardioinhibitory center and inhibition of the accelerator center, thus causing a reflex slowing of the

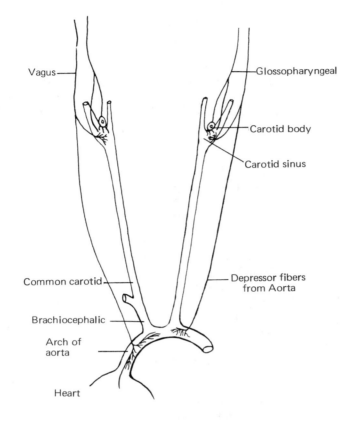

Vagus

Glossopharyngeal

Carotid body

Carotid sinus

Common carotid

Depressor fibers
from Aorta

Brachiocephalic

Arch of
aorta

Heart

Fig. 14-11. Diagram of the inner-vation of the arch of the aorta, the carotid sinus and the carotid body. Glossopharyngeal and vagus nerves are shown. Depressor fibers are those whose stimulation leads to a reflex fall in blood pressure. (After Hey-mans)

heart rate. At the same time, there is inhibition of the vasoconstrictor center which results in a re-flex vasodilatation of peripheral blood vessels. Both of these reflexes serve to lower the arterial blood pressure. On the other hand, if the arterial pressure begins to fall below normal levels, the pressoreceptors are less strongly stimulated and discharge fewer impulses; consequently, the car-dio-inhibitory center is less stimulated and the accelerator center is less inhibited, the end-result being a reflex increase in the heart rate. At the same time, the vasoconstrictor center is strongly stimulated and reflex vasoconstriction occurs in the peripheral blood vessels. Both of these reflexes tend to raise the arterial blood pressure.

The pressoreflexes are of fundamental impor-tance in regulating the activity of the heart and the blood vessels and in keeping the blood pres-sure within normal limits. The effects of changing arterial pressures and the variation in number of nerve impulses are illustrated in Figure 14-12.

Venous pressoreceptors are located in the walls of the terminal portions of the venae cavae and in the neighboring regions of the right atrium; their afferent fibers travel in the vagus nerve. They are stimulated by high venous blood pressure such as occurs when increased quantities of blood are being returned to the heart during exercise. Nerve impulses discharged by the venous presso-receptors lead to stimulation of the cardio-acceler-ator center and depression of the inhibitory cen-ter, thus causing an increase in the heart rate. This is called the *Bainbridge reflex,* and it provides for the rapid transfer of blood from the great veins

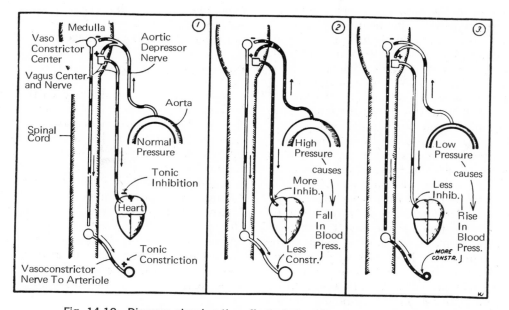

Fig. 14-12. Diagram showing the effect of changing pressure in the arch of the aorta. The afferent pathway is the vagus nerve (labeled aortic depressor nerve). Nerve impulses are shown as shaded segments. The arrows indicate the direction in which the impulses are being transmitted. The spacing of the impulses indicates the frequency of the impulses. The efferent nerves to the heart and blood vessels are indicated. The changes in the heart rate and size of blood vessels on changing from normal to high and low arterial pressures are indicated. With high pressure, the heart rate is slower and the vasoconstrictor center inhibited; with low pressures, the opposite is found. (Carlson, A. J., and Johnson, Victor: The Machinery of the Body, Chicago, Univ. Chicago Press)

to the systemic arterial circuits. At the same time, there is vasoconstriction of the arterioles in the skin and the viscera. These reflexes are partly responsible for the rapid heart rate and the high blood pressure which occur during exercise.

Effects of gravity

The pull of gravity tends to interfere with the return of blood from lower portions of the body when one assumes the upright position. However, after blood leaves the capillaries and enters the veins, its return trip to the heart is facilitated by several factors. These include: (1) the previously mentioned decreasing pressure gradient, (2) the contraction of various skeletal muscles which massage the veins and force blood onward through the one-way valves, and (3) the breathing movements that exert a sort of suction (due to negative intrapleural pressure, p. 430) which helps to pull blood upward into the thorax. In spite of the pull of gravity, venous return to the heart is good so long as one can move about and make full use of his muscular pumping devices.

A great strain is placed on the circulatory system of those persons who are required to stand quietly in one position for prolonged periods of time. A good example of this is to be found in the operating room; during long surgical procedures, doctors and nurses may stand in one place for several hours without relief. At such times, blood tends to accumulate (stagnate) in the extremities, causing them to feel uncomfortably full and swollen; the person may unconsciously begin to shuffle his feet and shift his weight in an attempt to get his muscular pump working. In extreme cases, so much blood may be pooled in the lower portions of the body that venous return becomes completely inadequate; the heart does not receive sufficient quantities of blood to supply the brain, and the person *faints*.

The essential cause of fainting is a lack of oxygen in the brain due to a decreased blood supply. Under such conditions the person loses consciousness and falls. This is nature's remedy, since consciousness is soon regained in the horizontal position as blood flow to the brain improves, and ve-

nous return is no longer a problem; well-meaning bystanders who prop the patient in a sitting position tend to defeat the entire purpose of the faint.

Fainting usually occurs only when other compensatory mechanism are inadequate. For example, as arterial blood pressure falls in the aorta and the carotid sinuses, reflex cardio-acceleration and peripheral vasoconstriction may restore the pressure and prevent fainting. However, when a person begins to feel faint, he should lie down if this is possible; if not, then he should sit down, bend over and get his head between his knees. Attempting to walk out of a room when feeling faint may result in an unnecessary fall.

Control by higher centers

Nerve pathways from many parts of the cerebral cortex and the hypothalamus converge on the medullary cardiovascular centers. Consequently, impulses traveling to the brain over *any* afferent nerve ultimately may have some effect on cardiac and vasomotor activity. For example, a frightening sight or sound can cause the heart to beat more rapidly and the skin to turn pale (cardio-acceleration and vasoconstriction). On the other hand, feelings of embarrassment or shame can make one blush (vasodilatation). Persons who are angry, fearful, anxious, too warm, too cold, suffering intense pain, etc., may experience marked changes in cardiovascular activities.

Chemical control of circulation

The chemical composition of the circulating blood plays an important part in regulating cardiovascular activities. The concentration of carbon dioxide, oxygen, lactic acid and certain hormones produced by the endocrine glands are of particular interest in this respect. These chemical agents may exert their effect in one of three ways: (1) stimulation of chemoreceptors in the aortic and the carotid bodies, (2) direct action on the vasomotor centers, or (3) direct action on the arteriolar walls.

Stimulation of Chemoreceptors. The aortic and the carotid bodies contain highly specialized receptor end organs which are sensitive to the concentration of oxygen in the circulating blood; for this reason, such end organs are called *chemoreceptors*. Clusters of chemoreceptors are found in the arch of the aorta and at the bifurcation of the common carotid arteries (Fig. 14-11). When the oxygen concentration in the blood is within normal limits, the chemoreceptors dispatch nerve impulses to the medullary centers at a moderate rate. However, a fall in the oxygen content results in a marked increase in the rate of discharge; this stimulates the cardio-accelerator and the vasoconstrictor centers, leading to an increase in the heart rate and a rise in the arterial blood pressure. Conversely, a rise in the oxygen level will result in a reduced rate of chemoreceptor discharge and a reflex decrease in the heart rate and in the arterial blood pressure.

Direct Action on the Vasomotor Centers. In addition to the effect produced by stimulation of the peripheral chemoreceptors, the activities of the vasomotor centers are influenced directly by chemical changes in the composition of the blood which flows through them. A high concentration of carbon dioxide in the blood stimulates the vasoconstrictor center and causes the constriction of blood vessels in the abdominal viscera; this tends to increase the arterial blood pressure. As the carbon dioxide level falls, there is less stimulation of the vasoconstrictor center, and the resulting reflex vasodilatation leads to a decrease in the arterial blood pressure.

Direct Action on the Arteriolar Walls. Peripheral blood vessels, especially the arterioles, are affected not only by nerve impulses but also by temperature and chemical factors in local areas. For example, during exercise the contraction of skeletal muscle tissue results in the production of heat, carbon dioxide and lactic acid; at the same time, large quantities of oxygen are used to oxidize the lactic acid as rapidly as possible. Consequently, the tissue fluid which bathes the arteriolar walls in the area becomes very warm, its carbon dioxide level rises, the pH falls, and the oxygen concentration is markedly reduced. All of these factors have a direct effect on the arteriolar walls, causing them to become greatly dilated and allowing

Rest

Skin   Muscle   Intestine

Activity

Skin Muscle   Intestine

Fig. 14-13. Highly diagrammatic representation of the shunting of blood from areas of lesser need to areas of greater need. (Top) During periods of rest, the blood supply to the skin and intestine is abundant, as indicated by the dilated vessels; the blood supply to skeletal muscle is limited. (Bottom) During muscular activity, less blood flows to the skin and intestine, as indicated by the constricted vessels, but the supply to the skeletal muscles is abundant.

more blood to flow through the area; this facilitates the removal of waste products and the delivery of fresh supplies of oxygen and glucose.

As previously described, stimulation of the peripheral chemoreceptors and direct stimulation of the vasomotor centers also are of importance during a bout of exercise. The resulting complementary chemoreflexes serve two purposes: first, blood is shunted away from the relatively inactive abdominal viscera, and, secondly, the arterial blood pressure is raised so that there is an increased rate of blood flow through the locally dilated arterioles in the active muscles (Fig. 14-13).

Another example of direct action on arteriolar walls is found in the cerebral circulation. A most striking feature of these vessels is their sensitivity to carbon dioxide. An increase in the level of carbon dioxide in arterial blood provokes marked cerebral vasodilatation and an increase in cerebral blood flow. On the other hand, a decrease in the level of carbon dioxide, such as produced by rapid and deep breathing (hyperventilation), causes vasoconstriction and a decrease in cerebral blood flow. This explains why one may feel dizzy or even lose consciousness after extreme hyperventilation; so much carbon dioxide is "blown off" that blood flow to the brain is impaired as a result of the cerebral vasoconstriction.

The purpose of all the cardiac and vascular reflexes is to keep the heart rate and the arterial blood pressure as near the normal level as possible and thereby maintain homeostasis. Sufficient examples have been presented to impress on the reader the beauty of the self-regulation in the cardiovascular system. There can be no changes in the heart rate or in blood pressure in any part of the system which do not set into action reflexes to restore conditions to normal so long as one remains "in circulatory health."

Finally, certain *hormones* produced by the endocrine glands also play a role in the regulation of cardiovascular activities. For example, epinephrine (Adrenalin) increases the rate and the force of the heartbeat and causes vasoconstriction of arterioles in the skin and the viscera. The endocrine glands and their secretions are described in Chapter 19.

Hemorrhage

Hemorrhage refers to an escape of blood from the vessels in which it is normally confined. An *external hemorrhage* is easily seen as the blood flows from the body, but an *internal hemorrhage* is concealed as blood escapes into the surrounding tissues or into a body cavity (e.g., the stomach, the peritoneal cavity, etc.). In either case, the body's compensatory mechanisms are quickly called into action. If the vascular injury is relatively slight, bleeding may be controlled by local vasoconstriction and the clotting mechanism (p. 308), but in extensive lesions the hemorrhage may be so great that it overwhelms the clotting process, and large quantities of blood may be lost before the flow can be stopped.

The signs and symptoms of hemorrhage are directly related to the amount of blood that escapes from the vascular sysem. A relatively small hemorrhage (up to 500 cc.) usually is tolerated quite well by most persons. On the other hand, a loss of 30 to 40 per cent of the total blood volume is a serious threat to life and should be treated immediately by transfusions (p. 312). There are 3 key links in the chain of events that trigger the body's response to a severe hemorrhage: (1) the great *reduction in blood volume* leads to (2) *decreased venous return* and (3) *reduced cardiac output*. As the cardiac output falls, so does the arterial blood pressure; this results in reflex acceleration of the heart and vasoconstriction in the skin and the abdominal viscera. (Note: the role of the kidney in combating hemorrhage is described on p. 529). The vasoconstrictor mechanism attempts to restore arterial blood pressure by reducing the capacity of the vascular system; it also helps in the redistribution of circulating blood so that larger amounts go to the CNS, the heart and the lungs, and correspondingly less to those organs which are not immediately essential to life (i.e., the skin and the abdominal viscera). A temporary restoration of blood volume may be promoted by the discharge of red blood cells from storage depots such as the liver and the spleen; at the same time, decreased filtration pressure in the capillaries leads to a *relative* increase in the colloidal osmotic pressure, and great quantities of tissue fluid are "pulled" into the blood stream. The latter results in dehydration of the tissues and accounts for the symptom of thirst that usually follows severe hemorrhage.

If the blood loss continues, the signs and symptoms increase in severity as the compensatory mechanisms are overwhelmed. In addition to pale, cold skin and falling blood pressure, the pulse is rapid and thready, generalized sweating may be observed, and the patient is very restless as nature endeavors to make use of the muscular pump mechanism to increase venous return. Breathing movements become rapid and labored (air hunger), there is loss of consciousness, and the patient will die if the bleeding is not controlled and if treatment has not been started promptly. One should be familiar with the signs and symptoms of hemorrhage, since early recognition of the condition may save a life.

Surgical shock

Surgical or traumatic shock is characterized by severe depression of the circulation, reduced blood pressure, rapid pulse, rapid and shallow breathing, and usually a low body temperature. Two of the most common predisposing causes of surgical shock are hemorrhage and injury to body tissues, but in either case the end-result is a critical decrease in the circulating blood volume.

Primary shock is that which manifests itself immediately after the trauma or injury. The person suddenly collapses in a manner that somewhat resembles an ordinary fainting spell. However, primary shock rarely is serious in itself, and the patient usually recovers spontaneously. The clinical importance of primary shock lies in the fact that it often serves as a warning that the more dangerous secondary or true shock may be imminent.

Secondary shock usually does not appear for several hours after the trauma. You will recall from the preceding discussion of hemorrhage that peripheral vasoconstriction is a compensatory device which is called into action when there is a reduction in arterial blood pressure. While this

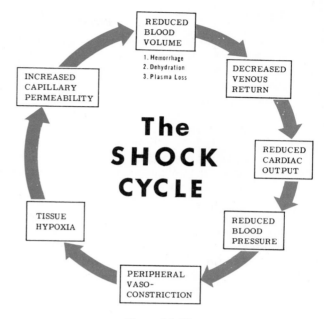

Figure 14-14.

mechanism does tend to raise arterial blood pressure, it may be thought of as a two-edged sword, since prolonged constriction of the blood vessels results in lack of oxygen in the tissues or *tissue hypoxia*. Prolonged tissue hypoxia not only injures the vital organs but also tends to damage capillary walls so that their permeability is abnormally increased and great quantities of fluid leak out into the surrounding tissues; this leads to a further loss of blood volume, and the vicious cycle of shock begins (Fig. 14-14). After shock progresses to a certain stage it becomes *refractory* (not yielding readily to treatment), and death may follow within a short time.

The most significant factor in refractory shock seems to be the oxygen deficit associated with inadequate blood flow to the tissues. Although the body's initial reaction (peripheral vasoconstriction) is an attempt to spare the vital centers, it cannot be allowed to continue indefinitely without serious consequences (e.g., anaerobic glycolysis leading to metabolic acidosis and, finally, irreversible cell damage).

SUMMARY

1. Circulating blood delivers vital substances and removes wastes in all parts of body; integration of all cardiovascular activities of fundamental importance
2. Blood pressure and blood flow
   A. Blood pressure is force exerted by blood against vessel walls
      a. Liquids flow only from areas of greater to lesser pressure
      b. Heart establishes initial high head of pressure
      c. Blood pressure measured in millimeters of mercury above atmospheric pressure
   B. Kinds of blood pressure
      a. Arterial: higher in systemic than in pulmonary circuit
         (1) Systolic generated during ventricular contraction; average 115 to 120 mm. Hg
         (2) Diastolic due to recoil of stretched arteries; average 75 to 80 mm. Hg
         (3) Difference between systolic and diastolic called pulse pressure; average 40 mm. Hg
      b. Capillary pressure: about 32 mm. Hg at arterial end, 12 at venous end
         (1) The driving force in filtration of tissue fluid
         (2) Very low in pulmonary capillaries; if raised may have pulmonary edema
      c. Venous pressure: about 12 mm. Hg in venules, gradually falls to zero in veins entering heart; increased in "heart failure" as blood tends to back up in veins
   C. Maintenance of arterial blood pressure depends on
      a. Rate and force of heartbeat
      b. Elasticity of large arteries
      c. Peripheral resistance
      d. Quantity of blood
      e. Viscosity of blood
      f. Age, weight, sex, emotions, exercise
   D. Method of measuring arterial blood pressure: sphygmomanometer
   E. Velocity of blood flow
      a. Most rapid where cross-sectional area of system is the least: arteries
      b. Slowest where cross-sectional area greatest: capillaries
      c. Picks up speed again after entering veins, but slower than in arteries
      d. "Arm to tongue" circulation time 10 to 16 seconds, "arm to lung" 4 to 8; increased in cases of circulatory obstruction
   F. Arterial pulse
      a. Wave of distention and recoil which sweeps over arterial system
      b. Reflects ventricular beat; travels 6 to 9 M./sec.
      c. Disappears completely in capillaries
      d. Radial artery frequently used for checking pulse rate, rhythm, volume and tension
   G. Central venous pulse due to pressure changes reflected from right atrium
3. Regulation of the circulation
   A. Cardiac reflex centers: inhibitory and accelerator; in medulla; stimulation of one associated with depression of other
   B. Vasomotor reflex centers: (functional) constrictor and dilator
      a. Vasoconstrictor nerves: sympathetic division of ANS; in skin and abdominal viscera; role in maintenance of peripheral resistance
      b. Vasodilator nerves: both divisions of ANS
         (1) Parasympathetic: to salivary glands, tongue, tonsils, pharynx and external genitalia
         (2) Sympathetic: to blood vessels of skeletal muscles and coronary arteries
         (3) Stimulation of above leads to active vasodilatation; passive dilation in other areas by suppressing vasoconstrictor center

C. Cardiovascular pressoreflexes
   a. Specialized nerve endings sensitive to pressure changes in blood vessel walls
   b. Arterial pressoreceptors in aortic arch and carotid sinuses
      (1) Rise in arterial pressure leads to reflex slowing of heart, vasodilatation of peripheral vessels; lowers pressure
      (2) Fall in arterial pressure leads to reflex acceleration of heart, vasoconstriction of peripheral vessels; raises pressure
   c. Venous pressoreceptors in terminal portions of venae cavae and adjacent walls of right atrium
      (1) Stimulated by increasing venous pressure; cause reflex speeding of heart; Bainbridge reflex
      (2) Provides rapid transfer of blood from veins to systemic arteries; valuable in exercise

D. Effects of gravity
   a. Pull of gravity interferes with return of blood from lower portions of body in upright position
   b. Venous return depends on decreasing pressure gradient, contractions of muscles, breathing movements
   c. Standing for prolonged time may lead to fainting as blood stagnates in extremities
   d. Fainting due to lack of oxygen in brain; horizontal position improves blood flow to brain and helps venous return

E. Control by higher centers
   a. Impulses traveling over any afferent nerve may influence medullary centers due to connections between cerebral cortex, hypothalamus and medulla
   b. Sights, sounds, external temperature, emotions, etc., may lead to vasoconstriction, vasodilatation, rapid heart or slow heart

F. Chemical control of circulation
   a. Stimulation of chemoreceptors: sensitive nerve endings in aortic and carotid bodies respond to changes in carbon dioxide and oxygen levels
   b. Direct action on vasomotor centers
   c. Direct action on arteriolar wall: affected by temperature and chemical changes, as during exercise
   d. Hormone: epinephrine increases rate and force of heart beat, causes vasoconstriction in skin and viscera

G. Hemorrhage
   a. External—flows from body; internal—into a body cavity, concealed
   b. Key links in chain that trigger response to hemorrhage
      (1) Reduction in circulating blood volume
      (2) Decreased venous return
      (3) Reduced cardiac output
   c. Signs and symptoms of hemorrhage: falling blood pressure; pale, cold skin; thirst; rapid, thready pulse; generalized sweating; restlessness; air hunger; loss of consciousness and, finally, death

H. Surgical shock
   a. Depression of circulation, reduced blood pressure, rapid pulse, rapid and shallow breathing, usually low body temperature
   b. Primary shock
   c. Secondary or true shock

PRACTICAL APPLICATIONS AND QUESTIONS

(Encircle the letter of the *best* answer to each of the following questions.)

A. *While working in the postoperative recovery room, you notice that Miss T. R. is restless and perspiring, her previously flushed skin is now pale and cold, and her pulse is extremely rapid. On examining the operative site, you observe that her bandages and the bed linens are soaked with bright red blood.*

1. On taking the patient's blood pressure you find that it has dropped from 130/90 to 85/50. This is probably due to the

a. increasing viscosity of the blood
b. reduced blood volume
c. restlessness and perspiration
d. excessive peripheral resistance

2. Her rapid pulse and pale cold skin are signs that certain compensatory pressoreflexes have been initiated to increase venous return and cardiac output. These are
   a. cardio-inhibition and peripheral vasodilatation
   b. peripheral vasoconstriction and cardio-inhibition
   c. cardio-acceleration and peripheral vasoconstriction
   d. peripheral vasodilatation and cardio-acceleration

3. Following severe hemorrhage, patients may complain of thirst. This is due to
   a. a relative increase in osmotic pressure of the blood
   b. excessive filtration rate in the capillaries

c. loss of red blood cells and platelets
d. accumulation of carbon dioxide

B. *Mr. F. W. is suffering from congestive heart failure ("backward failure of heart").*

1. Inability of the failing heart to generate an effective pumping pressure results in
   a. increased arterial blood flood to the kidney
   b. low capillary filtration rate
   c. increased venous pressure
   d. dehydration of tissues

2. Which of the following is *not* a sign of systemic congestion?
   a. dyspnea
   b. edema of dependent parts
   c. enlargement of the liver
   d. cyanosis

3. Pulmonary edema is caused by increased
   a. osmotic pressure
   b. filtration
   c. phagocytosis
   d. hemorrhage

"The breath of life"

PARADISE LOST ● JOHN MILTON

15

THE RESPIRATORY SYSTEM

Respiration is a broad term that is used in reference to the exchange of gases between a living organism and its environment. In aerobic organisms, respiration involves the taking up of oxygen and the giving off of carbon dioxide. A single-celled creature, such as the amoeba, has no great respiratory problem, since the exchange of oxygen and carbon dioxide takes place by simple diffusion through its cell membrane. However, in multicellular organisms as complex as man, provision must be made for the trillions of cells that are far removed from the external environment.

In solving this problem, nature has devised an ingenious respiratory plan that involves the combined services of two elaborate systems (respiratory and cardiovascular); this plan is conveniently divided into two phases which are referred to as external and internal respiration.

External respiration involves the exchange of gases between the circulating blood and the air. For this exchange, one needs a large, moist surface where air and blood can come in close contact; such an area for diffusion is provided by the lungs. In addition, there must be a passageway

External – blood + Air.
internal – blood + cells

through which fresh air can be moved into and stale air expelled from the lungs. The final requirement for external respiration is an air pump (like a bellows) such as the thoracic cage, with muscles to operate it and nerves to control it, as air is constantly renewed in the lungs.

Internal respiration involves the exchange of gases between the circulating blood and the various tissue cells as they use oxygen and produce waste carbon dioxide. One may think of the tissue cells as tiny chemical factories in which oxygen makes possible the reactions by which energy is released from the foods that you eat. A discussion of the many aspects of internal respiration is not within the scope of this chapter which is primarily concerned with the organs and the mechanics of external respiration as well as with the transport of respiratory gases in the blood.

ORGANS OF THE RESPIRATORY SYSTEM

The organs which are concerned with external respiration are the nose, the pharynx, the larynx, the trachea, the bronchi and the lungs in addition to the thoracic cage and the respiratory muscles and nerves.

The nose

The nose consists of an external and an internal portion. The *external portion* of the nose protrudes from the face and is highly variable in shape. The upper part of this triangular structure is held in a fixed position by the supporting nasal bones which form the "bridge" of the nose, but the lower portion is movable because of its pliable framework of fibrous tissue, cartilage and skin. Numerous sebaceous glands are found in the skin that covers the nose; obstruction of these glands may be followed by an inflammatory process and the formation of "pimples." Squeezing pimples in the region of the nose is a dangerous procedure as the ophthalmic veins connecting the facial veins and the cavernous venous sinuses may carry infection to the vessels of the brain.

The *internal portion* of the nose lies within the skull between the base of the cranium and the roof of the mouth, in front of the nasopharynx (superior portion of the throat). The skull bones that enter into the formation of the nose include the frontal, the sphenoid, the ethmoid, the nasal, the maxillary, the lacrimal, the vomer, the palatine and the inferior conchae; these bones are described in Chapter 3.

The nasal septum is a narrow partition that divides the nose into right and left nasal cavities. As shown in Figure 3-22, the anterior portion of this septum is composed primarily of cartilage and skin, while the middle and the posterior portions consist of bone (chiefly the vomer and the perpendicular plate of the ethmoid). In some individuals the nasal septum is markedly deflected to one side so that the affected nasal cavity is almost completely obstructed; this condition, called *deviated nasal septum,* can be corrected by surgery.

The nasal cavities open to the outside by means of the anterior *nares* or *nostrils;* posteriorly, they open into the nasopharynx by means of the posterior nares or *choanae.* The *vestibule* of each cavity is the dilated portion just inside the nostril. Anteriorly, the vestibule is lined with skin and presents a ring of coarse hairs which serve to trap dust particles. Posteriorly, the lining of the vestibule changes from skin to a highly vascular ciliated mucous membrane, called the nasal mucosa, which lines the rest of the nasal cavity. The total surface area of the nasal mucosa is greatly increased by the fact that it covers 3 plates of bone which project from the lateral wall of each nasal cavity. Arranged one above the other like sagging shelves, these bony projections are the *superior,* the *middle* and the *inferior conchae* (Fig. 15-1). The name *turbinate* also is used for these bones, as stated in Chapter 3.

The surface of the nasal mucosa is covered with mucus which is secreted continuously by goblet cells in the epithelial layer. As air passes over this wet vascular membrane, it is warmed or cooled (according to the outside temperature), moisture is added, and dust is collected by the mucus; the ciliated cells sweep particles of dust backward into the

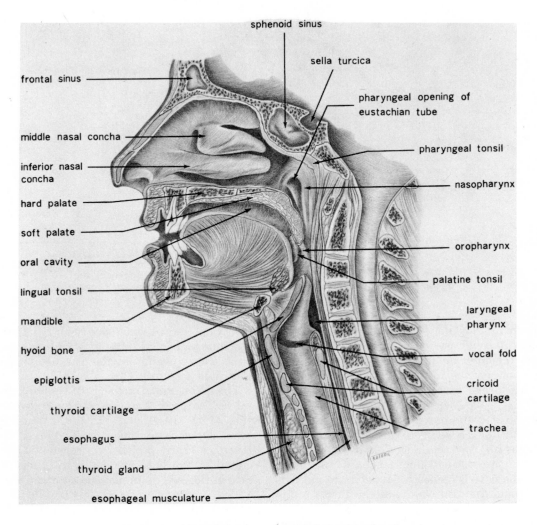

Fig. 15-1. Sagittal section of head. Lateral walls of oral,
nasal, pharyngeal and laryngeal cavities are shown.

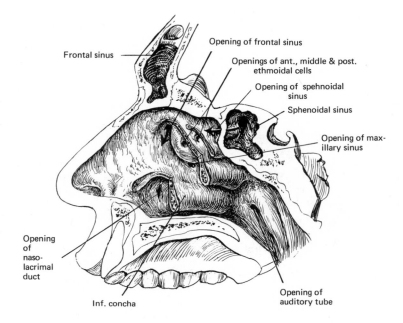

Fig. 15-2. Lateral wall of the nasal cavity. The nasal conchae, the
openings of the paranasal sinuses and the nasolacrimal duct are shown.

throat where they may be swallowed and then eliminated through the gastrointestinal tract. The **olfactory region** of the nasal mucosa is confined to the superior conchae and adjacent parts of the septum. The special sense of smell is described on page 270.

In summary, the nose serves not only as a passageway for air going to and from the lungs, but also as an "air conditioner" and as the sense organ for smell. The importance of breathing through the nose is obvious as it serves to moisten and filter and to warm or cool the air that is on its way to the lungs.

The paranasal sinuses are air spaces in certain bones of the skull. As described in Chapter 3, and illustrated in Figures 3-18 and 3-19, these spaces take the names of the bones in which they lie; thus they are called the maxillary, the frontal, the ethmoidal and the sphenoidal sinuses. Each sinus cavity communicates with the nasal cavity on its own side, and each is lined with ciliated mucous membrane that is continuous with the nasal mucosa. The openings of the paranasal sinuses are shown in Figure 15-2.

The nasolacrimal ducts (p. 273) open into the nasal cavity just below the inferior concha on each side (Figs. 10-14 and 15-2); the mucous membrane lining is continuous with that of the nasal mucosa. Tears, which are constantly being secreted by the lacrimal glands to cleanse the surface of the eye, drain into the nose and serve as an added source of moisture to humidify the air. A powerful bacteria-destroying enzyme (lysozyme) is found in tears as well as in the mucous secretions of the respiratory passages; this enzyme helps to destroy some of the millions of bacteria which we inhale every day.

Blood and Nerve Supply. The blood supply of the nose is derived from branches of the internal and the external carotid arteries. The olfactory nerve conducts impulses concerned with the sense of smell, and the trigeminal nerve conducts impulses concerned with general sensations (e.g., touch, temperature, etc.) in the skin and the nasal mucosa. The facial nerve supplies those muscles that move portions of the external nose.

Rhinitis. A common cold or rhinitis is an inflammation of the mucous membrane of the nose. It is characterized by an acute congestion of the mucous membrane and increased secretion. It is difficult to breathe through the nose because of the swelling of the mucous membrane and accumulated secretions.

Infection may spread from the nose into the nasolacrimal duct and lead to conjunctivitis, or into the paranasal sinuses and lead to pansinusitis (infection of all the sinuses). Pansinusitis may be acute or chronic.

The pharynx

The pharynx or throat is a tubular passageway that is attached to the base of the skull and extends downward behind the nasal cavities, the mouth and the larynx to continue as the esophagus ("food pipe"). Its walls are composed of skeletal muscle, and the lining consists of mucous membrane. The pharynx is subdivided from above downward into three parts: *nasal, oral* and *laryngeal.*

The nasopharynx is the superior portion of the pharyngeal cavity; it lies behind the nasal cavities and above the level of the soft palate. This portion of the pharynx is purely respiratory in function, and its ciliated mucosal lining is continuous with that of the nasal cavities. During the act of swallowing, food is prevented from entering the nasopharynx by the action of various muscles which elevate the soft palate and block off the nasal area.

There are 4 openings in the walls of the nasopharynx. Anteriorly, it communicates with the nasal cavities by way of the 2 *posterior nares* or choanae. In the lateral walls of the nasopharynx are the openings of the 2 *auditory* or *eustachian tubes* (Fig. 15-1) which communicate with the middle ear. The mucous membrane lining the auditory tube is continuous with that of the nasopharynx; thus it is possible for an infection of the throat to spread along this tube to the middle ear (otitis media). Such an extension of infection is relatively common in children, since their auditory tubes are shorter, wider and straighter than those of the adult.

The pharyngeal tonsil is a mass of lymphatic tissue that is located on the posterior wall of the nasopharynx (Fig. 15-1). During childhood this mass is frequently enlarged, at which time it is called *adenoids* (meaning "glandlike"). This enlargement of the pharyngeal tonsil may obstruct the upper air passage to such an extent that the child must breathe through his mouth. Mouth-breathing is undesirable because the air is not properly warmed, moistened and filtered before reaching the lungs. In other words, inspired air is not "air conditioned" unless it passes through the nose and the nasopharynx, as well as through the lower air passages.

The oropharynx is the middle portion of the pharyngeal cavity; lying behind the mouth, it extends from the soft palate to the level of the hyoid bone (Fig. 15-1). The only opening in the wall of the oropharynx is the *fauces* or archway into the mouth. The fauces is bounded by the soft palate above, the dorsum of the tongue below, and the *glossopalatine arches* (anterior pillars) laterally. Each glossopalatine arch extends downward from the palate to the base of the tongue on its own side; just behind these arches lie the *pharyngopalatine arches* (posterior pillars) which extend downward from the palate to the sides of the pharynx.

The palatine tonsils are prominent oval masses of lymphatic tissue situated between the glossopalatine and the pharyngopalatine arches on either side of the oropharynx. These tonsils are relatively larger in the child than in the adult, but their shape and size show considerable individual variation. Inflammation of the palatine tonsils is called *tonsillitis,* and the removal of tonsils is called a tonsillectomy. Acute inflammation of the tonsil and peritonsillar tissue with pus formation is referred to as peritonsillar abscess.

Underlying the mucous membrane at the root

of the tongue are collections of lymphatic tissue which compose the *lingual tonsil.* In addition to the formation of lymphocytes, the various masses of tonsillar tissue form a protective circular band of lymphatic tissue (Waldeyer's ring) which guards the opening into the respiratory and digestive tubes. This tonsillar ring consists of the two palatine tonsils laterally, the lingual tonsil below, and the pharyngeal tonsil above.

The laryngopharynx is the inferior portion of the pharyngeal cavity. As it extends downward from the level of the hyoid bone, the laryngopharynx opens into the larynx anteriorly and continues as the esophagus posteriorly (Fig. 15-1). In summary, the nasopharynx is purely respiratory in function, but the oropharynx and the laryngopharynx are common to both the digestive and the respiratory systems, since they serve as passageways for both food and air. The blood and nerve supplies are abundant.

The larynx

The larynx or "voice box" serves as a passageway for air between the pharynx and the trachea. It lies in the midline of the neck, below the hyoid bone and in front of the laryngopharynx. The unique structure of the larynx enables it to function somewhat like a valve on "guard duty" at the entrance to the windpipe, controlling air flow and preventing anything but air from entering the lower air passages. Exhalation of air through the larynx is controlled by voluntary muscles and so enables the larynx to become the organ of voice. During the act of swallowing, the larynx is pulled upward and forward in such a way that the air passageway is closed off, and food is shunted into the esophagus. Should food or other foreign matter enter the larynx, a cough reflex is set up in an attempt to expel it; a common expression for such a mishap is that one has "swallowed down the wrong throat."

The larynx is a triangular box composed of 9 cartilages that are joined together by ligaments and controlled by skeletal muscles. The larynx is lined with ciliated mucous membrane (except the vocal folds), and the cilia move particles upward to the pharynx.

Cartilages. There are 3 single cartilages in the larynx (cricoid, thyroid and epiglottis), and 3 paired cartilages (arytenoid, corniculate and cuneiform). The most prominent of these are illustrated in Figures 15-1 and 15-3.

The thyroid cartilage, shaped like a shield, is the largest in the larynx. It is composed of 2 broad plates, a right and a left, which meet and fuse in the midline in front like the bow of a ship. The plates form a more acute angle with each other in the male than in the female, and the ventral edges form the subcutaneous laryngeal prominence known as the *Adam's apple.*

The epiglottis is thin and leaf-shaped and extends above the thyroid cartilage in front of the entrance to the larynx. The aryepiglottic folds of mucous membrane are attached to its sides. As the larynx moves upward and forward during the act of swallowing, the free edge of the epiglottis is moved downward, thus helping to close the opening into the larynx.

The cricoid cartilage is shaped like a signet ring, with the band in front and the signet at the back of the larynx. It lies at the lower end of the larynx and is connected with the first ring of the trachea.

The arytenoid cartilages, which are above the cricoid cartilage, furnish attachment for the vocal ligaments. The position and the tension of these ligaments are altered by changes in position of the arytenoid cartilages. The apex of each arytenoid is covered by one of the *corniculate* cartilages.

The cuneiform cartilages are small, rodlike bodies found in the aryepiglottic folds, just anterior to the *corniculate* cartilages.

Ligaments. There are extrinsic and intrinsic ligaments in the larynx. The extrinsic ligaments connect the thyroid cartilage and the epiglottis with the hyoid bone and the cricoid with the trachea. The intrinsic ligaments connect the cartilages of the larynx with each other.

Cavity of the Larynx. The entrance to the larynx is bounded by the epiglottis, in front, the apices of the arytenoids and the corniculates, in the back, and the aryepiglottic folds, on the sides. The cav-

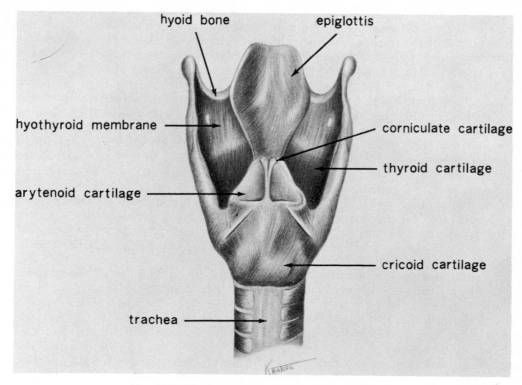

Fig. 15-3. The laryngeal cartilages. Posterior view.

Fig. 15-4. Interior of larynx, as seen with laryngoscope.
(Left) Rima glottidis, wide open; (right) rima closed.

ity of the larynx extends from the entrance to the lower border of the cricoid cartilage where it is continuous with that of the trachea. Two pairs of mucous membrane folds project like shelves into the laryngeal cavity and narrow it to an antero-posterior slit in two places. The upper paired folds are called the *ventricular folds* or "false vocal cords," indicating that they do not function in the production of sound. The lower paired folds are called the *vocal folds* or "true vocal cords"; each of these mucosal folds encloses a strong band of connective tissue (the vocal ligament), and each plays an important part in the production of sound (Fig. 15-4). Near the free edge of each vocal fold the mucous membrane is designed for rapid vibration and repeated contact; in contrast with the remainder of the air passageway, which has ciliated mucosa, the outer layer of the vocal mucosa consists of stratified squamous nonkeratinizing epithelium and contains no mucous glands or blood vessels.

The vocal folds form the *glottis,* and the opening between them is called the *rima glottidis* (meaning "slit of the glottis"); this is the narrowest part of the laryngeal cavity, and any obstruction (foreign body, edema, etc.) can easily lead to death by suffocation if not relieved promptly. The tension of the vocal folds and the size of the slit between them are controlled by muscles which act on the folds directly, and by other muscles that affect them indirectly by moving the cartilages (arytenoid) to which they are anchored.

A *laryngospasm* (laryngismus stridulus) is a sudden, violent, involuntary contraction of the muscles of the larynx. It is seen most commonly in young children as croup and is characterized by a sudden crowing inspiration followed by a stoppage of respiration for several seconds, with cyanosis, then ending with long, loud, whistling inspirations.

Laryngoscopy refers to a visual examination of the cavity of the larynx with a tubular instrument called the laryngoscope. This procedure is helpful in the diagnosis of various laryngeal diseases.

Blood and Nerve Supply. The blood supply to the larynx is derived from branches of the exter-

nal carotid arteries. The vagus nerves contain afferent fibers from the mucous membrane of the larynx, the latter being so sensitive that any irritation initiates a cough reflex. The vagus nerves also supply efferent fibers to the skeletal muscles of the larynx; the *recurrent laryngeal nerve* is a vagal branch of particular importance in this respect, since it supplies all but one of the laryngeal muscles.

Speech. As expired air passes through the larynx, it can be made to set the vocal folds into vibration, and this, in turn, sets the whole column of air above the vocal folds into vibration. The pharynx, the mouth and the nasal cavities (and the paranasal sinuses, perhaps) are resonating cavities. The muscles of the neck, the face, the tongue and the lips are used to modify the sounds into words. The speech center in the cerebral cortex integrates the activity of all the muscles concerned so that intelligible sounds or words may be spoken. The loudness of the voice depends on the volume and the force of the expired air and on the amplitude of vibrations of the vocal folds. The pitch of the voice is determined by the number of vibrations per second and the length and the tension of the vocal folds. Since women and children usually have shorter vocal folds than do men, their voices tend to be higher pitched. At puberty, the larynx in males increases in size, the cavity becomes larger, the thyroid cartilage is more prominent, and the vocal cords become longer and thicker. As a result, there is a marked change in the quality and the pitch of the voice.

Laryngectomy, or surgical removal of the larynx is necessary in cases of carcinoma of the larynx. Such patients are unable to speak in the usual way and may learn esophageal speech. This type of speech is accomplished by swallowing air into the esophagus and expelling it with an eructation or belch; the sound that is produced is then modified by the palate, the tongue and the lips.

The trachea

The trachea or windpipe is a flexible, tubular structure that extends from the larynx downward

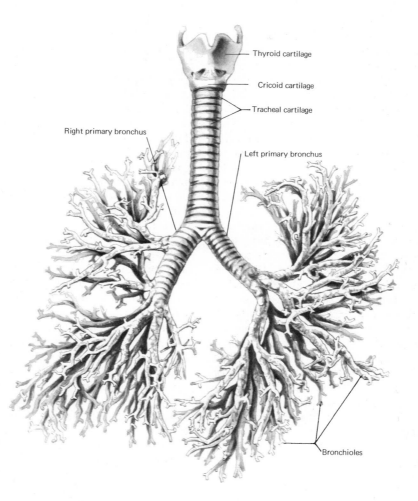

Fig. 15-5. Larynx, trachea and bronchial tree, anterior view.

through the midline of the neck and into the thorax. It is about 11 cm. in length and lies in front of the esophagus. Despite the flexibility of the trachea, its walls are very strong due to the presence of 16 to 20 U-shaped tracheal cartilages; these cartilages are placed horizontally, one above the other, at very close intervals (Fig. 15-5). The open end of the U is at the back, and the gap is bridged by connective tissue and smooth muscle. This arrangement permits expansion of the esophagus during swallowing of a *bolus* (meaning "a morsel" or "a swallow") of food, since it can encroach on the posterior wall of the trachea. The cartilage rings keep the trachea open at all times for the passage of air to and from the lungs. The trachea is lined with ciliated mucous membrane containing goblet cells. The dust particles stick to the mucus, and the cilia move them upward to the pharynx. The branches of the subclavian artery supply the tracheal structures with blood. The nerve supply is from the vagi.

Tracheostomy is a surgical procedure whereby an opening is made in the trachea to provide a free passageway for air. This may be a life-saving operation in cases of respiratory obstruction. For example, certain inflammatory conditions related to the larynx may produce a severe edema of the glottis; this condition can easily lead to death by suffocation if an alternate airway is not established immediately. After this operation, a patient requires special nursing care, for the tube which has been inserted into the trachea must be kept free of mucus. Patients with tracheostomy tubes are particularly susceptible to pulmonary infections, since the air is not "conditioned" before it reaches the lungs.

The bronchial tree

The trachea ends by dividing into right and left **primary bronchi** which extend to the lungs. Each bronchus enters the lung of its own side through the *hilus* (meaning an opening through which vessels, nerves, etc., enter or leave an organ). The right primary bronchus is more nearly vertical, shorter and wider than the left. Consequently, when foreign bodies enter the respiratory passages they are likely to be found in the right primary bronchus. As soon as each primary bronchus enters its respective lung it branches to form smaller or *secondary bronchi,* one for each lobe of the lung (i.e., 3 on the right and 2 on the left). The secondary bronchi continue to branch, forming still smaller tubes or **bronchioles** as shown in Figure 15-5.

Structurally, the primary bronchi are similar to the trachea in that their walls are strengthened by the same type of cartilaginous rings and their lining is ciliated mucous membrane. However, progressive structural changes accompany the continued subdivision of the bronchi. As they become smaller, less and less cartilage is present in their walls, and more and more smooth muscle appears. The smooth muscle completely encircles the lumen; it is arranged in right and left spirals. If you take two narrow ribbons and wind them around a pencil, winding one in a clockwise direction and the other in a counterclockwise direction, you will duplicate the spiral arrangements of smooth muscle in the small bronchi. The contraction of this smooth muscle narrows the lumen of the tube and throws the mucous membrane into longitudinal folds. The mucous membrane is ciliated and contains goblet cells; the mucus and the cilia help to keep the bronchi free of foreign particles.

Cranial autonomic fibers (parasympathetic), which travel in the vagus nerves, cause contraction of the smooth muscle in the walls of the bronchioles. Fibers from the sympathetic division cause relaxation of the smooth muscle and, therefore, dilate the lumens of the bronchioles.

Bronchitis is an infection of the mucous membrane of the bronchi, in which fluid collects in the passages and is expelled by coughing.

Bronchiectasis is the condition in which there is pathologic dilatation of a bronchus. It is characterized by spasms of coughing and the expectoration (coughing up and spitting out) of mucopurulent (mucus and pus) material.

Postural drainage refers to the removal of bronchial secretions or material by placing the patient head downward for a short time each day. It is recommended as a treatment for bronchiectasis.

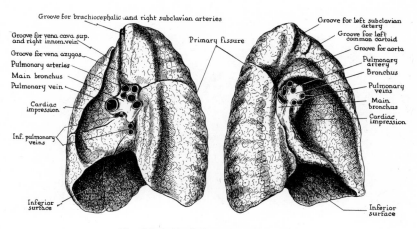

Fig. 15-6. Medial aspect of lungs.

Bronchoscopy is the visual examination of the interior of the primary bronchi.

Asthma. The word "asthma" means *panting.* Asthma is characterized by attacks of difficult breathing, coughing, wheezing, raising mucoid sputum and a sense of constriction of the chest. There is spasm of the bronchial muscles, edema of the mucous membrane and secretion of a mucoid substance. It is usually due to sensitivity to inhaled or ingested substances. The attacks are relieved by the use of drugs, such as epinephrine and ephedrine, which relax the constricted muscle and cause dilatation of the bronchioles.

The lungs

The lungs are the essential organs of respiration, since it is here that the exchange of gases between the blood and air takes place. They lie within the thoracic cavity, one on either side of the heart and the other contents of the mediastinum.

The thoracic cavity is the space above the diaphragm, within the walls of the thorax. It is closed, below, by the diaphragm; above, by the scalene muscles and the fascia of the neck; and, on the sides, the front and the back, by the ribs, the intercostal muscles, the vertebrae, the sternum and the ligaments. The size of the thoracic cavity changes constantly during the act of breathing.

The mediastinum is the space between the lungs. The contents of this cavity include (1) the heart and the pericardium, (2) the thoracic aorta, (3) the pulmonary artery and veins, (4) the venae cavae and the azygos vein, (5) the thymus, lymph nodes and vessels, (6) the trachea, the esophagus and the thoracic duct, and (7) the vagus, the cardiac and the phrenic nerves.

Description. The lungs are cone-shaped organs which fill their own halves of the thoracic cavity and lie against the rib cage both anteriorly and posteriorly. The right lung is shorter and broader than the left. The concave *base* of each lung rests on the diaphragm, and the *apex* extends into the root of the neck for a distance of about 2.5 cm. above the first rib. The medial surface (Fig. 15-6) of each lung also is concave and shows the imprint of the heart. Above and behind the cardiac imprint is the hilus, or slit, through which pass those structures that make up the *root* of the lung; the root structures include the primary bronchus, the pulmonary and the bronchial blood vessels, the lymphatics and the nerves. The lungs are freely movable except at the hilus where they are anchored by the root and the pulmonary ligaments.

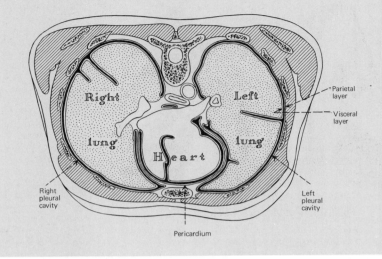

Fig. 15-7. The parietal and visceral pleurae are shown in transverse section. The pleural cavity is shown in black; this is a potential cavity between the two layers of pleura. (Adapted from Eycleshymer)

Each lung is invested by a transparent, serous membrane called the **pleura**. This membrane is arranged in the form of a closed sac and consists of 2 layers—a visceral layer and a parietal layer. The *visceral pleura* is closely applied to the surface of the lung and dips into the fissures between its lobes. The *parietal pleura* lines the inner surface of the chest wall, covers the upper surface of the diaphragm, and is reflected over the structures of the mediastinum (Fig. 15-7). The two layers of pleura are continuous with one another around the root of each lung.

Although the space between the visceral and the parietal pleurae is called the **pleural cavity**, it must be emphasized that this is purely a *potential* space. Normally, the pleural layers are held in close contact with one another by the cohesive effect of a thin film of serous fluid; this fluid also serves to lubricate the surfaces so that they can glide smoothly one over the other. To visualize the effect of the pleural fluid, place a thin film of water between two glass slides; note how the wet surfaces cling together, yet permit a slippery side-to-side movement.

Pleurisy is an inflammation of the pleura; it may manifest itself as *dry* pleurisy or as pleurisy with *effusion*. In dry pleurisy, the pain that accompanies every breath is due to friction between the two layers of pleura which are unable to glide smoothly over one another. In pleurisy with effusion there is a marked increase in the amount of fluid in the pleural cavity; if the fluid is purulent, the person is said to have *empyema*.

Structure. The lungs are light, porous and spongy in texture, and they will float when placed in water. Within the spongy tissue are the secondary bronchi and the bronchioles which pipe air to and from the respiratory units of the lung. An important feature of lung tissue is its great elasticity; this property is of fundamental importance during the act of breathing.

Deep fissures divide each lung into **lobes.** The right lung has 3 lobes (superior, middle and inferior), while the left lung has only 2 lobes (superior and inferior), as shown in Figure 15-6. The individual lobes are further subdivided into small **lobules.**

Lobules are irregular in shape and size, but

each is supplied with air by a bronchiole. As a bronchiole enters the substance of a lobule it branches repeatedly to form *terminal bronchioles*. Each terminal bronchiole, in turn, branches to form the *respiratory bronchioles* that lead into the functional lung units. As you inhale, air flows from the respiratory bronchiole down long corridors called *alveolar ducts*. Small cross-corridors, called *atria*, contain open "doors" that permit air to reach the all-important individual "rooms" or **alveoli.** The partitions between alveoli (walls between adjacent rooms) are capillary networks, supported by elastic and reticular connective tissue. It has been estimated that there are about 700 million alveoli in the human lungs, and the surface that they present for diffusion of gases is about 70 square meters. The alveolar walls are single layers of epithelial cells, and the walls of capillaries are single layers of endothelial cells; therefore, the air in the alveoli and the blood in the pulmonary capillaries are separated by microscopic partitions that are only 2 cells in thickness.

In summary, an anatomic and functional lung unit consists of a terminal bronchiole, a respiratory bronchiole, its alveolar ducts, atria and alveoli (Fig. 15-8) as well as the accompanying blood vessels and nerves.

Blood Supply. There are 2 separate arterial blood supplies for the lungs. The *pulmonary arteries* and their branches give rise to pulmonary capillaries in the walls of alveoli, through which exchanges of respiratory gases take place. The *bronchial arteries* and their branches supply the walls of the bronchi, the walls of blood vessels, the lymph nodes and the pleurae with blood. They are the nutrient arteries for the lung tissue and play no part in oxygenation of the blood.

Lymphatic vessels are present in the visceral pleura and in the dense connective tissue around bronchioles, bronchi, arteries and veins.

Disorders of the Lungs. *Atelectasis* means *incomplete expansion*. It refers to imperfect expansion of the lungs at birth or partial collapse of the lung after birth. The latter is caused by occlusion of a bronchus, perhaps by a plug of heavy mucus, with subsequent absorption of the air, or by external compression, as from a pleural

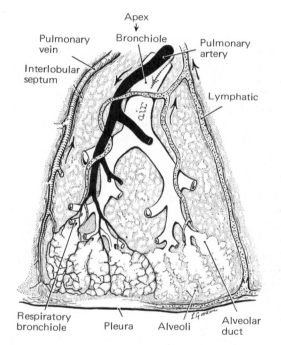

Fig. 15-8. Schematic drawing of a lobule of the lung. Only one set of blood vessels and lymphatics is shown.

effusion or a tumor. The atelectatic portion of the lung plays no part in the respiratory function.

Pulmonary emphysema is a serious lung disorder, characterized by the obstruction of bronchioles, the trapping of air in passages distal to the obstruction, disruption of those passages, and a loss of pulmonary elasticity. The end result is a state of chronic hyperinflation, as the victim is unable to empty his lungs on forced expiration; in severe cases the chest is enlarged in all dimensions ("barrel chest"). Pulmonary emphysema frequently is associated with chronic bronchitis, asthma, and other conditions that may cause inflammatory damage to the bronchioles; it is a chronic, slowly progressive disease, causing irreversible structural damage to the lung.

Pneumonia is the condition in which there is inflammation of lung tissue or of the walls of the bronchi. The former is called *lobar pneumonia* and the latter *bronchopneumonia*. There is also a "virus" pneumonia which is similar to influenza. When fluid collects in the alveoli, causing the lung to become solid and firm, the condition is called *consolidation*. In any condition in which the blood is not sufficiently oxygenated, such as lobar pneumonia, cyanosis results. This refers to a bluish coloration of the skin and is due to the large amount of reduced hemoglobin which gives the blood a dark color. Cyanosis is seen first in the finger tips, the lips and the lobes of ears, where capillaries are abundant in the skin.

Abscess. A lung abscess is a localized collection of pus in a lung.

Silicosis is a diffuse fibrosis of the lungs caused by the inhalation, over a period of many years, of dust having a large amount of silicon dioxide particles in it. It also is called *miner's asthma* and *grinder's asthma*. The lungs lose their elasticity as fibrous tissue replaces the normal elastic tissue.

Tuberculosis is an infectious disease characterized by the formation of tubercles. Pulmonary tuberculosis is treated by special drugs and by giving the infected lung as much rest as possible. In mild cases this may be accomplished by keeping the patient in bed. In advanced cases, the lung may be temporarily or permanently collapsed by various surgical procedures.

Carcinoma of the lung, is treated by lobectomy (the removal of a lobe), or by pneumonectomy which is the excision of an entire lung.

THE MECHANICS OF BREATHING

Breathing is the act of taking fresh air into, and expelling stale air from, the lungs. As noted previously, the external phase of respiration requires not only a large moist surface where blood and air can come in close contact, but also a bellows arrangement such as the lungs and the thoracic cage, with muscles to operate it and nerves to control it. Consequently, it is essential that one understand the mechanical and physical principles involved in the act of breathing.

Air pressure and flow

The basic principle underlying the movement of any gas is that it travels from an area of higher pressure to an area of lower pressure, or from a point of greater concentration to a point of lower concentration. This principle applies not only to the flow of air into and out of the lungs but also to the diffusion of oxygen and carbon dioxide through alveolar and capillary membranes. The respiratory muscles and the elastic lungs make possible the necessary changes in the pressure gradient so that air first flows into and then is expelled from the air passages. However, before studying the phases of a respiratory cycle (inspiration and expiration) one should be familiar with the following pressures: atmospheric, intrapulmonic and intrapleural.

Atmospheric pressure is that pressure exerted against all parts of the body by the surrounding air. It averages 760 mm. Hg at sea level. Any pressure that falls below atmospheric pressure is called a *subatmospheric* or *"negative"* pressure and represents a partial vacuum.

Intrapulmonic pressure is the pressure of air within the bronchial tree and the alveoli. During each respiratory cycle this pressure fluctuates below and above atmospheric pressure as air moves into and out of the lungs.

Intrapleural or **intrathoracic pressure** is that

pressure which exists between the two layers of pleura or between the walls of the thoracic cage and the lungs. Normally, the intrapleural pressure is a subatmospheric or "negative" pressure (752 to 756 mm. Hg), and the partial vacuum that exists in the pleural cavity is of great importance during inflation of the lungs. During each respiratory cycle the intrapleural pressure undergoes changes, but it is always negative or below atmospheric pressure in normal breathing. This pressure becomes positive only when one is coughing, lifting heavy objects, straining at stool, etc.

Inspiration

Inspiration is the act of taking air into the lungs. It involves a series of 4 events.

1. The diaphragm and the external intercostal muscles contract when impulses from the central nervous system (CNS) come to them by way of the phrenic and the intercostal nerves, respectively.

2. As the diaphragm contracts, its dome moves downward and enlarges the thoracic cavity from top to bottom. The contraction of the external intercostal muscles raises the ribs and, at the same time, rotates them slightly, thereby pushing the sternum forward. This enlarges the thoracic cavity from side to side and from front to back.

3. The enlargement of the thoracic cavity in its 3 dimensions is accompanied by a decrease in the intrapleural and the intrapulmonic pressures, which may be explained as follows. As the thoracic cavity enlarges, the parietal pleura tends to pull away from the visceral pleura, thus lowering the intrapleural pressure (i.e., it becomes more "negative"). However, as noted previously, the cohesion between the two pleural layers (due to the thin film of pleural fluid) is very great, and separation normally does not occur. Instead, the visceral pleura, and the elastic lung to which it is attached, expand with the enlarging thoracic cavity. As the lung increases in size, the intrapulmonic pressure immediately falls below atmospheric pressure. In other words, if one increases the volume of a gas container, there will be a decrease in the pressure of the gas within that container.

4. Since the lungs communicate freely with the outside air by way of the trachea, the pharynx, etc., air will flow into the lungs until the intrapulmonic pressure is equal to that of the atmosphere.

This series of events is necessary to complete the inspiratory phase of the respiratory cycle.

Expiration

Expiration is the act of expelling air from the lungs. It also involves a series of 4 events.

1. The diaphragm and the external intercostal muscles relax, due to a cessation of impulses from the CNS.

2. As these muscles return to their resting position, and the elastic lungs recoil, the thoracic cavity is decreased in its 3 diameters. This action is entirely passive during normal quiet expiration.

3. As the thoracic cavity and the lungs decrease in size there is a corresponding increase in the intrapleural pressure (i.e., it becomes less "negative") and in the intrapulmonic pressure which quickly rises above atmospheric pressure. In other words, if one decreases the volume of a gas container, there will be an increase in the pressure of the gas within that container.

4. Since the lungs communicate freely with the outside, air flows out until the intrapulmonic pressure again is equal to atmospheric pressure.

This series of events is necessary to complete the expiratory phase of the respiratory cycle (Fig. 15-9).

Summary of pressure changes

Intrapulmonic pressure is below atmospheric pressure during inspiration, equal to atmospheric pressure at the end of inspiration, above atmospheric pressure during expiration and again equal to atmospheric pressure at the end of expiration.

This series of changes in intrapulmonic pressure is repeated with each respiratory cycle. Whenever the size of the thoracic cavity remains constant for a few seconds, or in a position of rest, the intrapulmonic pressure is equal to atmospheric pressure.

Fig. 15-9. Drawn from x-rays of the bronchial tree. (Left) In full expiration. (Right) In full inspiration.

Although the *intrapleural pressure* is always "negative" or below atmospheric, it undergoes changes with each respiratory cycle, becoming lower or more "negative" during inspiration and higher or less "negative" during expiration. The "negative" intrapleural pressure not only plays a part in respiration but it also has a decided effect on venous return of blood to the heart (p. 408). This pressure has a sort of sucking effect and assists the inflow of blood into the thoracic veins from the abdominal area and from the large veins in the neck. Since the "negative" pressure is greater during inspiration, more blood is flowing into the thoracic veins at the same time that air is flowing into the lungs. In some individuals this increased return of venous blood to the heart initiates the Bainbridge reflex (p. 406), and there is a noticeable increase in the pulse rate during inspiration.

Modified breathing movements

Normally, both the diaphragm and the external intercostal muscles are used in inspiration. How-

ever, in some individuals the diaphragm predominates (abdominal type of breathing), and in others the external intercostals are more active (costal type of breathing). A record of a good balance between costal and abdominal factors is shown in Figure 15-10.

In the terminal stages of many diseases, breathing may become periodic. The most common type of periodic breathing is called *Cheyne-Stokes respiration*. In this type there is a period of *apnea* (temporary cessation of breathing) lasting several seconds; then breathing begins, at first, very short and shallow; then each becomes a bit deeper until a maximum is reached; and then it tapers off until apnea occurs again. Each time the period of apnea occurs, one may think that the person has expired. This type of breathing indicates a respiratory center that is badly damaged by hypoxia or toxins. Figure 15-11 is a record of Cheyne-Stokes respiration in a very ill person.

In *asthma* there is prolongation of the expiratory phase of respiration, and the ratio of inspiration to expiration is altered, since there is difficulty in getting air out of the lungs. In Figure 15-12,

Fig. 15-10. Respiratory movements in a normal subject. The upper line indicates the movements of the thoracic walls; the lower line indicates the movements of the abdominal walls. (Minnesota Med.)

Fig. 15-11. Cheyne-Stokes respiration.

Fig. 15-12. Respiratory movements in asthma. Prolongation of expiration is noted in the thoracic record. (Minnesota Med.)

ARTIFICIAL RESPIRATION

MOUTH-TO-MOUTH (MOUTH-TO-NOSE) METHOD

① If there is foreign matter visible in the mouth, wipe it out quickly with your fingers or a cloth wrapped around your fingers.

Tilt the head back so the chin is pointing upward.

② Pull or push the jaw into a jutting-out position.

④ Open your mouth wide and place it tightly over victim's mouth. At same time pinch victim's nostrils shut.

⑤ Or close the nostrils with your cheek.

⑥ Or close the victim's mouth and place your mouth over the nose.

Blow into the victim's mouth or nose. If you are not getting air exchange, recheck the head and jaw position (see drawings above at left).

⑦ If you still do not get air exchange, quickly turn the victim on his side and administer several sharp blows between the shoulder blades in the hope of dislodging foreign matter.

Resume breathing procedure.

Fig. 15-13. (From the American National Red Cross)

Fig. 15-14. Drinker machine for artificial respiration.

taken from an asthmatic patient, the prolongation of expiration is evident in the thoracic record. Wheezing in asthmatic persons is due to air being forced out through constricted bronchioles.

Hiccough is due to spasmodic contraction of the diaphragm, which causes a sudden inspiration. A sudden closure of the glottis shortens inspiration and gives origin to the characteristic sound. Often it is due to irritation of the stomach.

Pneumothorax refers to the presence of air in the pleural cavity. It may occur spontaneously as a result of any lung disease that leads to rupture of an alveolus or a bronchiole, and it always follows perforating wounds of the chest (accidental or surgical). In any case, collapse of the lung occurs, and breathing movements are of no avail on the affected side.

Artificial respiration

Artificial respiration is administered routinely by anesthetists during the course of lung and heart operations and often during long abdominal operations. It is administered during resuscitation after drowning, electric shock, asphyxiation and in poliomyelitis.

In the operating room an anesthetist compresses the bag of the anesthetic machine by hand, to administer artificial respiration by way of a catheter in the trachea or a mask over the nose and the mouth, attached to the gas machine. Artificial respiration is easy to manage by this method, and there should be a portable gas machine in all emergency stations for the administration of oxygen by artificial respiration.

Fig. 15-15. (Left) Spirometer: (1) spirometer bell or inverted cylinder; (2) double-walled tank, for water seal; (3) inspiratory and expiratory tubes, which connect with mouthpiece; (4) stopcock through which spirometer bell may be filled with oxygen or room air; (5) ink-writer, which traces the movements of the spirometer bell on the kymograph. (Right) Longitudinal section of spirometer: (1) water seal in double-walled tank; (2) spirometer bell or chamber; (3) soda-lime cannister through which expired air passes in order to remove carbon dioxide; (4) flutter valves which permit air to flow in only one direction, as indicated by arrows; (5) expiratory tube; (6) inspiratory tube. The tubes 5 and 6 are connected with a mouthpiece; the patient's nostrils are closed by a clip, and the respiratory tract is connected with the spirometer by means of the mouthpiece and the tubes.

Fig. 15-16. Spirogram of healthy young woman, in sitting position. Three minutes of normal respiratory movements are shown. From this portion of the record the rate, the tidal volume, the minute volume of respiration and the oxygen use (from slope of record) may be determined. A record of vital capacity is shown next; the deepest possible inspiration is followed by the deepest possible expiration; the vital capacity, the inspiratory reserve and the expiratory reserve air may be measured. Then follows a record of the deepest and fastest respiration possible for half a minute (soda-lime cannister out); from this the maximal breathing capacity is determined.

If no gas machine is at hand, or while waiting for a rescue squad, artificial respiration is administered by other methods. Oxygen must be brought to the alveoli quickly, so artificial respiration must be applied speedily after an emergency. Good pulmonary ventilation is needed, and the supply of blood to heart and brain must be maintained.

Investigation of the problem of artificial respiration has indicated that *"mouth-to-mouth"* breathing is the most effective method for ventilating a victim's lungs. It is shown in Figure 15-13. For a detailed explanation of this and other methods of artificial respiration one may obtain American Red Cross literature dealing with emergency procedures.

In severe cases of *poliomyelitis* the muscles of respiration frequently are paralyzed. In such cases, the Drinker respirator (iron lung) is a life-saving device, as it takes the place of the respiratory muscles. This respirator is shown in Figure 15-14.

CHANGES IN PULMONARY VOLUME

The volume of air that moves in and out of the lungs with inspiration and expiration can be measured by means of a spirometer. The inside parts of a spirometer and arrangement for recording are shown in Figure 15-15. The record produced by a person breathing in and out of a spirometer is called a *spirogram* (Fig. 15-16), and it resembles in some respects the record made during a basal metabolism test.

Pulmonary function tests

Tests of respiration, called *pulmonary function studies,* are very important in chest surgery. From spirograms, for example, the following information can be obtained:

1. **Rate of Respiration.** The number of respirations per minute can be counted. There are usually between 14 and 18 respiratory cycles per minute in the adult. In the newborn, the rate is about 40 per minute; in the infant, 30; and in a 5-year-old child, about 25 per minute.

2. **Tidal Volume.** This is the volume of air (or oxygen) moved in and out of the lungs with each respiratory movement. The average tidal volume is 500 ml. or 0.5 L.

3. **Inspiratory Reserve.** This is the volume of air, in excess of the tidal, that can be inhaled by the deepest possible inspiration. It averages 3,000 ml. or 3 L. Persons who play wind instruments can inhale much more than this.

4. **Expiratory Reserve.** This is the volume of air, in excess of the tidal, which can be exhaled by the deepest possible expiration. It is about 1,000 ml. or 1 L.

5. **Vital Capacity.** This may be defined in 2 ways. (A) It is the volume of air that can be exhaled by the deepest possible expiration after the deepest possible inspiration. (B) It is the sum of the tidal, the inspiratory reserve and the expiratory reserve air. The average vital capacity is 4,500 ml. or 4.5 L. Physical education students, athletes and persons who play wind instruments have much greater vital capacities than average persons.

Vital capacity is reduced in various cases of heart and lung disease. It also is reduced in any condition in which there is muscular weakness, since the patient is not capable of the increased muscular effort required in testing vital capacity. Reduced vital capacity is illustrated in Figure 15-17, and the measurable volumes of air are shown by diagram in Figure 15-18.

Bronchospirometry. It may be necessary to remove a lobe of one lung, or even an entire lung, from persons who have cancer of the lung. Before such an operation is done, it is essential to know the condition of the healthy lung. Bronchospirometry is the study of the function of the two lungs separately, at the same time. A bronchospirometer is a double spirometer; each lung is connected with one spirometer. The apparatus is shown in Figure 15-19.

Under local anesthesia a special catheter is introduced into the respiratory passages which establishes connection between each lung and its respective spirometer. An illustration of a record made by bronchospirometry is shown in Figure 15-20. The record from the right lung is above, and the one from the left lung is below. It is

Fig. 15-17. (Left) Vital capacity of 3,500 ml. in a normal individual. (Right) Vital capacity of 2,700 ml. in a patient with heart disease; the congested pulmonary capillaries encroach upon the space normally occupied by alveolar air.

Normal, 3500 cc.   In cardiac disease, 2700 cc.

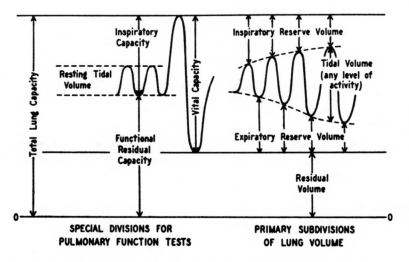

Fig. 15-18. Subdivisions of lung volume. (Federation Proc. 9:602)

Fig. 15-19. Bronchospirometer and Norris catheter. The bronchospirometer is a double spirometer, it permits the registration of the exchanges of each lung separately and simultaneously. In the catheter (right), 1 is the tube introduced into the left main stem bronchus; 2 is the balloon which, when distended, permits the passage of air to and from the left lung only through the tube; 3 is the face mask. 4 is the tube which permits the passage of air to and from the right lung. As the tubes leave the face mask they are connected with their respective spirometers (left), and the exchanges for each lung are recorded. The face mask is used instead of a mouthpiece. Bronchospirometry is done under local anesthesia of pharynx, larynx, trachea and bronchi; the patient is not in a basal state.

Fig. 15-20. Record obtained by bronchospirometry. In this record the right lung exchanges are above and the left below. Oxygen use, rate, tidal volume, minute volume and vital capacity for each lung can be determined from such a record. In chest surgery it is imperative to know the functional capacity of one lung before the other is removed.

obvious that the right lung is taking a much smaller share of the respiratory work than the left. Normally, the right lung does about 55 per cent of the total work, and the left about 45 per cent.

Other pulmonary volumes *re read.*

Residual Air. The residual air remains in the lungs even after the deepest possible expiration and cannot be removed by voluntary effort. The average volume of residual air is 1.5 L. It is eliminated only by collapse of the lungs. Thus, in the lungs we normally have 1.5 L. of residual air and 1 L. of expiratory reserve air or 2.5 L. at the end of a normal expiration. We breathe in only 0.5 L. with each inspiration and thus renew only one fifth of the air in the lungs with each respiratory cycle.

1.5L — 1500 me

Minimal Air. If a baby has taken even one breath, the lungs retain some air that is trapped in the alveoli and is not eliminated even by collapse of the lungs. This is called *minimal air,* and it is important in medicolegal practice to determine if a baby lived even briefly or was born dead.

Dead-space Air. The volume of air that remains in the passages during inspiration (larynx, trachea and bronchial tree) plays no part in gaseous exchanges of respiration; consequently, it is called *dead-space air.* It is about 150 ml. for men and 110 for women.

in passage

THE RESPIRATORY GASES

The air we breathe has a remarkably uniform composition insofar as oxygen (O_2), carbon dioxide (CO_2) and nitrogen (N_2) are concerned. Of these gases, only oxygen and carbon dioxide are of physiologic significance under ordinary circumstances, nitrogen serving merely to dilute the oxygen.

Composition of respired and alveolar air

The amounts of respiratory gases vary in inspired, expired and alveolar air, as indicated in the table. In each case, the remainder of the air is mostly nitrogen, which brings the total to 100 per cent.

	PERCENTAGE OF OXYGEN	PERCENTAGE OF CARBON DIOXIDE
Inspired air	21.00 *%*	0.04
Expired air	16.00 *%*	4.40
Alveolar air	14.00 *%*	5.50

You will note that expired air contains less oxygen and more carbon dioxide than inspired air, and that alveolar air contains less oxygen and more carbon dioxide than expired air. Expired air is really a mixture of alveolar and inspired air from the dead space. The composition of alveolar air is fairly constant, and only one fifth of the air in the lungs is renewed by each inspiration. In this way, sudden and marked changes in the composition of alveolar air are prevented.

In addition to the differences in content of oxygen and carbon dioxide, there are physical differences between inspired air and expired and alveolar air. Expired and alveolar airs are saturated with water vapor and warmed to body temperature. The amount of water vapor and the temperature of inspired air vary markedly in different localities and in different seasons. One loses heat by warming the inspired air whenever its temperature is below body temperature; one also loses heat by saturating inspired air whenever it is not saturated as it enters the respiratory passages.

⅕ of Air is renewed at each breath

Diffusion and exchange of gases

Gases diffuse rapidly from areas of higher to lower concentrations. As described in Chapter 2, this is due to the incessant motion of gas molecules which are constantly bumping into one another. Diffusion continues until concentrations are equal throughout the space in which the gases are contained.

In the body the concentration of oxygen is higher in alveolar air than it is in the blood coming to the lungs from the right ventricle; therefore, oxygen diffuses into the blood from the alveolar air. On the other hand, the concentration of oxygen is low in the cells of the body tissues and in tissue fluid; therefore, oxygen diffuses from the blood in the systemic capillaries into the tissue fluid and on into cells.

The concentration of carbon dioxide in the tissue cells and the tissue fluid is higher than it is in the blood in the capillaries. Therefore, carbon dioxide diffuses from tissue cells and tissue fluid into the blood. The concentration of carbon dioxide is higher in blood coming to the lungs from the right ventricle than it is in alveolar air, therefore, it diffuses from blood in pulmonary capillaries into the alveolar air.

Blood transport of respiratory gases

On entering the blood stream, both oxygen and carbon dioxide immediately go into simple physical solution in the plasma. However, since a fluid can hold only a small amount of gas in solution, most of the oxygen and the carbon dioxide quickly enter into chemical combinations with other blood constituents. A few of the more prominent chemical reactions are shown schematically in Figures 15-21 and 15-22. For a detailed discussion of this subject one should consult a textbook in biochemistry.

Oxygen Transport. Oxygen is carried in two ways by the blood constituents.

1. As mentioned previously, only a small amount of oxygen is carried in solution in the plasma. However, it is this oxygen that exerts "tension" or pressure and is available for immediate diffusion when blood reaches the systemic capillaries where the oxygen tension of the surrounding tissue fluid and tissue cells is low.

2. The remaining oxygen in the blood is combined with hemoglobin in the red blood cells to form *oxyhemoglobin* ($HHbO_2$). This oxygen is given up readily by the hemoglobin whenever the oxygen tension of the plasma decreases, so that as fast as oxygen diffuses from the plasma in tissue capillaries it is replenished by more from the oxyhemoglobin. Hemoglobin that has given up its load of oxygen is called *reduced hemoglobin* (HHb).

When blood returns to the lungs from the right ventricle, its reduced hemoglobin is ready to take up a new load of oxygen and become oxyhemoglobin again. The total amount of oxygen in 100 ml. of arterial blood is about 20 ml.; of this, 2.5 per cent or 0.5 ml. is dissolved in the plasma, and 97.5 per cent or 19.5 ml. are combined with hemoglobin in the red blood cells.

Hypoxia is a term that refers to any state wherein an inadequate amount of oxygen is available to the cells; it is generally classified on the basis of one of four causes.

1. *Anemic hypoxia* is due to a reduction in the oxygen-carrying capacity of the blood. For example, in anemia and hemorrhage there is a reduced amount of hemoglobin available for oxygen transport.

2. *Stagnant hypoxia* is due to a slow rate of circulation of the blood, as in heart disease. Oxygen is not delivered to the cells with sufficient rapidity to meet their needs.

3. *Hypoxic hypoxia* refers to decreased oxygen saturation of the blood due to insufficient oxygen in the alveolar air. This may occur in high altitude flying and in cases of respiratory obstruction.

4. *Histotoxic hypoxia* occurs when poisons, such as cyanide, enter the body. Such poisons destroy the enzyme systems present in cells, and the oxygen that is present cannot be used in the absence of these systems.

Carbon Dioxide Transport. Carbon dioxide is carried in several ways by the blood constituents.

1. A small amount of carbon dioxide is carried in solution in the plasma. Following the same principle that applied to oxygen transport, the carbon dioxide in solution exerts the necessary "tension" or pressure that makes it available for immediate diffusion when blood reaches the pulmonary capillaries where the carbon dioxide tension in the neighboring alveoli is low.

2. A moderate amount of carbon dioxide is carried in combination with hemoglobin, the resulting compound being called *carbamino-hemoglobin* ($HHbCO_2$). Thus hemoglobin does "double duty"; it not only serves to carry oxygen to the tissues but also helps in the removal of carbon dioxide.

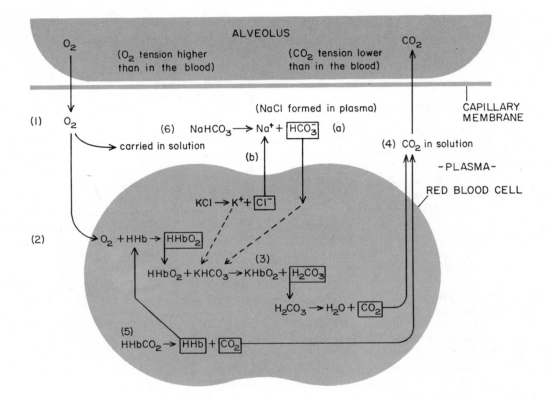

Fig. 15-21. Schematic representation of the exchange of gases between a pulmonary capillary and an alveolus. A few of the more prominent chemical reactions are included to illustrate the cooperative relationships that exist between the blood constituents as they pick up O_2 and release CO_2. As oxygen enters the bloodstream, some of it (1) is carried in solution in the plasma, but the remainder (2) combines with reduced hemoglobin (HHb) to form oxyhemoglobin ($HHbO_2$); most of the oxyhemoglobin then forms (3) potassium oxyhemoglobin ($KHbO_2$) for transport to the tissues. Simultaneously, the CO_2 in solution in the plasma (4) diffuses into the alveolus, thus lowering the plasma tension of CO_2; as a result, additional CO_2 can be released from (5) carbamino-hemoglobin ($HHbCO_2$) and from (6) sodium bicarbonate ($NaHCO_3$). Note that as the bicarbonate ion (a) from $NaHCO_3$ enters the red cell to form $KHCO_3$, it is replaced by a chloride ion (b) from KCl; this chloride movement is part of the chloride shift.

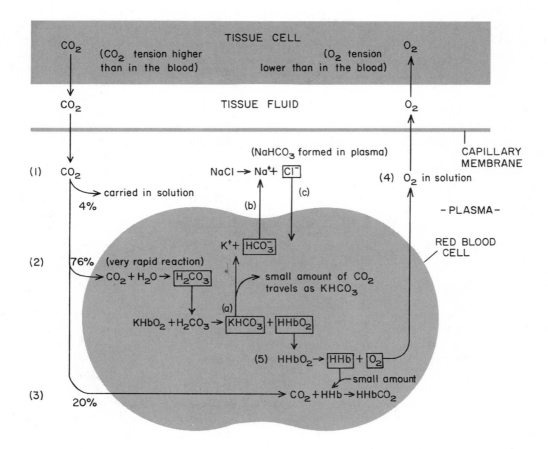

Fig. 15-22. Schematic representation of the exchange of gases between a systemic capillary and a tissue cell. A few of the more prominent chemical reactions are included to illustrate the cooperative relationships that exist between the blood constituents as they pick up carbon dioxide and release oxygen. As CO_2 diffuses into the bloodstream, some of it is carried in solution in the plasma (1), but most of it follows the chemical pathway (2) leading to the formation of (a) potassium bicarbonate ($KHCO_3$) in the red blood cell and (b) sodium bicarbonate ($NaHCO_3$) in the plasma. Note that as the bicarbonate ion (HCO_3^-) leaves the red cell it is replaced by (c) a chloride ion (Cl^-); this chloride movement is part of the chloride shift. The remaining CO_2 (3) combines with reduced hemoglobin (HHb) and is carried to the lungs as carbamino-hemoglobin ($HHbCO_2$). Simultaneously, the oxygen in solution in the plasma (4) diffuses into the tissue fluid and tissue cells, thus lowering the plasma O_2 tension so that additional supplies of O_2 are released from (5) oxyhemoglobin ($HHbO_2$).

3. A very large amount of carbon dioxide is carried in the form of bicarbonate, the most important being *sodium bicarbonate* ($NaHCO_3$) in the plasma. However, a small but significant amount is carried as *potassium bicarbonate* ($KHCO_3$) in the red blood cells.

The total amount of carbon dioxide in 100 ml. of venous blood is about 60 ml.; of this, about 4 per cent or 2.5 ml. is dissolved in the plasma, 72 per cent or 43 ml. is carried as sodium bicarbonate, 4 per cent or 2.5 ml. as potassium bicarbonate, and the remaining 20 per cent or 12 ml. is carried in hemoglobin as carbamino compound.

Nitrogen. Although there are no known metabolic reactions involving molecular nitrogen (N_2) in the human body, it is found in solution in the blood and in other tissues. Under ordinary circumstances this nitrogen is of no physiologic significance, but in the caisson worker, the deep-sea diver, or even the adventurous week-end scuba diver, dissolved nitrogen becomes a problem of immediate concern. These persons must breathe air that is under greatly increased pressure and, as the pressure increases, more nitrogen goes into solution in the plasma as well as in the tissue fluid. Excessive amounts of dissolved nitrogen may produce giddiness and other effects similar to those that follow the consumption of alcohol; this condition, called *nitrogen narcosis,* may imperil the life of the scuba diver who swims alone and has no contact with the surface.

Decompression sickness or "the bends" may follow too rapid ascent or return to normal pressure. In such cases, the excess nitrogen is released in the form of bubbles in the blood, and the severity of symptoms depends on where the bubbles become trapped. These bubbles may lodge in capillaries all over the body, but the most common symptom of decompression sickness is pain in the muscles and the joints. More serious symptoms include dyspnea, chest pain and muscular paralysis. Treatment of decompression sickness depends on recompression; the victim must be placed in a special chamber where the air pressure can be elevated until nitrogen once again is forced into solution. If decompression is carried out slowly, the nitrogen gradually is eliminated through the lungs and causes no further trouble.

Decompression sickness is not limited to tunnel workers and divers. In this age of high-flying jet aircraft, pressurized cabins and special pressure suits protect pilots from the same hazard of changing pressures. Without this protection, the nitrogen that normally is present in the blood would be released as bubbles during the rapid ascent from atmospheric pressure on the ground to the much lower pressure that prevails at high altitudes.

THE CONTROL OF BREATHING

Whether one is sitting quietly in a chair or playing a vigorous game of tennis, the breathing movements are controlled so as to meet the immediate oxygen requirements of the body. However, the respiratory muscles contract at the proper time and with the proper force only if they are so stimulated by nerve impulses from the CNS. Unlike the heart muscle, which can contract automatically, the skeletal muscles of respiration are completely dependent on their nerve supply. Therefore, in view of the constantly changing needs of the body, it follows that there must be a central control unit that is capable of coordinating and correlating the activities of the respiratory muscles; this vital unit, or respiratory center, and the many factors that influence it will be described briefly.

The respiratory center and efferent pathways

The respiratory center, consisting of inspiratory and expiratory neurons, is located primarily in the medulla oblongata and to a lesser extent in the lower part of the pons. Although nature has endowed the medullary center with an intrinsic rhythm, its activity is influenced by facilitatory and inhibitory centers in the pons. Connections with the spinal cord and with higher centers in the hypothalamus and cerebral cortex also are of importance in the control of breathing.

The medullary center is under constant bom

bardment by nerve impulses as it receives "information" from receptors in various parts of the body. These receptors "report," either directly or indirectly, on respiratory conditions in their area. In response to this stimulation, the respiratory center dispatches the appropriate "orders" for contraction of the respiratory muscles.

During normal, quiet breathing (called *eupnea*) the only muscles that contract to bring about inspiration are the diaphragm and the external intercostal muscles. Nerve impulses dispatched from the respiratory center reach the diaphragm by way of the phrenic nerves, and the intercostal muscles by way of the intercostal nerves. Quiet expiration normally is a passive act as the inspiratory muscles relax due to the cessation of impulses from the respiratory center.

In order to breathe more deeply, as during mild exercise, there must be more forceful contractions of the above muscles. More and more motor units are brought into action, and there are more impulses per unit of time conducted over each axon. There is a wide range of gradation possible in the depth of breathing, since any number of motor units may be brought into activity. In order to breathe more rapidly, there are shorter intervals of rest between bursts of impulses traveling over the phrenic and the intercostal nerves.

Following strenuous exercise, or in certain diseases that are accompanied by difficult breathing (called *dyspnea*), the respiratory center will call many more muscles into action as both *forced inspiration* and *forced expiration* are needed to meet the body's needs. Any muscle capable of lifting the ribs may be used during forced inspiration; some of these are the sternocleiodomastoids, the scalenes, the levatores costarum and the pectoralis major and minor muscles.

As noted previously, expiration is normally passive, but in forced expiration it becomes active, and muscles that depress the ribs are called into action. These include the internal intercostals, the quadratus lumborum and the muscles of the abdominal wall. In addition to pulling on the ribs, the abdominal wall muscles compress the abdominal viscera and force the diaphragm upward, thus decreasing the volume of the thorax and helping to expel air more rapidly.

Voluntary Control of Breathing

Nerve impulses originating in the motor areas of the cerebral cortex and traveling to the respiratory center enable one to consciously alter the rate and the depth of breathing. For example, during the act of speaking or singing, breath control is of considerable importance, and if a person wishes to swim under water he may hold his breath voluntarily for a short period of time. However, voluntary control is limited, and the respiratory center will "ignore" messages from the cortex when it is necessary to meet the body's basic needs. To prove this point to yourself, try to talk or to sing in a normal manner after a bout of strenuous exercise, or try to hold your breath for a prolonged period of time.

Chemical factors in the control of breathing

As metabolic activity in the body increases, usually there is a proportionate increase in the rate and depth of breathing; this sequence of events is quite logical in view of the fact that busy cells require more oxygen (O_2) and form more carbon dioxide (CO_2) and hydrogen ions (H^+). On the other hand, as metabolic activity declines, the cells need less O_2 and form less CO_2 and H^+, thus breathing activity is decreased. The respiratory center is able to issue the appropriate "orders" for changes in the rate and depth of breathing because it is alerted to any significant changes in the composition of the cerebrospinal fluid and the circulating blood. The "alerting mechanism" involves special sensory nerve endings, called *chemoreceptors*. These receptors, when stimulated by chemical changes in their natural liquid environment, initiate afferent nerve impulses that influence the activity of the respiratory center. The chemoreceptors are of two types: central and peripheral.

Central chemoreceptors, located on or near the ventral surface of the medulla, are strongly influenced by the H^+ and CO_2 content of the cerebrospinal fluid; to a lesser degree, they also may be influenced by the CO_2 in arterial blood. CO_2 diffuses readily through the walls of brain capillaries and into the cerebrospinal fluid that bathes the central nervous system; upon diffusing into the medullary chemoreceptor cells, carbon dioxide reacts with water to form carbonic acid ($CO_2 + H_2O \rightarrow H_2CO_3$), and some of the acid molecules dissociate to yield hydrogen ions ($H_2CO_3 \rightarrow H^+ + HCO_3^-$). As a result, nerve impulses are dispatched to the nearby respiratory center and one begins to breathe more deeply and more rapidly. As the excess carbon dioxide is blown off, and the amount of carbonic acid is reduced proportionately ($H_2CO_3 \rightarrow CO_2 + H_2O$), breathing returns to normal. On the other hand, if the blood level of carbon dioxide falls below normal levels there will be a temporary cessation of breathing (apnea). However, decreased carbon dioxide tension does not persist for any length of time, since carbon dioxide is produced constantly by metabolic processes in all cells, and it soon accumulates to the required level to stimulate the respiratory center again. Thus one can see that breathing plays a vital role in the maintenance of *acid-base balance*. As carbon dioxide is blown off with each expiration there is a corresponding reduction in the amount of acid in the blood.

This chemical control mechanism is responsible for the fundamental rhythm of the respiratory center, and it keeps us breathing both day and night without our giving the matter any conscious thought. It is this mechanism that comes to the rescue of the distraught mother whose child, in a fit of temper, is holding his breath until he becomes "blue in the face." If only the mother can remain calm for a few seconds, the child will breathe whether he wishes to do so or not, as the chemical control overcomes the voluntary effort, and the air in his rebellious little lungs will be freshened.

In some hospitals, *hyperventilation* is induced as a part of postoperative treatment. It consists of the administration of 7 to 10 per cent carbon dioxide for several minutes twice each day. This increases the depth of the respiratory movements. Some surgeons believe that the incidence of postoperative pneumonia is decreased by such periods of hyperventilation.

Various drugs may affect the respiratory center, and one of the most important of these is *morphine*. Morphine has a depressing effect on the respiratory center, and the slow rate of breathing in a morphine addict who had taken an overdose of the drug is illustrated in Figure 15-23. Respiratory failure due to overdose of morphine may occur if the respiratory center is not stimulated vigorously. When an injection of morphine is given to any patient it should be charted at once; otherwise it may be repeated by another person, and a serious depression of respiration might ensue.

If morphine is given to a woman in labor just

Fig. 15-23. Respiratory movements in morphine addict. The rate is very slow; the patient failed to recover. (Minnesota Med.)

before delivery the respiratory center of the new-born may be so depressed that it cannot function, and respiration cannot be established. The question of sedation and anesthesia is a vital one in obstetrics.

Peripheral chemoreceptors, located in the aortic and carotid bodies, play a role in the regulation of circulation (p. 408), but they are of even greater importance in regulating the oxygen content of the blood; under certain extreme conditions they also help to regulate the CO_2 and H^+ content of the blood. Whenever the amount of O_2 dissolved in the plasma falls, there is a corresponding decrease in the O_2 content of the tissue fluid bathing the chemoreceptor cells; this lack of O_2 serves to stimulate those cells, and nerve impulses are dispatched to the respiratory center. The vagus and glossopharyngeal nerves conduct impulses from the aortic and carotid bodies respectively (Fig. 14-11). When the respiratory center is stimulated by such incoming impulses it "orders" an increase in the depth and rate of breathing. This reflex is important, not only in normal daily living, but also when the oxygen supply to the body is decreased in heart disease, and in lung disease, such as emphysema.

Physical factors in the control of breathing

Although the chemical factors that regulate breathing are of fundamental importance, there are various physical factors that also are of significance. Some of these factors and the respiratory reflexes that they initiate will be described briefly.

Inflation of the lungs serves to stimulate receptor end organs which are sensitive to stretch or distention. These special nerve endings, located in the alveolar ducts, initiate a stream of nerve impulses which travel to the CNS by way of the vagus nerves. The inspiratory center is inhibited by these afferent impulses, and, as a result, impulses are no longer sent to the diaphragm and the external intercostal muscles. With relaxation of these muscles, passive expiration follows. This reflex, called the *Hering-Breuer* reflex, is of importance in the rhythmic control of normal, quiet

breathing. It the vagus nerves are cut, inspiration is greatly prolonged and of increased depth; however, the respiratory center eventually ceases to discharge efferent impulses, and expiration will occur. This indicates that there are other factors which continue to operate in the absence of the vagus nerves.

Changes in blood pressure stimulate pressoreceptors in the aortic and the carotid sinuses. These specialized receptor end organs are affected by sudden, marked changes in blood pressure. When arterial blood pressure rises suddenly, impulses are sent in from the pressoreceptors by way of the vagus and the glossopharyngeal nerves to the CNS. Such impulses depress the activity of the respiratory center, and respiration becomes slower and more shallow, temporarily.

When the arterial blood pressure falls suddenly, as after a severe hemorrhage, the number of impulses reaching the CNS from the pressoreceptors decreases, and the respiratory center increases its activity, thereby increasing the rate and probably the depth of respiration. However, it must be kept in mind that the pressoreceptors are not nearly as important in the control of respiration as they are in the control of circulation (p. 405).

Irritation of the respiratory passages stimulates sensitive receptors in the mucous membrane lining. An irritating substance in the nose, such as pepper, induces a *sneeze* which is a violent expiration of air through the nose. The presence of a crumb in the larynx or the trachea induces a spell of coughing. A cough is a sudden, violent expulsion of air after a deep inspiration and temporary closure of the glottis to build up pressure in the lower respiratory passages. Reflexes of this type are protective in nature and tend to remove the irritating substances from the body.

The temperature of the blood flowing through the respiratory center also may influence breathing. With an increase in body temperature, as during fever or severe muscular exercise, there is an increase in the respiratory rate. On the other hand, a subnormal temperature, as during hypothermia, results in a decreased respiratory rate.

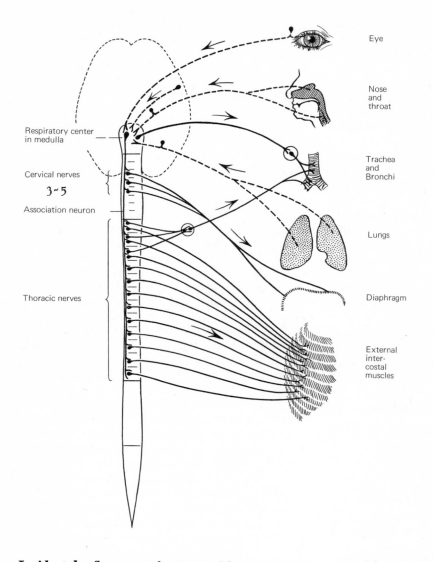

Eye

Nose and throat

Respiratory center in medulla

Cervical nerves

3~5

Association neuron

Trachea and Bronchi

Lungs

Thoracic nerves

Diaphragm

External inter- costal muscles

Fig. 15-24. Connections of the respiratory center in the medulla. Any afferent fiber, fibers from higher centers, from the respiratory passages and from the lungs may influence the activity of the respiratory center. Central (associational) neurons establish connections between the respiratory center and the cells in the spinal cord; axons from these cells go to the muscles of respiration. Hence, the respiratory movements may be altered by a variety of stimuli.

Incidental reflexes may be initiated by receptors of various kinds in other parts of the body. You may see something that makes you gasp or hold your breath momentarily. You may hear a shriek that either speeds up your respiratory rate or stops all respiratory movements for a few seconds. When you touch something cold and slimy, you may gasp. Thus, respiratory reflexes can be aroused by a variety of stimuli which affect many types of receptors.

Figure 15-24 illustrates the respiratory center and some of the afferent pathways by which impulses reach the CNS and alter activity in the respiratory system. The efferent pathways for all respiratory reflexes are the phrenic and the intercostal nerves, which are the final common paths for such reflexes.

SUMMARY

1. Respiration refers to exchange of gases between organism and environment
   A. External respiration—exchange between blood and air
   B. Internal respiration—exchange between blood and tissue cells
2. Organs of respiratory system
   A. Nose
      a. External—soft tissues except for bridge
      b. Internal—divided into 2 cavities by nasal septum; lined with vascular mucous membrane
      c. Serves to warm, moisten and filter air
      d. Paranasal sinuses and nasolacrimal duct open into nose
      e. Blood supply from carotid arteries; nerve supply by olfactory, trigeminal and facial cranial nerves
   B. Pharynx—tubular passageway from nose to esophagus
      a. Nasopharynx—superior portion; closed during swallowing. Has 4 openings in its walls: 2 posterior nares, 2 auditory tubes. Pharyngeal tonsil on posterior wall. Ciliated mucosa
      b. Oropharynx—middle portion; lies behind mouth with which it communicates by fauces. Palatine tonsils between anterior and posterior pillars. Lingual tonsil at root of tongue
      c. Laryngopharynx—inferior portion; opens into larynx anteriorly, continues as esophagus posteriorly
   C. Larynx: stands "guard" over trachea and serves as organ of voice
      a. Closed during act of swallowing
      b. Cartilages: thyroid, cricoid, epiglottis, arytenoid, corniculate and cuneiform; connected by ligaments
      c. Vocal folds or "true vocal cords" form glottis; narrow slit between them may be obstructed by foreign body. Tension of folds controlled by muscles during speech

   d. Blood supply from external carotid arteries; nerve supply, the vagus, particularly the recurrent laryngeal branch
   D. Trachea and bronchi
      a. Trachea a flexible tubular structure reinforced by cartilage rings. Lined with ciliated mucosa
      b. Bronchial tree
         (1) Trachea divides into primary bronchi which then divide to form secondary bronchi
         (2) Division continues to bronchioles; less cartilage, more smooth muscle
         (3) Smooth muscle of bronchioles supplied by both divisions of autonomics: parasympathetic promotes constriction; sympathetic relaxation
   E. Lungs: essential organs of respiration
      a. In thoracic cavity, one on either side of mediastinum
      b. Cone-shaped; base rests on diaphragm; apex extends above 1st rib
      c. Right lung shorter and broader; 3 lobes. Left lung, 2 lobes
      d. Visceral pleura applied to lung; parietal pleura lines thorax, covers diaphragm, reflected over mediastinum. Pleural cavity—potential space between visceral and parietal layers
      e. Light, porous and spongy; elastic; lobes divided into lobules
      f. Each lobule supplied with bronchiole; branches to terminal bronchiole, to respiratory bronchioles, to alveolar ducts, to atria and alveoli
      g. Blood supply: pulmonary and bronchial arteries
3. Mechanics of breathing
   A. Air pressure and flow
      a. Gases travel from area of higher to lower pressure or concentration
      b. Atmospheric pressure: exerted by outside air
      c. Intrapulmonic pressure: that within bronchial tree

d. Intrapleural pressure: that within pleural cavity; negative or subatmospheric pressure

B. Inspiration: act of taking air into lungs
   a. Contraction of inspiratory muscles
   b. Enlargement of thoracic cage
   c. Decrease in intrapleural and intrapulmonic pressures
   d. Air flows in until equal to atmospheric pressure

C. Expiration: act of expelling air from lungs
   a. Relaxation of inspiratory muscles; recoil of stretched tissues
   b. Decrease in size of thoracic cage
   c. Increase in intrapleural and intrapulmonic pressures
   d. Air flows out until equal to atmospheric pressure

D. Modified breathing movements
   a. Normally — balanced action between diaphragm and intercostal muscles, diaphragm predominates in abdominal breathing, intercostals in costal type breathing

E. Artificial respiration
   a. During heart and lung operations by special machine
   b. "Mouth-to-mouth" breathing gives best ventilation of lungs

4. Changes in pulmonary volume: measured by spirometer; record called spirogram
   A. Pulmonary function tests provide data on rate of respiration, tidal volume, inspiratory and expiratory reserve and vital capacity
   B. Bronchospirometry: study of lungs separately, at same time
   C. Other pulmonary volumes
      a. Residual air
      b. Minimal air
      c. Dead-space air

5. Respiratory gases
   A. Composition of respired and alveolar air
      a. Expired air contains less oxygen and more carbon dioxide than inspired air
      b. Composition of alveolar air fairly constant; only one fifth of air in lungs renewed by each inspiration
      c. Expired air and alveolar air warm and moist
   B. Diffusion and exchange of gases
      a. From higher to lower concentration
      b. Oxygen from alveoli to blood in pulmonary capillaries; carbon dioxide from pulmonary capillaries to alveoli
      c. Oxygen from systemic capillaries to tissue fluid; carbon dioxide from tissue fluid to systemic capillaries
   C. Blood transport of respiratory gases
      a. Oxygen: small amount in solution in plasma immediately available for diffusion; most of it in combination with hemoglobin (oxyhemoglobin)
      b. Hypoxia: inadequate amount of oxygen available to cells
      c. Carbon dioxide transport: small amount carried in solution in plasma; moderate amount carried as carbamino-hemoglobin; large amount carried as sodium bicarbonate in plasma; small amount as potassium bicarbonate in red cell
      d. Nitrogen of significance only in persons breathing air under pressure

6. Control of breathing
   A. Respiratory center and efferent pathways
      a. Located in medulla; coordinates and correlates breathing activities
      b. Dispatches orders to respiratory muscles stimulating contraction
      c. Forced inspiration involves any muscle capable of lifting ribs
      d. Forced expiration an active process; muscles that depress ribs and compress abdominal viscera are stimulated
   B. Voluntary control of breathing
      a. Nerve impulses from motor area of cortex may stimulate center and enable one to control rate and depth of breathing
      b. Limited by basic needs of body, which come first
   C. Chemical factors in control of breathing
      a. Stimulation of central chemoreceptors

by carbon dioxide and hydrogen ions in cerebrospinal fluid of fundamental importance; resultant increase in rate and depth of breathing enables one to blow off CO_2, reduce acid in blood. Limits voluntary control
   b. Peripheral chemoreceptor reflexes from aortic and carotid bodies when O_2 level falls
D. Physical factors in control of breathing
   a. Inflation of lungs; Hering-Breuer reflex
   b. Changes in blood pressure
   c. Irritation of respiratory passages
   d. Temperature of blood
   e. Incidental reflexes initiated by receptors elsewhere in body

PRACTICAL APPLICATIONS AND QUESTIONS

(Encircle the letter of the *best* answer to each of the following questions.)

A. *Three-year-old Sally was given a shiny new penny. Not long after receiving the penny she put it into her mouth and promptly aspirated it. She was taken to the broncho-esophagology department of a nearby hospital.*

1. On examination the doctor found that, as he had suspected, the penny was lodged in a branch of the right primary bronchus. Foreign bodies are most frequently found in the right lung because
   a. the right lung has 3 lobes and, therefore, is larger than the left
   b. the right primary bronchus is more nearly vertical and wider
   c. the walls of the right primary bronchus are more stiff and rigid
   d. there are no cilia in the right primary bronchus

2. Normally food and other foreign bodies bypass the air passages and are swallowed, because during swallowing the position of the larynx changes as it is pulled up and under the base of the tongue. The name of the cartilage which stands upright at the entrance of the larynx is the
   a. cricoid
   b. thyroid
   c. epiglottis
   d. arytenoid

3. Foreign objects must be removed almost immediately so that air may enter the lung to allow for exchange of gases. The area of exchange between the blood and inspired air is the
   a. terminal bronchi
   b. trachea
   c. pleura
   d. alveoli

4. When the bronchi subdivide their walls contain
   a. less cartilage and more smooth muscle
   b. more cartilage and more smooth muscle
   c. more cartilage and less smooth muscle
   d. less cartilage and less smooth muscle

5. The lining of the larynx, the trachea and the bronchial tubes is
   a. simple squamous epithelium
   b. nonciliated columnar epithelium
   c. ciliated mucous membrane
   d. serous membrane

6. After treatment and the removal of the penny, Sally had some hoarseness. The reason for this is that the vocal folds are located in the
   a. pharynx
   b. larynx
   c. trachea
   d. bronchi

B. *The respiratory rate is considered one of the vital signs in caring for an ill person. Therefore, it is one of the important procedures taught to student nurses.*

1. In counting the respiratory rate, the student nurses found that the rate in the adult usually was between
   a. 10 to 12 per minute
   b. 12 to 16 per minute
   c. 14 to 18 per minute
   d. 20 to 26 per minute

2. Respirations usually are counted by observing the rise and fall of the chest wall. However,

the main muscle action for enlarging the thoracic cavity is

    a. contraction of the diaphragm

    b. relaxation of the diaphragm

    c. relaxation of the intercostal muscles

    d. contraction of the pectoralis major

3. Since there is some amount of voluntary control of respiration, nurses record respiratory movements unobserved by the patient. The stimulus which keeps us breathing and limits voluntary control is

    a. nitrogen

    b. oxygen

    c. carbon dioxide

    d. equal parts of all three

4. The reflex regulation of respiration is important. The reflex which cuts short inspiration is

    a. aroused in the pressoreceptors

    b. the Hering-Breuer reflex

    c. a protective reflex from the larynx

    d. an incidental reflex from the skin

5. In times of stress, accessory muscles of breathing are brought into action. Forced expiration is brought about by

    a. relaxation of the diaphragm

    b. relaxation of abdominal muscles

    c. contraction of pectoralis muscles

    d. contraction of abdominal muscles

6. One respiratory cycle includes an inspiration and an expiration. The amount of air moved in and out of the lungs with one normal cycle is called

    a. inspiratory reserve air

    b. vital capacity

    c. tidal volume

    d. minimal air

16

THE DIGESTION
OF FOOD

Foods are substances taken into the body for one of three purposes: to yield energy, to build and repair tissues, and to regulate various metabolic processes. However, the mere act of swallowing a mouthful of food does not mean that it is "in the body"; not until the food material has been absorbed from the lumen of the digestive tube can it be said to have entered the body.

Some food substances can be absorbed with little or no change in the form in which they were ingested, but others must undergo extensive changes before they can enter the blood or lymph stream. It is the function of the digestive system to prepare foods for absorption so that they may be transported to cells in all parts of the body. Complex foods, such as meat, potatoes and gravy, must be broken down mechanically and chemically to small particles that can pass through membranes. Thus the digestive system is comparable in some ways to a mill as it modifies or "refines" food substances.

Let us consider briefly how it is possible for the protein and the starch in a grain of wheat to become part of the body. First the wheat must be ground and purified, the flour separated by chemical and physical processes and then retained while the waste is rejected. After the flour is made into bread, the bread is eaten and mechanically and chemically broken into small pieces during various digestive processes. The tiny end products of protein digestion are amino acids; those of starch digestion are simple sugars, such as glucose. These useful products of digestion are absorbed into the blood stream and carried to all parts of the body where they are used by the cells. Thus the original wheat has been subjected to *two* milling processes, first in making it into flour, and second in preparing the flour for absorption into the circulating blood.

It is the purpose of this chapter first to consider the various food groups and then the "machinery" of the digestive system "mill" and the way in which it prepares food for absorption. In Chapter 17 we shall discuss the absorption of food and the way in which it is utilized by the cells.

FOOD FOR THE MILL

The following discussion of foods is quite limited; for a more thorough presentation one should consult a textbook of biochemistry.

Foods may be divided into 2 general classes: inorganic and organic. The former comprises inorganic salts and water, and the latter comprises carbohydrates, lipids, proteins, and accessory foodstuffs or vitamins.

Inorganic

Inorganic salts in foods are primarily combinations of the following cations: sodium, potassium, calcium, iron, copper, magnesium and manganese and the following anions: chloride, bicarbonate, phosphate, sulfate and iodide. Proper amounts of inorganic salts are necessary for various body functions such as maintenance of osmotic relationships, excitability, conductivity, contractility, acid-base balance and for the coagulation of blood. Salts are lost each day in the urine and the feces and need to be replaced. Any marked departure from the normal amounts of various salts gives rise to pathologic conditions such as Addison's disease (p. 561) and tetany (p. 558).

Water, the most abundant of all constituents in living tissues, plays many important roles; the functions of water are described on page 15. Because it is so essential for all cellular reactions, there must be a balance between intake and output (p. 539).

Organic

Carbohydrates are our most abundant and economical source of energy. They are organic compounds containing carbon, hydrogen and oxygen. There are 3 groups of carbohydrates.

Monosaccharides or simple sugars, such as glucose (dextrose), fructose and galactose, are soluble in water. Glucose is the principal form in which carbohydrate is present in the blood, and it is a readily available source of energy.

Disaccharides or double sugars also are water-soluble. This group includes sucrose (cane sugar), lactose (milk sugar) and maltose (malt sugar).

Polysaccharides are multiple sugars, such as plant starch, cellulose, dextrin and glycogen (animal starch). They are insoluble in water and are a common form of storage for carbohydrate.

Lipids also are organic compounds, composed of carbon, hydrogen and oxygen, but they are generally insoluble in water. They consist of a group of substances that are classified together because of their solubility in fat solvents such as benzene or ether. For convenience, lipids may be divided into 3 main groups; simple, compound and steroid.

Simple lipids include the true fats, which consist of fatty acids and glycerol. They also are known as *triglycerides* because each molecule of glycerol is combined with 3 molecules of fatty acid. Fats provide a concentrated source of energy, protection from mechanical injury, and serve as heat insulators.

Compound lipids include the phospholipids and

glycolipids; they are lipids combined with other substances. For example, lecithin (a phospholipid) is a combination of phosphoric acid, choline, glycerol and fatty acids. A double layer of phospholipids associated with protein makes up the limiting membrane of the cell. Thus phospholipids play a vital role in cell permeability. They are so essential that a starving person dies before appreciable quantities are lost.

Steroids include the sterols, bile acids, vitamin D and various hormones. Cholesterol is a well known representative of this group; it is widely distributed in the body and serves as the precursor of many important steroids.

Proteins are organic compounds composed of carbon, hydrogen, oxygen and nitrogen; some contain sulfur and phosphorus. They are large molecules consisting of enormous numbers of amino acids, and they are in a constant state of change.

The proteins in the plasma, the liver and the cells of the tissues form a large protein pool, in which the proteins of all parts of the body are in dynamic equilibrium. An amino acid that is a component part of a plasma protein today may be in a liver cell tomorrow, in a muscle fiber the next day, in an enzyme on the fourth day, and so on. The circulating plasma is a means of exchange between various tissues.

Proteins are important in the growth or formation of new protoplasm, the repair of tissues and in resistance to infection; they are needed in extra amounts when one is recovering from an operation, during pregnancy and during lactation. If the protein in the diet is inadequate for the needs of the body, the condition of hypoproteinemia or low concentration of protein in the plasma exists.

The proteins that enable one to maintain a good state of nutrition at any age are called *complete* proteins. Most animal proteins are complete proteins. This means that they contain all of the *essential* amino acids that the body cannot synthesize. Most plant proteins lack one or more of the essential amino acids.

There are 2 main classes of protein: simple and conjugated. *Simple proteins* are those that consist only of amino acids; albumin and globulin are examples of simple proteins. *Conjugated proteins* are those that consist of other substances in addition to amino acids. For example, nucleoproteins in the chromosomes consist of protein linked with nucleic acid.

VITAMINS

Vitamins, which are organic compounds present in many natural foodstuffs, are required for growth and other processes. They produce no energy but play a role in transformations of energy and in the regulation of metabolism.

Most of the vitamins now known take part in enzymatic or oxidative reactions. Some act as catalysts, which means that they speed up reactions and enable them to take place at body temperature; in the absence of catalysts, the same reactions would require a much longer time and a much higher temperature. Some vitamins are precursors (forerunners) of enzymes. Some work as assistants to enzymes. Vitamins aim at various targets; some act on epithelial tissues, some on bone, and some aid the absorption of foods from the lumen of the intestine.

We receive most of the vitamins needed by the body from the food we eat. A few vitamins are synthesized by bacterial action in the large intestine and are absorbed into the blood.

If the supply of vitamins is insufficient, difficulties arise. There are several causes of vitamin deficiency, three of which will be mentioned: (1) a low intake, as a result of poor eating habits, loss of appetite or the use of special diets in the treatment of obesity, hypertension, allergy, peptic ulcer or as a result of a limited diet after an operation; (2) failure of absorption, as in prolonged vomiting or diarrhea, the absence of bile salts from the intestine (which affects the absorption of the fat-soluble vitamins) or the use of mineral oil as a laxative or in low-calorie salad dressings (mineral oil dissolves the fat-soluble vitamins and carries them out with it in the feces); (3) in liver disease, in which there may be a failure to convert precursors to active vitamins or a failure to store the vitamins.

Fat-soluble vitamins

The best known fat-soluble vitamins are A, D, E and K. They are soluble only in fats and are absorbed with them.

Vitamin A is formed in the body from precursors that are especially abundant in carrots, spinach, butter, cheese and egg yolk. It is stored in the liver of vertebrates; thus fresh liver and fish oils (e.g., cod-liver oil) are excellent natural sources of this vitamin. Vitamin A is concerned with the growth of bones and teeth, with the integrity of epithelial tissues, and with the formation of visual purple which is essential for vision in dim light.

Deficiency. The skin becomes dry and rough, there are degenerative changes in the epithelial layer of mucous membranes, and vision is poor in dim light (night blindness). In children, there is interference with normal growth and development.

Vitamin D is formed by irradiation of 7-dehydro-cholesterol in the skin with ultraviolet light. It is present in egg yolk and is particularly abundant in cod-liver oil. Vitamin D is required for the absorption of calcium and phosphorus from the intestine and for their utilization in the development of bones.

Deficiency. In children, a severe deficiency of vitamin D causes *rickets*. Bones are misshapen, soft and fragile; there is delayed closure of the fontanels and retarded eruption of teeth.

Vitamin E is found in wheat-germ oil, in egg yolk, and in the green leaves of many vegetables. It is essential for reproduction in certain lower animals, but the precise function of vitamin E in the human body is not yet known.

Vitamin K is found in liver, cabbage, spinach and kale. However, the synthesis of this vitamin by bacteria in the large intestine is of fundamental importance, and newborn infants are potential candidates for hemorrhage until their bacterial flora is established in the bowel. Vitamin K is required by the liver in the formation of prothrombin.

Deficiency. There is a reduction in the blood prothrombin level and a tendency to hemorrhage.

Water-soluble vitamins

The water-soluble vitamins are those of the B complex and vitamin C. These vitamins are soluble only in water and are absorbed with it.

The vitamin B complex consists of several distinct chemical substances. Some of these are synthesized by bacteria in the large intestine, but most of them occur naturally in such foods as liver, pork, egg yolk, yeast, whole-grain cereals, soybeans, nuts and milk products. Four important components of the B complex are thiamine, riboflavin, niacin and B_{12}.

Thiamine plays an important role in carbohydrate metabolism as it makes possible the oxidation of pyruvic acid. In cases of moderate deficiency, pyruvic and lactic acid accumulate in the blood, causing loss of appetite, irritability, muscle tenderness and fatigue. Severe deficiency results in beriberi which is characterized by peripheral neuritis, muscle incoordination, loss of appetite and loss of weight.

Riboflavin also is important in carbohydrate metabolism and is necessary for tissue repair. Symptoms of deficiency include glossitis, cracking and splitting of the lips at the corners of the mouth, and seborrheic dermatitis.

Niacin is important in the absorption and the metabolism of carbohydrate. Deficiency results in pellagra which is characterized by the 3 "d's": dementia, dermatitis and diarrhea; in severe cases it may be fatal.

Vitamin B_{12} is the erythropoietic factor described on page 302. A deficiency of this vitamin results in anemia.

Vitamin C (ascorbic acid) is found in citrus fruits and in many vegetables, such as spinach, cabbage, broccoli and potatoes. This vitamin is essential for the maintenance of normal intercellular substances throughout the body, which includes the formation of collagen, intercellular cement material, bone matrix and tooth dentin. Vitamin C also aids in the absorption of iron.

Deficiency. Lack of vitamin C causes scurvy. There is an increase in the susceptibility to infection, poor wound healing and retardation of growth. The gums are swollen and tender; there

Fig. 16-1. A diagram of the digestive system, showing the digestive tube, or alimentary canal, and accessory organs. The liver and gallbladder have been turned upward and to the right.

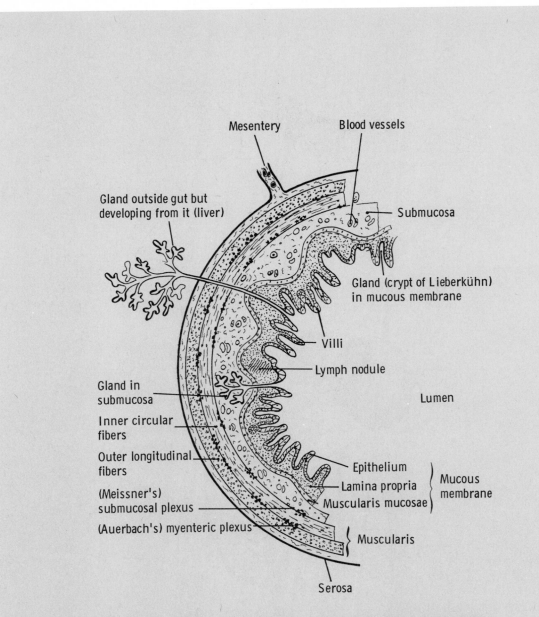

Fig. 16-2. The general cross-sectional plan of the gastrointestinal tract, showing glands in 3 locations: in the mucous membrane, in the submucosa, and outside the tract. (Modified from Ham, A. W.: Histology, ed. 2, Philadelphia, Lippincott)

is pain, tenderness, and swelling of thighs and legs.

THE DIGESTIVE TUBE

The digestive tube, or *alimentary canal,* is a long muscular tube lined with mucous membrane, extending from the lips to the anus. The total length is about 29 or 30 feet, of which 1½ feet are above the diaphragm. Each part of the tube is called by a different name—for example, mouth, pharynx, esophagus, stomach, small intestine and large intestine. Each part has its own special anatomic characteristics and performs its own particular functions, yet each makes an essential contribution to the process of making food available to the cells of the body. The functions of the digestive tube are enhanced by its accessory organs: the tongue, teeth, salivary glands, liver and pancreas (Fig. 16-1).

Structural layers

There are 4 main layers in the wall of the digestive tube: (1) mucous membrane lining, (2) submucous layer, (3) muscular layer, and (4) an external layer. The general plan is shown in Figure 16-2. Variations in the structural layers will be described as they occur throughout the tube.

The **mucous membrane** or **mucosa** is the innermost layer of the digestive tube. Its epithelium varies in structure according to the work being done in the part of the tube that it lines. For example, it is designed for protection (stratified squamous) in the mouth, the pharynx, the esophagus, and the anal region, but from the stomach to the anus it is designed for processes of secretion and absorption (columnar). In addition to 2 thin layers of smooth muscle tissue (the muscularis mucosae), the mucosa contains many glands, blood vessels and lymphatics.

The **submucous layer** serves to connect the mucous membrane with the main muscular layer. It is composed of loose connective tissue and contains networks of blood vessels. Nerve fibers and ganglion cells are interwoven to form a submucous plexus (Meissner's plexus) in which are found

components of both divisions of the autonomic system.

The **muscular layer** (muscularis externa) is the third main layer of the wall of the digestive tube. It is composed of 2 very substantial sheets of smooth muscle, an inner circular and an outer longitudinal sheet. The function of this muscular layer is to mix the contents of the lumen with the digestive juices and to move them onward through the alimentary canal.

A plexus of nerve fibers and ganglion cells called the *myenteric* or *Auerbach's plexus* is found between the 2 sheets of smooth muscle. This plexus resembles the submucous plexus in that both divisions of the autonomic system are represented in it.

The **external layer** of the tube is *fibrous* in nature above the diaphragm and *serous* below the diaphragm. The serous membrane below the diaphragm is known as the visceral peritoneum.

The peritoneum

Although the peritoneum is not limited to the digestive tube, it seems appropriate to discuss it at the present time. The peritoneum is the largest serous membrane in the body, and it consists of a double-walled sac. The outer layer of this sac, called the *parietal peritoneum,* lines the abdominal cavity and then is reflected (turned or bent back) over the viscera, forming the *visceral peritoneum* or inner layer of the sac. The space between these layers is called the *peritoneal cavity.* However, this is merely a potential space, and it contains nothing but a small amount of fluid which permits the viscera to glide freely on each other or against the wall of the abdominal cavity with a minimum of friction.

The *mesentery* is a fan-shaped extension of the peritoneum which encircles the intestine and serves to attach it to the posterior abdominal wall. Other folds of peritoneum that serve to connect organs within the abdominal cavity are called ligaments. The *greater omentum* is a special ligament, arranged like an apron of fat, that connects the stomach and the transverse colon. A second special ligament is the *lesser omentum,* which

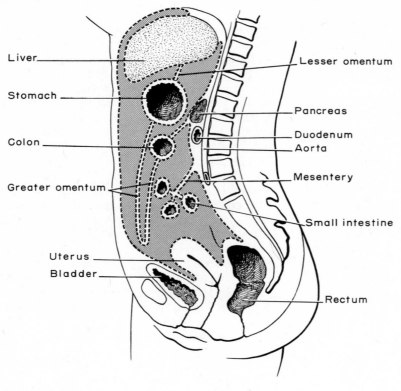

Fig. 16-3. Reflections of the peritoneum as seen in sagittal section.

connects the stomach and the first part of the duodenum with the liver. The complicated reflections of the peritoneum, as seen in sagittal section, are illustrated in Figure 16-3.

Inflammation of the peritoneum is called *peritonitis*. It is accompanied by rigidity of the muscles of the abdominal wall, tenderness over the abdomen, paralysis of the intestine, vomiting and pain.

The mouth

The mouth or *buccal cavity* is the first portion of the digestive tube. The vestibule of the mouth is the narrow, slitlike space bounded by the lips and the cheeks externally, and by the teeth internally. The mouth cavity proper is bounded laterally and in front by the teeth, above by the

hard and the soft palates, and below by the tongue (Fig. 16-4).

The lips are composed of connective tissue and striated muscle (orbicularis oris). The outer surface is covered with skin, and the inner surface is lined with mucous membrane. The free margins are covered with modified skin, the derma of which contains so many capillaries that it gives a red color to the lips.

The cheeks also consist primarily of striated muscle (buccinator). They are covered with skin and lined with mucous membrane. The submucous area contains elastic fibers and numerous blood vessels.

The roof of the mouth is formed by the bony hard palate anteriorly, and by the soft palate posteriorly. As described in Chapter 3, the hard palate is formed by the palatine processes of the

Fig. 16-4. The palate or roof of the mouth, teeth, tongue and palatine tonsils are shown. The hard palate, formed by the maxillary and the palatine bones, separates the mouth from the nasal cavity. The soft palate is composed of muscular tissue. The glossopalatine and the pharyngopalatine arches are described on page 419. The palatine tonsils lie between the palatine arches. The gingivae are the gums; they cover the alveolar processes of the maxillae and the mandible and surround the necks of the teeth. (Redrawn after Spalteholz) (Shapiro, H. H.: Maxillofacial Anatomy, Philadelphia, Lippincott)

maxillae and the horizontal plates of the palatine bones. The movable soft palate is attached to the posterior margin of the hard palate. It is drawn upward during the act of swallowing; this closes the nasopharynx and prevents food from entering the nasal cavities. The lower or posterior margin is free and forms an arch from one side of the pharynx to the other, with the uvula projecting from the middle of the arch, as shown in Figure 16-4. The soft palate is composed of interlacing striated muscle fibers, covered with mucous membrane. The passage from the mouth to the pharynx is called the *fauces*.

The tongue, an accessory organ, is composed of interlacing bundles of striated muscle fibers, arranged in longitudinal, vertical and horizontal planes, with fibroelastic connective tissue between. The mucous membrane on the undersur-

face is thin; it forms a fold, called the *frenulum linguae,* that extends from near the tip of the tongue to the floor of the mouth. Tonguetie (ankyloglossia) refers to the condition in which the frenulum linguae is abnormally short and prevents free movement of the tongue. This may interfere with sucking during infancy and with speech later.

The mucous membrane on the dorsum of the tongue is thick, and that over the anterior two thirds (or body of the tongue) is studded with *papillae,* as shown in Figure 16-5. The papillae are of 3 types: filiform, fungiform and vallate.

The filiform ("threadlike") *papillae* are tall narrow structures arranged in parallel rows across the tongue. In certain animals, such as the cat, these papillae are so horny that the tongue feels like sandpaper. In man, the filiform papillae are

EPIGLOTTIS

ROOT OF TONGUE

LINGUAL LYMPHATIC FOLLICLES

PHARYNGOPALATINE ARCH

PALATINE TONSIL (CUT)

GLOSSOPALATINE ARCH

VALLATE PAPILLAE

BODY OF TONGUE

DORSAL SURFACE OF TONGUE

MEDIAN LINGUAL SULCUS

FUNGIFORM PAPILLAE

FILIFORM PAPILLAE

LATERAL LINGUAL MARGIN

APEX OF TONGUE

Fig. 16-5. The surface of the human tongue as viewed from above. The palatine arches and tonsils have been cut through transversely. (Redrawn after Spalteholz) (Shapiro, H. H.: Maxillofacial Anatomy, Philadelphia, Lippincott)

not very highly developed, but they do permit one to lick substances (such as ice cream) in a satisfactory manner. These papillae also contain nerve endings for tactile sense (touch).

The fungiform papillae are scattered among the filiform papillae, but they are not nearly as numerous. The name "fungiform" is derived from their resemblance to little fungi, as they have narrow bases and expanded tops like mushrooms. Most of these papillae contain taste buds (p. 271).

The vallate papillae are arranged in a V-shaped line between the body and the root of the tongue (i.e., the posterior third); they have been described as resembling castles surrounded by moats or trenches. All of these papillae contain taste buds.

Underlying the mucous membrane at the root of the tongue (the pharyngeal portion) are collections of lymphatic tissue, which compose the lingual tonsil (p. 420).

The tongue is important in mastication (chewing), deglutition (swallowing) and speaking. The hypoglossal nerve is motor to the muscles of the tongue. The trigeminal nerve supplies receptors of touch, temperature and pain in the tongue. The facial and the glossopharyngeal nerves carry impulses from the taste buds, which give rise to taste sensations.

One of the first requests that the physician of old used to make was "Stick out your tongue." If the tongue was coated, the physician knew that all was not well with the alimentary tract. The appearance of the tongue is of diagnostic importance in such diseases as scarlet fever and pernicious anemia. Inflammation of the tongue is called *glossitis*.

The teeth also are accessory organs. Each person has 2 sets of teeth during his lifetime. The first set is called the *milk* or *deciduous* teeth. These begin to erupt (called *dentition*) at about

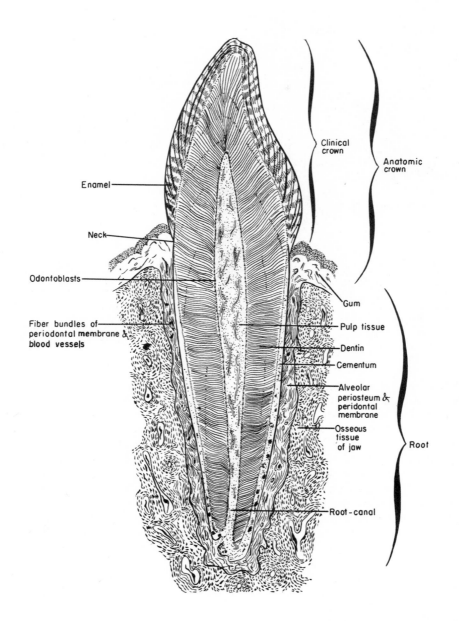

Fig. 16-6. Longitudinal section of canine tooth in situ. Semidiagrammatic.

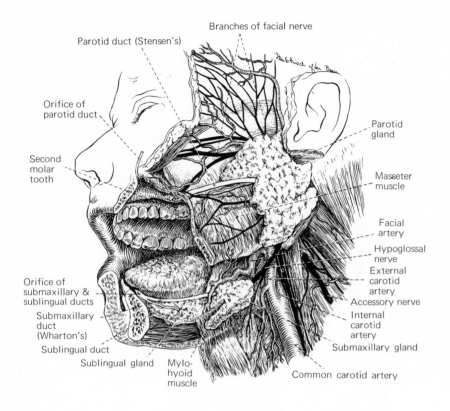

Fig. 16-7. Salivary glands, their ducts and orifices. Branches of the facial, the accessory and the hypoglossal nerves are shown. Common, external and internal carotid arteries are shown. (After Bonamy and Broca)

6 months of age, and one appears about each month thereafter until all 20 have erupted. The deciduous teeth are lost between 6 and 13 years of age.

The second set of teeth is called the *permanent set*. These appear between 6 and 17 years (except the wisdom teeth). There are 32 in the permanent set. They are named from their shape or function. Beginning at the midline and progressing laterally, in each jaw, the teeth are called: central incisor, lateral incisor, canine, 2 premolars or bicuspids, and 3 molars.

The incisors are shaped like chisels and serve to cut food.

The canines are shaped like dogs' teeth; they tear and shred food.

The premolars crush and tear food.

The molars crush and grind food.

The last molar tooth in each jaw is called a *wisdom tooth;* the 4 wisdom teeth may erupt between 17 and 25 years of age or may never erupt at all. The teeth are shown in Figure 16-4.

The 2 chief parts of a tooth are the crown and the root.

The crown or portion beyond the gum is covered with enamel, which is the hardest substance in the body. The bulk of the tooth is composed of dentin, which is calcified connective tissue. The central cavity in the shell of dentin is called the *pulp cavity* and is filled with soft, pulpy connective tissue. Blood vessels and nerves (branches of the trigeminal) enter the tooth by way of the root canal. The parts of a tooth are shown in Figure 16-6.

The roots of the teeth fit into sockets in the alveolar processes, which are projections from the mandible and the maxillae. The roots are covered with cementum and are bound to the bone of

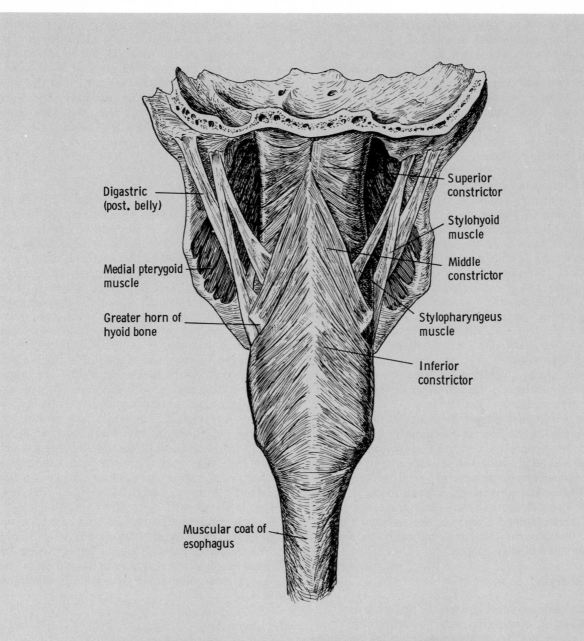

Fig. 16-8. Posterior view of the pharynx, showing the constrictor muscles.
(Thorek, Philip: Anatomy in Surgery, Philadelphia, Lippincott)

the sockets by a strong connective tissue membrane, the *periodontal* membrane.

The teeth are laid down in the embryo, so the diet of the mother should contain an abundance of calcium and vitamin D during pregnancy to insure proper development of teeth. The diet of the young child influences the permanent set of teeth, so it, too, should include abundant calcium and vitamin D in order to prevent dental caries.

The Salivary Glands. There are 3 pairs of salivary glands which pour their secretions into the mouth: parotid, submandibular and sublingual. These accessory organs manufacture saliva.

The parotid glands lie below and in front of the ears, between the mastoid processes of the temporal bones and the rami of the mandible. The location is shown in Figures 16-1 and 16-7. The duct (Stensen's) passes through the buccinator muscle and pours its secretion into the vestibule of the mouth opposite the upper second molar tooth, on each side. Inflammation of the parotid glands is called *parotitis* or mumps.

The submandibular (submaxillary) *glands* lie in contact with the inner surface of the mandible and the ducts (Wharton's) open into the floor of the mouth beside the frenulum linguae, behind the lower incisors (Fig. 16-7).

The sublingual glands lie beneath the mucous membrane of the floor of the mouth and open by means of several ducts in the floor of the mouth.

The secretions from the salivary glands may be thin and watery or thick and viscid, according to the type of stimulus which arouses them.

Branches of the external carotid arteries bring an abundant blood supply to the salivary glands. Both divisions of the autonomic nervous system supply the salivary glands.

The pharynx

The various subdivisions of the pharynx are described in connection with the respiratory system (pp. 419-420). At this time we shall mention only the muscular layers that are concerned with the act of swallowing.

Beneath the mucous membrane and fibrous tissue of the pharynx there is a thick layer of skeletal muscle. As shown in Figure 16-8, this muscular layer forms the superior, middle and inferior *constrictor muscles* of the pharynx. When a bolus of food enters the pharynx it is grasped by the constrictor muscles and moved onward into the esophagus. Another series of muscles raise the pharynx during swallowing, draw the sides laterally to increase its width, and elevate the soft palate to close the nasopharynx.

The esophagus

The esophagus (gullet) is a muscular, collapsible tube, about 10 inches long, which lies behind the trachea. It begins at the end of the laryngopharynx and passes through the mediastinum and the diaphragm to end in the stomach.

The muscular walls of the upper third of the esophagus contain striated muscle which is gradually replaced by smooth muscle as the tube descends toward the stomach. However, the aforementioned striated muscle is not under conscious control; it is supplied by autonomic fibers which travel in the vagus nerve and supply the smooth muscle as well. At the lower end of the esophagus, just above its junction with the stomach, the circular layer of the muscular wall is slightly hypertrophied. Although this is not a true anatomical sphincter, it functions as such by remaining tonically constricted until the third stage of swallowing (p. 484); thus the term *gastroesophageal constrictor* is more meaningful than "cardiac sphincter." A cross sectional view of the esophagus is shown in Figure 16-9.

As described in Chapter 13, the veins of the esophagus communicate with gastric veins of the portal system. In cases of portal hypertension (p. 377) the esophageal veins may become dilated and tortuous; such dilatations are called *esophageal varices*.

The stomach

Just below the diaphragm, the alimentary canal expands to form the stomach, a pouchlike structure that serves as a reservoir for food during the early stages of digestion. It lies in the upper part

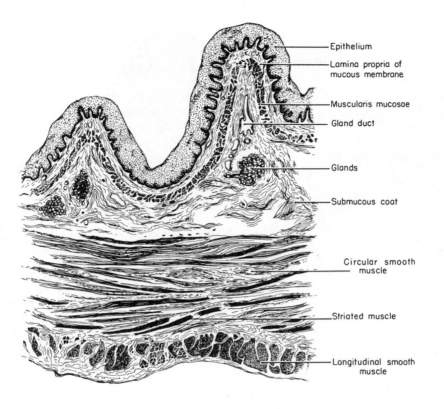

Epithelium

Lamina propria of mucous membrane

Muscularis mucosae

Gland duct

Glands

Submucous coat

Circular smooth muscle

Striated muscle

Longitudinal smooth muscle

Fig. 16-9. Cross section of esophagus, through middle third. × 18.

of the abdominal cavity, in the epigastric and left hypochondriac regions (Fig. 16-24).

Divisions. The esophagus opens into the upper end of the stomach through the *cardiac orifice,* an opening so named because of its proximity to the heart. The part of the stomach that lies above and to the left of the cardiac orifice is called the *fundus,* while the central portion is known as the *body.* The pyloric portion of the stomach is that beyond the body; it communicates with the small intestine by way of the *pylorus,* an opening that is surrounded by a muscular ring called the *pyloric sphincter.* Hypertrophic *pyloric stenosis* occurs most frequently in young male infants; in this condition the pyloric sphincter is in a state of persistent spasm, and hypertrophy of the sphinc-

ter results. The condition must be treated surgically. The medial border of the stomach is called the *lesser curvature,* and the lateral border the *greater curvature.* Figure 16-10 illustrates the divisions of the stomach.

Structural Variations. When the stomach is empty, the mucous membrane lining is thrown into folds called *rugae.* These folds gradually smooth out and disappear as the stomach becomes distended with food.

The epithelium of the mucous membrane consists of a single layer of columnar cells; this layer not only covers the surface of the membrane but also extends down into numerous little "wells" called the gastric pits. Opening into the bottom of each pit are 2 or 3 simple tubular glands; these

Duodenum

Fundus

Cardiac orifice

Cardiac portion

Pyloric valve

Pylorus

Pyloric antrum

Pyloric portion

Lesser curvature

Greater curvature

Fig. 16-10. Interior of the stomach, showing rugae. (Adapted from Lewis, W. H.: Gray's Anatomy of the Human Body, ed. 26, Philadelphia, Lea & Febiger)

Surface epithelium

Openings of gastric glands into gastric pits

Lymphatic nodule

Gastric glands

Mucosa

Submucosa

Muscularis mucosae

Smooth muscle layers

Serosa

Fig. 16-11. All the layers of the stomach. × 17. (After Braus) gastric glands produce the *gastric juice,* a secretion that is delivered into the pits, which, in turn, conduct it to the surface of the mucosa. Gastric juice contains hydrochloric acid, digestive enzymes, and mucus. The hydrochloric acid is produced by *parietal cells,* located near the opening of a gland into its gastric pit. The enzymes are produced by *zymogenic* or *chief cells,* located in the base or body of a gland. Protective mucus is produced by cells in the neck of each gland and by cells in the surface epithelium. The function of gastric juice is described on page 486. A special component of gastric juice, the "intrinsic factor," is described on page 302 in relation to the absorption of vitamin B_{12} and the maturation of red blood cells.

The main muscular layer of the stomach varies from the general structural plan in that it is composed of 3 layers of smooth muscle: an inner oblique, a middle circular and an outer longitudinal layer. The ringlike pyloric sphincter is formed by a thickening of the circular muscle fibers.

The outer serous layer of the stomach is composed of visceral peritoneum. The various layers of the wall of the stomach are illustrated in Figure 16-11.

The extensibility of the smooth muscle of the stomach is well known to all of us. We can eat a fairly large quantity of food at one meal, and the stomach stretches to accommodate it without an increase in pressure. The difference in size before and after a meal is illustrated in Figure 16-12.

The blood supply is derived from branches of the celiac artery; drainage is by way of gastric veins. Lymphatic vessels are abundant. Both divisions of the autonomic system supply efferent fibers to the stomach, and visceral afferent fibers conduct impulses from the stomach to the CNS.

The small intestine

The greatest amount of digestion and absorption take place in the small intestine, a convoluted (coiled) tube extending from the stomach to the large intestine. It is approximately 23 feet in length and 1 inch in diameter. The fan-shaped

Fig. 16-12. Stomach (top) before and (bottom) after a meal.

mesentery attaches the coiled intestinal loops to the posterior abdominal wall.

Divisions. The small intestine consists of 3 divisions: duodenum, jejunum and ileum.

The duodenum, about 10 inches in length, is the shortest, widest and most firmly attached portion of the small intestine. It is arranged in the shape of a letter "C," and the head of the pancreas lies in the concavity which it forms (Fig. 16-23).

The jejunum forms the next two fifths of the small intestine and extends from the duodenum to the ileum.

The ileum forms the remainder of the small intestine; it terminates by joining the large intestine at right angles. A muscular sphincter (ileocecal valve) guards this "exit gate."

Structural Variations. The mucous membrane of the small intestine differs markedly from that in the remainder of the alimentary canal. To increase the epithelial surface, and thus provide a large area for absorption of nutrients, the mucosa is arranged in circular folds and is studded with villi.

Fig. 16-13. Circular folds of jejunum. (Spalteholz, W.:
Hand Atlas of Human Anatomy, Philadelphia, Lippincott)

The circular folds (plicae circulares) are folds of mucosa that project into the lumen of the intestine, forming ridges that somewhat resemble an old-fashioned washboard (Fig. 16-13).

The villi are tiny, fingerlike projections of mucous membrane that are barely visible to the naked eye. Much like a forest of trees on a series of hills and dales, the villi are crowded so close together over the mucosal surface that they give it the appearance of velvet. The villi are highly specialized for the absorption of nutrients, and each contains a blood capillary and a lymph vessel (lacteal), Figure 16-14 shows villi enlarged many times.

Most of the epithelial cells lining the small intestine are tall, columnar cells that have numerous microvilli on their free border; the primary function of these cells is absorption, and the microvilli greatly increase the surface area for such activity. Distributed among these cells are true goblet cells (p. 38), which secrete mucus.

There is an abundance of lymphatic tissue just below the epithelium of the mucosa. This may appear as solitary nodules or in groups of nodules called *Peyer's patches*. The *intestinal glands* (crypts of Lieberkühn) also are found in this area. They open into the depressions between villi, and their function is to secrete enzymes which aid in the digestion of food.

The duodenal glands (Brunner's glands) are located in the submucosal layer; they are largest and most numerous near the pylorus. Their function is to secrete protective mucus.

The small intestine has an excellent blood supply provided by branches of the duodenal and the superior mesenteric arteries. After passing through capillary networks, the blood drains into veins that eventually enter the portal system. Lymphatic vessels begin as capillaries (lacteals) in the villi; their collecting vessels enter mesenteric lymph nodes where the lymph is filtered before it enters the thoracic duct. Visceral afferent nerves conduct impulses from the intestine to the CNS, and efferent fibers from both divisions

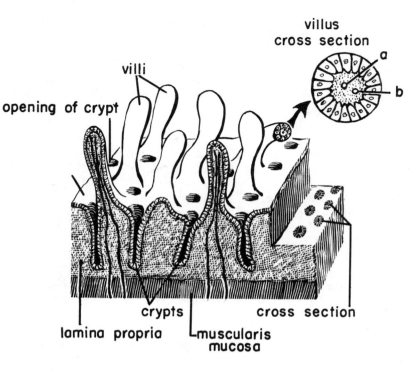

Fig. 16-14. Three-dimensional drawing of the mucous membrane of the small intestine. The villi are projections of epithelium containing cores of lamina propria. The glands (crypts of Lieberkühn) are located in the lamina propria. Vascular and lymphatic capillaries extend into the villi (a and b in the enlarged drawing shown by the arrow). (Modified from Ham, A. W.: Histology, ed. 2, Philadelphia, Lippincott)

of the autonomic system are supplied to the smooth muscle of the intestinal wall.

Intestinal obstruction may be due to: (1) hernial-sac incarceration or retention; (2) foreign bodies, especially at the ileocecal junction; (3) stricture from an ulcer, peritonitis or tumor; (4) volvulus, a knotting or twisting of the intestine; (5) intussusception or telescoping of one part of the intestine into another portion of it; and (6) bands that arise from adhesions. Any intestinal obstruction is exceedingly serious, since it upsets the water and salt balance of the body and cuts off the blood supply to a part of the intestinal wall.

Paralytic ileus is a condition in which the bowel is paralyzed. It may occur after any abdominal or pelvic operation and has the same effect as other types of obstruction. In some cases the condition is associated with a low concentration of potassium in the body fluids.

Ileostomy refers to the surgical formation of a fistula or an artificial anus through the abdominal wall into the ileum. This may be necessary for those who suffer from cancer of the colon or the rectum.

The large intestine

The large intestine is about 4½ to 5 feet in length and 2½ inches in diameter as it extends from the end of the ileum to the anus. It is larger in caliber than the small intestine and has a sacculated appearance.

Divisions. The large intestine may be divided into the cecum, the colon, the rectum and the anal canal (Fig. 16-1).

The cecum is a blind pouch about 2 to 3 inches long which hangs down at the junction of the ileum and the colon. The ileocecal valve lies at the upper border of the cecum and prevents the return of feces from the cecum into the small intestine. The vermiform appendix arises from the cecum about an inch below the ileocecal valve. It is a twisted and coiled tube whose walls contain all the layers of the intestine. Inflammation of the appendix, called *appendicitis,* is quite common. Since the appendix is a blind tube, wastes accumulate which cannot be moved by peristaltic contractions. Muscular rigidity, pain and vomiting are common. The chief danger is that of rupture, followed by peritonitis. If the appendix becomes inflamed, it should be removed (appendectomy) before it ruptures.

The function of the appendix has not yet been determined. However, recent studies carried out on the appendix of the rabbit suggest that this organ, like the thymus (p. 387), may play a role in the development of immunological competence.

The colon is subdivided into ascending, transverse, descending and sigmoid portions.

The ascending colon extends from the cecum to the undersurface of the liver, where it turns left to form the right or hepatic flexure.

The transverse colon crosses the upper part of the abdominal cavity from right to left and turns downward to form the left or splenic flexure.

The descending colon extends from the splenic flexure to the brim of the pelvis, where it turns toward the midline to become the sigmoid colon.

The sigmoid (pelvic) colon extends from the descending colon at the level of the pelvic brim to the rectum. It descends along the left pelvic wall, then passes transversely across the pelvis from left to right, to the right pelvic wall, where it bends upon itself, passes again to the left to join the rectum in the midline, at the level of the 2nd or 3rd sacral vertebra. It is evident that the sigmoid colon is really "S-shaped" as the name implies. *Colostomy* refers to the surgical formation of an artificial anus or opening from the colon to the exterior.

The rectum extends from the sigmoid colon to the anal canal and is about 5 or 6 inches in length. It descends along the hollow of the sacrum and the coccyx to the tip of the coccyx. Cancer may occur in any part of the colon, but it is more commonly found in the rectum.

The anal canal is the terminal portion of the large intestine. It extends from the rectum to the anus (opening to the exterior) and is about 1 to 1½ inches in length. The anal canal passes between the two medial borders of the levator ani muscles, which compress it to a mere slit. Powerful sphincter muscles guard the anal opening; these muscles are described below.

Structural Variations. The mucous membrane of the large intestine differs from that of the small intestine. There are no villi, and the epithelium contains large numbers of goblet cells. The glands (crypts of Lieberkühn) secrete mucus but no digestive enzymes. The mucosa of the upper end of the anal canal differs from that of other parts of the large intestine in that it is arranged in vertical folds, called *rectal columns* (Fig. 16-15). Beneath these columns are hemorrhoidal (rectal) veins which may become tortuous and dilated; this condition is referred to as *hemorrhoids.*

The main muscular layer differs from that in other parts of the alimentary canal in that the longitudinal muscle fibers are concentrated into 3 flat bands, called the *taeniae coli* (Fig. 16-16). These bands are not as long as the large intestine; consequently, the latter is gathered (shirred) into sacculations or pouchlike structures known as *haustra,* which are characteristic of this portion of the digestive tube.

In the anal canal, the circular muscle fibers are greatly thickened, forming the *internal anal sphincter;* this ring of smooth muscle helps to guard the exit of the alimentary canal, but it is not under control of the will. The *external anal sphincter* is a cylinder of skeletal muscle that also helps to close the anus, but it is under conscious control.

The visceral peritoneum forms little pouches containing fat. These pouches hang from the large intestine and are called appendices epiploicae. A section of the wall of the large intestine is shown in Figure 16-17.

The blood supply to the wall of the large intestine is derived from branches of the superior and the inferior mesenteric arteries. Blood leaving the capillaries in the large intestine enters the portal system. Lymphatic drainage is abundant.

Visceral afferent fibers conduct impulses from the large intestine to the CNS. Both divisions of the autonomic system supply efferent fibers to the wall of the large intestine.

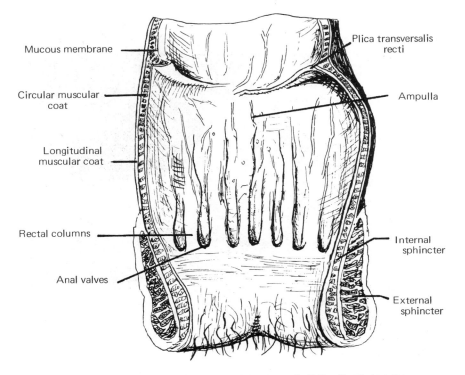

Mucous membrane

Circular muscular coat

Longitudinal muscular coat

Rectal columns

Anal valves

Plica transversalis recti

Ampulla

Internal sphincter

External sphincter

Fig. 16-15. Interior of rectum and anal canal. (After Spalteholz)

Fig. 16-16. Portion of descending colon, showing haustra, taeniae coli and epiploic appendages.

Taenia coli

Haustra

Appendix epiploica

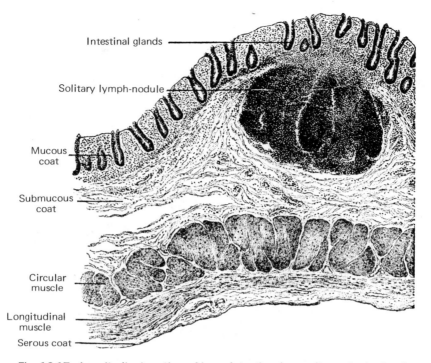

Intestinal glands

Solitary lymph-nodule

Mucous coat

Submucous coat

Circular muscle

Longitudinal muscle

Serous coat

Fig. 16-17. Longitudinal section of large intestine (ascending colon), showing the general arrangement of the coats and a solitary lymph nodule. × 30.

THE ACCESSORY ORGANS

The tongue, the teeth, and the salivary glands are accessory organs related to the mouth; they are described on pages 461–466. The liver, with its biliary apparatus, and the pancreas remain to be discussed.

The liver and biliary apparatus

The liver is the largest organ of the body, weighing about 3 pounds in an adult. It is located in the upper part of the abdominal cavity, under the dome of the diaphragm, in the epigastric and right hypochondriac regions (Fig. 16-24).

Description. The superior or diaphragmatic surface of the liver is relatively smooth and convex (Fig. 16-18). The inferior surface is more concave and shows impressions of the underlying organs, such as the stomach, the kidney, the duodenum and the colon (Fig. 16-19). The liver consists of 4 lobes. The 2 main lobes are the right and the left, separated by the falciform ligament. The right lobe is subdivided into right lobe proper, quadrate and caudate lobes. Each lobe, in turn, is further subdivided into tiny lobules.

The liver is almost completely covered with visceral peritoneum. In certain areas this peritoneum is thrown into folds (ligaments) which help to attach the liver to the diaphragm and to the anterior abdominal wall. Beneath the peritoneum there is a covering of fibroelastic tissue called *Glisson's capsule*, which accompanies the blood vessels into the interior of the liver. The porta is a fissure which extends transversely across the left portion of the right lobe. At the porta there is a

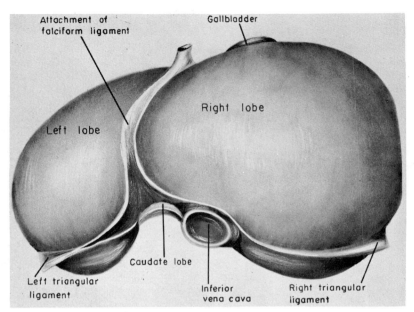

Fig. 16-18. The superior surface of the liver. (From model by His) (Adapted from Lewis, W. H.: Gray's Anatomy of the Human Body, ed. 26, Philadelphia, Lea & Febiger)

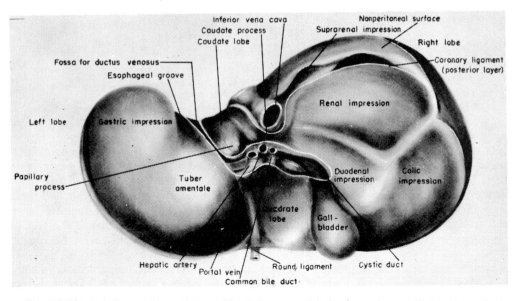

Fig. 16-19. Inferior surface of liver. The tuber omentale is a prominence that rests against the front of the lesser omentum and fits into the lesser curvature of the stomach. (From model by His) (Adapted from Lewis, W. H.: Gray's Anatomy of the Human Body, ed. 26, Philadelphia, Lea & Febiger)

Hepatic artery
Portal vein
Bile-duct

Central (intra-lobular) vein

Fig. 16-20. Section of liver, showing the general arrangement of the lobules, the interlobular and the intralobular vessels. × 120.

"tree trunk" of connective tissue, continuous with the capsule, which extends up into the substance of the liver. The "tree" branches extensively and furnishes internal support for the liver. It also provides pathways by which branches of the portal veins, the hepatic artery, the bile ducts and the lymphatic vessels can reach all parts of the liver.

At the porta, the portal vein and the hepatic artery enter the tree of connective tissue and branch with each branching of the tree. Lymphatic vessels and bile ducts, which have tributaries in every branch of the tree, leave the liver at the porta. The hepatic artery supplies the liver with arterial blood; hence, it supplies a large part of the oxygen used by the liver. The portal vein brings venous blood that has traversed the walls of the intestinal tract and is rich in absorbed food. Blood leaves the liver by way of the hepatic veins, which are not found in the branches of the tree of connective tissue. These veins begin in the central veins of the liver, which unite to form the sublobular and then the hepatic veins, which, in turn, empty into the inferior vena cava as it passes through a groove on the posterior surface of the liver.

A unit of liver substance is called a *liver lobule*. The lobules are separated by a small amount of

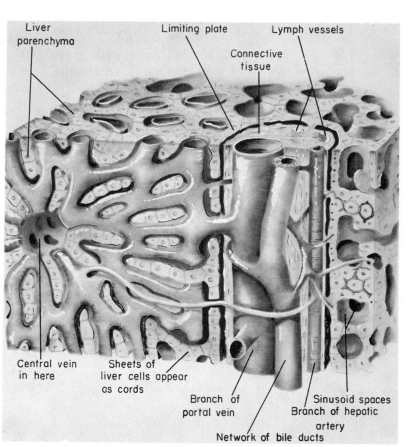

Fig. 16-21. Stereogram of a portion of a liver lobule. (After Hans Elias)

interlobular connective tissue in which are found terminal branches of the hepatic artery, the portal vein and the beginnings of bile ducts and lymphatic vessels (Fig. 16-20).

Structure Related To Function. The liver has over 100 known functions, and most of these activities depend upon the unique structure of the liver, as well as its location in the body. For example, the liver is famous for its production of bile. Thus we find that each liver lobule is so constructed that it meets all of the requirements of a secreting gland (i.e., cells to form the secretion, a blood supply to provide the raw materials, and a system of ducts whereby the secretion is carried away). The versatile hepatic cells also play an important role in "monitoring" all of the food-laden blood that is brought to them by way of the portal system of veins (p. 374); thus the location of the liver has great significance. A summary of liver functions will follow a brief description of important structural features.

The substance of each liver lobule consists of thin plates of hepatic cells that resemble cords as they radiate irregularly from the center of the lobule to its periphery (Fig. 16-21). Between the plates of cells are the *sinusoids*, microscopic channels that receive blood from the hepatic artery and the portal vein. The sinusoids are lined with

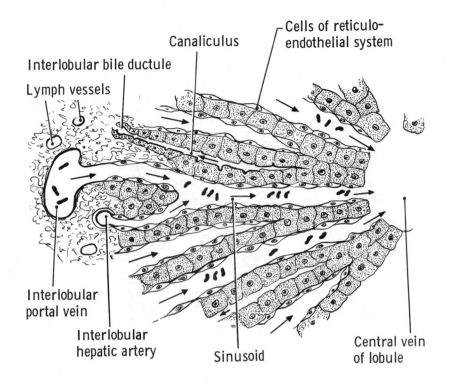

Interlobular bile ductule

Lymph vessels

Canaliculus

Cells of reticulo-endothelial system

Interlobular portal vein

Interlobular hepatic artery

Sinusoid

Central vein of lobule

Fig. 16-22. Drawing (at high-power magnification) to show how blood from the portal vein and the hepatic artery (at left) flows into sinusoids, lined by cells of the reticuloendothelial system that lie between liver cords, and empties into the central vein (right). The way that bile travels in the opposite direction in canaliculi to empty into bile ducts in portal areas also is shown. (Adapted from Ham, A. W.: Histology, ed. 2, Philadelphia, Lippincott)

phagocytic cells of the reticuloendothelial system; these cells (Kupffer's cells) engulf bacteria or other foreign particles that may gain entrance to the blood stream. Sinusoids differ from true capillaries in that they are wider and tend to have leaky walls, inasmuch as their lining cells are irregularly placed. Although the openings in the lining are too small for the passage of red blood cells, the plasma can come into direct contact with hepatic cells. After passing through the sinusoids, blood flows into the central vein of the lobule (Fig. 16-22) on its way to the hepatic vein and thence to the inferior vena cava. One should keep in mind the fact that the millions of sinusoidal spaces in the liver constitute a vast spongework, which can hold large quantities of blood

at any given time; thus the liver must be considered an important reservoir, which can influence the circulating blood volume as well as the cardiac output.

The bile drainage apparatus begins as microscopic, cleft-like spaces (canaliculi) between adjacent rows of hepatic cells within the plates (Fig. 16-22). As bile is produced by the hepatic cells it enters the canaliculi and drains toward the periphery of the lobule; here the canaliculi drain into bile ductules, which drain, in turn, into larger ducts. Ultimately, all bile is collected into one large duct from each lobe. Two main trunks, one from the right lobe and one from the left lobe, unite to form the *hepatic duct*. The hepatic duct descends to the right for a distance of about 1½

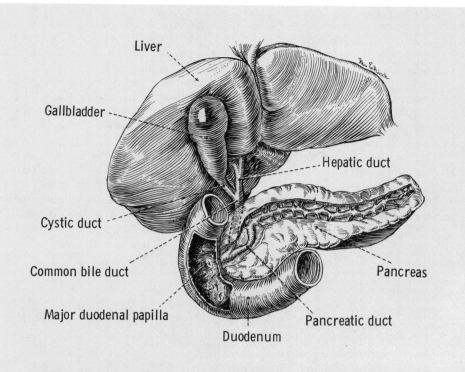

Liver

Gallbladder

Hepatic duct

Cystic duct

Common bile duct

Pancreas

Major duodenal papilla

Pancreatic duct

Duodenum

Fig. 16-23. Liver retracted upward to expose gallbladder. Bile ducts, pancreatic ducts and the entrance of the ducts into the duodenum are shown.

inches, at which point it is joined at an acute angle by the *cystic duct* from the gallbladder to to form the *common bile duct*. The common duct descends behind the head of the pancreas, where it usually joins the pancreatic duct, forming a single dilated tube known as the *ampulla of Vater;* the ampulla opens into the duodenum at the *duodenal papilla* (Fig. 16-23). Muscle tissue associated with the ampulla forms a very weak sphincter (of *Oddi*), but the bile duct (just before it fuses with the pancreatic duct) is guarded by a strong sphincter muscle (of *Boyden*). When this sphincter is closed, bile is prevented from entering the intestine and, as a result, passes by way of the cystic duct to the gallbladder, in which it is stored until needed.

The gallbladder is a musculomembranous sac with an average capacity of 40 to 50 ml. Roughly the size and the shape of a small pear, this organ is located in a fossa on the undersurface of the liver (Fig. 16-23). The gallbladder is lined with mucous membrane that is thrown into tiny folds when the organ is empty. Connective tissue and smooth muscle fibers form the framework of the wall. Except where it is attached to the liver, the external coat of the gallbladder is serous membrane (visceral peritoneum).

The function of the gallbladder is to store and concentrate bile. When food enters the duodenum, a hormone (cholecystokinin) is released by cells in the duodenal mucosa. Carried in the bloodstream to the gallbladder, this hormone stimulates the smooth muscular wall to contract and dispatch bile to the duodenum when it is needed. The importance of bile is discussed under liver function.

Functions of the liver

Of all the organs in the human body, the liver is the largest and the busiest. It performs an amazing variety of functions, many of them essential to life itself. Although the liver possesses a remarkable ability to regenerate and thus replace tissue lost by partial resection (surgical removal), we must stress the fact that severe injury to, or disease of, the liver may be rapidly fatal. A few of the broad areas of liver function are described briefly.

The Production of Bile. Bile, which is considered to be both a secretion and an excretion, is formed continuously by the hepatic cells; the average daily volume of bile is about 600 to 800 ml. It is a greenish-yellow fluid that contains water, bile salts, bilirubin, cholesterol, fatty acids, lecithin and various inorganic salts. Of these constituents, only the *bile salts* (formed from cholesterol) have important functions to perform in the digestive tube. Upon entering the small intestine, the bile salts have two important actions. First, they serve to *emulsify fats* by so lowering the surface tension that large fat globules are broken into tiny particles; this action is valuable, because the fat-splitting enzymes can attack many small units more efficiently than one large unit. Secondly, bile salts help in the *absorption of fatty acids* from the intestinal tract (p. 499).

Bilirubin, or bile pigment, is excreted by the liver; this yellowish substance is one of the major end-products resulting from the decomposition of hemoglobin. As previously described (p. 387), when worn-out red blood cells are removed from the circulating blood their hemoglobin is broken down by cells of the reticuloendothelial system; bilirubin, bound to a plasma protein, travels in the bloodstream to the liver, where it is conjugated (made water-soluble) and excreted into the bile.

Between meals, bile is stored in the gallbladder, in which it becomes very concentrated because of the absorption of water, sodium, chloride and other small electrolytes. The mechanism of emptying of the gallbladder is described on page 479.

Metabolic Functions. The liver plays a vital role in the metabolism of the 3 major food groups. A brief summary of these functions is presented below. Further details can be found in Chapter 17.

Carbohydrate Metabolism. The liver helps to maintain a normal concentration of glucose in the blood. For example, after meals when the glucose level tends to rise, the liver converts glucose to glycogen and stores it until needed; when the blood glucose level falls, glycogen is changed back to glucose and released to the blood. Other simple sugars, galactose and fructose, coming to the liver, are converted to glucose, which then may be stored or used immediately as required by the body. If the blood glucose level continues to fall, the liver has the ability to form glucose from non-carbohydrate sources, such as amino acids and the glycerol portion of fats; this activity is referred to as *gluconeogenesis.*

Lipid (Fat) Metabolism. Although the metabolism of fats probably can take place in most cells of the body, certain activities occur much more rapidly in the liver. For example, fatty acids are an important source of energy, but they must first be broken down to small molecules that can enter the citric acid cycle and be oxidized (p. 507); it is believed that about 60 per cent of all the preliminary breakdown of fatty acids in the body occurs in the liver. Other specific functions are the formation of large quantities of cholesterol and phospholipids, the formation of lipoproteins, and the synthesis of fat from glucose and amino acids.

Protein Metabolism. The liver plays its most vital role in the metabolism of protein. For example, except for the gamma globulins, essentially all of the plasma proteins (p. 307) are formed by the hepatic cells. The liver forms important chemical substances, such as phosphocreatine, from amino acids. It synthesizes certain amino acids, referred to as "nonessential" amino acids because it is not essential that they be in the diet, so long as the liver can provide them. The liver deaminizes amino acids (p. 510) so that they can be used for energy or can be converted to glucose or to fat. It removes ammonia from the blood by converting it to urea for elimination by the kidney.

Miscellaneous Metabolic Functions. The liver is capable of forming vitamin A from precursor substances in certain vegetable foods. It also stores large quantities of vitamin A, vitamin D, and vitamin B_{12}. Iron is stored in the liver in the form of ferritin. Various hormones (e.g., gonadal and adrenocortical) are inactivated in the liver and made more soluble, so that they can be excreted in the bile and in the urine. The liver also is concerned with the detoxification of harmful compounds, such as alcohol and certain drugs, so that these substances can be eliminated in the bile and urine.

Other functions of the liver include the formation of heparin, an anticoagulant, and the phagocytic action of the Kupffer cells, as previously described on page 478.

Tests of liver function

The liver performs such a variety of functions that no one test can give information about the liver as a whole. Only a few of the available tests are mentioned at this time.

Plasma Proteins. As noted in the table on page 311, a decrease in total plasma proteins may be indicative of liver disease.

Bilirubin *(van den Bergh test).* An abnormally high level of bilirubin in the blood may be indicative of liver disease, of obstruction of the biliary tract, or of increased rate of red blood cell destruction. However, if for any reason the rate of bilirubin excretion fails to equal that of production, the level of bilirubin in the blood increases. As the blood level of bilirubin rises (above 2 mg./100 ml.) there is a proportionate accumulation of bilirubin in the tissues, staining them and giving rise to the characteristic yellow pigmentation known as *jaundice* (icterus). Although any of the body tissues may become stained with bilirubin, jaundice makes its earliest appearance in the sclera of the eye and in the skin of the face and upper trunk.

Bromsulphalein (BSP) **Test.** Injected intravenously, BSP dye is eliminated almost exclusively by the liver and is a very sensitive indicator of hepatic disease. Normally, less than 5 per cent of the dye is retained after 45 minutes.

Gallbladder Function. The person ingests a special dye that is excreted by the liver into the bile; the dye-laden bile enters the gallbladder, where it is concentrated. Because the dye is opaque to X-rays, it outlines the gallbladder and makes it visible. The person then is given a fatty meal, and additional X-rays are taken to see whether or not the gallbladder has emptied properly.

The pancreas

The pancreas is both an exocrine and an endocrine gland; it is located in the epigastric and left hypochondriac regions of the abdomen. As illustrated in Figure 1-6, the head of this hammer-shaped organ rests in the concavity of the duodenum, the body extends toward the spleen, and the tail is in contact with the spleen. Fresh pancreas appears white, with a tinge of pinkish color, and the surface has a lobulated appearance.

Closer examination of the pancreas shows that it is composed of lobules in which the *exocrine* secretory units, called *acini*, resemble grapes hanging on stems. Each acinus consists of a single row of epithelial cells arranged around the lumen of a duct; these acinar cells are concerned with the production of *pancreatic juice*, the exocrine secretion of this important gland. As will be described later, the pancreatic juice contains various enzymes that are important in the digestion of foods. Figure 16-23 illustrates the duct system whereby pancreatic juice reaches the duodenum; the main *pancreatic duct* (of Wirsung) usually unites with the common bile duct, while an accessory duct (of Santorini) may open directly into the duodenum.

The *endocrine* secretory units consist of irregular clumps of cells referred to as the *islets of Langerhans;* these islets, scattered throughout the pancreas, contain extensive capillary networks that serve to carry off the endocrine secretions (hormones). Two types of cells may be distinguished in the islets, beta and alpha. The beta cells pro-

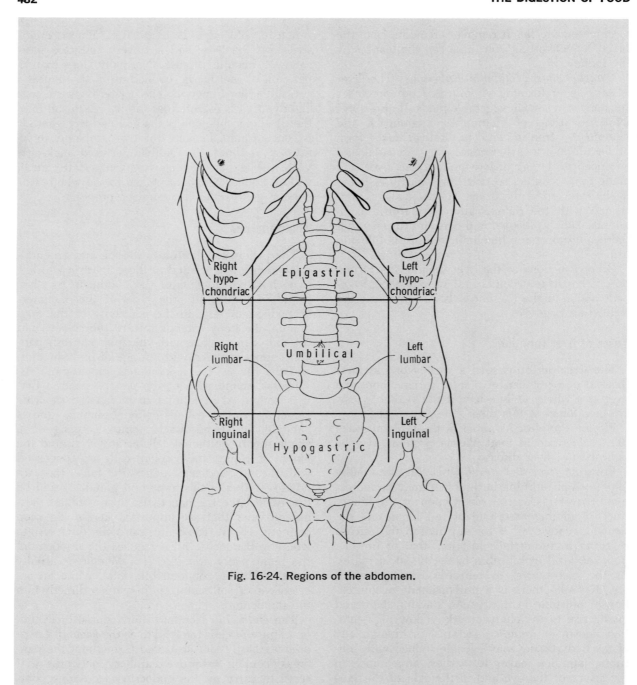

Fig. 16-24. Regions of the abdomen.

duce *insulin,* a hormone that is essential for normal carbohydrate metabolism; hypofunction of these cells causes *diabetes mellitus* (p. 563). The alpha cells produce *glucagon,* which raises blood sugar levels. Additional information on the endocrine function of the pancreas can be found on page 564.

The pancreas receives blood from branches of the splenic, gastroduodenal, and superior mesenteric arteries; its veins drain into the splenic and superior mesenteric veins, which in turn join to form the portal vein. The nerve supply is derived from both divisions of the autonomic system.

SURFACE PROJECTIONS OF DIGESTIVE ORGANS

The abdomen is divided arbitrarily into 9 regions for purposes of location of the viscera on the surface. The regions are shown in Figure 16-24. The location of the various viscera is given in the table.

DIGESTIVE PROCESSES

Attention already has been called to the fact that complex foods must undergo specific changes before they can be absorbed from the digestive tract; These foods are carbohydrates, fats and proteins. Others, such as water, vitamins and minerals, are ready for immediate absorption. Two types of activity are involved in preparing complex foods for absorption: mechanical and chemical.

Mechanical activity involves purely physical processes. These include the chewing of food, moving it along the digestive tube, mixing it with the various digestive juices, spreading it over the absorptive surfaces and, finally, the elimination of the residue.

Chemical activity involves the process of *hydrolysis,* the splitting of complex compounds into simple fragments by the addition of water. This process depends much on the presence of *digestive enzymes,* the organic catalysts that greatly

---

LOCATION OF ABDOMINAL VISCERA

Right Hypochondriac	**Epigastric**	**Left Hypochondriac**
Greater part of the right lobe of the liver, hepatic flexure of the colon and part of the right kidney	Greater part of left lobe and part of right lobe of liver with gallbladder, part of stomach, part of duodenum, pancreas, upper end of spleen, parts of kidneys and suprarenal glands	Part of stomach, part of spleen, tail of pancreas, splenic flexure of colon, part of left kidney and, sometimes, part of left lobe of liver
Right Lateral, or Lumbar	**Umbilical**	**Left Lateral, or Lumbar**
Ascending colon, part of right kidney and, sometimes, part of ileum	Greater part of transverse colon, part of duodenum, part of jejunum and ileum, part of mesentery and greater omentum, part of kidneys and ureters	Descending colon, part of jejunum, part of left kidney
Right Inguinal, or Iliac	**Hypogastric, or Pubic**	**Left Inguinal, or Iliac**
Cecum and appendix, termination of ileum	Ileum; bladder in children; bladder, if distended, in adults; uterus when pregnant; sigmoid flexure	Sigmoid colon, jejunum and ileum

increase the speed of hydrolytic reactions. Each enzyme acts on a certain type of food and requires a certain pH if it is to operate with greatest efficiency.

It is customary to name enzymes after the food acted upon by adding the suffix -*ase*. Thus *amylase* acts on starches, *lipase* acts on fats, and *protease* acts on proteins. However, some of the older, original names, such as pepsin and trypsin, still are in use. The names of the enzymes, the foods on which they act, and the products formed as a result of their activities are presented in tabular form on page 493.

Digestion in the mouth

Saliva is the first secretion encountered by the food eaten. It consists of a mixture of the secretions of the 3 pairs of salivary glands, as well as mucus and cells from the surface epithelium of the mouth. Saliva contains watery mucin, inorganic salts, and a digestive enzyme called *salivary amylase* (ptyalin). However, the mechanical functions of saliva probably are of greater importance than is its somewhat limited chemical contribution. Saliva protects the lining of the mouth against drying, facilitates speech, and lubricates food so that it can be chewed and swallowed; chemically, saliva begins the digestion of starches.

The secretion of saliva begins when one thinks about food, sees it, smells it, or hears it talked about; this preliminary flow of saliva is called the *psychic* secretion. When food is taken into the mouth it dissolves to some extent in the saliva and stimulates the taste buds; as a result of this stimulation, saliva continues to flow while one actually is eating. The daily secretion of saliva ranges between 1000 and 1500 ml.; its pH is between 6.0 and 7.0, a favorable range for the action of salivary amylase.

Mechanical activity in the mouth depends on saliva, the tongue, the teeth, and the muscles of mastication. As one chews or masticates food, it is ground into small particles and thoroughly mixed with saliva, which serves as an important lubricant.

Chemical activity in the mouth depends on the presence of *salivary amylase;* this enzyme attacks complex starch molecules and breaks them down to dextrins and maltose. Dextrin molecules are intermediate in size between starch and maltose; because food does not remain in the mouth for a long period of time, and because salivary action is inhibited by the acid gastric juice, the conversion of all starches to dextrins and of all dextrins to maltose may not occur until they reach the small intestine.

Role of the pharynx and esophagus

Food is carried from the mouth to the stomach by the act of swallowing, or deglutition. For convenience of description, this is divided into 3 stages.

The first stage of swallowing consists of collecting the bolus or mass of food on the dorsum of the tongue. Then a sudden elevation of the tongue throws the mass into the pharynx. The first stage of swallowing is under voluntary control.

The second stage of swallowing is the passage of the bolus through the pharynx. The air passages are shut off, as previously described (p. 420) and respiration is inhibited. The bolus is grasped by the constrictors of the pharynx and passed along into the esophagus. Figure 16-25 indicates the changes that occur in the position of the soft palate and the larynx during swallowing. The second stage is involuntary although muscles of the pharynx are striated.

The third stage is the passage through the esophagus. The muscle in the upper portion of the esophagus in man is striated but not under the control of the will. The muscle in the lower portion of the esophagus is smooth. It exhibits waves of contraction called *peristaltic* (meaning "to send around") waves. A typical peristaltic wave is preceded by relaxation. The function of peristaltic waves is to move food along the digestive tube in a caudal direction. The gastroesophageal constrictor relaxes as a peristaltic wave in the esophagus approaches.

Achalasia of the esophagus is a condition in

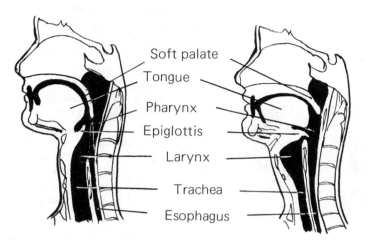

Soft palate
Tongue
Pharynx
Epiglottis
Larynx
Trachea
Esophagus

Fig. 16-25. Diagram showing elevation of soft palate and larynx and closure of glottis during swallowing. (After Tigerstedt.)

which the gastroesophageal constrictor fails to relax properly during swallowing. The subject complains that the food "sticks in his throat."

The only secretion produced by glands in the pharynx and the esophagus is mucus, which facilitates swallowing of a bolus of food by making it slippery. No enzymes are produced in this portion of the digestive tube.

Digestion in the stomach

Gastric juice is the highly acid secretion produced by glands in the mucosa of the stomach (p. 469). The secretion of this digestive fluid occurs in 3 phases.

The cephalic phase is stimulated by the sight, smell, taste, or even by the thought of food; this phase derives its name from the fact that the related receptors and afferent nerves are located in the head. Efferent impulses travel over the vagus nerves and promote the reflex secretion of gastric juice. The cephalic phase is important in that it assures the presence of gastric juice as soon as food enters the stomach; thus one can see the value of preparing appetizing food that is attractively arranged. This phase of secretion accounts for ¼ to ⅓ of all the gastric juice normally associated with eating a meal.

The gastric phase occurs because of the presence of food in the stomach; this food is thought to stimulate secretion in two ways. First, owing to its actual bulk, there is a mechanical stimulus involved in stretching the wall of the stomach. Second, a chemical stimulus is provided by the presence of partially digested protein and certain food extractives. These mechanical and chemical factors both serve to stimulate the production of a hormone, *gastrin*, by cells in the pyloric portion of the gastric mucosa. Gastrin enters the blood stream and is carried to glands in the fundus and body of the stomach, where it stimulates the production of gastric juice.

The intestinal phase of gastric secretion involves the presence of chyme in the duodenum. (After food has become mixed with gastric juice it is referred to as *chyme*.) Small amounts of gastric juice continue to be secreted as long as chyme is present. The mechanism is not well understood, but it is thought that a hormone, produced by the intestinal mucosa, is carried to the stomach by way of the blood. The total amount of secretion for all phases averages about 2000 ml. each day.

Fig. 16-26. Section of frozen stomach of rat during digestion to show stratification of food given at different times. Food was given in three portions and colored differently. (Redrawn after Grützner: Pflüger's Arch. ges. Physiol. 106:463)

Mechanical activity in the stomach depends upon rhythmic contractions of the smooth muscular wall, which serve to mix the food with gastric juice. The waves of contraction begin as shallow ripples near the cardiac end of the stomach and become deeper as they move toward the pylorus.

As digestion proceeds, small amounts of liquid chyme are emptied from the stomach into the duodenum. The rate of emptying of the stomach is influenced by such factors as the fluidity of the chyme, the amount of chyme already present in the duodenum, the acidity of the chyme and the type of food in the chyme. For example, the presence of fat in the chyme stimulates cells in the duodenal mucosa to secrete a hormone (*entero-*

gastrone) that is carried to the stomach by way of the blood stream; enterogastrone not only inhibits the secretion of gastric juice but also inhibits the muscular contractions of the stomach wall. On the other hand, carbohydrates in the chyme have only a mild delaying effect; protein has an intermediate effect.

Chemical activity in the stomach depends primarily on the secretion of *pepsin* (gastric protease); this enzyme is highly active in an acid medium (optimal pH = 2.0); thus the secretion of hydrochloric acid is equally important for the digestion of protein in the stomach. On the other hand, gastric acidity inhibits the activity of the incoming salivary amylase; therefore, inasmuch as food is layered as it enters the stomach (Fig. 16-26), salivary digestion continues only in the center of the stomach contents, or until such time as the food is mixed thoroughly with the highly acid gastric juice.

Pepsin is secreted in an inactive form, called *pepsinogen,* which is converted to the active enzyme by the hydrochloric acid (HCl) in the stomach; if pepsin were secreted in its active form it would digest the protein in the very cells that produced it. Once activated in the lumen of the stomach, pepsin attacks amino acid linkages in the center of protein molecules, thus liberating protein fragments rather than amino acids.

The surface epithelial cells tend to be protected from the corrosive effects of gastric juice by the mucous secretion that coats the lining of the stomach; however, it is believed that these cells do have a high rate of mortality, and that they are replaced by cells from deeper parts of the gastric pits (p. 467). A defect in the mucosal defense may result in *gastric ulcer* formation.

Gastric lipase, secreted in very small quantities, is of questionable value in the adult. Inasmuch as it principally acts on emulsified fats, it has practically no effect on the large fat globules that make up the bulk of the fat in one's diet.

Feeding Other Than by Mouth. A person who cannot take food by mouth may receive fluids by intravenous injection, by gavage or by gastrostomy. *Gavage* means a feeding that is given by way of a tube passed through the nose or the mouth and the esophagus into the stomach. If the esophagus is obstructed, a surgeon may perform a *gastrostomy;* this involves the creation of an opening through the abdominal wall into the stomach.

Gastric analysis refers to the study of stomach contents after a test meal or the injection of histamine, which stimulates the parietal cells to secrete hydrochloric acid; if no acid is present, the patient is said to have *achlorhydria;* this is a finding in pernicious anemia. Less than the normal amount of acid is called *hyposecretion* and occurs in cancer of the stomach. If there is an unusually high content of acid, the patient is said to have *hyperacidity* or hypersecretion.

Gastric lavage refers to repeatedly washing out the stomach, as after one has taken poison or an overdose of sleeping pills.

Nausea, meaning "seasickness", is a term that has been in use for 3,000 years. It is a feeling of discomfort, accompanied by salivation, aversion to food, weakness, trembling and perspiration. Usually it precedes vomiting. Nausea is common in the early months of pregnancy, in gastrointestinal disturbances from various causes, and disease of the inner ear (especially of the semicircular canals).

Vomiting. Morning sickness of pregnancy, brain tumors and upsets or infections of the digestive system usually are accompanied by vomiting. In the act of vomiting, there is compression of the stomach by the muscles of the abdominal wall against the liver and the diaphragm. The gastro-esophageal constrictor relaxes, and the contents of the stomach are ejected. Emetics are substances which are given to produce vomiting when the stomach needs to be emptied, in cases in which the individual has taken poison or some other harmful substance.

Digestion in the small intestine

The greatest amount of digestion occurs in the small intestine for the following reasons. First, food entering the intestine already has undergone an extensive preliminary breakdown owing to mechanical and chemical activities in the mouth and stomach. Second, the small intestine receives secretions that provide all of the enzymes necessary for the complete digestion of each major food group. Third, food remains in the small intestine for a relatively long period of time, thus giving the enzymes ample opportunity to complete their tasks.

Three secretions are emptied into the small intestine: pancreatic juice, intestinal juice, and bile. The rates of production and flow of these secretions are influenced by nerve impulses and by hormones produced in the mucosa when acid chyme enters the duodenum.

Pancreatic juice, the exocrine secretion of the pancreas (p. 481), is produced very slowly between meals. However, the entry of acid chyme into the duodenum results in a marked increase in the rate of production owing to stimulation of the pancreas by two hormones: secretin and pancreozymin; these hormones are released by cells in the duodenal mucosa and carried to the pancreas by way of the blood stream.

Secretin causes the pancreas to produce a thin, watery juice that is rich in sodium bicarbonate; sodium bicarbonate helps to neutralize hydrochloric acid in the chyme. Because the duodenal mucosa is not as well equipped as the stomach to withstand the corrosive effect of gastric juice, neutralization of the hydrochloric acid is an important protective mechanism. Persons who develop a *duodenal ulcer* usually have an accompanying hypersecretion of hydrochloric acid, but this is only one of many possible factors that could be involved. Another important effect of this secretion is the provision of a favorable duodenal pH (6.0 to 7.0) so that the pancreatic enzymes may operate efficiently.

Pancreozymin is a hormone that stimulates the pancreas to produce a thick, viscid secretion that is rich in amylase, lipase, and 3 proteases; the digestive effects of these enzymes are described under chemical changes.

Nervous mechanisms in the regulation of pancreatic secretion are far less important than hormonal regulation. However, during the cephalic phase of gastric secretion, vagus nerve impulses are transmitted to the pancreas, as well as to the stomach. These impulses stimulate the production of enzyme-rich pancreatic juice, which is stored temporarily in the acini.

The total secretion of pancreatic juice averages about 1200 ml. per day.

Intestinal juice or *succus entericus* is produced by the glands of the small intestine (p. 470). The flow of this juice is initiated by distention of the intestine, by the presence of food, and by parasympathetic (vagus) stimulation. On the other hand, sympathetic nerve stimulation inhibits intestinal secretion, particularly of the mucus-producing duodenal glands. This tends to leave the mucosa unprotected and may be a factor in the development of duodenal ulcer.

Enzymes associated with intestinal juice include enterokinase, proteases ("erepsin"), sucrase, maltase, and lactase; in addition there are very small quantities of amylase and lipase. The digestive effects of these enzymes are described under chemical changes.

Bile formation and the mechanism of emptying of the gallbladder were previously described on pages 479–480. Two duodenal hormones are involved: *secretin,* which stimulates the production of bile in the liver, and *cholecystokinin,* which provokes evacuation of the gallbladder. Although bile contains no digestive enzymes, the bile salts play an important role in the digestive process, as they emulsify fats.

Mechanical activity in the small intestine involves segmental and pendular "mixing" contractions, as well as the propulsive movements of peristalsis.

Segmentation consists of a squeezing and mixing of the intestinal contents by means of ringlike contractions of the circular muscle; at times the intestine resembles a chain of little link sausages owing to the local constrictions. Segmental contractions occur at the rate of 8 or 9 per minute in the duodenum, and at progressively slower rates in the jejunum and ileum. Segmentation produces no onward movement of the intestinal contents, but it does serve to mix them with the various digestive juices and to bring them into contact with the mucosa, so that absorption can take

GASTROINTESTINAL HORMONES

Hormone	Where Produced	Agents Stimulating Production	Action
Gastrin	Gastric mucosa of pyloric region	Distention and protein derivatives	Stimulates production of gastric juice
Enterogastrone	Duodenal mucosa	Fatty acids, fats, and certain sugars	Inhibits secretion of gastric juice and motility of stomach
Secretin	Duodenal mucosa	Acidity of duodenal contents	Stimulates production of bile and of bicarbonate-rich pancreatic juice
Pancreozymin	Duodenal mucosa	Chyme	Stimulates production of enzyme-rich pancreatic juice
Cholecystokinin	Duodenal mucosa	Fats, fatty acids, dilute HCl	Stimulates emptying of gallbladder

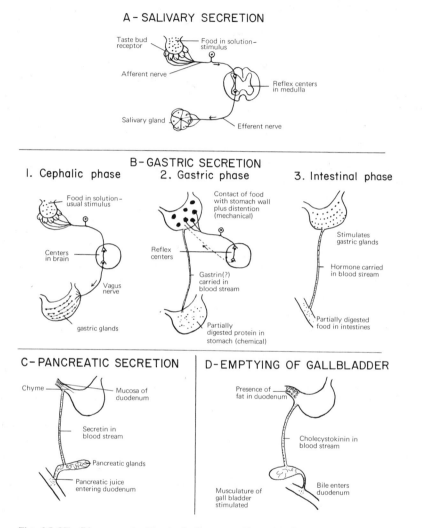

A – SALIVARY SECRETION

Taste bud receptor
Food in solution – stimulus
Afferent nerve
Reflex centers in medulla
Salivary gland
Efferent nerve

B – GASTRIC SECRETION

1. Cephalic phase
2. Gastric phase
3. Intestinal phase

Food in solution – usual stimulus
Centers in brain
Vagus nerve
gastric glands

Contact of food with stomach wall plus distention (mechanical)
Reflex centers
Gastrin(?) carried in blood stream
Partially digested protein in stomach (chemical)

Stimulates gastric glands
Hormone carried in blood stream
Partially digested food in intestines

C – PANCREATIC SECRETION

Chyme
Mucosa of duodenum
Secretin in blood stream
Pancreatic glands
Pancreatic juice entering duodenum

D – EMPTYING OF GALLBLADDER

Presence of fat in duodenum
Cholecystokinin in blood stream
Musculature of gall bladder stimulated
Bile enters duodenum

Fig. 16-27. Diagrams to illustrate the secretion of saliva, gastric juice and pancreatic juice. The mechanism of the emptying of the gallbladder is shown also. (A) Reflex control of salivary secretion. (B) Gastric secretion: 1. Cephalic phase, reflex. 2. Gastric phase, possibility of both reflex and hormonal control. 3. Intestinal phase, hormonal control. (C) Hormonal control of pancreatic secretion through secretin. (D) Hormonal control of gallbladder evacuation through cholecystokinin.

place. Segmental contractions in no way depend upon nerve impulses, but their intensity can be increased by parasympathetic nerve impulses or decreased by sympathetic impulses.

Pendular movements consist of small constrictive waves that sweep forward, then backward, over a few inches of the intestine. The function of these movements is uncertain, but a certain amount of mixing of intestinal contents must occur.

Peristalsis is responsible for the onward movement of the intestinal contents. These wavelike contractions may begin in any part of the small intestine and move along for variable distances. Those that travel for relatively short distances are called peristaltic *waves;* those that travel longer distances are referred to as peristaltic *rushes.* If one applies a stethoscope to the abdomen, these propulsive waves can be heard as long continued rumbles; they occur one to twelve times per minute.

When one begins to eat, and food enters the stomach, peristaltic activity of the small intestine is greatly increased; the existence of this *gastroenteric reflex* is one reason for not giving food by mouth immediately after surgical operations on the small intestine, as the increased activity might result in a tearing of tissues at the suture lines. The rate of movement of chyme through the intestine varies with its composition. However, the "head" of an average meal usually reaches the ileocecal valve in 3 to 4 hours, and the last of the meal leaves the ileum about 8 or 9 hours after ingestion.

Although smooth muscle of the intestinal tract is able to initiate spontaneous contractions, the integration of peristaltic activity depends upon autonomic nerve fibers. Parasympathetic fibers conduct impulses that stimulate peristalsis, while those of the sympathetic division inhibit peristalsis.

Chemical activity in the small intestine is of fundamental importance in the breakdown of all 3 major food groups. Although some digestion occurs in the mouth and stomach, it should be emphasized that the pancreatic and intestinal enzymes (together with the emulsifying action of bile) are capable of initiating and carrying through the entire digestive process.

Carbohydrate enters the duodenum partly in the form of dextrins and maltose (produced by the action of salivary amylase), starches and glycogen (that escaped digestion in the mouth), or as sucrose and lactose (cane sugar and milk sugar ingested with the food). Pancreatic *amylase* attacks starch, dextrins, and glycogen, converting them to maltose (a disaccharide). Intestinal enzymes then complete the digestion of carbohydrate to simple sugars (monosaccharides): *maltase* splits maltose to 2 molecules of glucose; *sucrase* splits sucrose to one molecule of glucose and one of fructose; *lactase* splits lactose to one molecule of glucose and one of galactose.

Fats are attacked by pancreatic *lipase* and split into glycerol and fatty acids. Although lipase can and does attack large fat globules, its action is much more effective when fats first are emulsified (split into tiny particles) by the action of bile salts.

Protein and protein fragments resulting from the action of pepsin are attacked by a series of enzymes in the small intestine, where they are broken down to amino acids. Generally speaking, the pancreatic proteases initiate the digestion of large protein molecules and fragments, splitting them into still smaller fragments. Although a few amino acids are split off by the pancreatic enzymes, the intestinal proteases do the bulk of the work in completing the digestion of protein fragments to their constituent amino acids.

Because the pancreatic proteases will attack native protein, they are secreted in inactive forms to prevent digestion of the pancreas itself; these forms (trypsinogen, chymotrypsinogen, and procarboxypeptidase) become activated only after they enter the small intestine. *Enterokinase,* an enzyme in the intestinal juice, triggers the activation process by converting trypsinogen to active *trypsin.* Trypsin, in turn, activates chymotrypsinogen to active *chymotrypsin,* and procarboxypeptidase to active *carboxypeptidase.*

Intestinal proteases (aminopeptidase and dipeptidase) do not attack native protein and can be produced in their active form. They complete the

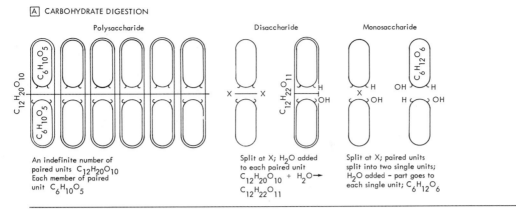

A CARBOHYDRATE DIGESTION

Polysaccharide

Disaccharide

Monosaccharide

An indefinite number of paired units $C_{12}H_{20}O_{10}$
Each member of paired unit $C_6H_{10}O_5$

Split at X; H_2O added to each paired unit
$C_{12}H_{20}O_{10} + H_2O \rightarrow$
$C_{12}H_{22}O_{11}$

Split at X; paired units split into two single units; H_2O added – part goes to each single unit; $C_6H_{12}O_6$

B FAT DIGESTION

Neutral fat, a large cube, consisting of a great number of small cubes; the formula of each small cube is

CH$_2$O – OCR
CHO – OCR
CH$_2$O – OCR

Bile emulsifies neutral fat and greatly increases its surface. We may consider the large cube split into its small component cubes under the action of bile.

Pancreatic lipase then acts on the small cubes and splits them at the three points marked X.

CH$_2$OH   RCOOH
CHOH   RCOOH
CH$_2$OH   RCOOH

Three molecules of water are added to each small cube, as indicated; the products which result are one molecule of glycerol and three molecules of fatty acid.

C PROTEIN DIGESTION

The protein molecule may be considered as an indefinite number of amino acid molecules; these are united through the loss of one H from the NH$_2$ group and of an OH from the COOH group of the next amino acid.

Proteins

Proteoses

Peptones

Amino acids

Gastric protease splits the prepared protein molecule into proteoses (and peptones) by the addition of water; these are derivatives which contain fewer amino acid molecules.

Pancreatic protease splits proteoses (and peptones) into peptones (and amino acids) by the addition of water.

Intestinal protease splits the peptones into amino acids by the addition of water.

in presence of HCL

water

Fig. 16-28. Diagram of digestion. (A) Carbohydrates: polysaccharides hydrolyzed to disaccharides by amylase; disaccharides hydrolyzed to monosaccharides by disaccharases. (B) Fats: emulsified by bile, then hydrolyzed to glycerol and fatty acids by lipases. (C) Proteins: HCl supplies the proper pH for protein digestion in the stomach. Protein is hydrolyzed to amino acids in the intestine by pancreatic and intestinal proteases. Although the chemical union is between the nitrogen of the NH$_2$ group and the carbon of the COOH group, it is indicated in the diagram as between H and O for simplicity, in consideration of the addition of H$_2$O.

digestive processes initiated by the pancreatic enzymes; thus amino acids are made available for absorption.

Digestion in the large intestine

Activity in the large intestine is limited to mechanical and bacterial activity. The only secretion produced in this portion of the digestive tube is mucus. In addition to its role as a protector of the intestinal wall, mucus serves to hold fecal matter together and to facilitate its movement toward the rectum. There are no enzymes secreted by the glands of the large intestine.

Mechanical activity involves rather sluggish mixing and propulsive movements. The mixing movements are similar to the segmentation contractions of the small intestine (p. 488); these contractions promote the reabsorption of water as the intestinal contents are churned about and brought into contact with the mucosa.

Propulsive movements, or "mass movements," propel the fecal contents toward the anus; these movements occur only a few times each day, usually after meals (gastrocolic reflex). Mass movements are most abundant after breakfast, and many persons take advantage of this reflex as they establish the habit of emptying the bowel each morning. The parasympathetic autonomic nerves are the nerves of "emptying," as they stimulate contraction of the smooth muscle in the wall of the colon and cause relaxation of the sphincters of the anal canal. The sympathetic nerves are the nerves of "retention," as they promote relaxation of the muscular wall of the colon and contraction of the sphincters of the anal canal.

Bacterial Action. The large intestine is filled with bacteria, which act on the undigested residues. They produce fermentation of carbohydrate and putrefaction of proteins. Some of the split products are eliminated with the feces, and others are absorbed. Those that are absorbed are phenol, indol and skatol; these are conjugated with other substances in the liver and then excreted by way of the urine.

Bacteria that inhabit the large intestine synthesize vitamin K, which is then absorbed, provided that bile is present in the intestine. Some components of the vitamin B complex are produced by intestinal bacteria, and these likewise are absorbed and used by the body. Patients who are taking sulfonamide or antibiotic drugs may develop a vitamin deficiency if a sufficient number of these helpful bacteria are destroyed.

Defecation (emptying of the rectum). The sigmoid colon is filled with feces by the mass movements of the large intestine. The rectum remains empty until just before defecation. As the feces enter and stretch the rectum the desire to defecate is aroused. If unheeded, the desire disappears (due to adaptation of stretch receptors), and the feces remain in the rectum where they become hard and dry; defecation then becomes difficult and painful. Infrequent, or difficult evacuation of the feces is referred to as *constipation.*

Contractions of the smooth muscle in the walls of the rectum are accompanied by relaxation of the internal and the external sphincters and by contraction of the voluntary muscles of the abdominal walls and the pelvic floor. The levator ani muscles assist in expelling the last of the fecal contents.

Composition of Feces. The feces contain water and mucus as well as great numbers of bacteria. Also present are epithelial cells that have been sloughed off the intestinal mucosa, various food residues, such as undigestible cellulose, and various food substances which have escaped digestion and absorption in the small intestine. Elements such as calcium, potassium, iron, nitrogen and magnesium also are lost in the feces. The bile pigments (bilirubin and biliverdin) give the normal brown color to feces. If for any reason bile fails to enter the intestinal tract, the feces will be "clay colored" or chalky in appearance. If old blood from the upper part of the gastrointestinal tract is present, the stools have the color and the consistency of tar (ulcer or cancer of stomach). Fresh blood appears as red streaks in the stools and often is due to hemorrhoids or to cancer of the rectum.

The stools should be examined for eggs or segments of parasites in certain types of disturbances of the gastrointestinal tract. Thus, it is obvious that stool examinations are of considerable diagnostic importance.

Diarrhea. In this condition there are frequent bowel movements, and the fecal material is liquid, since it is moved so rapidly through the digestive tube that absorption cannot occur. Usually it is due to the intake of spoiled food or infection in the digestive system. Laxatives and cathartics may lead to diarrhea.

Vomiting and diarrhea can become very serious conditions if they persist for a few days. One loses large volumes of liquid and salts in both conditions. Normally, about 8,000 ml. of fluid are poured into the digestive tube from the blood in a day (in the form of digestive juices). As stated previously, this is taken back into the blood by absorption, so that it is not lost to the body. If either vomiting or diarrhea occurs, the patient becomes dehydrated due to the loss of part of the digestive juices. If vomiting persists for a couple of days, alkalosis may occur, since a large amount of HCl is lost in the vomitus. If diarrhea persists, with a loss of pancreatic, as well as intestinal juices, acidosis may occur due to the loss of $NaHCO_3$. These conditions are especially serious in infants.

BRIEF SUMMARY OF DIGESTIVE ACTIVITIES
(See text for details)

Glands	Secretions	Acts On	Products Formed
Salivary	Salivary amylase (ptyalin)	Starch & glycogen	Dextrins
		Dextrins	Maltose
Gastric	Hydrochloric acid	Activates pepsinogen	Pepsin
	Gastric protease (pepsin)	Protein	Protein fragments (partially digested protein)
	Gastric lipase (?)	Emulsified fats	Fatty acids and glycerol
Pancreas (acinar cells)	Pancreatic amylase (amylopsin)	Starch, glycogen and dextrins	Maltose
	Pancreatic lipase (steapsin)	Emulsified fats	Fatty acids and glycerol
	Pancreatic proteases (trypsin, chymotrypsin, and carboxypeptidase)	Protein (intact or fragmented)	Protein fragments and amino acids
Intestinal (crypts of Lieberkuhn)	Enterokinase	Activates trypsinogen	Trypsin
	Proteases ("erepsin")	Protein fragments	Amino acids
	Maltase	Maltose	Glucose
	Sucrase	Sucrose	Glucose and fructose
	Lactase	Lactose	Glucose and galactose
Liver	Bile salts (no enzymes)	Large fat globules	Emulsified fats (tiny droplets)

SUMMARY

1. Digestive system prepares food for absorption

2. Foods
   A. Inorganic: inorganic salts, water
   B. Organic
      a. Carbohydrate: mono-, di- and polysaccharides; energy
      b. Lipids: simple, compound, and steroid; stored energy and special compounds
      c. Protein: simple and conjugated; building blocks

3. Vitamins
   A. Required for growth and other processes; take part in various reactions
   B. Most obtained in diet, some synthesized in intestine
   C. Fat-soluble vitamins
      a. Vitamin A: growth of bones and teeth; formation of visual purple
      b. Vitamin D: for absorption of calcium and phosphorus and their use in bone
      c. Vitamin E: function in human body unknown
      d. Vitamin K: for formation of prothrombin in liver
   D. Water-soluble vitamins: vitamin B complex and vitamin C
      a. Thiamine: in oxidation of pyruvic acid, carbohydrate metabolism
      b. Riboflavin: for tissue repair and carbohydrate metabolism
      c. Niacin: for absorption and metabolism of carbohydrate
      d. Vitamin B_{12}: erythropoietic factor
      e. Vitamin C: maintain intercellular substance

4. The digestive tube
   A. Structural layers
      a. Mucous membrane lining
      b. Submucous layer
      c. Muscular layer
      d. External: fibrous above diaphragm and serous below
   B. Peritoneum
      a. Double-walled sac: outer layer lines cavity (parietal peritoneum); inner layer covers organs (visceral peritoneum); peritoneal cavity is space between
      b. Mesentery: attaches intestine to posterior abdominal wall
      c. Greater omentum connects stomach and transverse colon
      d. Lesser omentum connects stomach with liver
   C. Mouth or buccal cavity
      a. Vestibule: space between lips and teeth
      b. Lips and cheeks covered with skin, lined with mucosa; muscular walls
      c. Roof of mouth: bony hard palate anteriorly; soft palate posteriorly
      d. Tongue: aids chewing, swallowing, speaking. Papillae on dorsum contain taste buds
      e. Teeth: concerned with chewing food; first set called deciduous, 20 in number; second set permanent, 32 in number. Named for shape or function. Chief parts are crown and root
      f. Three pairs of salivary glands secrete saliva:
         (1) Parotid
         (2) Submandibular
         (3) Sublingual
   D. Pharynx
      a. Constrictor muscles aid swallowing
   E. Esophagus
      a. Muscular tube; behind trachea
      b. Conveys food to stomach
   F. Stomach
      a. Food reservoir; in epigastric and left hypochondriac regions
      b. Divisions: cardiac orifice; fundus and body; pylorus surrounded by pyloric sphincter; greater and lesser curvatures

  c. Structural variations: mucosal folds form rugae; special mucosal cells secrete gastric juice; 3 layers of smooth muscle highly extensible

 G. Small intestine
  a. Coiled tube: stomach to large intestine
  b. Divisions: duodenum, jejunum and ileum; ileocecal valve guards opening into large intestine
  c. Structural variations: circular folds and villi; each villus contains a blood and a lymph capillary; duodenal glands secrete mucus; intestinal glands secrete digestive enzymes

 H. Large intestine
  a. Extends from ileum to anus
  b. Divisions: cecum and appendix; colon (ascending, transverse, descending, sigmoid); rectum; anal canal, guarded by sphincters
  c. Structural variations: no villi; glands secrete mucus but no enzymes; longitudinal muscle fibers in bands (taeniae coli), form pouches or haustra; circular muscle in anal canal forms internal anal sphincter (involuntary); skeletal muscle forms external anal sphincter (voluntary)

5. Accessory organs: tongue, teeth, salivary glands related to mouth
 A. Liver and bile ducts
  a. Located under dome of diaphragm; epigastric and right hypochondriac regions
  b. Description: superior surface smooth and convex; inferior concave; 4 lobes (right, left, quadrate, caudate), subdivided into lobules; attached to diaphragm and body wall by folds of peritoneum; Glisson's capsule, accompanies vessels into interior of liver; connective tissue extends from porta throughout liver, provides pathway for vessels and bile ducts; hepatic artery supplies oxygenated blood; portal vein supplies blood rich in end products of digestion; hepatic veins drain liver and empty into inferior vena cava
  c. Microscopic appearance: branching plates of hepatic cells radiate from center of lobule; sinusoids between cords receive blood from hepatic artery and portal vein, are lined with phagocytic cells; much blood can be held in sinusoids (reservoir effect)
  d. Biliary apparatus: bile canaliculi originate between liver plates; drain into larger ducts, finally into hepatic duct which joins cystic duct from gallbladder to form common bile duct that empties into duodenum at duodenal papilla. Gallbladder a musculomembranous sac on undersurface of liver; receives bile for storage

 B. Functions of liver
  a. Production of bile
  b. Metabolic functions:
   (1) Carbohydrate: regulation of blood sugar level
   (2) Lipid: synthesis; breakdown fatty acids for oxidation
   (3) Protein: deaminizes amino acids, forms new ones; forms plasma proteins
   (4) Miscellaneous: Forms vitamin A; stores vitamins A, D and B_{12}; stores iron; steroid hormone inactivation; phagocytosis; forms heparin; detoxifies

 C. Pancreas
  a. Head rests in concavity of duodenum, body and tail extend toward spleen
  b. Composed of lobules and secretory units which produce pancreatic juice; secretion emptied into duodenum via pancreatic ducts
  c. Groups of irregular cells (islands of Langerhans) secrete hormone insulin and glucagon

6. Digestive processes
   A. In the mouth
      a. Mechanical: mastication and insalivation
      b. Chemical: salivary amylase converts starch to dextrin and maltose

   B. Deglutition or swallowing
      a. Formation of bolus
      b. Passage of bolus through pharynx; constrictor muscles
      c. Passage of bolus through esophagus; peristaltic waves

   C. In the stomach
      a. Secretion of gastric juice in 3 phases: cephalic, gastric, intestinal
      b. Mechanical: mixing; forms chyme
      c. Chemical: see table on page 493

   D. In the small intestine
      a. Pancreatic juice: flow stimulated by presence of chyme in duodenum; hormones secretin and pancreozymin; vagal impulses
      b. Intestinal juice: flow stimulated by distention, presence of food, vagal impulses
      c. Bile: secretin stimulates production; cholecystokinin evacuates gallbladder
      d. Mechanical: segmentation, pendular, peristalsis
      e. Chemical: see table on page 493

   E. In the large intestine
      a. Mechanical: segmentation; mass movements
      b. Bacterial action: synthesis of vitamin K and some B complex; putrefaction, fermentation
      c. No digestive enzymes
      d. Defecation: emptying of rectum and elimination of waste
         (1) Feces contain water, mucus, bacteria, various food residues, elements and bile pigments

PRACTICAL APPLICATIONS AND QUESTIONS

(Encircle the letter of the *best* answer to each of the following questions.)

A. *Mr. J. R. was admitted to the hospital for treatment of a gastric ulcer.*

1. Gastric ulcers invade the lining of the stomach wall. The lining is called the
   a. serosa
   b. fibrosa
   c. mucosa
   d. submucosa

2. Occasionally a gastric ulcer will erode completely through the stomach wall, permitting the contents of the stomach to enter the abdominal cavity. As a result there may be a generalized inflammation of the membrane which lines the cavity and covers the viscera. This membrane is called the
   a. pleura
   b. peritoneum
   c. mesentery
   d. greater omentum

3. A subtotal gastrectomy was performed with an anastomosis between the remaining upper portion of the stomach and the middle portion of the small intestine. This section of small intestine is called the
   a. cecum
   b. ileum
   c. duodenum
   d. jejunum

B. *Mrs. S. F. was admitted to the hospital for treatment of an obstruction of the common bile duct.*

1. This patient was placed on a low fat diet since bile was not able to reach the small intestine where it serves to
   a. absorb fats
   b. synthesize fats
   e. emulsify fats
   d. deaminize fats

2. Fats are an important constituent of the diet because they
   a. are a good source of energy
   b. constitute the framework of protoplasm
   c. provide fatty acids needed to maintain acid-base balance
   d. catalyze various metabolic reactions

3. Which of the following hormones is produced by the duodenal mucosa when fat enters the small intestine?
   a. gastrin
   b. pancreozymin
   c. secretin
   d. cholecystokinin

4. Fats, along with other food materials, are moved along the digestive tract by muscular contractions called
   a. deglutition
   b. pendular movements
   c. peristalsis
   d. rhythmic segmentation

17

"There is a place for everything,
In earth, or sky, or sea,
Where it may find its proper use,
And of advantage be..."

AUGUSTINE'S PHILOSOPHY
STANZA 1
BENJAMIN B. WARFIELD

THE ABSORPTION AND UTILIZATION OF FOOD

We have shown, in Chapter 16, how complex foods are mechanically and chemically broken down to absorbable forms. Through the action of powerful digestive enzymes, carbohydrate, fat, and protein have been hydrolyzed to simple sugars, fatty acids, glycerol and amino acids. The stage now is set for these nutrients to "enter" the body, in the truest sense of the word, and to follow various metabolic pathways that are open to them.

ABSORPTION

Absorption involves the transfer of the products of digestion through the epithelial lining of the digestive tube into the blood or the lymph streams. Two of the processes involved in this activity are *osmosis* and *diffusion*. However, physical processes alone cannot account for all of the intricacies of absorption, and *active transport* must be given credit for much of the action. These processes are described on pages 23–26.

From the mouth and stomach

There is no absorption of food from the mouth. However, certain drugs, such as nitroglycerin, can pass through the oral epithelium into the blood stream.

Absorption from the stomach is very limited. Alcohol, a small amount of water, and a few drugs are thought to be absorbed from this part of the digestive tube.

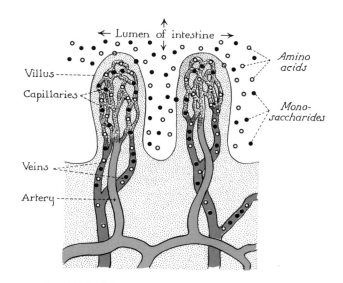

Fig. 17-1. Diagram of absorption of carbohydrate and protein; monosaccharides and amino acids enter the capillaries of the villi.

From the small intestine

The greatest amount of absorption takes place from the small intestine for several important reasons: (1) food is in an absorbable form inasmuch as all of the enzymes required for complete digestion are readily available; (2) the circular folds, the villi, and the microvilli provide a great surface area for absorption (in addition, villi are in constant motion owing to the activity of smooth muscle fibers in the mucosa; this helps to stir the intestinal contents and promote maximal contact between the absorptive surface and the nutrients); (3) blood and lymph vessels are abundant; (4) food remains in the small intestine for a relatively long period of time.

Absorption of Organic Materials. The *simple sugars*—glucose, galactose and fructose—are absorbed by an active transport carrier mechanism. They enter the blood stream in the intestinal capillaries as shown in Figure 17-1.

Fatty acids and *glycerol*, products of fat digestion, enter the epithelial cells of the intestinal mucosa separately. Glycerol enters as such, but bile salts help to "ferry" the fatty acids across the cell membranes; energy is not required for this process. During their passage through the epithelial cells, fatty acids and glycerol are resynthesized to microscopic droplets of neutral fats (Fig. 17-2). Most of these neutral fats then enter the lymphatic capillaries (lacteals) in the villi (Fig. 17-3) and are carried off in the lymph which ultimately flows into the blood stream. Small quantities of short-chain fatty acids may be absorbed directly into the blood stream rather than being converted to chylomicrons, the latter being too large to enter a blood capillary.

Amino acids are absorbed by an active transport system and enter the blood capillaries, as shown in Figure 17-1. For all practical nutritional purposes, protein is absorbed only in the form of amino acids. However, extremely small quantities

Fig. 17-2. Diagram of absorption of fat. Glycerol enters the epithelial cells as such; fatty acids combine with bile salts which help to "ferry" them into the epithelial cells. Within the cells, the fatty acids are freed, and they unite with the glycerol to form neutral fat, which enters the lacteals. Some short chain fatty acids may be absorbed directly into the blood stream.

of *whole protein* may be absorbed at times, probably by the process of pinocytosis (p. 26); inasmuch as protein can act as an antigen, this may have some relation to food allergies.

Absorption of Inorganic Materials. *Sodium* and some *chloride* are absorbed by active transport; however, the transport of sodium (Na$^+$) creates sufficient electrical potential to pull chloride (Cl$^-$) with it. *Potassium* is absorbed passively. *Calcium* absorption is related to body needs; parathyroid hormone (p. 558) and vitamin D are thought to play an important role in regulating the absorption of this important ion. *Iron* also requires a special mechanism for transport, which depends, in part, on body needs.

Water is absorbed principally by osmosis. As the inorganic salts and nutrients are absorbed, the intestinal fluid becomes hypotonic, which means that water then will be absorbed by the osmotic process.

From the large intestine

Great quantities of water are absorbed in the large intestine, as witnessed by the fact that fecal material entering the cecum is in a liquid state, but by the time it reaches the rectum it is normally a soft, semisolid mass. There is no significant absorption of food in this part of the alimentary canal.

Fig. 17-3. Lacteals or lymphatic capillaries in intestine of rat; filled with dye. In man there is a single lacteal in each villus. (After Ranvier)

METABOLISM

Metabolism refers to all the changes in foodstuffs from the time they are absorbed from the small intestine until they are excreted as waste products from the body. Metabolism consists of 2 phases: *anabolism* (meaning "a building up") and *catabolism* (meaning "to throw down"). In other words, during the phase of anabolism, substances are built up, while during the phase of catabolism, substances are broken down by oxidative processes with the release of energy, as heat and work, or the storage of energy, in the form of "high energy-bond" phosphate.

The processes of metabolism are carried out by means of **enzymes** within the cells. These intracellular enzymes are so important that if even one of them is missing or malfunctioning, the effects may be quite serious; such persons are said to have an *inborn error of metabolism*. For example, phenylketonuria is a condition in which the amino acid phenylalanine cannot be properly metabolized in the body, due to the absence of a single enzyme (phenylalanine hydroxylase). If left untreated, phenylketonuria interferes with brain development and results in mental retardation.

Without their normal complement of enzymes, cells cannot reproduce, they cannot convert food substances to energy or to new protoplasm, etc.

Many of the enzymatic reactions, in turn, are dependent on the presence of certain vitamins, as noted in the preceding chapter; these reactions also are regulated by hormones which are produced by the endocrine glands.

Energy metabolism

Energy is involved in every activity that occurs within the body. The beating of the heart, the digestion and the absorption of food, the building and repair of tissue, etc., cannot occur without energy. In fact, the very organization of each living cell depends on complicated chemical reactions that require a constant supply of energy. Without energy there is disorganization of cells, illness and death. Thus, the energy needs of the body must take precedence over all others.

To supply the constant demand for energy, nature has devised an ingenious process, called *biologic oxidation*, that enables one to procure energy from food without burning up body tissue at the same time. Due to the catalytic action of intracellular enzymes, food can be burned at low temperatures which are compatible with the life of the cell. Biologic oxidation is a step-wise process that has been compared with the orderly progression of a boat through a series of locks in a river, rather than plunging over the falls. As illustrated in Figure 17-4, the end products of digestion are ultimately oxidized in a series of steps by way of the *citric acid cycle* (Kreb's cycle). In addition to carbon dioxide and water, a tremendous amount of energy is liberated; some of this energy keeps the body warm, and the remainder is stored temporarily in the high-energy phosphate bonds of **ATP** (adenosinetriphosphate).

ATP frequently is compared to a cocked and loaded gun in that it is always ready to "fire" and release its energy when needed by the cells. In Chapter 4 we discussed the utilization of the energy derived from ATP during muscle contraction, but this is only a small part of the total picture. ATP is found in every living cell, where it provides the energy required not only for mechanical work but also for chemical work, such as the building and repair of protoplasm.

Carbohydrates, fats and proteins all contain stored energy that can be transferred to ATP following biologic oxidation in the citric acid cycle. This potential energy value of food is referred to as the caloric or heat value. A large calorie, abbreviated Cal., is the amount of heat required to raise the temperature of 1 Kg. (2.2 lbs.) of water 1 degree centigrade.

Carbohydrates are very easily burned, and they serve as a quick source of energy. Each gram of carbohydrate releases 4 Cal. of heat when it is oxidized. Fats have an even higher caloric value as they yield 9 Cal./Gm. when oxidized. Under normal conditions, only a relatively small amount of protein is used to supply energy, but each gram yields 4 Cal. on oxidation. When food intake is severely restricted, as in starvation, the oxidation of body protein is of major importance. Since energy needs take precedence over all others, the very protoplasm of the cells is oxidized to meet those needs. It is obvious that death will be the ultimate result if food intake is not resumed.

Basal metabolism refers to the energy output required to keep a person alive; that is, to maintain his body temperature and to keep his respiration and circulation going. It is related to one's surface area, being about 1,000 Cal. per square meter of body surface per day. This is about 38 to 40 Cal. per square meter per hour for men, and 36 to 38 for women. Variations of plus or minus 10 per cent are permitted in the normal range. This means that on the basis of 40 Cal. for men, the limits are 36(40−4) and 44(40+4) Cal. per square meter per hour. The basal metabolic rate, or B.M.R., commonly is reported as a percentage of normal. For example, if a man's B.M.R. is recorded as "+30" it means that it is 30 per cent higher than the normal for a person of his size, age, and sex.

In the laboratory, the basal metabolic rate can be determined by an "indirect" method; this means that only the oxygen consumption is measured. The subject breathes into a special chamber by means of a rubber tube leading to his mouth, his nose being clamped off. After a given period of time the amount of oxygen used from the chamber is measured. Each liter of oxygen consumed is equivalent to a certain number of calories, and from this the B.M.R. can be calculated. During the test, the subject must be at complete rest and have had nothing to eat since dinner the previous evening.

Several factors influence the basal metabolic rate. For example, it varies with age, being higher in children, since they are growing rapidly. It is higher in men than in women, the former generally being larger and having more muscle tissue. It varies also with the state of nutrition, being low in malnutrition. Abnormal activity of the thyroid gland may cause marked changes in the B.M.R., since the thyroid hormone plays an important role in determining the rate at which chemical reactions proceed in the cells. If this gland is overactive, the basal metabolic rate is elevated beyond the normal limits, and, if underactive, the basal rate is depressed below the normal limits. However, the B.M.R. measures only the over-all oxygen consumption; it may be increased in unrecognized infections, congestive heart failure and various other conditions not related to the thyroid. For this reason, determination of the amount of protein-bound iodine (PBI) in the plasma is of greater diagnostic value than is the B.M.R. in regard to thyroid function (p. 555).

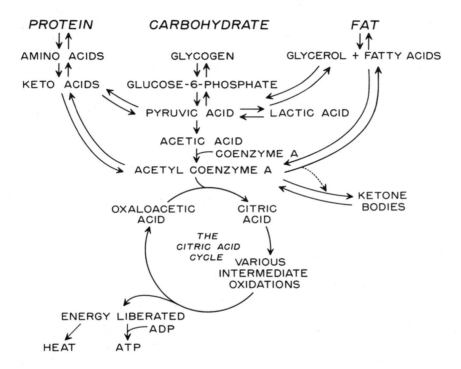

Fig. 17-4. Diagrammatic representation of ways in which all major foods may enter the citric acid cycle (Kreb's Cycle) for biologic oxidation and related energy liberation. Arrows also indicate pathways whereby one food group may be converted to another: e.g., amino acids to carbohydrate, carbohydrate to fat, and so on. Oxidative reactions of the citric acid cycle take place within the fluid interior of each mitochondrion, while ATP formation takes place nearby along the folds of the inner membrane.

The total caloric requirement is subject to great individual variation, since it depends on the energy expended when one is eating, working or playing, in addition to the basic needs previously described. For the average sedentary student a maximum of 2,400 Cal. is sufficient, but a man at very hard muscular work may require 6,000 to 8,000 Cal. to meet his energy needs. In any case, caloric intake should be balanced by energy output. Difficulty arises when one who follows a sedentary occupation takes in the amount of food needed by a heavy laborer.

Obesity or overweight frequently is due to an excessive intake of food, beyond the needs of the body. The excess is stored as adipose tissue. For weight control, the caloric intake should be reduced, yet the diet can be balanced and contain essential salts and vitamins. Peculiar diets are usually not satisfactory, and "reducing pills" may be harmful.

Carbohydrate metabolism

Carbohydrate metabolism includes all the reactions undergone in the body by carbohydrates which have been ingested as part of the diet and by those which are formed in the body from other sources, such as pyruvic acid, lactic acid, amino acids and glycerol. However, the main purpose underlying all carbohydrate metabolism is the ultimate provision of *energy* through oxidative reactions in the citric acid cycle. Only a small amount of carbohydrate is involved in the building of tissues.

Utilization of Glucose. In discussing the highlights of carbohydrate metabolism we shall list the various pathways that are open to glucose following its absorption from the small intestine into the blood stream.

1. Some glucose may enter the tissues immediately and be oxidized to carbon dioxide and water, with the release of energy needed to maintain body temperature and to enable one to do muscular work.

2. Glucose that is not needed for the moment will be converted to glycogen (glycogenesis) for temporary storage in the liver and in muscle cells. ATP provides the necessary energy for the synthesis of glycogen. Slightly less than one pound of carbohydrate can be stored in the body.

3. When the glycogen "storage bins" are filled, another portion of glucose is changed to fat and stored as adipose tissue. There are fat depots in the subcutaneous tissues, around the kidneys, in the mesentery and the greater omentum as well as in various other regions of the body.

4. If there is a large intake of carbohydrate within a short period of time, such as when one eats a generous amount of candy at one sitting, some of the glucose may be eliminated by the kidneys. When the "factories" that normally handle glucose are flooded by a sudden large intake, the excess spills over into the urine (alimentary glycosuria). A similar spillage may occur in cases of uncontrolled diabetes mellitus. Due to a deficiency of insulin, diabetic patients are unable to metabolize carbohydrate efficiently, their blood sugar level is high, and much glucose is lost in the urine.

5. When the blood sugar level begins to fall, as it usually does between meals, the liver responds in two ways. First, it converts its stores of glycogen into glucose for release into the blood stream (glycogenolysis). Secondly, liver cells have the necessary skill to form glucose molecules from noncarbohydrate sources (gluconeogenesis). For example, some of the lactic acid and the pyruvic acid produced during muscle contraction is carried in the blood stream to the liver and there converted to glucose. Amino acids and glycerol also can be utilized by the liver in forming blood sugar when necessary to meet the energy needs of the body.

The average range for blood glucose is between 80 and 110 mg. per 100 ml. of blood. Normally, the blood glucose level varies continually, but within rather narrow limits due to the homeostatic mechanisms described above.

Catabolism of Carbohydrate. There are two catabolic processes involved in the liberation of energy from carbohydrates. The first, or *anaerobic phase,* results in the breakdown of glycogen with the formation of pyruvic and lactic acids;

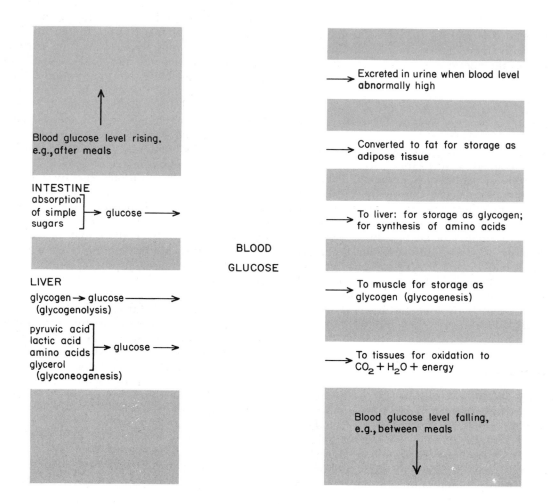

Fig. 17-5. Diagrammatic summary of carbohydrate metabolism. Sources of blood glucose are indicated on the left, and means of utilizing glucose are indicated on the right. Note that as the blood glucose level begins to fall below normal levels, the liver converts glycogen and other substances to glucose and releases it into the blood. As the blood glucose level rises above normal levels, glucose is stored as glycogen and fat; in extreme cases, it is eliminated by the kidneys.

oxygen is not required in this process, and only a few ATP molecules are formed (Fig. 4-10).

In the second, or *aerobic phase,* pyruvic acid (and lactic acid that is converted to pyruvic acid) is oxidized to acetic acid. The acetic acid then reacts with a special substance, called coenzyme A, forming *acetyl coenzyme A* (acetyl CoA). Acetyl CoA also is known as "active acetate," as it is chemically more active than is acetic acid; ATP provides the energy source for this activation process:

ATP

acetic acid + coenzyme A → acetyl coenzyme A

As shown in Figure 17-4, acetyl coenzyme A reacts with oxaloacetic acid to form citric acid, and the great cycle of oxidation is underway. The detailed reactions that occur during the citric acid cycle are beyond the scope of this textbook, but an important result of these reactions is the liberation of a large amount of energy. Forty per cent of this energy is stored primarily in the high-energy phosphate bonds of ATP, and 60 per cent is liberated as heat, which is distributed to all parts of the body by way of the blood stream. The regulation of body temperature is described on pages 510–517.

Lipid metabolism

Absorbed lipids are transported in the blood partly as chylomicrons, and partly as lipoprotein complexes. In addition, there may be free fatty acids loosely combined with albumin. Chylomicrons are composed primarily of triglycerides (simple lipids) combined with a small amount of cholesterol, phospholipid and protein; the lipoprotein complexes contain less triglyceride and more cholesterol, phospholipid and protein. The sources of these lipids are: absorption from the small intestine, mobilization of depot fat, and synthesis in the liver.

Utilization of Lipids. Lipids are vital constituents of all living cells and, when oxidized, they also are an important source of energy. The stor-

age of lipids in the form of adipose tissue provides insulation and mechanical protection as well as energy reserves. The liver serves as a "central clearing house" in lipid metabolism, as it is the principal site for the synthesis of lipids and also for their degradation (i.e., making them less complex by splitting off one or more groups).

The storage of fats (simple lipids) involves the formation of adipose tissue in various parts of the body. Because one can store only a small amount of carbohydrate (less than one pound), these fat deposits constitute the bulk of stored, energy-producing food in the body. Depot fat is in a continuous state of change, which means that it is constantly being deposited and remobilized; however, "deposits" may exceed "withdrawals" when there is an excessive intake of food.

Under normal conditions, the liver is able to oxidize any fat that is conveyed to it; thus there is no accumulation. However, should large quantities of fat be mobilized from the depots and transferred to the liver, there may be an accumulation resulting in the condition known as *fatty liver;* this may occur in such conditions as untreated diabetes mellitus, starvation, and the consumption of a high-fat diet.

The oxidation of fatty acids involves a complex series of reactions that result in the formation of a number of molecules of acetyl CoA, the two-carbon compound previously described above. For example, one typical fatty acid (palmitic) consists of a chain of 15 carbon atoms attached to the carbon of a carboxyl group (COOH), giving a total of 16 carbons:

Palmitic acid

The first step in the breakdown of the above molecule involves its activation; this is accomplished by a coupling with coenzyme A (CoA) to form fatty acyl CoA:

(Fatty acyl CoA)

Next, through a series of reactions involving the removal of hydrogen atoms and the addition of water, the compound splits between the alpha and beta carbons (the alpha carbon is that attached to the COOH group, the beta is that next to alpha). The long portion of the chain then combines with a new molecule of CoA, while the short portion remains combined with the original CoA, thus forming a molecule of acetyl CoA:

(Fatty acyl CoA)

and

(Acetyl CoA)

The beta-oxidation of fatty acids takes place mainly in the liver cells, but it can occur in other tissues as well. In any event, the process is repeated until the entire molecule of fatty acid has been broken down and 8 molecules of acetyl CoA

have been formed. Inasmuch as each triglyceride molecule usually contains 3 long-chain fatty acids, one can see why fats have a greater caloric yield than do carbohydrates (i.e., one molecule of glucose provides only 2 molecules of acetyl CoA).

Although the liver cells generate far more acetyl CoA than is required for their own metabolic needs, this valuable compound normally does not go to waste. Instead, when there is an excess, the liver condenses two molecules of acetyl CoA to form one molecule of *acetoacetic acid.* This keto acid diffuses into the blood stream and is carried to active tissues throughout the body. Upon entering a tissue cell, the process is reversed and two molecules of acetyl CoA are formed; these molecules then enter the citric acid cycle and are oxidized with the liberation of energy. Normally, the amount of acetoacetic acid in the blood rarely exceeds 1 mg. per cent, but in certain metabolic disorders it may accumulate and lead to ketosis.

Ketosis. The so-called "ketone bodies" include *acetoacetic acid* along with two substances that are derived from it, *beta-hydroxybutyric acid* and *acetone.* When these substances accumulate in the blood (ketonemia) and are found in the urine (ketonuria), a state of *ketosis* is said to exist.

Ketosis may be severe when carbohydrate metabolism is depressed and the body is deriving most of its energy from the metabolism of fats. For example, in untreated diabetes mellitus a lack of insulin prevents the transport of glucose into the cells; thus the body must turn to fat as an alternative source of energy. As a result, large quantities of acetyl CoA are generated, and ketone bodies pour out of the liver for delivery to the cells. Unfortunately the tissue cells are limited in their ability to metabolize ketone bodies; thus these substances begin to accumulate and ketosis develops. In a similar manner, ketosis can occur in starvation, or in consumption of a high-fat diet.

Acetoacetic acid and beta-hydroxybutyric acid are relatively strong organic acids; thus an excessive accumulation may cause severe *acidosis* for 2 reasons. First, their mere presence in the blood tends to deplete the basic or alkaline half of the buffer systems (p. 298). Second, and even more important, large quantities of these acids are accompanied by sodium during their excretion by means of the kidney; this not only decreases the amount of base available to buffer acids, but also leads to dehydration, because water is lost whenever sodium is lost. Acetone is eliminated in two ways. Because it is a volatile substance, small quantities are blown off in expired air from the lungs, and persons with severe ketosis have the odor of acetone on their breath. Acetone also is eliminated in the urine.

Various laboratory procedures are utilized in analyzing the total concentration of ketone bodies, thus enabling a physician to determine the degree of ketosis that exists. Treatment must be started promptly, because uncontrolled ketosis ultimately leads to coma and death.

Biosynthesis of Lipids. Although the major pathway for acetyl CoA is its oxidation by means of the citric acid cycle, this two-carbon compound actually serves as a "bridge" between catabolism and anabolism. In other words, acetyl CoA serves not only as a source of energy, but also as the major precursor in the synthesis of fatty acids, acetylcholine, cholesterol and other steroids. Free glycerol serves as the precursor for the triglycerides and some of the phospholipids.

Protein metabolism

The primary function of protein is to supply the amino acids necessary for building new protoplasm, blood proteins, enzymes and many of the hormones that regulate the chemical processes of the body. Proteins also are burned for energy, but this is not their chief function.

There are 3 sources of amino acids in the blood: absorption from the small intestine, synthesis by liver and tissue cells and catabolism of tissue protein. The amino acids in the blood constitute a pool that can be drawn on for all purposes of protein metabolism. In other words, the story of protein metabolism is essentially the story of what happens to amino acids as they enter and leave this dynamic plasma pool (Fig. 17-7).

Amino Acid Synthesis. All amino acids are needed by the body, but only certain ones can be formed within the body. Those which cannot be synthesized are called *essential* amino acids, and they must be obtained from ingested food. On the other hand, *nonessential* amino acids can be synthesized in the liver if they are missing from the diet. For example, the liver cells can transfer the amino group (NH_2) from an amino acid to a keto acid and so form a different amino acid (transamination). These amazing cells also can form an amino group from some other nitrogen-containing compound (e.g., ammonia) and add it to a keto acid, forming an amino acid (amination). In this way new substances are formed.

The amino acid nitrogen in the body is shifting continually from one amino acid to another, being added to the pool, then withdrawn from the pool

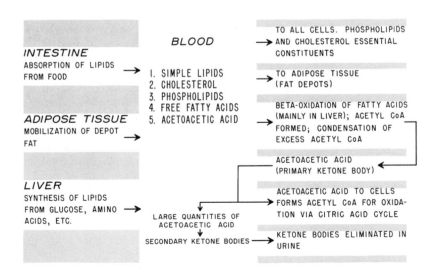

Fig. 17-6. Diagram of lipid metabolism. Sources of blood lipids are indicated on the left. The means of utilizing these lipids and related substances are indicated on the right.

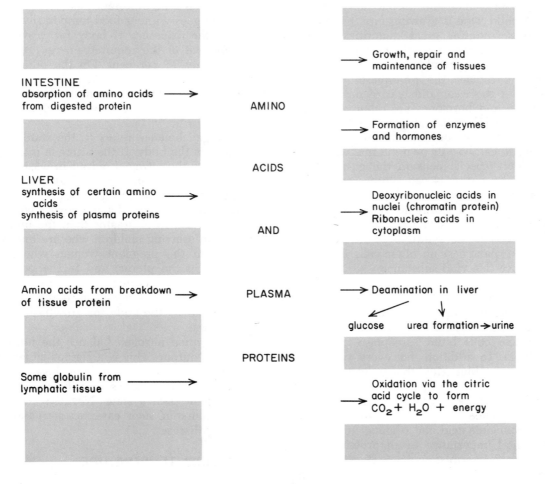

INTESTINE
absorption of amino acids ⟶
from digested protein

AMINO

⟶ Growth, repair and
maintenance of tissues

⟶ Formation of enzymes
and hormones

ACIDS

LIVER
synthesis of certain amino ⟶
acids
synthesis of plasma proteins

AND

⟶ Deoxyribonucleic acids in
nuclei (chromatin protein)
Ribonucleic acids in
cytoplasm

Amino acids from breakdown ⟶
of tissue protein

PLASMA

⟶ Deamination in liver

glucose   urea formation ⟶ urine

PROTEINS

Some globulin from ⟶
lymphatic tissue

⟶ Oxidation via the citric
acid cycle to form
$CO_2 + H_2O$ + energy

Fig. 17-7. Diagram of protein metabolism. Sources of amino acids and plasma proteins are indicated on the left, and the means of utilizing amino acids are indicated on the right.

and incorporated into tissue, liver or plasma protein, then split and again returned to the pool. Urea is the chief nitrogenous waste product. Lesser ones are creatinine and ammonium salts.

Protein Synthesis in Body Tissue. As blood flows through the vast capillary networks of the body, each tissue selects the specific amino acids needed to build the kinds of protein required for growth, maintenance and proper function of that tissue. A child, who is growing rapidly and building tissues, requires great quantities of amino acids as new protoplasm is being formed all over his body. As one gets older, amino acids still are required to replace the protoplasm that breaks down under the wear and tear of daily living.

Enzymes and hormones are other examples of protein synthesis by the body tissues. While every cell in the body can produce the enzymes that are necessary to catalyze its own internal chemical reactions, only special cells in the gastrointestinal tract and the pancreas can synthesize the extracellular enzymes needed to digest food. The production of certain hormones also requires the services of highly specialized cells. A good example of this is the synthesis of insulin by islet cells in the pancreas; no other cells in the body can produce this vital substance.

The most fascinating aspect of the whole subject of protein synthesis by the tissue cells concerns the mechanism whereby cells "know" what to build from the amino acids in the blood—i.e., why muscle cells build sarcoplasm rather than hemoglobin. In addition, for every type of protein there is a "blueprint" that indicates the exact sequence of amino acids; i.e., one arrangement of amino acids results in a molecule of albumin, but another sequence is required to produce globulin. Deoxyribonucleic acid and ribonucleic acid are of fundamental importance in all protein synthesis, as previously described on pages 29–30.

Catabolic pathways are followed by protein molecules when they are needed as a source of energy, and in the ingestion of a high-protein diet. In either case, amino acids are *deaminized* in the liver to form ammonia and keto acids. The ammonia is converted to urea and eliminated in the urine. Some of the keto acids are converted to glucose, others to ketone bodies; these substances, in turn, provide sources of acetyl CoA or other constituents of the citric acid cycle. When energy needs must be met, acetyl CoA enters the citric acid cycle (Fig. 17-4). However, if energy is not required and if structural protein supplies are adequate, the acetyl CoA can be converted to glycogen or to fat for storage; thus it is possible to "get fat" on a high-protein diet.

If one goes without food temporarily (a fasting state), the oxidation of body fat provides about 85 per cent of the required energy, protein supplying only 15 per cent. On the other hand, in starvation, when the fats have been used up, *all* energy comes from protein catabolism; emaciation and death will follow if food intake is not resumed.

Nitrogen balance refers to the state of protein balance in the body. If the nitrogen intake in food is equal to the nitrogen output in waste products, one is said to be in nitrogen balance; this is the healthy state of an average adult.

A *positive* nitrogen balance exists when the intake of nitrogen is greater than the output. This occurs in growing children who are building new tissues, in the pregnant woman whose baby is growing in the uterus, and in the postoperative patient who is repairing tissues. In such cases less deamination is going on, since the amino acids are needed by the body for growth and repair of protoplasm.

In *negative* nitrogen balance the intake is less than the output. This is a serious situation, since nitrogen must be coming from the breakdown of the person's own tissues, and life cannot continue for long in such a state. Negative nitrogen balance occurs in such cases as starvation and in wasting diseases.

THE BODY TEMPERATURE

The maintenance of a fairly constant body temperature in man is another example of homeostasis in which many activities are correlated to accomplish one purpose. As long as one is alive, heat is produced. The amount produced in health varies greatly in accordance with the activity of

Activity of cardiac and smooth muscles
Unconscious tensing of muscles
Voluntary activity, skeletal muscles
Secretion, digestion, absorption   Vaporization
Specific dynamic action of food   Conduction
Basal heat production   Radiation
Posterior hypothalamus heat production   Anterior hypothalamus heat loss

Fig. 17-8. Balance between heat production and heat loss. Heat production is increased when one is exposed to either very hot or very cold environments, by increase in the rate of metabolism. It is increased, also, by thyroxin and by epinephrine. Heat loss is decreased by wool clothing, vasoconstriction, piloerection, and decreasing the body surface by certain postures. It is increased by scant cotton clothing, sitting in a breeze, vasodilatation, sweating, the ingestion of cold food and beverages, inhaling cold air, increasing the radiating surface by certain postures. (From Greisheimer, E. M., Physiology and Anatomy, ed. 8, Philadelphia, Lippincott.)

skeletal muscles, the type of food eaten, the temperature of the surroundings and the condition of certain endocrine glands. If an adult man rested for 24 hours and took no food, he would produce about 1,700 Cal. of heat. If he were moderately active he would produce about 3,000 Cal., and if he did heavy work he would produce about 7,000 Cal. Not only are there such wide variations in health, but the variations may be equally wide in infectious diseases and glandular disturbances. Whatever the amount of heat produced in the body, the cooperation of the circulatory system is needed to distribute the heat throughout the body.

Since heat is produced continuously during life, it must be lost continuously (Fig. 17-8). If there were no heat loss, the temperature of the body under basal conditions would rise by 1.8° F. per hour; with moderate activity it would rise by 3.6° F. per hour. It is evident that not only must there be continued loss of heat, but the amount lost must vary also in accordance with changes in heat production. Most of the heat loss takes place through the skin and is regulated by the amount of blood flowing through the cutaneous vessels and also by the activity of the sweat glands.

In order to maintain a balance between heat production and heat loss, fine adjustments are needed. A device somewhat like a thermostat is required, but the regulating mechanism in the body differs from a thermostat in that heat production cannot be "turned off completely," no matter how hot the external environment becomes. Heat production in the body cannot drop below the *basal* level.

The mechanisms for temperature regulation are so efficient in health that only when one does exceedingly heavy work or when the environmental conditions interfere with heat loss does the body temperature depart from the normal range. Since one adjusts so well to both external and internal "threats," a departure from normal body temperature has come to be one of the cardinal signs of disease.

HEAT PRODUCTION

Heat production in man cannot be decreased below the basal level even when the temperature of the external surroundings is so high that life is in danger. In fact, heat production increases in proportion to the temperature of the external environment. Thus, it adds an internal threat to the external threat.

On the other hand, heat production increases also when one is exposed to a cold environmental temperature, but it cannot be increased to such an extent that it protects a person against extreme cold, and he can "freeze" to death.

Activity of muscles and glands

Heat is produced by the oxidation of foodstuffs in all the cells of the body, but since a great part of the body is composed of **skeletal muscles**, most of the heat is produced by oxidations in them. When skeletal muscles are relaxed, as during rest or sleep, heat production is lowest; it is highest during strenuous exercise. If the body temperature begins to fall, and one does not voluntarily do something to correct this condition, a reflex mechanism will initiate shivering to increase the production of heat.

Heat also is produced during the secretory activities of the **glands.** Since the liver is the largest and busiest gland in the body, it is an important source of heat, particularly when the skeletal muscles are relaxed during sleep.

The heat that is produced in any tissue is distributed to all parts of the body by means of the circulating blood. This prevents overheating in any one organ.

Food Intake. The intake of food is associated with increased heat production. This is due in part to the activity of the smooth muscle tissue of the gastrointestinal tract and to the marked activity of the glands that secrete the digestive juices. Heat also is produced by the epithelial cells of the small intestine during their activities connected with the absorption of foodstuffs.

One of the requirements for basal metabolic tests is that no food be eaten during the preceding 14 to 18 hours. The reason for this is to avoid the increased heat production associated with digestive and absorptive processes.

HEAT LOSS

The major channel of heat loss is the skin, but a certain loss also occurs through the lungs and the excreta. Heat is lost from the body by the physical processes of radiation, conduction, convection, and vaporization (Fig. 17-9).

Radiation

Radiation is the transfer of heat through the air from the surface of one object to the surface of another without physical contact. One loses heat by radiation only if the surroundings are cooler than the body. If the surroundings are warmer, heat will be transferred to the body; this may be a distinct disadvantage under certain circumstances and may interfere with the "physiologic" regulation of temperature. Under ordinary conditions, in a temperate climate, the greatest loss of body heat occurs through radiation from the skin. The amount and type of clothing that one wears, as well as the amount of heat brought to the skin by the circulating blood, will greatly influence the radiation process.

Conduction

Conduction refers to the transfer of heat from one object to another by direct physical contact. Man loses heat by conduction to the air that is in contact with the skin (if it is cooler than the skin), to clothing, to air in the respiratory passages, to cold food and beverages in the alimentary canal, to cold furniture, etc. Since man protects himself by clothing, the loss of heat by conduction through the skin may not be great. Air is a poor conductor of heat, and the protective value of clothing is proportional to the thickness of the layer of still air trapped in the meshes or between the layers of material.

Convection

The movement of air is known as convection, and heat may be lost from the body by convection air currents. As heat is conducted to the air surrounding the body, it warms that air; the heated air rises and is replaced by denser, cool air. Electric fans, cool winds, and the like cause the warm air to be replaced more rapidly. Clothing, on the other hand, reduces heat loss by convection.

Vaporization

Vaporization refers to loss of heat when water evaporates or changes from the liquid to the vapor state. Each gram of water that evaporates (at body temperature) requires 0.58 Cal. of heat.

Some of our body heat is lost by saturating the expired air with water vapor from the lining of the respiratory tract, but the amount lost in this way depends on the temperature and humidity of the inspired air. The amount of water lost by vaporization from the lungs is about 300 ml. daily.

The greater part of heat loss by vaporization is through the skin. A continuous loss of heat through the "insensible" loss of water occurs, since one loses from 300 to 800 ml. of water daily by this means. The loss of heat by evaporation of perspiration ("sensible" loss) varies with the tem-

Fig. 17-9. Heat loss in different climatic conditions, by conduction (including convection), radiation, and vaporization from the skin. (From Greisheimer, E. M., Physiology and Anatomy, ed. 8, Philadelphia, Lippincott.)

perature and the relative humidity of the external air. The maximum rate of vaporization of sweat is about 1.6 L. per hour, such as occurs during work in a hot dry atmosphere.

The flexibility of the skin temperature in man is the most important device for adjusting heat loss. The water of the plasma takes up heat in the warmer parts of the body, such as the liver and the skeletal muscles, and gives it up in cooler regions, such as the skin. The amount of heat distributed to a cutaneous area is determined by the rate of blood flow through the area. If the vessels are constricted the blood flow is curtailed, and there is less heat to be eliminated by radiation, conduction, convection and vaporization. If there is vasodilation the skin is warmer, and more heat will be eliminated. The amount of blood flowing through the skin can be varied markedly; it can be decreased to almost zero or increased to as much as 12 per cent of the total blood flow. In the fingers the blood flow can be changed from about 1 ml. to 90 ml. per 100 Gm. of tissue per minute. The blood flow through the hands and the feet is particularly significant, since these are very important areas for dissipation of heat. Not only can the blood flow through arterioles, capillaries and venules be varied, but there are also arteriovenous anastomoses in the extremities through which blood can be shunted from arteries to veins without going through capillaries. This makes possible a great increase in the amount of blood flowing through the area concerned.

TEMPERATURE REGULATION

The hypothalamus is the center of integration for the regulation of body temperature. In the anterior portion there is an area that is sensitive to heat and protects the body against overheating. This is accomplished by dilatation of cutaneous blood vessels, stimulation of sweat glands and relaxation of skeletal muscles. If the anterior portion of the hypothalamus is damaged, fever will ensue, and there will be a permanent inability to regulate the body temperature on exposure to hot environments.

In the posterior region there is an area that is sensitive to cold and protects the body against overcooling. This is accomplished by vasoconstriction of cutaneous vessels, inhibition of sweat glands and stimulation of skeletal muscles (shivering). If the posterior portion of the hypothalamus is damaged, there is inactivity, no shivering and no vasoconstriction on exposure to cold.

It is evident that both somatic and visceral efferent nerves are involved in the body's response to temperature changes in the environment. If a resting individual is exposed to heat or cold, the thermal-sensitive receptors in the skin are stimulated. The afferent impulses course to the hypothalamus, and the appropriate responses are mediated.

In addition to the cutaneous thermal receptors, it is assumed that there are temperature-sensitive receptors in the hypothalamus. When a redistribution of blood, a change in skeletal muscle activity and a change in pulmonary ventilation are required in the regulation of body temperature, it is likely that the central receptors are more important than the cutaneous ones. In other words, the latter are involved when one is passive, and the former when temperature must be regulated during strenuous exercise.

PHYSIOLOGIC VARIATIONS IN BODY TEMPERATURE

The range of temperature found in a large number of healthy, young adults was 96.5° to 99.3°, with an average of 98.1° F.

There is a daily or diurnal variation in body temperature, which is established at about 1 year of age. The temperature is lowest in the early morning, after several hours of rest in bed, when one is inactive and not digesting food. The temperature is highest in the late afternoon and the early evening, after a day of activity and after the evening meal. If the temperature is taken every hour over a 24-hour period, as much as 3° F. variation may be found, but the usual variation between the early morning and the late afternoon is about 1° F.

There is some variation in basal temperature with the menstrual cycle. Ovulation is thought

Fig. 17-10. Diagram of regulation of body temperature. Impulses from cutaneous and hypothalamic receptors initiate reflexes in somatic (skeletal muscles) and visceral (smooth muscle and glands) effectors that aid in maintaining homeostasis or relative constancy of body temperature. (From Greisheimer, E. M., Physiology and Anatomy, ed. 8, Philadelphia, Lippincott.)

to occur at the low point of the monthly temperature curve; the basal temperature then rises, reaching a peak within 24 hours after ovulation.

ABNORMAL VARIATIONS IN BODY TEMPERATURE

High external temperatures

Heat Exhaustion. When one is subjected to high external temperatures, one may perspire so much that heat exhaustion supervenes. This is possible because temperature regulation has priority over the maintenance of water and salt balance, and sweating continues even though it produces severe dehydration and marked sodium chloride loss. Heat exhaustion is characterized by the following: severe muscle cramps, pallor, low blood pressure, vertigo, weakness, nausea, vomiting and fainting. The symptoms are due to sodium chloride depletion and can be prevented by taking enough sodium chloride and water to make up for the excessive loss by perspiration.

Heat Stroke. This is seen most frequently in the person who has a pre-existing acute or chronic disease. When first exposed to excessive heat these persons perspire, and the loss of water leads to a decrease in plasma volume, with a decrease in cardiac output. This means a decreased blood flow through the skin. As the cutaneous blood supply becomes inadequate, sweat secretion diminishes and then ceases completely as circulatory failure supervenes.

When a major pathway of heat loss, namely, evaporation of sweat, is closed, the body temperature rises with explosive suddenness, and the general condition of the person becomes very critical. The skin is dry and flushed. As the body temperature rises to dangerously high levels the patient becomes comatose. The absence of sweat is the most striking characteristic of heat stroke. Death invariably occurs if the body temperature rises above 114° F. due to coagulation of the protein of protoplasm and irreversible inactivation of enzymes.

Low external temperatures

If the body is subjected to excessive cold, or if there is too great a loss of heat through insufficient clothing or by immersion in cold water, the body temperature falls markedly. As the body temperature falls, there is a feeling of exhaustion and an uncontrollable desire to sleep.

The respiration becomes slow, the blood pressure falls, the dissociation of oxyhemoglobin decreases, and coma occurs. One case is reported in which there was recovery after the body temperature had fallen to 64° F. The person was a woman who went to sleep in the street in very cold weather, while intoxicated. The body was stiff when found, but there was a faint sound, which was interpreted as a heart sound, about 12 times a minute. By means of excellent care, recovery took place, but amputation of both legs and of several fingers later was necessary, since the tissues had been irreparably damaged, probably due to the formation of crystals of ice within the cells.

Fever

Fever is an elevation of body temperature. It may be due to an infection, a reaction to a foreign protein, drugs, injury to the brain or lesions in the upper portion of the spinal cord.

The typical onset of chills and fever due to an infectious disease is as follows: (1) The person feels cold, is pale, has a dry skin and gooseflesh. (2) He cannot seem to get warm, even with extra clothing. (3) If he goes to bed and lies under several blankets, even with hot water bottles and heating pads, he still feels cold. (4) His teeth chatter, and he has such a severe chill (shivering) that he may shake the bed. (5) If his oxygen use were measured during the chill it would be found to be about 3 times as great as normal, which means that he is producing a large amount of heat. (6) In spite of increased heat production and minimal heat loss, the feeling of cold persists during the chill. (7) The extra heat is being stored in the body, and, at the end of the chill, the body temperature is elevated, having risen 3° or more during the chill.

The heat production of the body is increased during the course of the fever. It is increased about 7 per cent for each degree rise in body temperature. However, the heat loss keeps pace with heat production during the course of the fever, so it seems as if the thermostat is set at a higher level during the course of fever.

At the end of a fever that is permitted to run its course, the temperature may fall suddenly to the normal range. This sudden drop is called a *crisis*. It is the opposite of a chill, in that heat loss is increased markedly over heat production. The skeletal muscles are relaxed, the skin is flushed, and perspiration is profuse. The temperature returns to normal in the course of a few hours. When the return to normal temperature occurs slowly it is called *lysis*.

The significance of fever is unknown. It is possible that bacteria do not grow as well at the higher temperature, and perhaps the body forms antibodies more readily at the elevated temperature. Phagocytosis is increased during fever.

Defective regulation

Temperature regulation is poorly developed in newborn babies and is especially lacking in premature babies. In infants, a fit of screaming can cause a marked rise in body temperature, and warm and cold baths can alter the temperature more than in adults.

In elderly persons the temperature usually is subnormal. The body is less active, the circulation feeble, and there is less power of compensation for changes in external temperature. These persons are intolerant of extremes of external temperature.

Taking the temperature

Temperature may be taken several times a day in hospitalized persons, and physicians usually examine the temperature charts before they make their daily calls.

The close observation of body temperature in ill persons is most important, since the "optimum" body temperature for man extends over a limited range. The enzymes that take part in all cellular activities are very sensitive to temperature change, and may be irreversibly inactivated at high body temperatures.

The temperature may be taken in the mouth, the rectum or the axilla.

The *mouth temperature* is most variable. It is influenced by hot food or beverages, cold food or beverages, smoking, mouth breathing, talking, and evaporation of sweat from the face. The thermometer should be left in place for 3 minutes (under the tongue).

The *rectal temperature* is about 0.5° to 0.7° F. higher than that of the mouth and is the best guide to the internal temperature of the body. The thermometer should be inserted to a depth of 2 inches and left in place 3 minutes. Rectal temperatures are taken in preference to oral temperatures in small children, in very ill persons and in those that are delirious.

Axillary temperatures are about 1° F. lower than mouth temperatures. The thermometer should be left in place in the axilla for about 10 minutes.

Temperatures of 101° to 105° are found after severe muscular exercise and during infectious diseases, in which the temperature regulating mechanisms are efficient, but the thermostat is set at a higher level. The temperature during fever therapy may rise to 106° F. During heat stroke temperatures of 106° to 112° F. are found, but in this condition the temperature regulating mechanisms are impaired. Below 94° F., there is also an impairment of temperature regulation, and the ability to regulate temperature is lost completely when the body temperature falls to 82° F.

"Dehydration fever" is seen occasionally in children with low plasma volumes. It seems to be due to depression of sweat glands and responds readily to administration of water and sodium chloride.

SUMMARY

1. Absorption
   A. In stomach: slight; water, alcohol, certain drugs
   B. In small intestine: greatest here—food in diffusible form, large surface area, blood supply good, long time for contact
      a. Simple sugars and amino acids absorbed into blood stream; active transport
      b. Fatty acids "ferried" by bile salts into cells of mucosa, join glycerol to form neutral fats (tiny particles); most enter lymph stream (lacteal); some enter blood
      c. Na^+ and Cl^- absorbed by active transport, K^+ passively, Ca^{++} and Fe^{++} according to need
      d. H_2O absorbed by osmosis
   C. In large intestine: much water absorbed
2. Metabolism: all changes in foodstuffs from time of absorption until excreted
   A. Types: anabolism, catabolism

B. Enzymes within cells, vitamins and hormones play important role
C. Energy metabolism
   a. Energy needs take precedence over all others
   b. Biologic oxidation; citric acid cycle—release of large quantities of energy; stored in ATP
   c. Potential energy value of foods called caloric or heat value
   d. Basal metabolism: energy output required to keep one alive
   e. Total caloric requirement varies according to activity
D. Carbohydrate metabolism: main purpose is provision of energy
   a. Glucose pathways
      (1) To tissues for immediate oxidation and release of energy
      (2) Storage as glycogen or as adipose tissue until needed
      (3) Eliminated in urine if intake sudden and excessive, in diabetes mellitus when insulin deficient
      (4) If blood sugar falls, liver releases glucose (from glycogen stores), also forms glucose from noncarbohydrate sources
   b. Catabolism of carbohydrate
      (1) Anaerobic phase—break-down of glycogen to pyruvic and lactic acid
      (2) Aerobic phase—pyruvic acid to acetic acid to acetyl CoA, which then reacts with oxaloacetic acid to enter citric acid cycle; much energy released
E. Lipid metabolism: triglycerides, cholesterol, phospholipids, and free fatty acids found in blood
   a. Sources: absorption from intestine, depot fat, synthesis in liver
   b. Utilization: constituents of all cells; energy; protection
   c. Stored as adipose tissue
   d. Beta-oxidation of fatty acids yields acetyl CoA; excess forms ketone bodies
   e. Ketosis: accumulation of ketone bodies; excessive—causes acidosis
   f. Biosynthesis of lipids: acetyl CoA precursor for many
F. Protein metabolism: primary function to build and repair tissue, etc.
   a. Amino acid synthesis
      (1) Essential amino acids cannot be synthesized; must be obtained in diet
      (2) Nonessential amino acids can be formed in liver if necessary; transamination and amination to form new amino acids
   b. Urea is chief nitrogenous waste product
   c. Synthesis in body tissues
      (1) Each tissue selects needed amino acids from blood
      (2) Builds new protoplasm (child), repairs worn protoplasm (adult), forms intracellular enzymes
      (3) Special cells produce digestive enzymes, hormones, etc.
      (4) Under control of DNA and RNA
   d. Catabolic pathways; get rid of excess; provide energy; deamination
      (1) Amino acids converted to ammonia and keto acids
      (2) Ammonia converted to urea for elimination by kidney
      (3) Some keto acids converted to glucose, some to ketone bodies. Ultimately oxidized by way of citric acid cycle or converted to glycogen and fat
   e. Nitrogen balance: intake in food equal to output in waste
      (1) Positive balance—intake greater than output (e.g., child)
      (2) Negative balance—output greater than intake (e.g., starvation)
3. Heat production
   A. Cannot be decreased below basal level; cannot be increased to prevent freezing
   B. Activity of muscles and glands
      a. Heat produced by oxidation of foodstuffs in all cells, most prominently in skeletal muscles; production lowest during sleep, highest during exercise

b. Heat produced during glandular activity; liver is important source of heat during sleep

c. Heat produced during digestion and absorption of foods; activity of smooth muscle and glands

4. Heat loss
   A. Radiation: transfer through air without direct physical contact; from warmer to cooler object; most important channel for heat loss in temperate climate is radiation from skin
   B. Conduction: transfer from warmer object to cooler object by direct contact; man protects self by use of clothing; air a poor conductor of heat
   C. Vaporization: loss of heat by evaporation of water; e.g., perspiration from the skin; heat loss by this source varies with temperature and humidity of air
   D. Convection: heat loss through movement of air surrounding body
   E. Constancy of body temperature depends on balance between heat production and heat loss; skin most important in regulating heat loss
   F. Blood flow through the skin
      a. Increased or decreased by vasomotor activity
      b. Amount of blood flowing through skin determines amount of heat loss by radiation, conduction and convection

5. Temperature regulation
   A. Center of integration
      a. Anterior portion of hypothalamus protects against overheating
         (1) Vasodilatation of skin vessels
         (2) Stimulation of sweat glands
         (3) Maximum relaxation of skeletal muscles
      b. Posterior hypothalamus protects against overcooling
         (1) Vasoconstriction of skin vessels
         (2) Inhibition of sweat glands
         (3) Increased skeletal muscle tone
         (4) Shivering
      c. Hypothalamus stimulated by afferent impulses from skin and by temperature of blood flowing through
      d. Efferent impulses cause vasomotor changes, secretion of sweat, shivering

6. Physiologic variation in body temperature
   A. Average temperature range 96.5° to 99.3° F.
   B. Daily variation from 1° to 3° F.
      a. Lowest in early morning; highest in late afternoon and early evening
      b. Some variation with menstrual cycle

7. Abnormal variations in body temperature
   A. High external temperatures
      a. Heat exhaustion: extreme sweating; dehydration and salt loss
      b. Heat stroke: sweating ceases; explosive rise in temperature
   B. Low external temperatures
      a. Falling body temperature if too great heat loss
      b. Feeling of exhaustion, slow respiration, falling blood pressure, coma
   C. Fever: elevation of body temperature
      a. Patient feels cold, has dry skin, cannot seem to get warm, shivers; this sequence typical of fever onset in case of certain infectious diseases
      b. During course of fever, body temperature rises as heat production increases
      c. Fever may end with sudden drop in temperature (crisis), or slowly (lysis)
   D. Defective regulation: temperature regulation poorly developed in infant; elderly persons usually have subnormal temperature, body less active
   E. Temperature may be taken by mouth, by rectum or by axilla

---

PRACTICAL APPLICATIONS AND QUESTIONS

(Encircle the letter of the *best* answer to each of the following questions.)

A. Mr. H. B. was suffering from severe malnutrition after being lost in the mountains for a prolonged period of time. His total weight loss was 70 pounds.

---

1. Under ordinary circumstances the most abundant and economical source of energy is
   a. carbohydrate
   b. protein
   c. fat
   d. vitamins

2. When food intake is markedly reduced, the body first
   a. deaminizes protein
   b. forms glycogen to store energy
   c. mobilizes depot fat
   d. increases the production of vitamins

3. When all reserve food supplies have been exhausted the body will begin to oxidize constituents of the protoplasm of the cells because
   a. amino acids are released when protoplasm is broken down
   b. energy needs take priority over all others
   c. oxidation of amino acids provides a supply of protein in emergencies
   d. cholesterol in the cell releases fatty acids when oxidized

B. *One of the first symptoms Mr. L. L. experienced before his attack of pneumonia was a "chill." After being admitted to the hospital, he was told that he had a fever and that his temperature-regulatory mechanisms were temporarily out of balance.*

1. During a chill
   a. hcat production exceeds heat loss
   b. heat loss exceeds heat production
   c. heat loss and heat production are equal
   d. heat production temporarily stops completely

2. The center for temperature regulation is in the
   a. cerebellum
   b. medulla
   c. midbrain
   d. hypothalamus

3. On the fifth day, Mr. L. L.'s temperature dropped by crisis. Most of the heat lost during the crisis was lost by
   a. conduction
   b. radiation
   c. evaporation
   d. vasoconstriction

4. After Mr. L. L.'s temperature returned to normal, the nurses continued to take his temperature for 3 consecutive days. It was shown that there is a diurnal variation in man's body temperature of about
   a. 1°
   b. 5°
   c. 10°
   d. 0.1°

18

THE WORK OF THE KIDNEYS

The various metabolic activities of all living cells not only provide for the growth, the repair and the maintenance of tissues, but also result in the production of waste products which must be removed from the body. One of these waste products (carbon dioxide) is volatile, like smoke from a furnace, and is eliminated in the air that is exhaled from the lungs. Certain other waste products, such as food residues, are comparable to ashes in the furnace and are eliminated by way of the large intestine. Water is eliminated through all channels of excretion (lungs, skin, large intestine and kidneys). The remaining waste products (some inorganic salts and most of the nitrogenous waste products) require the special services of the kidneys for their elimination.

Waste products are formed continuously and must be eliminated continuously. In previous chapters we have considered the work of the skin, the lungs and the large intestine as they contributed to the removal of waste products. It now remains to discuss the work of the kidneys as they remove nitrogenous waste products from the blood and concentrate them in a fluid called urine. The elimination of urine, in turn, requires 2 ducts (the ureters) to convey urine from the kidneys to the urinary bladder, where it is stored temporarily, and another duct (the urethra) to carry urine from the bladder to the exterior of the body.

The production of urine is not the only function performed by the kidneys. The amount of water that they can eliminate is not limited to that needed to keep waste products in solution but can vary widely beyond this amount. This means that in health one's kidneys can produce either very dilute or very concentrated urine, and this flexibility or adjustability in elimination of water makes it possible for the kidneys to play a very important role in maintaining water balance. They serve as a "spillway" for water not needed by the body.

The amount of inorganic salts, particularly sodium chloride, excreted by the kidneys can vary widely also, and this indicates the essential function of the kidneys in the maintenance of salt balance. The kidneys also have the ability to manufacture ammonia and to substitute it for sodium and in this way to help maintain the acid-base balance of the body.

In summary, the kidneys contribute a generous share to homeostasis or maintenance of the constancy of the internal environment by removing and excreting waste and by conserving useful substances and returning them to the plasma. Without normally functioning kidneys it would be impossible to preserve the normal composition of the plasma and the tissue fluid.

THE KIDNEYS

Location

The kidneys are located in the posterior part of the abdominal cavity, one on either side of the vertebral column, behind the peritoneum. The kidneys are surrounded by masses of adipose tissue and loose areolar connective tissue. They rest on the psoas major and the quadratus lumborum muscles and on part of the diaphragm. The location is

shown in Figure 18-1, and the surface projections in Figure 1-7.

Fixation

The kidneys are not fixed in a rigid position against the abdominal wall, since they move with the diaphragm during inspiration. However, they are embedded in a mass of *adipose tissue* around which is found a supporting layer of fibrous tissue called the *renal fascia*. The large renal arteries and veins also give a measure of support to the kidney.

Gross appearance

The kidney presents a bean-shaped appearance, as its lateral border is convex, and the medial is concave. In the central portion of the concave border there is a deep longitudinal fissure, called the *hilus*, where vessels and nerves enter and leave and from which the ureter descends toward the urinary bladder. The kidney is covered with a fibrous capsule or tunic that provides a firm, smooth covering.

Longitudinal section

If a longitudinal or coronal section is made through the kidney, as illustrated in Figure 18-2, 3 general regions may be observed: the renal cortex, the renal medulla, and the renal pelvis.

The renal cortex, or outer portion of the kidney, is granular and reddish-brown in appearance. It arches over the pyramids of the medulla and dips in between adjacent pyramids; these inward extensions of cortical substance are called the *renal columns* (of Bertin).

The renal medulla is darker in color and consists of striated, cone-shaped masses called the *renal pyramids.* The pyramids vary in number, but the average is 12. The base of each pyramid is directed toward the cortex, and the free end or apex projects centrally toward the renal pelvis where it forms a *papilla*. The summit of each papilla resembles a sieve, as it is studded with a variable number of openings; urine flows through

Fig. 18-1. Dissection of the abdomen, showing kidneys in position. Course and relations of ureters and urinary bladder also are shown.

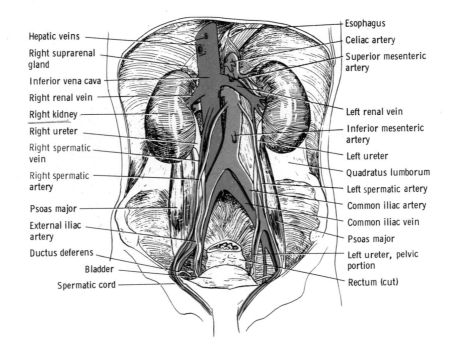

Hepatic veins

Right suprarenal gland

Inferior vena cava

Right renal vein

Right kidney

Right ureter

Right spermatic vein

Right spermatic artery

Psoas major

External iliac artery

Ductus deferens

Bladder

Spermatic cord

Esophagus

Celiac artery

Superior mesenteric artery

Left renal vein

Inferior mesenteric artery

Left ureter

Quadratus lumborum

Left spermatic artery

Common iliac artery

Common iliac vein

Psoas major

Left ureter, pelvic portion

Rectum (cut)

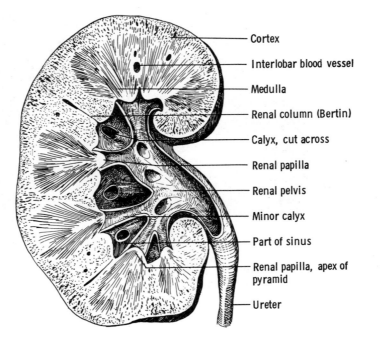

Cortex

Interlobar blood vessel

Medulla

Renal column (Bertin)

Calyx, cut across

Renal papilla

Renal pelvis

Minor calyx

Part of sinus

Renal papilla, apex of pyramid

Ureter

Fig. 18-2. Longitudinal section of kidney, showing divisions of renal substance and relations of renal pelvis and calyces. Striations on pyramids indicate course of collecting tubules toward papillae.

Fig. 18-3. Retrograde pyelogram. Sodium iodide was injected through catheters, which are shown in position. The pelves of the kidneys and the ureters are shown. The right kidney is a little lower than the left, which is normal. (X-ray taken through the back.)

Fig. 18-4. Intravenous urogram. Visualization of the urinary tract 15 minutes after the injection of the dye. The patient was pregnant; the head of the fetus is shown compressing the urinary bladder. (Dr. Vastine: Woman's College Hospital) (X-ray taken through the abdomen.)

nephron made up of a capsule and a renal corpuscle. This corpuscle made up of a glomerulus and a capsule

these openings into an extension (calyx) of the renal pelvis.

The renal pelvis is a funnel-shaped sac that forms the upper expanded end of the ureter. It receives urine from all parts of the kidney by way of the *calyces,* which are cup-shaped extensions of the sac. Each kidney has a variable number of calyces, since a single calyx may surround more than one papilla. X-ray studies of the renal pelvis and the calyces are shown in Figures 18-3 and 18-4.

Kidney stones (renal calculi) may form in the pelves of the kidneys; they frequently cause pain and hematuria (blood in the urine).

Microscopic appearance

The microscopic unit of structure is the **nephron,** and there are over 1 million of them in each human kidney. Each nephron consists of a renal corpuscle and a renal tubule.

A **renal corpuscle** consists of a glomerulus and a surrounding capsule, called the capsule of Bowman, as shown in Figure 18-5.

The *glomerulus* is a tuft of capillaries. The vessel that conveys blood to the glomerulus is called the *afferent arteriole,* and it divides to form the capillary loops. These loops then unite to form the *efferent arteriole* that drains blood from the glomerulus. Note that this vessel is not called a vein, even though it drains blood from capillaries. The efferent arteriole has the structure of a typical arteriole (p. 344), and it conveys blood from the glomerulus to the region of the renal tubule, where it arborizes to form the peritubular capillaries (Fig. 18-6).

The afferent arteriole is not a typical arteriole, and its diameter is greater than that of the efferent vessel. The tunica intima and tunica externa are poorly developed; thus the diameter of the afferent arteriole is large because its tunica media consists of a very substantial layer of smooth muscle. A further modification involves a cluster of unusual cells in the tunica media just before this arteriole gives rise to the glomerulus; these cells are known as *juxtaglomerular cells,* because they are near to or adjoining the glomerulus. The

juxtaglomerular or JG cells are concerned with the production of a chemical substance called *renin;* the importance of renin is discussed on page 529.

The *capsule of Bowman* is the beginning of a renal tubule, and it is invaginated by the glomerulus. The visceral layer of the capsule is intimately attached to the glomerulus, but there are large pores or openings in it. The outer or parietal layer is intact. The space between the two layers contains fluid that has filtered out of the glomerulus; this fluid is referred to as the *glomerular filtrate.*

A renal tubule is called by different names in its tortuous course. It begins in the capsule of Bowman and then becomes the *proximal convoluted tubule,* the *loop of Henle* and, finally, the *distal convoluted tubule,* which is the end of the nephron unit. The distal convoluted tubule empties its contents into a branch of a straight collecting tubule or duct. The collecting tubule courses through a renal pyramid and joins other collecting tubules to form one of the papillary ducts that open into a calyx at the summit of a papilla. Many nephron units drain into each collecting tubule. Figure 18-5 illustrates the various structures described above.

Location of Microscopic Structures. All of the renal corpuscles are confined to the cortex. The proximal and the distal convoluted tubules also are located in the cortex, close to the renal corpuscles. However, the descending limb of each loop of Henle dips downward for a variable distance into the medulla, bends on itself to form the loop, and then returns to the cortex as the ascending limb. The collecting tubules begin in the cortex and unite at short intervals with one another to form a series of larger tubes that descend into the medulla. These larger tubes converge to form the papillary ducts and are responsible for the striated appearance of the renal pyramids.

Blood supply

Blood is conveyed to the hilus of each kidney through a *renal artery.* On entering the kidney,

glomerulus is only a tuft of capillaries.

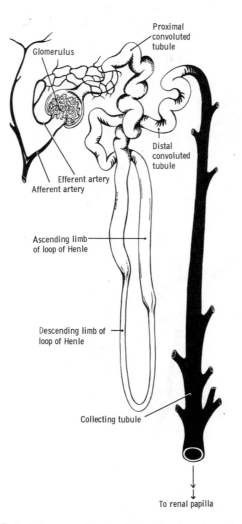

Fig. 18-5. Diagram of a nephron showing its union with a collecting tubule. (From Greisheimer, Esther M.: Physiology & Anatomy, ed. 8., Philadelphia, Lippincott, 1963.)

Proximal convoluted tubule

Distal convoluted tubule

Efferent arteriole

Interlobular artery & vein

Peritubular capillary

Glomerulus

Bowman's capsule

Afferent arteriole

Venule

Collecting tubule

Henle's loop

Fig. 18-6. Diagram of blood supply to kidney showing interlobular artery, a glomerulus with its afferent and efferent arterioles, a peritubular capillary network and its venous drainage.

the renal artery branches to form the *interlobar arteries;* these vessels pass between adjacent pyramids and give off small branches as they course toward the cortex. As the interlobar arteries approach the cortex they arch over the bases of the medullary pyramids where they become the *arcuate arteries.* Branches of the arcuate arteries, the *interlobular arteries,* extend into the cortex. Some of the interlobular arteries give off the afferent arterioles of the glomeruli (Fig. 18-6) while others send terminal branches to the capsule of the kidney.

After passing through the glomeruli, blood flows through the efferent arterioles into capillary beds that surround the renal tubules; these microscopic networks are called the *peritubular capillaries.* On leaving the peritubular capillaries, blood flows into stellate veins and then into the interlobular veins; from this point, the veins that drain the kidney follow the same general course as the arteries and lie beside them.

Reduced Blood Supply. Any condition that markedly reduces the blood supply to the kidneys will cause the juxtaglomerular cells (p. 526) to release an enzymelike substance called *renin.* On entering the blood stream, renin combines with a plasma protein, leading to the formation of a pressor substance called *angiotensin.* Generally speaking, angiotensin helps to raise the blood pressure in two ways. First, it helps to increase peripheral resistance by causing a generalized vasoconstriction of arterioles in other parts of the body. Secondly, angiotensin stimulates the adrenal cortex (p. 559) to increase its secretion of *aldosterone.* Aldosterone acts on the renal tubule cells and promotes the reabsorption of sodium; because sodium is accompanied by water. This leads to an increase in the circulating blood volume. These changes lead to an increase in blood pressure and in blood flow through the vital organs, including the kidney. Such a response is protective when the reduction in renal blood flow is due to hemorrhage. However, when the renal blood flow is reduced by obstruction of the renal artery or by certain kidney diseases, an abnormal elevation of blood pressure may ensue (renal hypertension).

Nerve supply

The kidneys are supplied with visceral afferent fibers that transmit impulses from the kidneys to the CNS. The blood vessels of the kidneys are supplied with vasoconstrictor fibers from the thoracolumbar division of the autonomic system. The cells of the tubules have no nerve supply.

THE EXCRETORY PASSAGES

In each kidney, urine flows from the papillary ducts of the pyramids into the calyces leading to the renal pelvis. From the pelvis, urine flows into the ureter which leads to the urinary bladder. Urine ultimately passes to the exterior of the body by way of the urethra.

The ureters

Location. The ureters are tubes, about 10 or 12 inches long, that convey urine from the kidneys to the urinary bladder. Lying behind the parietal peritoneum, each ureter descends along the posterior abdominal wall to the pelvic brim of its own side. After crossing the brim of the pelvis, the ureters pass along the lateral wall of the pelvis and follow a downward and medial course along the pelvic floor to reach the urinary bladder (Fig. 18-1). They enter the bladder by passing obliquely through its muscular wall. There is no valve at the ureteral opening, but a fold of the mucous membrane lining the bladder serves to prevent backflow when the pressure of urine within the bladder begins to rise.

Description. Each ureter is lined with mucous membrane that is continuous with the mucosal lining of the renal pelvis above and the urinary bladder below. The muscular portion of the ureteral wall consists of a longitudinal and a circular layer of smooth muscle; contractions of these muscular layers produce the peristaltic waves that move urine toward the urinary bladder. The adventitia or outer layer of the ureteral wall consists of fibrous connective tissue and some elastic fibers.

The blood supply to the ureters is derived from

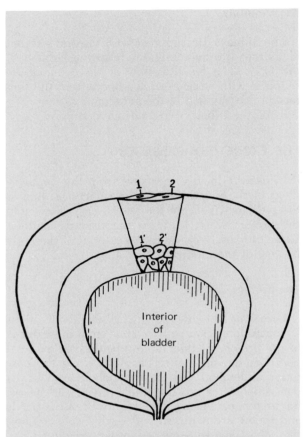

Interior
of
bladder

Fig. 18-7. Transitional epithelial cells in empty and distended bladder. The cells flatten out, as in 1 and 2, when the bladder is distended; they are spherical, as in 1' and 2', when the bladder is not distended.

branches of the spermatic (testicular) or the ovarian arteries. Visceral afferent and efferent nerve fibers from both divisions of the autonomic system also are supplied to the ureters. Kidney stones that escape from the renal pelvis into the ureter may cause excruciating pain (renal colic) as they move toward the urinary bladder.

The urinary bladder

Location. The urinary bladder is a thick-walled, muscular sac that lies behind the pubis, below the parietal peritoneum. It serves as a reservoir for urine and is emptied periodically. The location of the bladder is shown in Figure 18-1.

Description. The mucous mebrane lining of the bladder is thrown into folds or _rugae_ when the bladder is empty; these folds disappear as the bladder becomes distended with urine. The epithelium of the mucosa is of the transitional type, that is, its appearance varies with the state of emptiness or fullness of the bladder as shown in Figure 18-7. The _trigone_ is a small triangular area in the floor of the bladder. Its anterior angle is formed by the internal opening of the urethra, and its posterolateral angles by the openings of the ureters. There are no rugae in the trigone, and its mucosal surface is always smooth.

Cystitis is an infection of the mucosa of the bladder. Pain and frequency (desire to empty the bladder every few minutes) are two symptoms of this condition.

The muscular coat of the bladder consists of an inner longitudinal, a middle circular and an outer longitudinal layer of smooth muscle; the entire muscular coat is called the _detrusor muscle_. The middle layer of muscle is thickest toward the lower part of the bladder where it forms a sphincter that guards the exit of the urethra.

The blood supply is derived from the internal iliac arteries, and the drainage is into the internal iliac veins.

The nerve supply consists of visceral afferent and visceral efferent fibers. Those fibers which are part of the sympathetic division of autonomics are called the "nerves of retention," which means that they promote relaxation of the bladder wall

Fig. 18-8. Diagrammatic representation of innervation of the bladder and the urethra in man. On the left, the nerves of "emptying" are shown; these are motor to the bladder wall and inhibitory to the sphincter. On the right, the nerves of "retention" are shown; these are inhibitory to the bladder wall and motor to the sphincter. Both bladder wall and urethra are supplied with afferent fibers. (After Learmonth) (Best, C. H., and Taylor, N. B.: Physiological Basis of Medical Practice, ed. 5, Baltimore, Williams & Wilkins)

Fig. 18-9. Cystograms of male bladder, showing bladder containing about 20 cc. of sodium iodide solution (top) and 500 cc. (bottom). (Redrawn from Morris)

and contraction of the sphincter. On the other hand, parasympathetic fibers are called the "nerves of emptying," since they promote contraction of the wall and relaxation of the sphincter. The nerve supply is illustrated in Figure 18-8.

A **cystoscopic** examination is one in which the interior of the bladder is examined visually. In certain conditions it is necessary to wash out the bladder, and such a procedure is called a bladder *irrigation*. Figure 18-9 shows the appearance of the urinary bladder when distended with different amounts of fluid.

The urethra

The urethra is the tube that conveys urine from the urinary bladder to the exterior. In men it has both an excretory and a reproductive function, but in women it is concerned only with excretion.

The female urethra is only 1 to 1½ inches in length. As it curves obliquely downward and forward from the bladder, the posterior wall of the urethra is united firmly with the anterior wall of the vagina. The external orifice of the urethra is located directly in front of the vaginal opening as shown in Figure 20-12. The wall of the urethra is composed of mucous membrane and a muscular layer. An external sphincter of striated muscle surrounds the orifice and enables one to control the escape of urine.

The male urethra is made up of 3 portions: the prostatic, the membranous and the cavernous portions.

The *prostatic* portion is about 1 inch long and extends from the urinary bladder to the pelvic floor. During its course it is completely surrounded by the prostate gland. When this gland enlarges, as it commonly does in elderly men, it compresses this portion of the urethra and interferes with the flow of urine.

The *membranous* portion of the urethra extends through the pelvic floor or body wall, from the apex of the prostate gland to the bulb of the urethra, and is about ½ inch long.

The *cavernous* portion of the urethra is in the penis (p. 576). It is between 5 and 6 inches long and extends from the bulb of the urethra to the external orifice. The parts of the male urethra are shown in Figure 20-1.

Urethritis is an inflammation of the urethra. It may be followed by a *stricture* or narrowing of the urethra due to adhesions. When this condition exists, frequency and dribbling of urine may be noted due to incomplete emptying of the bladder.

Micturition

This refers to the emptying of the urinary bladder. The 3 layers of muscle of the bladder wall, called the *detrusor muscle,* act as a unit in emptying the bladder. When about 300 ml. of urine have accumulated in the bladder, stretch receptors in the wall are stimulated by distention, and afferent impulses are sent over visceral afferent nerve fibers to the CNS which arouse a desire to empty the bladder. Then there is a removal of voluntary control, which is essential to the release of a chain of reflexes. The act of micturition is actually started by a relaxation of the voluntary muscles of the perineum.

The first reflex appears as a series of rhythmic contractions of the detrusor muscle that become more and more powerful. These contractions of the wall of the bladder are accompanied by a relaxation of the internal sphincter of the bladder.

As urine passes along the urethra other receptors are stimulated which call forth additional reflexes. Further rhythmic contractions of the wall of the urinary bladder occur, and these are accompanied by a relaxation of the external sphincter of the urethra. These additional contractions of the wall assure complete emptying of the bladder.

Although the emptying of the urinary bladder is reflex in nature, it is initiated by an effort of the will and a voluntary removal of restraint. It can be stopped at various stages. The external sphincter of the urethra can be closed voluntarily, but is is opened as a part of a chain of coordinated reflexes.

If the urinary bladder is not emptied when the desire to do so first is noted, it will be distended further. Micturition can be inhibited voluntarily until about 700 ml. of urine have accumulated. By this time a sensation of pain may be aroused, and micturition becomes urgent.

Pathologic distention of the bladder may occur in both the conscious and the unconscious patient. In extreme cases, the bladder may distend to the level of the umbilicus, but this is rare when medical attention is available. Retention of urine may follow an obstruction or an infection of the urethra, an enlargement of the prostate gland, damage to the nerve supply of the bladder, etc.

Catheterization of the bladder refers to emptying it by insertion of a tube or catheter through the urethra into the bladder.

It is done to relieve distention or for continuous drainage in incontinent patients. It is done also when a "catheterized" specimen is requested for analysis. In women, the urine eliminated spontaneously may be contaminated by vaginal discharge; therefore, it is frequently essential to draw a specimen by catheter to rule out such a possibility.

Sterile equipment and technic must always be used when inserting catheters into the bladder. The introduction of bacteria may result in cystitis or even a pyelitis. *Pyelitis* is an infection of the renal pelvis that may follow infection of the bladder, since it is easy for infection to spread along the mucous membrane of the ureters from that of the bladder.

CHARACTERISTICS OF URINE

Urine is a watery solution of nitrogenous waste and inorganic salts that are removed from the plasma and eliminated by the kidneys. The color usually is amber but varies with the amount produced. The reaction is acid on a mixed diet and alkaline on a vegetable diet. The specific gravity usually is between 1.016 and 1.020, but may vary from 1.002 to 1.040 in normal kidneys, according to whether the urine is very dilute or very concentrated. The quantity of urine is about 1½ L. daily. An increase in daily output that is persistent is called *polyuria,* and a temporary increase is called *diuresis.* A decrease below the average amount is called *oliguria.*

The composition varies with the waste products to be removed and with the need for maintenance of homeostasis. About 95 per cent of urine is water. The average amount of solids excreted per day is about 60 gm.; of this, about 25 gm. consist of inorganic salts and 35 gm. consist of organic substances. The composition of urine of an adult man on a mixed diet is as follows:

Inorganic Constituents		Organic Constituents	
NaCl	15.000 gm.	Urea	30.000 gm.
K	3.3	Creatinine	1.0
SO$_4$	2.5	Uric acid	0.7
PO$_4$	2.5	Hippuric acid	0.7
NH$_3$	0.7	Indican	0.01
Mg	0.1	Acetone bodies	0.04
Ca	0.3	Undetermined	2.945
Fe	0.005		
Other	0.2		

FORMATION OF URINE

The work of the kidneys centers on maintaining the normal composition, volume and pH of body fluids. In accomplishing this task, each kidney removes from the blood variable amounts of water, organic and inorganic constituents, as well as toxic substances, and eliminates them in the urine.

Urine formation begins in the renal corpuscles by the process of glomerular filtration. It is completed in the renal tubules where processes of osmosis, diffusion, tubular reabsorption, tubular secretion and tubular excretion all help in the conversion of glomerular filtrate to urine. Some of these processes involve an expenditure of energy by the tubular cells as certain substances are moved by active transport.

Glomerular filtration

As previously described, each glomerulus is a tuft of capillaries to which blood is brought by an afferent arteriole and from which blood is drained by an efferent arteriole of smaller diameter. This anatomic arrangement favors the maintenance of a relatively high blood pressure throughout the capillary loops in the glomerulus. The pressure of the fluid in Bowman's capsule is low, and the walls of the capillaries and the inner

layer of the capsule are thin and permeable. Consequently, the glomerulus is an ideal filtering apparatus as water and true solutes are "pushed" out of the blood stream into the capsular beginning of the renal tubule. Since large particles, such as red blood cells and most plasma proteins, are unable to pass through a normal membrane, they remain in the blood stream as it flows out of the glomerulus.

More than 500 ml. of blood enter each kidney every minute, but the amount of filtrate produced depends on such factors as the glomerular blood pressure and the permeability of capillary and capsular walls, among others. An average amount of glomerular filtrate is 120 ml. per minute or approximately 170 L. in 24 hours. The fact that only 1 to 1½ L. of urine is eliminated each day points to a very large reabsorption of fluid during the tubular phase of urine formation.

Tubular reabsorption

As the glomerular filtrate flows through the renal tubule, many constituents are reabsorbed into the blood stream. This is particularly true of substances that are needed by the body. For example, water, glucose, amino acids, sodium, chloride, bicarbonate and other tiny particles are mechanically filtered through the glomerular membrane along with various waste products. However, by highly complicated mechanisms of active transport, in addition to simple osmosis and diffusion, the useful substances are removed from the tubular fluid and returned to the blood as it flows through the peritubular capillaries.

Active Transport. This process requires the expenditure of energy and the presence of highly specific enzymes, as certain substances are "pumped" across the tubule cells and into the surrounding tissue fluid. At the same time, these transported substances are prevented from diffusing back to the tubular lumen from whence they came. Thus they enter the peritubular capillary and are carried away in the blood stream.

Some constituents of the glomerular filtrate, such as **potassium,** are reabsorbed almost completely, regardless of their concentration. Others, such as **glucose,** have a well-defined limit or "renal threshold," which means that excessive amounts are eliminated in the urine. For example, if one eats a large amount of candy within a short period of time, the blood is loaded with glucose, and large amounts are filtered into the renal tubules; the resulting overload on the active transport mechanism is responsible for the appearance of glucose in the urine. Other important threshold substances include amino acids, acetoacetic acid, vitamins, and uric acid.

Large quantities of filtered **sodium** (Na^+) are delivered constantly to the tubules, chiefly as chloride (Cl^-) and bicarbonate (HCO_3^-). However, Na^+ is reabsorbed efficiently, and less than 1 per cent is excreted in the urine. The active reabsorption of Na^+ represents the most massive operation carried out by the kidney, aside from the reabsorption of water which moves more or less passively. About 80 per cent of the filtered sodium is reabsorbed in association with chloride, and about 20 per cent with bicarbonate.

Passive Transport. The reabsorption of water is accomplished by the simple process of osmosis (p. 34). As sodium and other solutes are transported from the lumen of the tubule, their concentration in the surrounding tissue fluid is increased as their concentration in the tubular fluid is diminished. Thus there is a net diffusion of water from the tubule into the peritubular tissue fluid. Diffusion from the tissue fluid into the peritubular capillary blood is facilitated by the relatively high colloidal osmotic pressure of that blood; two factors are operative in maintaining this effective "pulling pressure." First, unlike water, the plasma proteins are not readily filtered through the glomerular membrane; thus they remain in the blood as it leaves the glomerulus and flows into the peritubular capillary. Second, the hydrostatic or "pushing pressure" of the blood is reduced as it flows toward the venous end of the peritubular capillary bed. Because of these factors, all but about 1 or 1½ L. of the water that filters through the glomerular capillary membrane ultimately is reabsorbed and returned to the blood stream. The role of antidiuretic hormone (ADH) will be described presently.

Another form of passive transport involves the establishment of *electrical gradients.* For example, when positive ions (e.g., Na^+) are actively transported out of the tubule, the surrounding tissue fluid becomes electropositive; thus negative ions (e.g., Cl^-) will follow the positive ions in the reabsorptive process.

Urea is the chief nitrogenous constituent of the blood, constituting over one-half of the NPN (non-protein-nitrogen). This substance also is the chief organic constituent of the urine. Although urea is a waste product, some of it can and does diffuse from the tubular fluid back into the blood stream. As you might expect, this "backward diffusion" is most pronounced when urine flow is decreased; thus, in kidney disease the blood urea nitrogen (BUN) may greatly exceed the normal levels of 10 to 15 mg. %.

Tubular secretion

The kidney plays an important role in regulating the acid-base balance of the body. Through the ability of its tubular cells to secrete varying amounts of hydrogen ions and ammonia, the kidney can increase or decrease the acidity of the urine. These secretory activities occur primarily in the distal portion of the tubules and are part of the final phase of urine formation.

Hydrogen ions (H^+) are secreted into the lumen of the tubule in exchange for sodium (Na^+) ions. Na^+, accompanied by bicarbonate (HCO_3^-), returns to the blood stream where it serves as part of the basic buffer system described on page 298.

As the acidity of the urine increases, **ammonia** (NH_3) is formed by the tubule cells by deamination of amino acids. The NH_3 diffuses into the tubule lumen and unites with H^+ to form the non-diffusible ammonium radical (NH_4^+); the NH_4^+ then combines with chloride (Cl^-) to be excreted as ammonium chloride. The excretion of NH_4Cl, rather than $NaCl$, is an additional way of conserving sodium for the body and thus safeguarding its total available base.

Another secretory function of the renal tubule is the regulation of the amount of **potassium** (K^+) in the body. Since almost all of the filtered K^+ is reabsorbed in the proximal tubule, that which appears in the urine is primarily due to the active secretion of K^+ by the distal tubule cells in exchange for sodium. This not only serves to eliminate excess K^+ but is an additional way of saving sodium.

Tubular excretion

By processes of active transport, the tubule cells can transfer substances from the blood into the tubular lumens. In contrast to the secretory processes, the substances to be moved include those that are of no use to the body (e.g., creatinine) as well as those that are completely foreign to the body (e.g., penicillin and certain dyes). In the latter case, tubular excretion supplements glomerular filtration in that it facilitates the elimination of compounds that could not otherwise be disposed of by metabolic processes.

Tubular excretion of foreign substances is clinically important in that it provides the basis for certain laboratory tests of kidney function. For example, the dye **phenolsulphonphthalein** (commonly called **P.S.P.**) is injected into the body, and urine specimens are collected at timed intervals. Normal kidneys eliminate 60 to 80 per cent of the injected dye within a specified time, but impaired kidneys eliminate proportionately less according to the amount of tubular damage.

Hormonal effects

Chapter 19 is devoted to the endocrine glands and their chemical "messengers" or hormones. However, it seems advisable at this time to introduce two particular hormones that greatly influence the formation of urine.

The antidiuretic hormone (ADH) is a neurosecretion produced by nerve cell bodies in the hypothalamus and passed along axons to the posterior lobe of the pituitary gland for storage. The hypothalamus is concerned not only with the production of ADH but also with its release from the pituitary into the blood stream.

As the name implies, "antidiuretic" means that this hormone is "against diuresis" or against the excretion of urine; its chief effect is on the kidney tubules in which it accelerates the rate of water reabsorption, possibly by widening the pores in cell membranes. ADH acts on cells in the loop of Henle, in the distal convoluted tubule and in the collecting ducts.

The role of the hypothalamus in regulating water balance was previously described on page 225, but a brief summary may prove helpful at this time. The rate at which ADH is released from the posterior lobe of the pituitary gland depends on the concentration of solutes (e.g., salt) in the circulating blood as it flows through the hypothalamus. If the concentration of solute is high, the hypothalamus "orders" the pituitary to release ADH; as a result, the reabsorption of water is accelerated until the concentration of solute is reduced to normal levels. On the other hand, if the solute concentration in the blood is too low, the secretion of ADH is inhibited; as a result, more water is lost in the urine until the solute concentration is increased to normal levels.

Aldosterone, sometimes called a "salt and water" hormone, is secreted by cells in the cortex of the adrenal glands (p. 559). This hormone plays an important part in the active transport of both sodium and potassium. When the concentration of aldosterone is high, sodium is retained in excessive amounts in the body, and potassium is excreted in greater amounts than usual. On the other hand, when there is a deficiency of aldosterone, as in Addison's disease (p. 561), potassium is retained while excessive sodium is lost from the body and with it an equivalent amount of water; as a consequence, body fluid is progressively reduced to lethal levels.

Urinalysis

Routine analysis of the urine involves a description of the color and turbidity, determination of the specific gravity, pH, and the presence or absence of abnormal constituents. A microscopic examination of the sediment also may be ordered.

Specific Gravity. Normal kidneys are able to vary the specific gravity of urine from 1.002 to

1.040. This ability is tested by the Mosenthal and by the concentration-dilution tests. In the former, the daily variation in specific gravity and volume of urine is determined; in the latter, the differences in specific gravity of urine on a "dry" diet and after the intake of a large amount of water within a short period of time are determined.

If the kidneys are diseased, the variation in specific gravity of urine is limited. In fact, the specific gravity may be "fixed" and remain about 1.010 regardless of variations in intake of water. These tests of flexibility of specific gravity are easy to perform, and the information derived is valuable, since lack of ability to concentrate the urine is one of the earliest signs of kidney damage.

Color and Turbidity. The color may vary with the specific gravity, or with various drugs and other abnormal constituents. Urine may become cloudy on standing; in acid urine this is due to urates, and in alkaline urine it is due to phosphates. The cloudiness may also be due to pus or mucus.

Abnormal constituents include blood, pus, albumin, sugar, and ketone bodies.

Blood. The presence of blood in the urine is called *hematuria*. It may be due to contamination from vaginal discharge, cystitis, tumors, and stones in the kidney, the ureter or the bladder. Whenever blood is found in the urine, additional examinations are imperative to determine the origin of the blood.

Pus. The presence of pus in the urine is called *pyuria*. It may be due to infection of the bladder or of the renal pelvis.

Albumin. The presence of albumin in the urine, called albuminuria, may be a symptom of serious kidney disease. However, before such a diagnosis can be made, other causes of albuminuria must be ruled out; for example, the urine may have been contaminated with vaginal discharge, or there may be an existing bladder infection, or the like. Orthostatic albuminuria also must be ruled out. This is a condition in which albumin is present in specimens of urine collected during the day, when the person is in the upright position; the specimens collected after resting in bed are free of albumin. This is purely a circulatory phenomenon; in the standing position there is enough pressure on the renal veins to cause a disturbance in filtration. There is no disease of the kidneys present. If all other causes for albuminuria, such as those listed above, have been ruled out, then it is safe to conclude that there is pathology of the kidneys in the form of glomerulonephritis (primarily involvement of glomeruli) or nephrosis (primarily involvement of tubules).

Sugar. The presence of sugar in the urine is called *glycosuria;* it may be *alimentary glycosuria,* due to large intake of sugar. It may be due to emotional upsets, such as during examinations (epinephrine causes excessive glycogenolysis, with marked elevation of blood sugar to above renal threshold concentration). If glycosuria is found in a pregnant or lactating woman, lactosuria must be ruled out. When all other causes have been ruled out, diabetes mellitus may be suspected, and additional tests (glucose tolerance) are imperative.

Ketone bodies. The presence of acetone, acetoacetic acid, or beta-hydroxybutyric acid (the so-called ketone bodies) in the urine is called *ketonuria*. However, a small number of ketone bodies may be present in the urine of healthy persons, particularly in the fasting state. As previously described (p. 507), ketone bodies tend to accumulate when carbohydrate metabolism is depressed and the body is deriving most of its energy from the metabolism of fats (e.g., untreated diabetes mellitus, starvation, and so forth).

Microscopic Examination. When a drop of abnormal urine (which has been centrifuged) is examined, erythrocytes, tiny stones (renal calculi) and casts may be noted. The casts are tiny masses of material that have hardened in the tubular lumens, and they assume the shape of the lumen. The presence of casts indicates kidney injury.

Diuresis

Diuresis refers to an increased excretion of urine. It may be caused by a variety of factors, a few of which will be described.

Water diuresis follows the intake of a large amount of water within a short period of time. This lowers the solute concentration in the blood and inhibits the secretion of antidiuretic hormone (ADH), as mentioned previously. Most of the water will be eliminated by normal kidneys within 2 hours after it has been taken in.

Osmotic diuresis is due to the presence of large amounts of waste products in the glomerular filtrate.

Urea is a natural diuretic. When one eats a large amount of protein, the diuretic effect of urea is noted.

Glucose in an untreated diabetic is a waste product and is responsible for the large amount of urine (polyuria) eliminated by such persons.

Waste products in the lumens of the tubules hold enough water (by osmosis) to keep themselves in solution and cause diuresis by opposing the reabsorption of water.

Mercurial diuretics include those drugs that in some way promote the excretion of sodium which, in turn, takes water with it.

Digitalis, used in treating certain types of heart disease, has a diuretic effect, since it improves the blood flow through the kidney.

Caffeine causes a dilatation of the renal blood vessels and, since more blood flows through the kidney, more urine is formed.

Ethyl alcohol inhibits the release of ADH, thus more urine is formed.

Characteristics of urine in certain diseases

In untreated **diabetes mellitus** a large amount of urine is produced; it is pale in color, has a high specific gravity and contains glucose and a large amount of acetone.

In **diabetes insipidus** a very large amount of urine is produced (as much as 30 L. per day); it is pale in color, has a very low specific gravity and contains neither glucose nor abnormal amounts of acetone.

In **glomerulonephritis** there are both hematuria and albuminuria. In the acute stage the urine volume is low, and the specific gravity is high, while in the chronic stage there is usually polyuria, with low specific gravity (fixed around 1.010). There will be other alterations in the body as a result of the kidney impairment, such as re-

tention of waste products (uremia, acidosis), low plasma protein with edema and depletion of salt.

In **tubular nephritis** (commonly called *nephrosis*) polyuria, hematuria and albuminuria may be present. The specific gravity of the urine is low. Other alterations in the body are edema and probably acidosis, since the kidneys cannot manufacture ammonia. It is difficult to find conditions in which injury is confined to glomeruli alone or to tubules alone; sooner or later all parts of the nephrons are involved.

Hemodialysis

Hemodialysis refers to the removal of crystalloid substances from the blood stream by taking advantage of their ability to diffuse through a porous membrane. Because of their large size, red blood cells and plasma proteins are unable to pass through the membrane; thus they remain in the blood stream. Hemodialysis may mean the difference between life and death for a person who has taken an overdose of certain drugs (e.g., barbiturates), for a patient whose kidneys have temporarily stopped producing urine (e.g., in acute nephritis), and for various other conditions related to renal excretion.

The equipment used for hemodialysis frequently is referred to as the "artificial kidney." Briefly, it consists of a long cellophane tube arranged in coils and submerged in a temperature-controlled bath solution; the chemical composition of the bath solution usually approximates normal extracellular fluid, but it may be altered in various ways as necessary to meet the specific needs of the patient.

Dialysis begins when blood from one of the patient's arteries is pumped through the tubing. Crystalloid substances that need to be removed from the blood (e.g., potassium and urea in the case of kidney failure, or barbiturates in the case of drug overdosage) diffuse across the cellophane membrane from the area of higher concentration in the blood to the area of lower concentration in the bath solution. The bath solution is changed at intervals to prevent the accumulation of these substances and to maintain the diffusion gradient.

[handwritten annotation at top:] 800cc. lost by perspiration & breathing GI tract looses 100-200cc

After passing through the length of tubing, the blood is returned to the patient's circulation by way of a vein.

WATER BALANCE

Water is the most abundant constituent of the body, making up about 70 per cent of the total body weight. The various functions of water are described on page 15, and summarized as follows: water is important (1) as a solvent, (2) in all chemical reactions occurring in the tissues, (3) in the regulation of body temperature, and (4) in the excretion of waste products.

Intake

Exogenous water is that taken into the body as a beverage and as a constituent of food.

The amount of water taken in the form of beverage varies widely. In one person studied, the intake varied from 880 to 2,440 ml. on different days, at rest. When the same person worked, his intake varied from 2,225 to 4,550 ml. daily. On an average mixed diet, one takes from 700 to 1,200 ml. daily as part of the food eaten (even meat has a high water content).

Thirst is an important signal that more water is needed by the tissues. It is closely related to the concentration of dissolved substances in the blood and the general state of supply in the cells of the body.

Endogenous water is that made available by the metabolic activities taking place within the cells. As previously described, water is formed in the metabolism of all 3 major foodstuffs. About 300 ml. of water is obtained from this source every day.

Output

Water is eliminated through all 4 channels of excretion.

Lungs. It is lost by way of the lungs in saturating the expired air. The amount lost by this channel varies with the humidity of the air inspired, with the depth and the rate of breathing and with the temperature of the inspired air.

Large Intestine. The amount of water lost by way of the large intestine is small; the average daily amount is about 150 ml. If there is diarrhea, the water lost by this channel may become very great.

Skin. The loss by way of the skin may be divided into the "insensible" loss and the "sensible" loss by perspiration. The insensible loss varies from 300 to 800 ml. daily; it goes on throughout the day, and we are unaware of it. The rate of loss is fairly constant for any individual.

The loss of water in perspiration is purely an emergency mechanism required in the regulation of the body temperature. It varies with exercise, external temperature and body temperature. We perspire more (1) when we exercise, (2) when the environmental temperature is high, and (3) when the body temperature is high, as in fever. Loss of water by perspiration is a safety factor in temperature regulation but a hazard when the body supply of water is low, as there is no way to decrease this loss even if we are totally deprived of water.

Kidneys. The amount of water lost by the kidneys varies greatly and depends on the available supply of body water. The kidneys act as a spillway for water not lost through other channels and not needed by the body. If the supply of water is low, the waste products are excreted in a small amount of water, and the urine is very concentrated, with a specific gravity approaching 1.040. If the supply of water is overabundant, as in drinking a large amount of water within a few minutes, a very dilute urine can be produced, in which the specific gravity approaches 1.002. The "obligatory" loss of water by the kidneys depends on the waste to be excreted; sufficient water must be excreted to keep the waste products in solution. The amount lost by this channel, therefore, depends on the intake, respiration and perspiration. If abnormal conditions arise, such as vomiting and diarrhea, the amount of water lost by the kidneys is curtailed immediately.

Balance between intake and output

In health, the balance between intake and output of water is perfect, so there is no edema, water intoxication or dehydration. One suffers no harmful effects, from taking either a small or a large amount of water, provided there is enough to regulate body temperature and excrete waste products. This is possible only if the kidneys are normal.

ELECTROLYTE BALANCE

The functions of inorganic salts are discussed on page 16. Some of their functions are the maintenance of osmotic relationships, acid-base balance, conductivity of nerves, contractility of muscles, transport of gases and aiding in the coagulation of the blood.

Intake

With the exception of sodium chloride, which is voluntarily added to food as it is cooked or served, one takes in enough inorganic salts on a mixed diet to satisfy requirements.

Output

Inorganic salts are excreted by 3 channels: kidneys, skin and intestine. Calcium, magnesium, iron and phosphorus are excreted by the kidneys and the large intestine. Sulfur, sodium, potassium and chloride are excreted chiefly by the kidneys, but the skin excretes a small amount of sodium chloride in the perspiration.

The amount of sodium chloride excreted by the kidneys varies. In health, a person probably runs into difficulty with salt balance only when he perspires profusely and loses more chloride than he takes in.

Water and sodium chloride "move" together. If a patient is in difficulty in connection with water balance, he is quite likely to be in difficulty with salt balance, also.

Fluid compartments of the body

The water of the body is divided into 3 fluid compartments for purposes of discussion. These compartments are shown in Figure 18-10. Water enters the blood from the small and the large intestines, after being taken in as beverage, as a component of food and by reabsorption of digestive juices. It leaves the body by way of the lungs, the large intestine, the kidneys and the skin.

Vascular compartment

The first compartment is the vascular compartment, occupied by the blood plasma. The water in this compartment forms about 5 per cent of the body weight. In this compartment there is a rapid circulation of fluid, and it is under pressure in the blood vessels.

Interstitial fluid compartment

The second compartment comprises the interstitial or tissue fluid, lymph, aqueous humor, pericardial fluid, pleural fluid, peritoneal fluid and cerebrospinal fluid. The fluid in this compartment forms about 15 per cent of the body weight.

The fluid in the vascular compartment and that in the interstitial fluid compartment together make up the *extracellular fluid*, which is concerned with the transport of nutritive products to all parts of the body, transport of waste products from cells to organs of excretion, osmotic relationships, water balance, salt balance and acid-base balance.

The chief difference between plasma and interstitial fluid is in protein content; the interstitial fluid contains very little protein compared with plasma. The barrier between these two compartments is the capillary wall, which is permeable to all the solutes of plasma except protein. Blood pressure supplies the filtering force that moves fluid from the vascular into the interstitial fluid compartment. The force that pulls it back into the vascular compartment from the interstitial compartment is the osmotic force of the plasma proteins.

Intracellular fluid compartment

The third fluid compartment comprises the intracellular fluid, which is a constituent of the protoplasm of cells. This is the water in which cellular oxidations occur. The intracellular fluid forms about 50 per cent of the body weight. Therefore, the total amount of fluid in the 3 fluid compartments makes up about 70 per cent of the entire body weight.

There are several differences in composition between the extracellular and the intracellular fluids. Sodium and chloride are present in higher concentration in the former than in the latter, while potassium and phosphates are present in higher concentration in the latter. Protein is more abundant inside the cells than in the fluid bathing the cells. In order to make possible such differences in composition, there must be a highly selective barrier between the interstitial and the intracellular compartments, and the cell membrane with its special properties constitutes such a barrier.

Water moves from one compartment to another freely, but certain salts are more restricted in their movements.

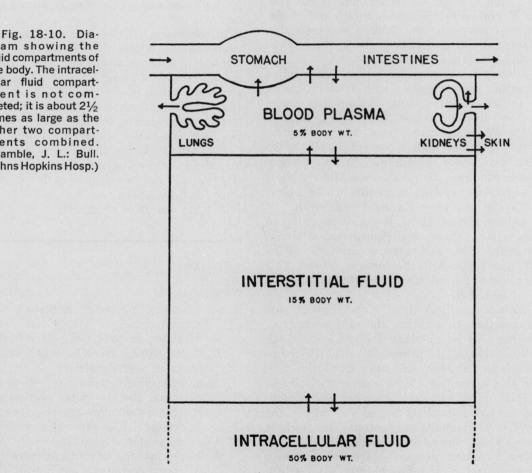

Fig. 18-10. Diagram showing the fluid compartments of the body. The intracellular fluid compartment is not completed; it is about 2½ times as large as the other two compartments combined. (Gamble, J. L.: Bull. Johns Hopkins Hosp.)

Disturbances in water and electrolyte balance

Disturbances in water and electrolyte balance involve changes in volume and composition of extracellular fluid, and, if prolonged, changes in intracellular fluid occur also.

A decrease in extracellular fluid volume (dehydration) follows prolonged vomiting, diarrhea or profuse perspiration, as well as deprivation of water. As soon as a decrease in extracellular fluid occurs, there is impairment of circulation; this means less blood flow to the kidneys. If the kidneys are not supplied abundantly with blood, they cannot perform their functions properly, so waste products begin to accumulate. If the condition is not permitted to continue, and if dehydration is corrected, the changes in composition are corrected automatically as soon as the kidneys can function again.

In prolonged vomiting, one loses water in saliva and gastric juice, together with HCl in gastric juice. In this condition, then, alkalosis may ensue, in addition to dehydration. In diarrhea, there is loss of water in pancreatic juice, bile and intestinal juice, together with a loss of $NaHCO_3$, so acidosis may ensue, in addition to dehydration. The same condition can result when Miller-Abbott or Wangensteen suction tubes are in use, unless care is taken to replace the fluid withdrawn.

In kidney disease there is retention of nitrogenous waste, sulfates and phosphates. Albumin is lost in the urine, and water accumulates in the subcutaneous tissues in the form of edema. This water is lost to the vascular compartment as surely as if it had left the body.

In diabetes mellitus there is dehydration due to the polyuria. In addition, the keto acids (e.g., acetoacetic) to be eliminated carry out sodium with them (eliminated as sodium salts). Dehydration leads to renal impairment, with all the difficulties that accompany it. Whenever the kidneys are impaired, not only do waste products accumulate in the blood and lead to acidosis, but also the production of ammonia is impaired. This leads to further acidosis due to loss of sodium.

When a person perspires excessively he may suffer from lack of sodium chloride, especially if he drinks plenty of water but does not replace the sodium chloride lost. There are cramps, lassitude, apathy, stupor, headache, weakness, nausea and vomiting. All of these symptoms can be prevented by taking extra salt or salt tablets with water, or by drinking dilute salt solution instead of water.

Water Intoxication. It is possible to produce water intoxication in a person whose kidneys are impaired. This condition is accompanied by headache, vertigo, vomiting, muscle cramps and edema, and really is due to decrease in salt concentration of the extracellular fluid. Death may occur in coma or convulsions, since there is edema of the brain and an increase in intracranial pressure.

In conclusion, it is evident that there are many conditions in which disturbances in water and electrolyte balance may occur, and a disturbance in one is seldom found without a disturbance in the other. When one is "out of balance" the functions of the various cells of the body (nervous system, heart muscle, smooth muscle, skeletal muscle, liver, etc.) are not performed properly.

The extent of the disturbances can be ascertained by determinations of sodium, potassium, chloride, pH and bicarbonate of the plasma. These same determinations can be made in order to follow the results of treatment.

SUMMARY

1. Kidneys
   A. Location: posterior abdomen; retroperitoneal
   B. Fixation: adipose tissue and renal fascia
   C. Gross appearance: bean-shaped; hilus in concave medial border
   D. Longitudinal section
      a. Renal cortex—outer portion of kidney
      b. Renal medulla—composed of pyramids
      c. Renal pelvis—funnel-shaped sac with extensions called calyces
   E. Nephron—the unit of structure
      a. Renal corpuscle—glomerulus and Bow-

man's capsule; renal tubule—proximal portion, loop of Henle, distal portion
  b. Drain into straight collecting tubules which join to form papillary ducts that open into calyces of pelvis
  c. Most of nephron unit in cortex; loop of Henle and collecting tubules in medulla
F. Blood supply: renal artery branches to interlobar arteries to arcuate to interlobular to afferent arteriole of glomerulus; efferent arteriole of glomerulus to peritubular capillaries to stellate vein to interlobular veins to arcuate veins to interlobar veins to renal veins
G. Nerve supply: visceral afferent fibers; visceral efferent fibers to vessels

2. Excretory passages
  A. Ureters
    a. Retroperitoneal tubes; convey urine to bladder
    b. Muscular layers produce peristaltic waves to move urine; mucosal lining continuous with that of kidney and bladder
  B. Urinary bladder
    a. Thick-walled muscular sac; behind pubis, reservoir for urine
    b. Mucosa in folds (rugae) in empty bladder
    c. Muscular coat—the detrusor muscle
    d. Sympathetic nerves of retention; parasympathetic nerves of emptying
  C. Urethra: conveys urine from bladder to exterior
    a. Female: 1 to 1½ in. long; external orifice in front of vagina; excretory function only
    b. Male: prostatic, membranous and cavernous portions; 6 to 8 in. long; both excretory and reproductive functions
  D. Micturition: act of emptying the urinary bladder; series of reflexes following release of voluntary control

3. Characteristics of urine
  A. Watery, amber-colored solution of nitrogenous waste and inorganic salts
    a. Specific gravity averages 1.016 to 1.020; acid reaction on mixed diet
    b. Quantity about 1½ L. daily
  B. Composition varies with products to be removed to maintain homeostasis

4. Formation of urine
  A. Glomerular filtration
    a. High blood pressure in glomerulus; water and true solutes filter into Bowman's capsule; red cells and protein remain in blood
    b. Average 170 L. daily
  B. Tubular reabsorption: osmosis, diffusion and active transport as substances are returned to blood stream
    a. Some substances (e.g., glucose) have "renal threshold"; excess is eliminated
    b. Active transport requires expenditure of energy and presence of specific enzymes
    c. Passive transport: osmosis; electrical gradients
  C. Tubular secretion: active transport and diffusion
    a. Kidney important in acid-base balance by increasing or decreasing acidity of urine
    b. H^+ secreted into lumen of tubule in exchange for Na^+; latter combines with HCO_3^- and returns to blood; conserves base
    c. Ammonia formed by tubule cells also conserves base; excreted as ammonium salt, thus saving Na^+
    d. Excess potassium actively secreted by tubule cells in exchange for Na^+
  D. Tubular excretion: active transport of substances of no use to body as well as those foreign to body (e.g., penicillin and P.S.P.)
  E. Hormonal effects
    a. ADH accelerates reabsorption of water by tubules; under control of hypothalamus
    b. Aldosterone important in active transport of Na^+ and K^+
  F. Urinalysis: examine for color, turbidity, pH, presence or absence of abnormal con-

stituents; microscopic examination of sediment

G. Diuresis (increased excretion of urine): water diuresis; osmotic diuresis; drugs; ethyl alcohol

H. Hemodialysis: removal of crystalloid waste products from blood as it flows through cellophane tubing submerged in special bath solution

5. Water balance

A. Intake: exogenous—in food, etc.; endogenous—from metabolic processes

B. Output: water eliminated through lungs, large intestine, skin and kidneys

6. Electrolyte balance

A. Intake: satisfactory on mixed diet; NaCl added to food voluntarily

B. Output: excreted by kidneys, intestine and skin

7. Fluid compartments of body

A. Vascular compartment: blood plasma; about 5% of body weight

B. Interstitial compartment: tissue fluid, lymph, special fluids (e.g., pleural fluid, cerebrospinal fluid, etc.); about 15% of body weight

C. Fluids of vascular and interstitial compartments make up extracellular fluid of body: concerned with transport of nutrients and wastes

   a. Chief difference between plasma and interstitial fluid—plasma has far more protein

D. Intracellular compartment: fluid constituent of protoplasm of cells; about 50% of body weight

   a. Sodium and chloride in lower concentration in cell than in tissue fluid

   b. Potassium and phosphates present in higher concentration in cell

   c. Cell membrane constitutes a highly selective barrier in maintaining this electrolyte balance

E. Disturbances in water and electrolyte balance involve changes in volume and composition of extracellular fluid

PRACTICAL APPLICATIONS AND QUESTIONS

(Encircle the letter of the *best* answer to each of the following questions.)

A. *Mrs. B. D. was admitted to the hospital for treatment of a severe bladder infection. The doctor immediately ordered a catheterized urine specimen for analysis.*

1. In catheterizing a female patient, one must remember that

   a. there is a sphincter of smooth muscle guarding the external urethral opening

   b. the female urethra is only about 1½ in. in length

   c. the urethral orifice is located behind the vagina

   d. the female urethra is common to both the excretory and the reproductive systems

2. Which of the following constituents would not be found in a normal catheterized urine specimen?

   a. sodium chloride

   b. urea

   c. creatinine

   d. albumin

3. The urinary bladder receives urine

   a. by peristaltic waves from the ureters

   b. drop by drop from the urethra

   c. directly from the kidneys by way of the hilum

   d. by force of gravity from the urethra

4. The stimulus that initiates the act of emptying the bladder is the

   a. concentration of the urine

   b. pressure of urine within the rectum

   c. stretching of the bladder wall

   d. increasing specific gravity of the urine

B. *An experiment on urine production in a mammal was demonstrated to a class in the physiology laboratory. From this experiment, the students were able to arrive at the following conclusions:*

1. The primary function of the kidney tubules is to

   a. return plasma proteins to the blood

b. reabsorb urea from the glomerular filtrate
c. act as a filter to prevent plasma proteins
   from leaving the blood
d. reabsorb water, glucose and electrolytes
   from the glomerular filtrate

2. When glucose is found in the urine, it usually
indicates that
   a. the kidney tubules are damaged
   b. tubular excretion is inactive

c. the active transport mechanism is over-
   loaded
d. there has been an injury to the glomerular walls

3. Increased secretion of antidiuretic hormone
(ADH) results in
   a. increased reabsorption of water
   b. increased excretion of urine
   c. decreased reabsorption of water
   d. no change in the reabsorption of water

19

". . . for I am fearfully and wonderfully made:"

PSALMS 139:14

THE ENDOCRINE SYSTEM

The maintenance of homeostasis is highly dependent upon the two great communication systems of the body—the nervous system and the endocrine system. The most rapid communication service is provided by the nervous system, which is roughly comparable to the telephone system of a great city; nerve impulses, traveling swiftly to and from the central nervous system "switchboards" over peripheral nerve fiber "wires," enable one to make rapid adjustments in both the external and the internal environments. The endocrine system, in contrast to the nervous system, provides a slower form of communication, because its messages are carried in the blood stream in the form of highly specialized chemical substances (hormones). However, the functions of these two communication systems are closely coordinated; each one depends on the other for its optimum performance. For example, certain hormones, such as epinephrine, have a profound effect on the central nervous system. On the other hand, discovery of the relationships between the central nervous system and the pituitary gland led to the development of a whole new subdivision of endocrinology, called *neuroendocrinology*. In this chapter we shall consider the many and varied activities of the endocrine communication system.

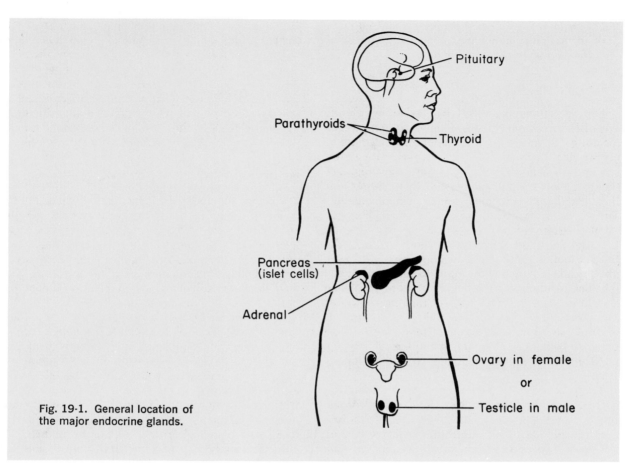

Fig. 19-1. General location of the major endocrine glands.

Endocrine Glands

The endocrine system consists of hormone-producing cells, which are called endocrine glands. These glands are relatively simple structures, consisting of clumps or cords of secretory cells that lie close to capillary networks and are supported by delicate reticular fibers. Because endocrine glands have no ducts, their secretions are discharged into the capillaries rather than onto the surface, or into a cavity, of the body; thus these glands also are referred to as *ductless glands,* or the *glands of internal secretion.*

As described on page 41, and illustrated in Figure 2-19, some of the endocrine glands are derived from epithelium that grows inward from the covering or lining surfaces of the body; certain other endocrine glands are derived from the nervous system and from other fetal tissues. However, regardless of their derivation, endocrine glands have one important feature in common —their secretory products are carried primarily in the blood stream.

The glands of the endocrine system do not form an anatomic system in the sense that they are in continuity, as are the organs that comprise other systems. However, even though the individual glands are located in widely separated regions of the body (Fig. 19-1), they do form a system from a functional point of view (i.e., the functioning of one affects the functioning of others).

Hormones

The secretions produced by endocrine glands are called *hormones,* a term derived from words meaning "to arouse" or "to spur on." Hormones are specific organic substances that are transported to various parts of the body, where they regulate the rates of specific processes. In carrying out their regulatory functions, some hormones are essential to life itself and others are not. For example, certain adrenal cortical hormones regulate the vital fluid and electrolyte balance of the body, but hormones produced by the ovaries and testes are considerably less important to mere survival.

When studying the function of hormones, one should not lose sight of the fact that the action of one hormone can affect the activities of others. For example, one hormone may reinforce another, two or more hormones may act in sequence, and one hormone may sensitize tissues to the action of another.

The production of each hormone is regulated in a particular way; for example, by the level of the blood sugar (insulin), by the level of sodium chloride in the blood (antidiuretic hormone), by the level of blood calcium (parathormone), by the nervous system (epinephrine) or by the blood level of a hormone from another gland. An example of the last is a trophic or regulatory hormone, such as the thyrotrophic hormone of the anterior lobe of the pituitary which regulates the production of thyroxin by the thyroid gland. The glands whose activities are regulated by trophic hormones are called *target organs.* The blood level of a hormone from a target gland reciprocally controls the production of the corresponding trophic hormone.

In order to have mental and physical health and to preserve homeostasis, a delicate and intricate balance must be maintained in the endocrine system. Too little secretion by any one gland not only leaves its own particular function undone but also affects the functions of other hormones.

Too much secretion by any one gland, such as occurs in adenomata or tumors of glands, likewise disturbs its own function and those of other hormones. This applies to all the components of the endocrine system, which comprises the pituitary, the pineal, the thyroid, the parathyroids, the adrenals, the gonads, the islets of Langerhans of the pancreas, and the mucosa of the stomach and the duodenum, which produces several hormones.

Methods of Study

Various methods of study have been used to collect information regarding the endocrine glands and, with the passage of time, these methods have become progressively more discriminating and precise. In addition, new techniques, have been evolved to meet the needs of investigators in the field of neuroendocrinology. A brief summary of methods and techniques is as follows:

(1) Clinical observation of persons with endocrine disorders correlated with findings at autopsy (both gross and microscopic); (2) surgical removal of a gland, or depression of its secretion by x-ray or radioactivity, to determine the effects of a lack of a particular hormone; (3) the administration of a hormone (natural or synthetic) to normal human beings and animals, as well as to those who have a deficiency of that hormone; (4) chemical analysis of body fluids and tissues to determine the presence or absence of hormones—the use of radioactive isotopes has been particularly valuable in study of the thyroid gland; (5) the placement of either destructive or stimulating electrodes in certain parts of the brain (e.g., the hypothalamus) has been of particular value in studying the interrelations of the nervous system and the endocrine system.

Pathology

A detailed presentation of the effects of hypofunction and hyperfunction of the various endocrine glands is not within the scope of this textbook. However, a few results of dysfunction will be mentioned briefly following the description of each gland.

THE PITUITARY GLAND

General Description

The pituitary gland, or *hypophysis cerebri,* lies at the base of the brain, to which it is attached by a thin stalk (Fig. 8-2). The ovoid body of this gland is enclosed by dura mater and rests in the sella turcica of the sphenoid bone; this arrangement provides maximum protection for what is probably the most important single endocrine gland. Pituitary hormones dominate the activities of the thyroid gland, the adrenal cortices, and the gonads. In addition, they exert important independent effects that will be described shortly.

The pituitary gland has two primary lobes or divisions: anterior and posterior. The anterior lobe is called the *adenohypophysis* because of its glandular nature. It arises in the embryo as an outpouching of epithelial tissue from the roof of the primitive mouth. Structurally, the anterior lobe consists of irregular cords or nests of large, polyhedral cells supported by delicate reticular fibers; sinusoids (capillary-like blood vessels) lie between the nests of cells (Fig. 19-2). There are relatively few nerve endings in this part of the pituitary gland.

The posterior lobe of the pituitary is an outgrowth of the hypothalamus; thus it is called the *neurohypophysis,* because it is derived from the nervous system. Thousands of axons descend into this lobe from cell bodies located in the hypothalamus; these nerve fibers are supported by pituicytes, cells that resemble the neuroglia of the CNS. Capillary networks are found near the endings of the nerve fibers.

Role of the hypothalamus

Almost all secretory activity of the pituitary gland is controlled by that small but complicated area of the brain known as the hypothalamus (p. 224). In response to various messages coming from the internal and external environments, the hypothalamus sends "signals" down the pituitary stalk and orders appropriate changes in the secretory activity of the anterior lobe and the discharge of stored hormones by the posterior lobe of this gland.

Control of the Anterior Lobe. A special arrangement of nerve fibers and tiny blood vessels provides the pathway for hypothalamic control of secretory activity in the anterior lobe; these vessels and nerve fibers are referred to as the *pituitary portal system,* or the hypothalamico-hypophyseal portal system (Fig. 19-2). Branches of the internal carotid arteries supply blood to a rich capillary plexus in the proximal portion of the pituitary stalk; blood from these capillaries then flows into a number of tiny venules, called portal vessels, that course down the stalk to empty into the sinusoids of the anterior lobe.

Special nerve cell bodies at the base of the hypothalamus produce hormones, called *neurosecretory substances* or "releasing factors." These substances trickle down the axons for storage at nerve fiber endings near the capillary plexus in the stalk. When appropriate messages reach the hypothalamus these special neurons are stimulated, causing their fiber endings to secrete one or more of the stored "releasing factors." These factors then enter the pituitary portal system, described above, and are transported to the anterior lobe, where they serve to promote the secretion of its hormones.

Control of the posterior lobe. In contrast to the anterior lobe, which receives only a few nerve fibers, the posterior pituitary is distinguished by its abundant nerve supply. As previously described on page 225, thousands of axons descend into the posterior lobe from highly specialized nerve cell bodies in the hypothalamus (Fig. 19-2). These hypothalamic nerve cell bodies produce two neurosecretions (antidiuretic hormone and oxytocin) that trickle down the axons and are stored at the fiber endings in the posterior lobe. When the hypothalamus detects a need for these substances, nerve impulses are dispatched over the appropriate fibers and the stored hormones are released for entry into the neighboring capillaries. Thus, the posterior lobe is under direct nervous control.

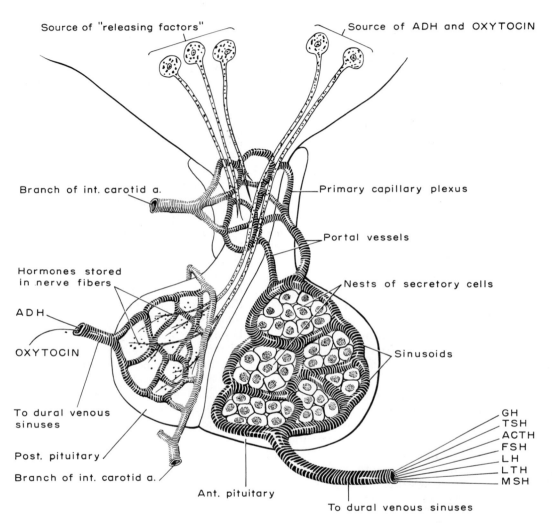

Fig. 19-2. Diagram of certain neural and vascular relationships between the hypothalamus and the pituitary gland. See text, pp. 549–552, for description.

Hormones of the Anterior Pituitary (Adenohypophysis)

At least 6 physiologically important hormones are produced by cells in the anterior lobe of the pituitary gland. These include the growth hormone or *somatotrophin, thyrotrophin, adrenocorticotrophin* and 3 gonadotrophins: *follicle stimulating* (FSH), *luteinizing* (LH) and *lactogenic* or luteotrophic (LTH). In addition to these major hormones, a seventh distinct endocrine substance, melanocyte-stimulating hormone (MSH), is found in the pituitary; however, its physiological importance has not yet been established in man.

With the exception of MSH, the anterior pituitary hormones are concerned with normal growth and metabolism, and, in addition, they exert an important measure of control over certain other endocrine glands. All 7 of these hormones are protein or polypeptide in nature.

Growth hormone or *somatotrophin* is concerned with the growth of bones, muscles and other organs of the body. It increases the rate of protein synthesis in all cells and promotes cell division. By acting on the cartilage cells in the epiphyses of long bones, this hormone plays an important part in controlling the growth of the skeleton. Growth hormone also promotes the utilization of fats as an energy source (ketogenic effect) while decreasing the rate of utilization of carbohydrates (diabetogenic effect).

Regulation of growth hormone secretion involves a somatotrophin-releasing factor (SRF) formed in the hypothalamus and transported to the anterior lobe by way of the pituitary portal system. The factors that influence the formation of SRF are not yet known; however, studies of the problem suggest that depletion of cellular proteins probably is a major stimulus for the secretion of SRF.

Thyrotrophin or *thyroid-stimulating hormone* (TSH) promotes the growth and the secretory activity of the thyroid gland. Regulation of thyrotrophin production is related reciprocally to the blood level of thyroid hormone (p. 556) and to the formation of a thyrotrophin-releasing factor (TRF) in the hypothalamus.

Adrenocorticotrophin (ACTH) controls the growth and the secretory activity of the adrenal cortex. Control of ACTH production is related reciprocally to the blood level of cortical hormones (p. 560) and to the formation of corticotrophin-releasing factor (CRF) in the hypothalamus in response to various biological stresses (e.g., pain, hypoglycemia, hypoxia, bacterial toxins, extremes of heat or cold, and so on).

Gonadotrophins are hormones that control the growth, development, and functioning of the ovaries and testes. These hormones are described in Chapter 20, and only a brief summary of their activities is presented here.

1. *Follicle-stimulating hormone* (FSH): stimulates development of ovarian follicles and the secretion of estrogen; stimulates development of seminiferous tubules and maturation of spermatozoa in male.

2. *Luteinizing hormone* (LH): works with FSH in final stages of follicular growth; provokes ovulation; stimulates formation of corpus luteum and secretion of progesterone. Male hormone called *interstitial cell-stimulating hormone* (ICSH); stimulates secretion of testosterone.

3. *Lactogenic hormone* or *luteotrophin* (LTH): maintains the corpus luteum and its secretion of progesterone; stimulates secretion of milk by prepared mammary glands (i.e., made responsive by action of ovarian hormones) at the end of pregnancy.

Melanocyte-stimulating hormone (MSH) may have a certain effect on the melanin granules in pigmented skin. Although its physiologic importance has not yet been established, there is increasing evidence that it plays a role in controlling skin pigmentation in man. The chemical structure of MSH is similar to that of ACTH, and both of these hormones can cause increased pigmentation of the skin under certain circumstances.

Hormones of the Posterior Pituitary (Neurohypophysis)

The two hormones found in the posterior lobe of the pituitary actually are produced by special

Fig. 19-3. Effects of pituitary disease, showing a giant and a dwarf; the woman is of normal height. (Boyd, William: An Introduction to Medical Science, ed. 4, Philadelphia, Lea & Febiger)

Fig. 19-4. Acromegaly, showing protrusion of lower jaw, heavy lips and "spade" hands. (Karsner, H. T.: Human Pathology, ed. 7, Philadelphia, Lippincott)

nerve cell bodies in the hypothalamus. These substances (antidiuretic hormone and oxytocin) trickle down the axons of their respective cell bodies and are stored at the fiber endings in the posterior pituitary until needed.

Antidiuretic hormone (ADH) also is referred to as *vasopressin,* because, when present in large quantities, it causes contraction of smooth muscle in the walls of blood vessels and can raise the blood pressure; large doses of ADH also can cause contraction of smooth muscle in the intestinal tract and in the uterus. However, in routine daily living, the antidiuretic effect is more pronounced, because even small quantities of ADH in the blood stream promote the reabsorption of water from the renal tubules and thus cause decreased excretion of water by the kidneys.

The role of the hypothalamus in regulating the secretion of ADH is described on page 225, and the specific action of ADH is described in more detail on page 536.

Oxytocin promotes contraction of the muscle of the uterus, particularly at the end of gestation. It also is most important at the time during which a mother nurses her baby—it causes milk to be expressed from the glandular tissue by acting on myoepithelial cells of the breast. When the hypothalamus receives afferent nerve impulses, initiated by dilatation of the cervix or by suckling stimuli on the nipple of the breast, it orders the release of oxytocin from the posterior lobe of the pituitary. Under certain conditions, commercial preparations of this hormone (e.g., Pitocin) are used clinically to induce uterine contractions during and after childbirth.

Pathology

Hypofunction of the Anterior Lobe. If a child is deficient in anterior pituitary hormones, the most obvious symptom is *dwarfism* or a failure to grow (Fig. 19-3). In addition, varying degrees of hypothyroidism, adrenal cortical insufficiency, and hypogonadism may occur.

Hypofunction in the adult may result in a condition known as *Simmonds' disease.* It is characterized by premature senility, weakness, emaciation, mental lethargy, and wrinkled, dry skin. In addition, there is loss of pubic and axillary hair and, sometimes, loss of the teeth.

Hyperfunction of the Anterior Lobe. The excessive quantity of growth hormone dominates this picture. If the condition develops before puberty, *gigantism* results; there is overgrowth of the entire body, and persons with this condition frequently reach a height of 7 or 8 feet (Fig. 19-3).

If hyperfunction occurs after the epiphyses of the long bones have closed, only the face, the hands and the feet are affected, and these become larger. The condition is called *acromegaly* (Fig. 19-4). The lower jaw becomes prominent, and the lower teeth separate; as the face enlarges the features become coarser. The skin is greasy and moist, and pigmentation may be increased. Headaches due to increased intracranial pressure, and even visual disturbances due to pressure on the optic chiasma, may occur.

Hypofunction of the Posterior Lobe. This condition, is characterized by the output of a large volume of dilute, sugar-free urine caused by the lack of antidiuretic hormone. The average daily output usually is 4 or 5 L., but in some cases it may be as great as 15 or 20 L., depending primarily on how much water the person drinks. Because there is an inability to concentrate the urine, the specific gravity usually is about 1.004 or less.

The absence of sugar in the urine led to the name of *diabetes insipidus* for this condition. The name stems from the ancient practice of physicians who diagnosed diabetes by tasting the urine; in diabetes mellitus ("sugar diabetes") the urine tasted as sweet as honey, but in diabetes insipidus the lack of sugar gave it an uninteresting or insipid taste.

Persons suffering from diabetes insipidus may have a great thirst (polydipsia) that is essentially a compensatory symptom for the loss of a large volume of urine (polyuria). However, such persons usually prefer ice-cold beverages and, inasmuch as urine is excreted at body temperature, considerable body heat may be lost; this is a good example of heat loss by conduction to the contents of the digestive tube.

Hyperfunction of the posterior lobe is not recognized clinically.

THE PINEAL GLAND

General Description

The pineal gland, or *pineal body,* is a small cone-shaped structure that extends posteriorly from the third ventricle in the diencephalon, lying just above the roof of the midbrain. Its functions have been under intensive study in recent years, and investigators hope that the mystery surrounding this organ soon will be solved. Inasmuch as study of the human pineal gland presents obvious technical difficulties, much of the laboratory work has been done on rats. However, a mounting body of evidence indicates that the mammalian pineal gland is an intricate and highly sensitive "biological clock," which participates in regulating the gonads, or sex glands.

The Pineal Hormone

In some way not yet completely understood, the amount of light in the environment influences the production of **melatonin,** a hormone that apparently is produced only by pineal cells. This hormone inhibits the activity of the gonads. It is believed that nerve impulses from the retina are relayed over sympathetic nerve fibers to the pineal gland, where they influence the secretion of melatonin. Light stimulates sexual maturation in the rat, but apparently inhibits such maturation in the human being. For example, a study of girls who either were born blind or lost their sight in the first year of life showed that blindness was associated with an early onset of puberty. In another study involving photosensitive albino girls whose retinae were inadequately protected from light, there was a great delay in the onset of puberty.

Further evidence that the pineal mechanism affects human gonads is found in cases of true pineal tumors; youngsters with such tumors have a delayed onset of puberty. On the other hand, tumors that destroy the pineal gland cause precocious puberty.

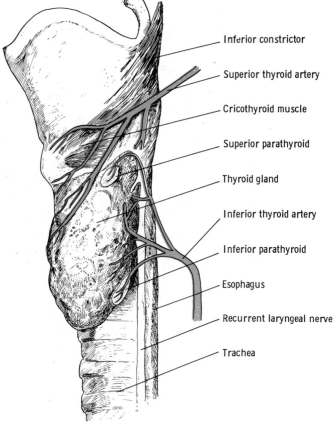

Inferior constrictor

Superior thyroid artery

Cricothyroid muscle

Superior parathyroid

Thyroid gland

Inferior thyroid artery

Inferior parathyroid

Esophagus

Recurrent laryngeal nerve

Trachea

Fig. 19-5. Thyroid and parathyroid glands.

THE THYROID GLAND

General Description

The thyroid gland is located immediately below the larynx in the anterior middle portion of the neck (Fig. 19-5). Lying on either side of, and anterior to, the trachea, this gland consists of two lobes united by a strip called the *isthmus.* It is covered with a capsule of connective tissue; partitions, or septa, extend inward from the capsule and divide the gland into irregular lobules.

The thyroid gland is provided with an abundant blood supply through branches of the exter-nal carotid artery and either the subclavian artery or its thyrocervical trunk. The thyroid veins empty into the internal jugular or the brachiocephalic veins. The nerve supply to this gland is derived from both divisions of the autonomic system; stimulation of parasympathetic fibers increases blood flow, but stimulation of sympathetic fibers decreases blood flow. However, nerve impulses do not directly affect secretion of the thyroid hormones.

The structural units of the thyroid gland are tiny sacs or "bags" known as follicles. Each follicle is formed by a single layer of epithelial cells surrounding a cavity that contains a secretory prod-

Fig. 19-6. Section of the thyroid gland. The follicles, which are lined with simple cuboidal epithelium, show varying degrees of distention with colloid material. ×100. (Greisheimer, Esther M.: Physiology and Anatomy, ed. 8, Philadelphia, Lippincott.)

Follicle containing colloid

Connective tissue

uct known as *colloid* (Fig. 19-6). Colloid is a viscous homogeneous fluid consisting mainly of a glycoprotein-iodine complex called *thyroglobulin*. Between the follicles is a network of reticular fibers with an extensive capillary bed, lymphatics and nerves.

The Thyroid Hormones

The thyroid gland produces 3 hormones: *thyroxin, triiodothyronine,* and *thyrocalcitonin,* the last secretion being a relatively recent discovery. Thyroxin represents over 95 per cent of the circulating thyroid hormone; triiodothyronine represents less than 5 per cent. Despite its relatively low concentration, triiodothyronine passes out of the blood stream more readily than does thyroxin; it has a more rapid action, and may account for as much as one-fourth to one-third of the total metabolic effect of the two secretions.

Thyroxin and triiodothyronine are stored in the follicular colloid as part of the thyroglobulin molecules. When these hormones are needed by the body, an enzyme in the colloid splits the thyroglobulin molecules and frees the hormones for entry into the blood stream. Upon entering the blood stream, thyroxin and triiodothyronine combine with specific plasma proteins and are transported to all parts of the body as "protein-bound" iodinated compounds. Thus, laboratory tests (p. 557) that determine the amount of "protein-bound" iodine (PBI) in the plasma reflect the level of circulating thyroid hormone.

Functions. *Thyroxin* and *triiodothyronine* control the metabolic rate of the body—i.e., the rate of oxidation in the cells and the resulting heat production. They are essential for normal growth and development of the body, including mental development and the attainment of sexual maturity. They have widespread effects on all aspects of metabolism, such as promoting protein synthesis and protein breakdown, maintaining normal blood levels of cholesterol and fatty acids, increasing the rate of glucose absorption and utilization, and promoting gluconeogenesis. They also assist in maintaining fluid and electrolyte balance.

Thyrocalcitonin has been found to lower the level of calcium in the blood. There is considerable evidence that it works directly on bone tissue and promotes the uptake of calcium. Secretions of the parathyroid glands (p. 558) also assist in maintaining calcium homeostasis.

Control of Secretion. *Thyroid-stimulating hormone* (TSH) from the anterior pituitary controls the growth and secretory activity of the thyroid gland. It increases the size and number of follicular cells and increases their ability to take up iodide. TSH also promotes the breakdown of thyroglobulin in the follicles with the resultant release of thyroxin and triiodothyronine.

The secretion of TSH by the anterior pituitary is regulated by the concentration of thyroxin and triiodothyronine in the circulating blood. When the concentration of these hormones is decreased, the pituitary cells are stimulated, both directly and indirectly, by way of the hypothalamus to secrete more TSH. On the other hand, an increase in the amount of these hormones in the blood serves to inhibit the production of TSH.

The stimulus for release of thyrocalcitonin apparently is an elevation of the level of calcium in the blood.

Pathology

Iodine Deficiency. If the iodine intake is insufficient, a simple or "colloid goiter" occurs. The gland is enlarged due to an increase in the number and the size of epithelial cells, but there is not an increased amount of colloid in the follicles. Usually the gland, because of its increased size, makes enough thyroxin so there are no symptoms of hypofunction, and the only evidence of pathology is the enlargement of the gland. In some persons the gland may be so large that it exerts pressure on the trachea and leads to choking sensations.

Persons who live near the sea, where iodine is abundant in the food and in the water, ingest adequate quantities of iodine in the diet. However, those who live in the inland sections of the United States generally find that iodine is lacking in the diet. The incidence of colloid goiter in the latter areas has been greatly reduced by the use of iodized table salt.

Hypothyroidism. Persons who fail to produce sufficient quantities of thyroxin and triiodothyronine are said to be *hypothyroid*. When the thyroid gland is underactive in an infant, a condition called *cretinism* develops. The first signs of cretinism appear at about 6 months of age, when it is noted that both mental and physical development are slow. Thereafter the infant does not sit up, walk and talk at the usual age. The mental development is so retarded that the child may become an idiot. The physical growth is so retarded that the child remains a dwarf.

The teeth are poorly developed, and ossification of bones is delayed. The tongue is large and protrudes from the mouth. The skin is thickened and dry. There is poor tone in the skeletal muscles. The secondary sexual characteristics do not develop. The body temperature is low, the blood pressure low, the heart rate slow, and the basal metabolic rate is about 25 per cent below the normal range. A typical cretin is shown in Figure 19-7.

When pronounced hypofunction of the thyroid gland appears in an adult the condition is called *myxedema*. A myxedematous patient undergoes a complete change of personality and mental ability and becomes slow, lethargic and stupid. The hair falls out, and the skin becomes thick and dry. Obesity is common. The heart dilates, but there is no evidence of cardiac failure, and digitalis therapy has no effect on cardiac function. The cholesterol of the blood is elevated, and the basal metabolic rate is low.

Hyperthyroidism. Persons who produce excessive quantities of thyroxin and triiodothyronine are said to be *hyperthyroid*. In such cases the thyroid gland usually is enlarged to some extent. Most commonly this enlargement is diffuse (toxic diffuse goiter), but occasionally it is nodular (toxic nodular goiter).

Toxic diffuse goiter, or *Graves' disease*, is characterized not only by the signs and symptoms of hyperthyroidism but also by protrusion of the eye-

Fig. 19-7. Cretinism. At the time the protograph was taken, the patient was 42 years of age, weighed 88 pounds and was 45 inches tall. The I.Q. was 12. The patient died 4 months after the photograph was taken; no thyroid tissue could be found at autopsy. (Minnesota School for the Feeble Minded)

Fig. 19-8. Exophthalmic goiter. The patient's thyroid was diffusely enlarged, hyperthyroidism had been present for about 4 years. Exophthalmos and increased lid space are evident. The pulse rate was 134; the left ventricle was enlarged; the basal metabolic rate was plus 69 per cent. (Minneapolis General Hospital)

balls (exophthalmos). It is believed that the cause of this disease is an excessive production of thyroid-stimulating hormone (TSH) by the anterior pituitary.

Some of the signs and symptoms of hyperthyroidism are as follows: high basal metabolic rate, rapid respiration, sweating and flushing of the skin (a means of promoting heat loss to keep pace with heat production and maintain normal body temperature), increased appetite, diarrhea, weight loss, tachycardia and increased cardiac output, fine tremors of skeletal muscles, high level of protein-bound iodine and low cholesterol in the blood, restlessness, nervousness and emotional instability.

The eye changes in toxic diffuse goiter include the aforementioned protruding eyeballs and a widening of the space between the lids (Fig. 19-8). Because the eyelids do not close completely when the person blinks or even when he is asleep, the epithelial surfaces of the eyes become irritated and often infected.

Treatment of hyperthyroidism centers on reducing the amount of circulating thyroid hormone. This may be accomplished by the use of drugs that depress the activity of the thyroid gland (e.g., propylthiouracil) or by removing a portion of the gland (subtotal thyroidectomy).

Laboratory Tests. Determination of the PBI *("protein-bound" iodine)* is a diagnostic test of considerable clinical importance in regard to thyroid function. The normal PBI range is between 4 and 8 micrograms per 100 ml. of plasma. Decreased levels (as low as 0.8 microgram) are found in hypothyroidism, and increased levels (as high as 24 micrograms) are found in hyperthyroidism. The B.M.R. *(basal metabolic rate)* also is decreased in hypothyroidism and increased in hyperthyroidism, but it should be noted that the B.M.R. measures only the over-all oxygen consumption and not thyroid function specifically; for example, the B.M.R. is increased in various infections, in pregnancy and in other conditions not related to thyroid disorders.

The radioiodine uptake is another test of thyroid function. The patient swallows a measured dose of radioactive iodine in distilled water; 24 hours later a radiant energy counter is placed near the thyroid gland to determine the amount of radiation from that area. In hypothyroidism the uptake usually ranges from zero to 15 per cent; in normal glands, from 15 to 50 per cent; in hyperthyroidism, 50 to 100 per cent.

THE PARATHYROID GLANDS

General description

The parathyroid glands are located on the posterior surface of the thyroid gland (Fig. 19-5). They lie beneath the capsule and actually may be embedded in the substance of the thyroid gland. Usually there are 4 parathyroid glands.

The parathyroid glands receive blood by way of branches of the external carotid, the subclavian or the thyrocervical trunk; and the veins drain into the internal jugular or brachiocephalic veins.

The nerve supply is from the vagus and the lateral sympathetic chain ganglia.

The parathyroid hormones

The major hormone produced by the parathyroid glands is called **parathormone.** However, there is considerable evidence that a second hormone, **calcitonin,** also is produced by these little organs.

Parathormone and calcitonin serve to maintain the proper level of calcium and phosphorus in the blood. In this way they help to preserve the normal excitability of muscle and nerve tissue. For example, excitability is increased when the blood calcium is low, and depressed when the calcium level is high. The formation and maintenance of functional bone also requires parathyroid hormones.

Parathormone has effects on three tissues that participate most prominently in maintaining the blood calcium level: bone, kidney and intestine. The role played by parathormone apparently is one of influencing the *rates* at which calcium is transported across membranes. For example, when blood calcium is low parathormone promotes the mobilization of calcium from bones and also increases its rate of absorption from the in-

testinal tract. In the kidney, parathormone promotes the excretion of phosphate, thus permitting more calcium to be added to the blood. The latter is possible because of the reciprocal relationship that exists between calcium and phosphate; this means that if the level of one begins to fall, the other rises, because the product of the two is a constant.

Calcitonin has the opposite effect of parathormone in that it decreases the blood calcium. As previously described (p. 556), thyrocalcitonin from the thyroid gland also decreases the calcium ion concentration in the blood. Little is known, as yet, about the biochemical mechanisms of action.

Control of Secretions. The secretion of parathormone is triggered by a decrease in the concentration of blood calcium ions below the normal level of 10 mg. per cent. Contributing factors include low calcium diets, lack of vitamin D, pregnancy, lactation, and kidney disease in which there is retention of phosphates.

The stimulus for release of calcitonin apparently is an elevation of the blood calcium level.

Pathology

Hypoparathyroidism. The symptoms of this disorder are related to the low blood calcium level that results from a lack of parathormone. The most striking change is increased excitability of the nervous system with latent or frank *tetany.* An early manifestation of tetany is carpopedal spasm, a sharp flexion of the wrist and ankle joints as illustrated in Figure 19-9; this is accompanied by muscle twitchings and cramps. Generalized convulsions may occur, leading to respiratory paralysis and death by asphyxiation unless the blood picture is corrected by the intravenous injection of calcium salts. Fortunately, this condition is not common, but it may develop following accidental removal of the parathyroid glands during thyroidectomy.

Hyperparathyroidism. This relatively rare disease usually is caused by a tumor in one or more of the parathyroid glands. With the continual production of an excess of parathormone, the blood level of calcium begins to rise; however, in mild

Fig. 19-9. The hands and feet of a patient with tetany, showing the typical position of the hands (main d'accoucheur) and the feet assumed in carpopedal spasm. (Grollman, Arthur: Essentials of Endocrinology, ed. 2, Philadelphia, Lippincott)

cases the rise may not be too great, probably because of the moderating effect of thyrocalcitonin. In severe cases, the blood calcium level may rise to 15 mg. per cent or higher as parathormone promotes withdrawals from the body's calcium "bank" in bone tissue. As a result, x-rays may show demineralized, cystic areas in the bones (osteitis fibrosa cystica), and multiple, spontaneous fractures are frequent.

Another complication of hyperparathyroidism is the formation of kidney stones: this occurs because with a high calcium level in the blood more calcium is excreted in the urine. Other symptoms include decreased excitability of nerve tissue and weakness of skeletal muscles.

ADRENAL GLANDS (SUPRARENAL)

General description

The adrenal glands are located above the kidneys. Figures 1-7 and 18-1 show the location of these glands. Each consists of an outer portion called the *cortex* and an inner portion called the *medulla.*

The blood supply to the adrenal glands is very abundant. They receive blood by way of branches from the inferior phrenic (superior suprarenal), the aorta (middle suprarenal) and the renal (inferior suprarenal) arteries. The blood is collected into the suprarenal veins; the right empties into the inferior vena cava, and the left into the renal vein.

The nerve supply consists of preganglionic fibers from the thoracolumbar division by way of the splanchnic nerves and also twigs from the vagus.

Hormones of the adrenal cortex

The specialized cells of the adrenal cortex produce 3 types of steroid hormones, some of which are essential to life.

1. **The mineralocorticoids** are hormones that are of fundamental importance in the maintenance of fluid and electrolyte balance. They also are called the "salt and water" hormones, since they regulate the absorption and the excretion of sodium, chloride, potassium and water.

Aldosterone is the most important mineralocorticoid secreted by the adrenal cortex. It acts on the cells of the renal tubules of the kidneys where it promotes the reabsorption of sodium chloride and water and the elimination of potassium. *The production of aldosterone* is controlled primarily by the intake of sodium salts, but it is influenced also by the volume of fluid within the body. For example, there is an increase in the secretion of aldosterone when the body is deprived of sodium; there may also be an increase during blood loss (p. 529) and dehydration. Adrenocorticotrophic hormone (ACTH) exerts only a slight amount of control over the secretion of aldosterone.

2. **The glucocorticoids** or "sugar hormones" constitute the second type of adrenal cortical hormones. *Cortisol* (hydrocortisone) and *corti-*

sone are members of this group. These hormones not only have important effects on the metabolism of all 3 groups of foodstuffs but also they are concerned with one's capacity to withstand stresses of many types. For example, the secretion of glucocorticoids is increased in such stressful situations as heavy muscular exercise, exposure to cold, hypoglycemia, hypoxia, trauma, infection, allergy, and the like.

The hormones of this group are concerned with preservation of the carbohydrate reserves of the body. They have a catabolic effect on protein metabolism, as they promote the mobilization of amino acids from the cells. The amino acids then are available for conversion to glucose (gluconeogenesis). In addition to promoting gluconeogenesis, the glucocorticoids also promote the deposition of glycogen in the liver, the mobilization of depot fat and the oxidation of that fat in the liver. Thus these hormones serve as functional antagonists to insulin because they conserve carbohydrate.

Although aldosterone is the main salt-retaining hormone of the adrenal cortex, the glucocorticoids also have an effect on fluid and electrolyte balance. This is particularly true when they are present in excessive quantities.

Of major clinical importance is the fact that glucocorticoids have an *anti-inflammatory effect*. Not only do they tend to suppress inflammatory reactions, but they also tend to limit the destructive effects of such reactions. Although injections of glucocorticoids are highly beneficial in controlling such conditions as rheumatoid arthritis, excessive quantities may work to one's disadvantage in other situations in which the inflammatory response (p. 305) is part of the normal mechanism for combating infection and promoting healing. The glucocorticoids also have an *anti-allergic effect,* possibly by interfering with the liberation of histamine.

The exact mechanism of the anti-inflammatory effect is not yet known. However, it is possibly related to the ability of the glucocorticoids to prevent the disruption of lysosomal membranes (lysosomes are cellular organelles that contain powerful digestive enzymes, as described on page 21).

Other effects that follow the injection of glucocorticoids include a reduction in the size of lymphatic organs and a decrease in the number of circulating lymphocytes and eosinophils.

The production of glucocorticoids is primarily under the control of adrenocorticotrophin (ACTH). For example, a decrease in the blood level of glucocorticoids stimulates the anterior pituitary to release ACTH, which, in turn, stimulates the adrenal cortex to increase its secretory activity. As the level of glucocorticoids rises, it serves to "shut off" the secretion of ACTH. The blood level of glucocorticoids is believed to stimulate the pituitary cells directly as well as indirectly by means of the hypothalamus, which secretes a corticotrophin-releasing factor (CRF) into the pituitary portal system.

In addition to being chemically stimulated by the blood flowing through it, the hypothalamus also produces CRF in response to nerve signals from various parts of the body. For example, stress situations, such as physical injury, pain, fright, and so on, initiate nerve impulses that are relayed to the hypothalamus, stimulating it to secrete CRF. The CRF then promotes secretion of ACTH, causing an increased output of glucocorticoids. The significance of this increased output is not yet completely understood; however, one theory is that in some cases the rapid mobilization of amino acids and fats from cellular "storehouses" provides not only a source of energy but also raw materials for the synthesis of substances that are essential to the lives of cells in injured tissues.

3. **The sex hormones** constitute the third group of hormones secreted by the adrenal cortex. Several moderately active male sex hormones (17-ketosteroids) plus minute quantities of female sex hormones are produced by the adrenals in both men and women. Their role in normal body function is not yet known.

Hormones of the adrenal medulla

The adrenal medulla produces a mixture of epinephrine and norepinephrine, thereby constituting an important link between the nervous system and the endocrine system. The secretory activity of the cells of the adrenal medulla is under the control of the sympathetic division of the autonomic nervous system. On stimulation, it is thought that the adrenal medullae liberate from 2 to 5 times as much epinephrine as norepinephrine.

Epinephrine, also known as *Adrenalin* (a trade name), is believed to be produced especially during such emergencies as emotional crises, hypoglycemia, mild hypoxia and hypotension. It induces constriction of arterioles (except those of the skeletal muscles and heart muscle); it increases the rate and the force of the heart beat and raises the blood pressure. It dilates the bronchioles by relaxing the smooth muscle in their walls. It increases the blood sugar by increasing the breakdown of glycogen in the liver. In general, the effects are the same as stimulation of the sympathetic division of the autonomic nervous system, and the function of epinephrine is to reinforce these activities and prolong them. In addition, it stimulates the production of ACTH, which, in turn, stimulates the production of adrenal cortical hormones.

Clinically, epinephrine is used in the treatment of bronchial asthma, urticaria (hives), cardiac failure, circulatory collapse and with local anesthetics in operations on eye, nose and throat. It constricts blood vessels and decreases bleeding, causes the blood to coagulate faster and delays the absorption of the local anesthetic.

Norepinephrine also is known by various trade names (e.g., *Levophed, Noradrenalin,* etc.). It differs from epinephrine in that it does not affect carbohydrate metabolism in muscle and liver tissue, nor does it cause hyperglycemia. While both hormones produce an elevation of the systolic blood pressure, norepinephrine produces a rise in the diastolic pressure as well. This is due to the fact that norepinephrine causes vasoconstriction in the skeletal muscles as well as in the skin and the viscera. As a result of this widespread vasoconstrictor effect, there is a marked increase in the peripheral resistance.

In addition to its production by the cells of the adrenal medullae, norepinephrine (sympathin)

also is released at the neuro-effector junctions of most sympathetic postganglionic nerve fibers; here it acts as a chemical transmitter substance that serves to excite (or to inhibit) the effector cells.

Pathology

Chronic adrenalcortical insufficiency, or chronic *hypofunction* of the adrenal cortex, leads to a condition known as Addison's disease. Some of the signs and symptoms that characterize this disease are as follows: (1) marked muscle weakness and easy fatigability; (2) gastrointestinal disturbances, manifested by vomiting, diarrhea and weight loss; (3) excessive loss of sodium and chloride, and retention of potassium; (4) reduced extracellular fluid volume with fall in blood pressure and secondary impairment of kidney function; (5) disturbances in carbohydrate metabolism, manifested by decreased gluconeogenesis, low blood sugar, and low liver glycogen; (6) a peculiar pigmentation of the skin (referred to as *bronzing* of the skin); (7) decreased capacity to adapt to even minor changes in the internal or external environments, decreased ability to withstand any form of stress, and acute prostration from even minor infections.

Hyperfunction of the adrenal cortex may involve excessive production of all 3 groups of hormones, or of just one group. *Cushing's syndrome* is the classic form of hyperactivity; it may be caused by various pituitary tumors that are the source of excess ACTH and lead to hyperplasia of the adrenal cortex. In this condition, the secretion of excess cortisol usually predominates over that of the other cortical hormones. Manifestations of the over-all catabolic effect of excess cortisol are marked muscle wasting (especially in the extremities), loss of elasticity and thinning of the skin, a tendency to bruise easily, poor wound healing, and osteoporosis. Persons with Cushing's syndrome have an abnormal distribution of fat characterized by a rounding of the face (moon face), deposits of fat in the shoulders (buffalo hump), and a pendulous abdomen; the extremities appear thin. The blood glucose is elevated, probably because

Blood vessel

Islet cells

Acinar cells

Fig. 19-10. Section of the pancreas, showing some details of the islets of Langerhans. ×190. (Greisheimer, Esther M.: Physiology, ed. 8, Philadelphia, Lippincott)

of the enhanced gluconeogenesis; if this persists for many months, the insulin-producing cells in the pancreas may "burn out" and lead to frank diabetes mellitus. There is slight sodium retention, slight potassium depletion, a mild increase in the extracellular fluid volume, and moderate hypertension.

Adrenogenital Syndromes. Excessive secretion of the 17-ketosteroids (male sex hormones) by children results in sexual precocity in boys. In girls, the most obvious sign is masculinization of the external genitalia. In the adult male, an excess of the 17-ketosteroids may not be recognized, inasmuch as they would tend to increase his characteristic "maleness." However, hypersecretion in the female may have devastating, masculinizing effects such as baldness, increased growth of facial and body hair, atrophy of the breasts and uterus,

enlargement of the clitoris, and increased skeletal muscle mass.

Hyperfunction of the Adrenal Medulla. Hypersecretion of the medullary hormones accompanies the presence of a tumor known as a *pheochromocytoma.* Two major syndromes are related to this condition—one of intermittent hypertension and one of sustained hypertension.

Intermittent, or paroxysmal, hypertension involves recurrent attacks of extreme, but transient, elevation of the blood pressure. During such attacks the systolic pressure may rise above 300 mm. Hg. The sustained, or chronic, type of hypertension is very similar to malignant hypertension (p. 393). In addition to a consistently high blood pressure, victims of this syndrome have signs of hyperthyroidism (e.g., nervousness, sweating, and so forth), but their PBI is normal.

ISLET CELLS OF THE PANCREAS

(The Islets of Langerhans)

General Description

The pancreas is an important accessory organ of the digestive system, and, as such, it was previously described on page 481. At this time we shall concern ourselves with its endocrine function—the secretion of insulin and glucagon.

Irregular clumps of cells, called the islets of Langerhans, constitute the endocrine secretory units of the pancreas. These little islets are scattred throughout the pancreas, and it has been estimated that there are anywhere from 20,000 to 2,000,000 of them.

The islet cells are separated from the surrounding acinar cells by a film of reticular tissue (Fig. 19-10). Each islet has an extensive capillary network to carry off the secretions. Special staining techniques reveal the presence of two cell types in the islets—alpha and beta. These cells are responsible for the secretion of glucagon and insulin.

Hormones of the islet cells

Insulin is secreted by the beta cells of the islands of Langerhans, and its production is controlled primarily by the level of glucose in the blood. This important hormone is essential for normal carbohydrate metabolism.

Insulin performs many functions. It lowers the blood sugar by (1) increasing the utilization of glucose by the tissues, (2) stimulating the formation and the storage of glycogen in the liver, (3) decreasing gluconeogenesis from amino acids, and (4) stimulating the formation of fat from glucose.

The effects of insulin are antagonized by several hormones: (1) *epinephrine* stimulates the breakdown of glycogen in the liver and produces hyperglycemia; (2) *adrenal cortical hormones* (glucocorticoids) stimulate gluconeogenesis; and (3) thyroxin stimulates gluconeogenesis.

Glucagon, a hyperglycemic factor, is secreted by the alpha cells of the islets of Langerhans when stimulated by a falling blood sugar. It causes a marked, but temporary, rise in blood sugar level by promoting rapid glycogenolysis in the liver followed by the release of glucose into the blood. Thus it appears that glucagon and insulin constitute a "team" of hormones, whereby the islet cells help to regulate blood sugar level.

Pathology

Diabetes mellitus is a chronic disorder of carbohydrate metabolism due to a relative or absolute insulin deficiency. There is a high incidence of this condition throughout the world, and diabetics require medical supervision for some time. Diabetes mellitus most frequently develops during and after middle life. It occurs more often in women than in men and is influenced by heredity and obesity.

Many metabolic disturbances occur in diabetes mellitus, but the cardinal symptom is *hyperglycemia* (high blood glucose level) due to the impaired metabolism of carbohydrates. The resulting glycosuria as well as the secondary alterations in protein and fat metabolism lead to polyuria, ketosis, acidosis, dehydration, coma and death. Abnormal metabolism is described on page 507.

The worst complication in diabetes mellitus involves changes that occur in the walls of the blood vessels. Capillary lesions may produce disastrous results, particularly in the retina of the eye and in the glomeruli of the kidneys. Changes in the walls of the arteries (atherosclerosis and arteriosclerosis) occur more frequently in the diabetic patient and at an earlier age than in the nondiabetic person.

The diabetic person has a marked tendency to develop infections; thus, careful and frequent cleansing of the skin is emphasized. Injuries heal slowly and with difficulty, particularly in the lower extremities where circulation frequently is impaired. Ulcers are common, and gangrene may necessitate the amputation of some of the toes. A diabetic ulcer with gangrene of the toes is illustrated in Figure 19-11.

A commonly used test for hypofunction of the beta cells of the islets is the glucose tolerance

Fig. 19-11. Gangrene of the feet in untreated diabetes mellitus. (Williams, J. R.: North Carolina M. J. 4:129)

test. In performing this test, the fasting blood sugar is determined, and then a definite amount of glucose is given (dependent on the body weight), and the blood sugar is determined at definite intervals thereafter for about 2 hours. The variations in blood sugar, after the ingestion of glucose, give information with respect to the production of insulin.

Many obese, adult diabetics respond to dietary management and weight reduction alone, but practically all of the younger persons require insulin therapy as well as regulation of the diet. Although insulin is not a cure, it does enable carbohydrate, fat and protein metabolism to approach the normal pattern.

Insulin must be given by hypodermic injection, since it is destroyed by the digestive enzymes if taken by mouth. There are 2 principal types of insulin preparations available: soluble or unmodified insulin (rapid acting), and modified preparations (slow acting). Unmodified, *crystalline* insulin acts over a period of 6 to 8 hours. On the other hand, the modified preparations consist of insulin combined with basic proteins and zinc to slow absorption and prolong the effect. For example, *protamine zinc insulin* (PZI) has a period of action of up to 30 hours; *neutral protamine Hagedorn* (NPH) insulin and *Lente* insulin act for about 24 hours. The insulin dosage is estab-

lished by the physician. If an overdose is given, convulsions may occur as the blood sugar falls to dangerously low levels. If the dose is too small, acidosis and diabetic coma may occur.

Insulin also has been used in the production of shock for the treatment of certain mental disorders. The very low level of glucose in the blood caused by an excessive dose of insulin alters the activity of the cells of the CNS.

Hyperinsulinism refers to the persistent excessive secretion of insulin by beta cells of the islands of Langerhans. It induces hypoglycemia (low blood glucose level) and is characterized by attacks of weakness, profuse perspiration and trembling. The attacks occur when meals are delayed, or when unusual exertion is undertaken. In the early stages, the symptoms are relieved by the taking of food or sugar.

THE GONADS

The cells that produce the gonadal hormones are located in the ovaries and the testes as described in Chapter 20.

The gonadal hormones

Testosterone is produced by the interstitial cells of the testes. The production of this hormone is under the control of ICSH of the anterior lobe of the pituitary gland. Testosterone is responsible for the development of the secondary sexual characteristics of the male and for the development and the maintenance of the male organs of reproduction.

Estrogen, produced by the cells of the ovarian follicles, frequently is referred to as the "growth hormone" of the female reproductive system. It is concerned with the development of the secondary sexual characteristics at the age of puberty and with their maintenance during adult life. Estrogen plays an important role in the first half of the menstrual cycle, as it promotes the repair of the endometrium following each menstrual period. It also induces cyclic changes in the breasts and in the vaginal mucosa.

The production of estrogen is controlled by the follicle-stimulating hormone (FSH) of the anterior portion of the pituitary gland; this is described in more detail on page 583.

Progesterone is produced by the cells of the corpus luteum, under the control of the luteinizing and luteotrophic hormones of the anterior lobe of the pituitary gland. Progesterone prepares the uterus for implantation of the fertilized ovum and for the nourishment and the development of the embryo in the early stages of its growth. It supplements the action of estrogen on the mammary glands.

Pathology

Hypofunction of the Ovaries. If the ovaries are removed before puberty, or if the anterior lobe of the pituitary gland is underactive, the secondary sexual characteristics fail to develop at the age of puberty. The menstrual cycles never are established. If the ovaries are removed after the age of puberty, the uterus, the vagina and the external genitalia undergo atrophy.

Hypofunction of the Testes. If the testes are removed before puberty, or if the gonadotrophic hormones of the anterior lobe of the pituitary gland are lacking, the secondary sexual characteristics fail to develop. The voice remains high-pitched, and there is no growth of hair on the face and the trunk. There is a deposit of fat around the hips and in the pectoral and the gluteal regions. The epiphyses close late; consequently, the person is tall. The lower extremities are disproportionately long in comparison with the trunk. The accessory reproductive organs remain small, and the person is sterile.

If the testes are removed after puberty, there is atrophy of the accessory reproductive organs.

In concluding this chapter, we wish to note that the possibility of an endocrine secretion from the thymus is discussed on page 387. The gastrointestinal hormones are reviewed, with others, in the table on pages 567 and 568.

SUMMARY

1. Nervous and endocrine systems are two great communication systems
   A. Closely coordinated, each depends on other
   B. Neuroendocrinology subdivision of endocrinology
2. Endocrine glands also called ductless glands, glands of internal secretion
   A. Secretions called hormones, carried in blood stream
   B. Hormone production regulated in various ways, delicate balance
3. Pituitary gland (hypophysis cerebri)
   A. Located at base of brain in sella turcica
   B. Anterior lobe, adenohypophysis
   C. Posterior lobe, neurohypophysis
   D. Hypothalamus controls most activity
      a. Anterior lobe: pituitary portal system; releasing factors
      b. Posterior lobe: direct nervous control
   E. Hormones of anterior lobe (see table on p. 567)
   F. Hormones of posterior lobe (see table on p. 567)
   G. Pathology
      a. Anterior lobe
         (1) Hypofunction—dwarfism in child; Simmond's disease in adult

(2) Hyperfunction—gigantism in child; acromegaly in adult

  b. Posterior lobe

    (1) Hypofunction—diabetes insipidus

    (2) Hyperfunction — not recognized clinically

4. Pineal gland

  A. Secretion: melatonin

  B. "Biological clock" in regulating gonads (?)

5. Thyroid gland

  A. Located below larynx, anterior neck

    a. Composed of follicles containing colloid, thyroglobulin

  B. Hormones: (see table on p. 567)

    a. Stored as part of thyroglobulin molecules

    b. Carried in blood as PBI compounds

  C. Pathology

    a. Iodine deficiency—colloid goiter

    b. Hyperthyroidism—toxic diffuse goiter (Graves' disease); exophthalmus

    c. Hypothyroidism — cretinism in child; myxedema in adult

    d. Lab tests: PBI, BMR, radioiodine uptake

6. Parathyroid glands

  A. Located on posterior surface of thyroid; usually 4 in number

  B. Hormones: (see table on p. 567–568)

  C. Pathology

    a. Hypoparathyroidism—tetany

    b. Hyperparathyroidism — spontaneous fractures, kidney stones, muscle weakness

7. Adrenal glands

  A. Located above kidneys; outer cortex, inner medulla

  B. Hormones: (see table on p. 568)

  C. Pathology

    a. Adrenal cortex

     (1) Hypofunction—Addison's disease

     (2) Hyperfunction — Cushing's syndrome, adrenogenital syndromes

    b. Adrenal medulla

     (1) Hypofunction — not recognized clinically

     (2) Hyperfunction — intermittent or sustained hypertension

8. Islet cells of pancreas

  A. Pancreas located in epigastric and left hypochondriac regions

  B. Hormones: (see table on p. 568)

  C. Pathology

    a. Insulin deficiency—diabetes mellitus

    b. Hyperinsulinism—hypoglycemia, weakness, trembling, sweating

9. Gonads

  A. Secretory cells in ovaries and testes

  B. Hormones: (see table on p. 568)

  C. Pathology

    a. Hypofunction before puberty: failure of secondary sex characteristics to develop; sterility

    b. Hypofunction after puberty: atrophy of reproductive organs; sterility

PRACTICAL APPLICATIONS AND QUESTIONS

(Encircle the letter of the *best* answer to each of the following questions.)

When Miss G. reported to duty, she found that a new patient had been admitted. The diagnosis was listed as tumor of the pituitary gland. Remembering the hormones related to this gland, Miss G. began to consider some of the possible symptoms that might be presented by this patient.

1. Because of the location of the pituitary gland, one of the symptoms most likely to result from pressure would be

  a. ringing in the ears

  b. visual disturbances

  c. slurring of speech

  d. disturbance of gait

2. If the thyroid gland should be affected because of the thyrotrophic hormone,

  a. spontaneous fractures would occur

  b. general body metabolism would be disturbed

  c. there may be an increased absorption of water by the kidney tubules

d. there might be periodic episodes of high blood pressure

3. The adrenal cortices might not function properly because the production of their hormones is influenced by the following pituitary secretion:
   a. FSH
   b. LTH
   c. ICSH
   d. ACTH

4. The follicle-stimulating hormone of the pituitary gland stimulates the production of

a. gonadotrophic hormone
b. testosterone
c. estrogen
d. adrenosterone

5. The parathyroid glands are not directly influenced by the pituitary gland; therefore, there would be no disturbance in the patient's
   a. mental and physical growth
   b. salt and water metabolism
   c. calcium and phosphorus metabolism
   d. renal tubular function

ENDOCRINE SYSTEM IN SUMMARY

Endocrine Gland and Hormone	Principal Site of Action	Principal Processes Affected
Pituitary gland		
(a) Anterior lobe		
Somatotrophin (Growth hormone)	General	Growth of bones & other organs
Thyrotrophin	Thyroid	Growth & secretory activity of thyroid gland
Adrenocorticotrophin	Adrenal cortex	Growth & secretory activity of adrenal cortex
Follicle-stimulating	Ovaries	Development of follicles & secretion of estrogen
	Testes	Development of seminiferous tubules, spermatogenesis
Luteinizing or interstitial cell stimulating	Ovaries	Ovulation, formation of corpus luteum, secretion of progesterone
	Testes	Secretion of testosterone
Lactogenic or luteotrophin	Mammary glands and ovaries	Secretion of milk; maintenance of corpus luteum & secretion of progesterone
Melanocyte-stimulating	Skin	Pigmentation (?)
(b) Posterior lobe Antidiuretic (vasopressin)	Kidney	Reabsorption of water; water balance
	Arterioles	Blood pressure (?)
Oxytocin	Uterus	Contraction
	Breast	Expression of milk
Pineal gland		
Melatonin	Gonads (?)	Sexual maturation (?)
Thyroid gland		
Thyroxin & triiodothyronine	General	Metabolic rate; growth & development; intermediate metabolism
Thyrocalcitonin	Bone	Calcium uptake; lowers blood level of calcium
Parathyroid glands		
Parathormone	Bone, kidney, intestine	Maintaining blood calcium & phosphorus levels

ENDOCRINE SYSTEM IN SUMMARY (Continued)

Endocrine Gland and Hormone	Principal Site of Action	Principal Processes Affected
Parathyroid glands (continued)		
Calcitonin (?)	Bone	Calcium uptake; lowers blood level of calcium
Adrenal glands		
(a) Cortex		
Mineralocorticoids (e.g. aldosterone)	Kidney	Reabsorption of sodium chloride & water; elimination of potassium
Glucocorticoids (e.g. cortisol)	General	Preservation of carbohydrate reserves; response to stress; anti-inflammatory
Sex hormones	General (?)	Secondary sex characteristics (?); function of reproductive system (?)
(b) Medulla		
Epinephrine and norepinephrine	Cardiac muscle, smooth muscle, glands	Same effects as stimulation of sympathetic division of autonomics.
Islet cells of pancreas		
Insulin	General	Lowers blood sugar; utilization and storage of carbohydrate
Glucagon	Liver	Raises blood sugar; glycogenolysis
Testes		
Testosterone	General	Development of secondary sex characteristics
	Reproductive organs	Development and maintenance; normal function
Ovaries		
Estrogen	General	Development of secondary sexual characteristics
	Mammary glands	Development of duct system
	Reproductive organs	Maturation and normal cyclic function
Progesterone	Mammary glands	Development of secretory tissue
	Uterus	Preparation for implantation; maintenance of pregnancy
Gastrointestinal tract		
Gastrin	Stomach	Production of gastric juice
Enterogastrone	Stomach	Inhibits secretion and motility
Secretin	Pancreas & liver	Production of bile and watery pancreatic juice (rich in $NaHCO_3$).
Pancreozymin	Pancreas	Production of pancreatic juice rich in enzymes
Cholecystokinin	Gallbladder	Contraction and emptying

THE REPRODUCTIVE SYSTEM

The ability to reproduce is one of the properties that characterize living matter. Under suitable conditions various forms of life are capable of reproducing themselves from one generation to the next. One-celled organisms reproduce by division of the parent cell into 2 so-called *daughter* cells. In higher forms of life a new individual can be produced only by the union (fertilization) of an ovum of a female and a spermatozoon of a male.

The union of an ovum and a spermatozoon may take place after they have left the body, as is the case in fishes. In birds the union takes place in the body of the female; then the fertilized ovum leaves the body and develops outside, if kept at the proper temperature.

In mammals the young are born alive, since the fertilized ovum remains in the uterus of the female, where it grows until ready for independent existence. We find, as we study the development of a new human being, that this is the greatest of the innumerable miracles in human life.

In both men and women, the organs of the reproductive system may be divided into 2 groups:

(1) the gonads (testes and ovaries), which perform the double function of producing germ cells (spermatozoa and ova) and hormones (testosterone, estrogen and progesterone) and (2) a series of ducts for the transportation of germ cells. In the male, a part of the duct system (penis) is modified for the transfer of germ cells into the body of the female. In the female a part of the duct system (uterus) is modified to support the growth and development of the new individual.

The differentiation of the sexes is a remarkable process. During the first few weeks of intra-uterine life there is no structural difference to indicate whether the developing individual is going to be a male or a female. After this, differentiation begins and, normally, the reproductive organs are completely differentiated, but immature, at birth. At *puberty*, which is initiated by the hormones of the anterior lobe of the pituitary gland (p. 551), the organs of reproduction become functionally mature. This occurs between 10 and 14 years in girls and between 14 and 16 years in boys, in temperate climates. Puberty occurs earlier in warmer and later in colder climates.

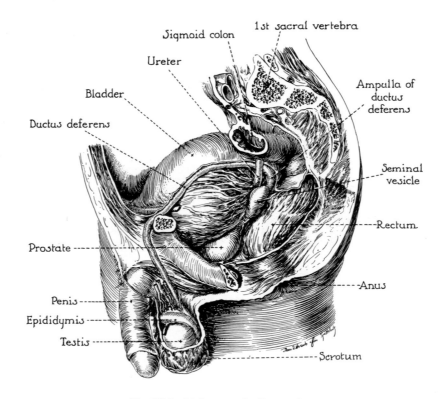

Fig. 20-1. Male reproductive system.

MALE REPRODUCTIVE SYSTEM

The male reproductive system consists of a pair of male gonads or testes and a system of excretory ducts with their accessory structures. The ducts are the epididymis, the ductus deferens and the ejaculatory ducts. The accessory structures are the seminal vesicles, the prostate gland, the bulbourethral glands and the penis.

The testes

The two testes are suspended outside of the abdominal cavity in a pouchlike sac called the *scrotum* (meaning "bag"), as shown in Figure 20-1. The scrotum is located between the upper thighs. In early fetal life the testes lie in the abdominal cavity, near the kidneys. As the fetus

grows, the testes move downward through the inguinal canal and usually enter the scrotum a short time before birth.

The descent of the testes into the scrotum is exceedingly important, since the formation of male sex cells (spermatogenesis) can occur only at the scrotal temperature, which is lower than that within the abdominal cavity. Failure of the testes to descend from the abdomen is called *cryptorchidism,* and the end-result is sterility (inability to reproduce).

Each testis is an oval, white body about 1½ inches in length and covered with visceral peritoneum. Beneath this serous membrane is a white fibrous covering that sends partitions into the testis and subdivides it into lobules. Within the lobules are tiny, coiled *seminiferous tubules* (Fig. 20-2) that are concerned with the production of

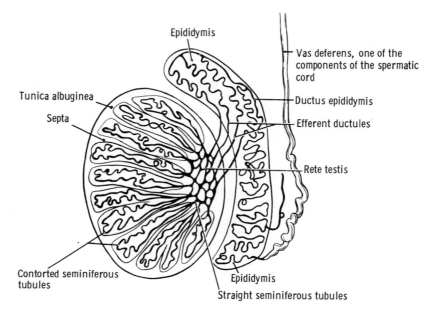

Epididymis

Vas deferens, one of the components of the spermatic cord

Tunica albuginea

Ductus epididymis

Septa

Efferent ductules

Rete testis

Contorted seminiferous tubules

Epididymis

Straight seminiferous tubules

Fig. 20-2. Diagram showing the parts of the testis and the epididymis. (Modified from Ham, A. W. Histology, ed. 2, Philadelphia, Lippincott)

spermatozoa, the male sex cells. These tubules have a total length of about one-half mile.

Spermatogenesis. The walls of the seminiferous tubules consist of many layers of epithelial cells (the so-called germinal epithelium). As shown in Figure 20-3, the cells farthest from the lumen are called *spermatogonia* (singular: spermatogonium); these are the spermatogenic, or sperm-producing cells. The spermatogonia divide by mitosis (p. 26). Half of the daughter cells remain as spermatogonia, while the other half undergo certain changes before dividing again to produce a new generation of germ cells called *primary spermatocytes.* After a prolonged prophase, the primary spermatocytes undergo a modified form of mitosis called reduction division (meiosis), in which the number of chromosomes is reduced by one-half. Although there is a division of the cytoplasm, there is no splitting of chromosomes, and each of the two cells, or *secondary spermatocytes,* that are formed have only 23 chromosomes instead of 46. In one secondary spermatocyte there are 22 regular chromosomes and an "X" sex chromosome; in the other secondary spermatocyte

there also are 22 regular chromosomes but the sex chromosome is a "Y".

The two secondary spermatocytes then undergo ordinary mitosis and give rise to 4 cells called *spermatids.* Two of the spermatids will have an "X" sex chromosome and two will have a "Y" sex chromosome, in addition to 22 regular chromosomes. The spermatids then undergo a complex transformation to *spermatozoa,* each developing a head, a middle piece and a tail piece. The stages of development are shown in Figure 20-4.

When fully formed, spermatozoa enter the lumen of a seminiferous tubule and are moved out of the testis into the duct system of the epididymis (Fig. 20-2). Spermatozoa that have just escaped from the testes are not capable of fertilizing an ovum, but by the time they reach the tail end of the epididymis they have become fully mature and actively motile. By lashing their tails they can move at the rate of 2 or 3 mm. per minute; this makes it possible for them to swim up the female reproductive tract after being deposited in the vagina.

Spermatozoa obtain their energy chiefly from

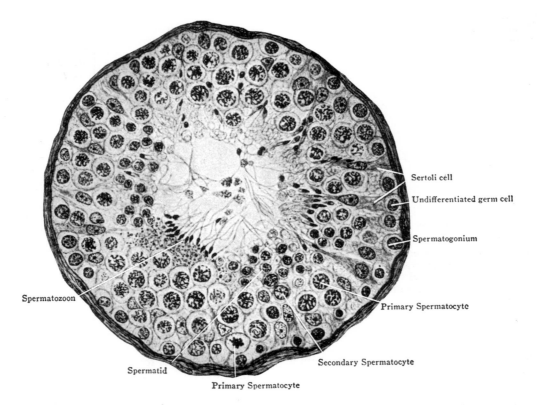

Fig. 20-3. Cross section of a seminiferous tubule, showing various stages of spermatogenesis.
× 550. (After Stieve) (Hotchkiss, R. S.: Fertility in Men, Philadelphia, Lippincott)

the fermentation of simple sugars; thus they can live under anaerobic conditions. This is important because sperm spend considerable time in relatively oxygen-poor environments such as the lumens of various ducts in the male system, and the vagina, uterus and uterine tube in the female system. Fructose is thought to be a major metabolic fuel for sperm because it is present in large quantities in the semen.

In the human testes, spermatogenesis begins at puberty (between 14 and 16 years of age) and continues throughout life. It is influenced directly and indirectly by two pituitary gonadotrophins: follicle-stimulating hormone (FSH) and interstitial cell-stimulating hormone (ICSH). The germinal epithelium is maintained and stimulated directly by FSH, but ICSH has an indirect effect

through its role in stimulating the production of testosterone. Temperature is another factor that affects spermatogenesis; the testes must be maintained at a somewhat lower temperature than that of the body as a whole. Vitamin E is essential for reproductive capacity in lower animals, but its precise function in the human body is not yet known. With advancing age, the seminiferous tubules undergo a slow decline in their ability to produce mature germ cells, but apparently never completely cease to function until death.

Testosterone is the male sex hormone (androgen) that is produced by the testes. It is secreted by little clumps of endocrine cells that lie in the connective tissue stroma between the seminiferous tubules; these cells are known as the *interstitial cells* of the testes, and their secretory activity is

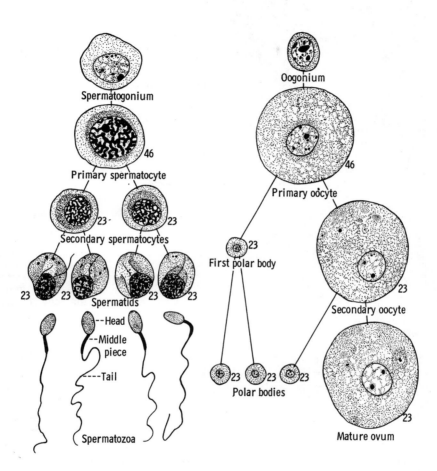

Fig. 20-4. Diagram of gametogenesis. The various stages of spermatogenesis are indicated on the left; 1 spermatogonium gives rise to 4 spermatozoa. On the right, oogenesis is indicated; from each oogonium, 1 mature ovum and 3 abortive cells are produced. In gametogenesis, the chromosomes are reduced to one-half the number characteristic for the general body cells of the species. In man, the number in the body cells is 46, and that in the mature spermatozoon and secondary oocyte is 23.

SURFACE OF
URINARY BLADDER

URINARY BLADDER OPENED

SEMINAL VESICLE

EJACULATORY DUCT

PROSTATIC
URETHRA

PROSTATE GLAND

SPONGY
URETHRA

MEMBRANOUS
URETHRA

PENIS

DUCTUS
DEFERENS

EPIDIDYMIS

URETHRA

TESTIS

SEMINIFEROUS
TUBULES

Fig. 20-5. Male repro-
ductive system. The various
organs of the male repro-
ductive system are shown.
The path of the spermato-
zoa from the time they leave
the testis until they leave
the body is indicated.

controlled by ICSH from the anterior pituitary.
Testosterone is essential for the maintenance of
a functional reproductive system in the male and
for the secondary sexual characteristics (e.g.,
beard, body structure, and so on) that appear at
puberty.

The blood supply of the testes is derived from
the testicular (spermatic) arteries, and the venous
drainage is into the testicular (spermatic) veins.
Lymphatic vessels accompany the blood vessels
and drain into the inguinal lymph nodes. Both
divisions of the autonomic system supply nerve
fibers to the testes.

The Duct System

The duct system serves to transport spermatozoa from each testis to the urethra. It includes

the epididymis, the ductus deferens and the ejaculatory duct.

The epididymis is a long, narrow, flattened
structure that is attached to the posterior surface
of the testis (Fig. 20-1). Efferent ductules from
the testis unite to form the greatly coiled ductus
epididymis, as illustrated in Figure 20-2. Spermatozoa complete their process of maturation while
passing through this part of the duct system,
before entering the ductus deferens.

The ductus deferens, or *vas deferens,* is a duct
that conveys spermatozoa from the epididymis to
the ejaculatory duct (Fig. 20-5). As shown in
Figure 20-1, the left ductus emerges from the
scrotum and enters the abdominal cavity by way
of the left inguinal canal. Curving around the
urinary bladder, it passes in front of, and medial
to, the ureter; the ductus then turns sharply down-

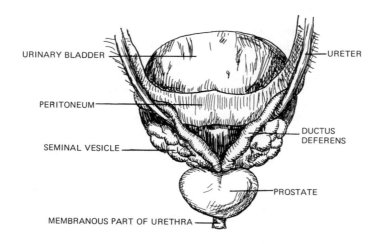

URINARY BLADDER

URETER

PERITONEUM

DUCTUS
DEFERENS

SEMINAL VESICLE

PROSTATE

MEMBRANOUS PART OF URETHRA

Fig. 20-6. Posterior view of the urinary bladder, the ductus deferens (Vas),
the seminal vesicles and the prostate gland. (After Gray)

ward to reach the base of the prostate gland between the bladder and the rectum (Fig. 20-6). Each ductus deferens terminates by joining with the duct of the seminal vesicle of its own side to form an ejaculatory duct (Fig. 20-5).

The spermatic cord is composed of the testicular arteries, veins, lymphatics, nerves and the ductus deferens, together with some connective tissue "wrappings." Each spermatic cord extends from the testis to the deep inguinal ring of its own side (Fig. 5-27).

The ejaculatory duct is formed by the union of a ductus deferens with a duct from a seminal vesicle on the same side (Fig. 20-5). The two ejaculatory ducts then enter the posterior surface of the prostate gland and continue through the substance of this gland for less than an inch before they end in the prostatic portion of the urethra. Thus the male urethra (p. 532) has both excretory and reproductive functions.

Accessory Structures

The accessory structures of the duct system of the male include the seminal vesicles, the prostate gland, the bulbo-urethral glands and the penis.

The seminal vesicles are elongated, musculomembranous structures (Fig. 20-6) that lie behind the bladder and in front of the rectum. Each has a mucous membrane lining that is thrown into an extremely large number of folds, thus providing great secretory area and also permitting the vesicle to become distended with stored secretion.

The mucosal cells secrete a thick, yellow, alkaline material that contains large quantities of fructose; this material is emptied into the ejaculatory ducts at the same time that the ductus deferens delivers the spermatozoa. The seminal vesicle secretion serves to provide nourishment for the spermatozoa and to enhance their motility by reducing acidity in their environment. It should be noted that although the duct of each seminal vesicle joins the ductus deferens of its own side, spermatozoa do not enter the seminal vesicle; spermatozoa and the seminal vesicle secretion pass directly into the related ejaculatory duct (Fig. 20-5).

The prostate gland is a firm, glandular and muscular organ that is approximately the size of a horse chestnut. Lying below the urinary bladder (Fig. 20-5), it surrounds the proximal, or prostatic, part of the urethra, as well as the two ejaculatory ducts that pass anteriorly to join the urethra.

Beneath a thin, firm, covering capsule of connective tissue is a dense layer of smooth muscular tissue; another dense layer of smooth muscular fibers encircles the prostatic urethra. Strong bands of smooth muscular tissue throughout the prostate form a meshwork in which the glandular tissue is embedded. Contraction of the smooth muscle of the prostate provides part of the force needed for expulsion of the semen (ejaculation).

The glandular substance of the prostate consists of a large number of branched, tubular glands whose ducts open separately into the prostatic urethra. The bulk of the prostatic secretion is a thin, milky, alkaline fluid that aids motility of the sperm by helping to maintain an optimum pH.

Benign prostatic hypertrophy is relatively common in older men. In this condition there is an enlargement or overgrowth of the glandular substance. As the prostate enlarges, urination becomes difficult because of compression of the prostatic urethra. When the bladder is not emptied completely, the residual urine leads to distention of the bladder and, in severe cases, to distention of the ureter and kidney (hydroureter and hydronephrosis). Residual urine also favors the occurrence of cystitis. Persons with this condition may become incontinent (i.e., unable to control the emptying of the bladder) and dribble urine. Prostatic hypertrophy usually is treated by surgical removal of the gland.

Cancer of the prostate occurs fairly frequently in elderly men, accounting for 2 to 3 per cent of all male deaths. Malignant tumors of the prostate may be treated by surgical removal of the testes (castration), because the growth of tumor cells, like that of the prostatic cells, is influenced by testosterone. The administration of female hormones (estrogens) also may inhibit the growth of tumor cells.

The bulbo-urethral glands (*Cowper's glands*) are small, rounded bodies, yellow in color and about the size of peas. They are inferior to the prostate gland, lying posterior and lateral to the membranous portion of the urethra. Their ducts pass forward to open into the cavernous portion of the urethra. The bulbo-urethral glands secrete an alkaline, mucoid substance that coats the lining of the urethra prior to ejaculation; this probably neutralizes acidity and provides a suitable environment for the spermatozoa.

The penis is an external genital organ through which the urethra passes to the exterior of the body (Fig. 20-5). It is composed of three cylindrical masses of erectile (cavernous) tissue that are bound together by elastic connective tissue and covered with skin. Two of these masses, called the *corpora cavernosa,* are located side by side in the dorsal half of the penis. The third mass, called the *corpora cavernosum urethrae,* conducts the urethra in its substance; it lies ventral to the corpora cavernosa. The distal end of the latter cavernous body is expanded into a blunt cone, called the *glans penis;* The glans is covered with a fold of skin called the *prepuce,* or foreskin. Occasionally the prepuce may fit so tightly that it cannot be drawn back over the glans, a condition referred to as *phimosis.* Surgical removal of the prepuce is called *circumcision.*

The substance of the cavernous bodies is a network of connective tissue and smooth muscle, with spaces between. The penis is soft and relaxed when this spongelike network is empty, but when the spaces become filled with blood the penis is firm and erect, a state that is essential for the deposition of spermatozoa in the vaginal canal of the female. The parasympathetic division of the autonomic system is responsible for the dilatation of penile arteries and the resultant state of erection. On the other hand, stimulation of the sympathetic system results in constriction of the penile arteries and a return to the flaccid state.

Semen

The spermatozoa, plus the secretions of the seminal vesicles, of the prostate gland and of the bulbo-urethral glands, make up the semen, which is ejaculated during the male sexual act. This thick, grayish-white fluid has an average pH of about 6.5.

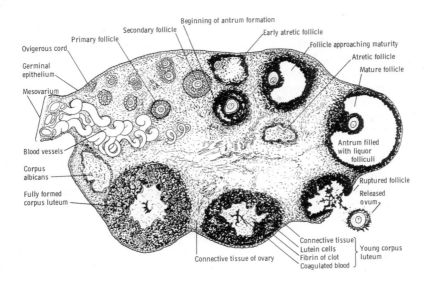

Fig. 20-7. Schematic diagram of an ovary, showing the sequence of events in the origin, the growth and the rupture of an ovarian (graafian) follicle and the formation and the retrogression of corpus luteum. Atretic follicles are those that show signs of degeneration and death. For proper sequence, follow clockwise around ovary, starting at the mesovarium. (Patten, B. M.: Human Embryology, New York, Blakiston Division of McGraw-Hill)

Semen is ejected by means of contraction of the smooth muscle of the prostate gland and the contraction of the bulbo-cavernosus muscle which compresses the cavernous portion of the urethra. In the average male, each cubic centimeter of semen contains about 100 million spermatozoa, and the average amount of ejaculate varies between 2 and 4 cc. However, only one spermatozoon can fertilize an oocyte, and the remainder disintegrate.

FEMALE REPRODUCTIVE SYSTEM

The female reproductive system consists of the paired gonads or ovaries, the paired uterine tubes, a single uterus and a vagina. The associated structures include the external genitalia and the mammary glands.

The ovaries

Description. The ovaries are small, almond-shaped bodies that are about 1½ inches in length. They are located one on either side of the uterus, below the uterine tubes, and attached to the posterior surface of the broad ligament of the uterus (Fig. 20-9). The medial end of each ovary is attached to the uterus by a rounded cord called the *ovarian ligament.* The lateral end of the ovary is in intimate contact with the free end of the uterine tube (Fig. 20-8).

Structurally, each ovary consists of an outer zone, or *cortex,* and an inner zone or *medulla.* The outermost layer of the cortex consists of the *germinal epithelium,* a single layer of cuboidal cells which covers the free surface of the ovary. Immediately below this surface layer is the connective tissue stroma of the cortex, and it is here that the ovarian follicles are formed. Each *primary follicle* consists of a central germ cell (oogonium) surrounded by a layer of epithelial cells (Fig. 20-7). The medulla is composed of loose connective tissue with numerous blood vessels; there are no follicles in this zone of the ovary.

Development of follicles. At birth several hundred thousand primary follicles are present in the ovary. However, this number decreases steadily throughout life, as most of them degenerate and die (atresia). During the reproductive years of the average female, only 300 to 400 follicles reach maturity and release their oocytes. This great limitation exists because maturation of follicles does not begin until puberty, and then usually only one follicle and oocyte reach maturity each month.

Under the influence of follicle-stimulating hormone (FSH) from the anterior pituitary, a variable number of primary follicles begin to develop into secondary follicles. By the process of mitosis, the single layer of follicular cells becomes several layers, and the oogonium, which has increased in size, now is referred to as a *primary oocyte.* The follicular cells continue to proliferate by mitosis and fluid begins to accumulate. The oocyte also continues to grow, but not in proportion to the epithelium, which soon makes up the bulk of the follicle as it approaches maturity.

It should be mentioned at this time that the follicular cells not only "house" the oocytes but also secrete estrogen, the primary hormone of the ovary. Estrogen is essential for the growth and development of all female reproductive organs, and then for keeping them in a functional state. The development and maintenance of the secondary female sexual characteristics (e.g., breasts, hair distribution, fat deposits, and so on) also depend on adequate estrogen production.

As described in the discussion of the menstrual cycle (p. 583), it appears that both FSH and LH (luteinizing hormone) are necessary for the secretion of estrogen. However, FSH is the predominating hormone in the mixture.

During follicular development, the primary oocyte undergoes a *reduction division* in which the number of chromosomes is reduced by one half (Fig. 20-4). This division gives rise to one *secondary oocyte,* containing 22 regular chromosomes and an "X" sex chromosome, and a small abortive cell that is called a polocyte (polar body); the polocyte also contains 22 regular chromosomes and an "X" sex chromosome. The secondary oocyte then begins an ordinary mitotic division, but this is not completed unless fertilization occurs (usually within the uterine tube).

Although a variable number of follicles begin this process of development, usually only one reaches maturity each month. At maturity, the follicle is greatly distended with fluid and actually bulges on the surface of the ovary (Fig. 20-7). The rising tide of estrogen produced by the follicular cells now inhibits the secretion of FSH and stimulates a sharp increase in the secretion of LH. In some way not yet completely understood, this predominantly LH mixture provokes ovulation.

Ovulation involves a bursting of the follicular wall and liberation of the secondary oocyte into, or close to, the uterine tube. Rupture of the wall occurs in the area where the follicle bulges on the surface of the ovary and where the overlying tissue is very thin.

Ovulation usually occurs every 28 to 30 days, from puberty to the *menopause* (end of the reproductive period of life); an exception to this is during pregnancy when follicles do not mature, and ovulation cannot occur. Usually only a single oocyte is discharged, but, if more than one follicle reaches maturity, additional oocytes may be released. After the oocyte is discharged from the follicle, it enters the distal end of the uterine tube where it may be fertilized if spermatozoa are present. If not fertilized within a few days after ovulation, the oocyte disintegrates and disappears.

The Corpus Luteum. At the site of ovulation the wall of the follicle collapses, and there is a small amount of bleeding into the follicular cavity. The follicular cells enlarge, and a yellowish substance (lutein) accumulates in their cytoplasm. As the entire follicle becomes filled with lutein cells it is called the corpus luteum (meaning "yellow body"); capillaries grow into this mass of cells, forming a fairly typical endocrine structure.

Fig. 20-8. Schematic drawing of female reproductive organs showing path of oocyte from ovary into uterine tube; path of spermatozoon also is shown. The usual site of fertilization in the uterine tube is marked with a cross and by the letter f. The path of the fertilized ovum from the uterine tube into the uterus and a frequent site of implantation are shown; the latter is marked with a cross and by the letter i. The left tube and ovary are shown in their natural position, but on the right they are spread out and cut open to show their internal structure.

The lutein cells secrete progesterone, the secondary ovarian hormone, and estrogen. The chief function of progesterone is to promote the final preparation of the endometrium (lining of the uterus) to receive a fertilized ovum. It also serves to maintain pregnancy by quieting the uterine muscle and by inhibiting ovulation and menstruation. Late in pregnancy, progesterone promotes the development of secretory tissue in the breasts.

Returning to the corpus luteum, we find that two possible courses are open to it: (1) if the oocyte is not fertilized, the corpus luteum continues to grow for about 10-12 days and then regresses, eventually becoming a small, white, ovarian scar called a *corpus albicans;* or, (2) if the oocyte is fertilized, the corpus luteum becomes very large, forming the corpus luteum of pregnancy. It continues to function for approximately 3 months and then slowly degenerates, leaving a white scar on the ovary.

Luteinizing hormone (LH) is responsible for the formation of the corpus luteum and the secretion of progesterone. However, there is some evidence that luteotrophic hormone (LTH) from the anterior pituitary also plays a role in the production of progesterone.

Blood and Nerve Supply. The ovaries are supplied with blood by the ovarian arteries and by ovarian branches of the uterine arteries. Venous drainage is into a plexus that empties into the ovarian veins. The ovaries are supplied with visceral efferent fibers from both autonomic divisions.

The uterine tubes

Description. The uterine tubes are known also as the *fallopian tubes* and *oviducts*. They are shown in Figures 20-8 and 20-9. Each tube lies in the upper part of the broad ligament of its own side and is about 4½ inches long. The proximal end penetrates the uterine wall and opens into the uterine cavity. Distally the trumpet-shaped, free end is in intimate contact with the ovary; this extremity of the tube also is called the fimbriated end due to the presence of fringelike projections or *fimbriae*.

Structure and Function. The lining of the uterine tube is a mucous membrane that is thrown into longitudinal folds; some of its epithelial cells are ciliated, and others are secretory. The middle coat is composed of circular and longitudinal layers of smooth muscle tissue that are responsible for peristaltic contractions of the tube. The outer coat is serous membrane (visceral peritoneum). An anatomic relationship of considerable clinical significance should be noted at this point. At the open end of the uterine tube the mucosal lining is continuous with the visceral peritoneum. Since the mucosa of the tube also is continuous with that of the uterus and the vagina, it is possible for harmful bacteria to enter the vaginal opening and ultimately cause an infection that could spread to the peritoneal cavity.

Unlike a spermatozoon, the oocyte is incapable of independent movement. Following ovulation, the oocyte enters the uterine tube and is moved along toward the uterus by peristaltic contractions of the tubal wall and by the sweeping action of the ciliated cells. During its passage, one of 2 courses is possible for the oocyte: (1) it may be fertilized (penetrated by a spermatozoon) in the tube, or (2) if not fertilized, it eventually disintegrates and disappears in the tube or in the uterus. If fertilized, the oocyte completes its mitotic division and becomes a mature *ovum.*

Normally, a fertilized ovum will reach the uterus in 4 or 5 days and continue to develop there for the duration of the pregnancy. If for any reason the fertilized ovum fails to reach the uterus, the woman is said to have an *ectopic* pregnancy. For example, an oocyte may remain attached to the ovary and be fertilized there; the result is an *ovarian pregnancy*. Even if the oocyte enters the tube and is fertilized there, its subsequent passage to the uterus may be prevented by adhesions. The result is a *tubal pregnancy*. In ectopic pregnancy there is great danger of fatal hemorrhage, because the uterus is the only place that is properly prepared to retain and sustain the growing embryo. Pregnancies that begin to develop elsewhere are a threat to both the new individual and the mother whose function it is to provide a "proper home" for the newcomer in her uterus.

The uterus

Description. The uterus is a hollow, thick-walled, muscular organ. Its cavity communicates with those of the uterine tubes above and with that of the vagina below. The uterus resembles an inverted pear that is somewhat flattened from front to back; this means that its cavity is slit-like with the anterior and posterior walls close together. The upper portion of the uterus is called the *body*, and the lower constricted portion is called the *cervix*. The portion of the body above the entrance of the uterine tubes is referred to as the *fundus* (Fig. 20-9).

The upper portion of the uterus is free and movable and rests on the upper surface of the urinary bladder (Fig. 20-10). Consequently the position of the uterus changes with the size of the bladder; when the latter is filled, the uterus may be tilted backward (retroversion). The lower portion of the uterus is embedded in the pelvic floor between the bladder and the rectum. The distal end of the cervix projects into the vagina where it terminates in thick, prominent lips that surround the external orifice (os) of the uterus.

Support. The muscles and the fascia of the pelvic diaphragm, particularly the *levator ani* (p. 160), constitute the principal support of the uterus. However, 4 paired ligaments offer an additional measure of support as they hold the uterus in its proper position in the pelvis. The principal liga-

Fig. 20-9. Female reproductive organs, posterior view. The posterior wall of the vagina has been opened and spread out. (Schaeffer, J. P.: Morris' Human Anatomy, ed. 11, New York, Blakiston Division of Mc-Graw-Hill)

ments of the uterus are the broad, the cardinal, the round and the uterosacral ligaments.

Each *broad ligament* is a transverse sheet of fibrous tissue, covered on both sides with peritoneum, that extends from the lateral border of the uterus across the pelvis to the pelvic wall and floor. It encloses the round and the ovarian ligaments, the uterine tube, the blood vessels and the nerves of its side. Each *cardinal ligament* is a fibrous sheet of fascia that extends from the cervix and the vagina across the pelvic floor as the base of the broad ligament of its own side. Each *round ligament* is a flattened band of fibrous tissue that passes from the lateral border of the uterus, in front of and below the entrance of the uterine tube of that side, through the broad ligament to the lateral pelvic wall; then it passes through the inguinal canal in a course similar to that of the ductus deferens in the male and merges with the tissue of the external genitalia (labium majus). Each *uterosacral ligament* is a prominent band of fibrous tissue that curves along the lateral pelvic wall of its own side, from the cervix to the sacrum. It is a posterior continuation of the tissue which forms the cardinal ligament.

The Uterine Wall. The wall of the uterus is composed of 3 main layers: the peritoneum, the myometrium and the endometrium.

The peritoneum or serosal covering of the uterus merges laterally with the peritoneum of the broad ligament. Anteriorly, it is reflected over the urinary bladder. Posteriorly, it forms a deep pouch as it is reflected on to the anterior surface of the rectum; this pouch, called the *cul-de-sac* or *pouch of Douglas,* is the lowest point in the pelvic cavity (Fig. 20-10).

The myometrium consists of smooth muscle. It is very thick and forms the main part of the uterine wall. The size of the uterus is capable of great change; its capacity is about 2 to 5 ml. before pregnancy and between 5,000 and 7,000 ml. at the height of pregnancy (term). It weighs about 60 Gm. at puberty and about 1,000 Gm. at the end of pregnancy, which is an increase of more than 16 times. The increase in size is due to both hyperplasia (increase in the number of cells) and hypertrophy (increase in size of original cells).

The change in size of the uterus during pregnancy truly is remarkable. It is due in part to hormones, both estrogen and progesterone, and in large measure to the distention by the growing fetus, which is a very effective stimulus to growth. There is also some stretching of the uterine wall, so the elastic and fibrous components of the wall are involved, as well as the smooth muscle. The

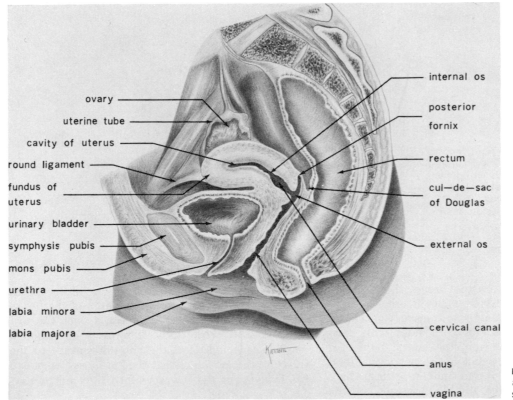

ovary

uterine tube

cavity of uterus

round ligament

fundus of
uterus

urinary bladder

symphysis pubis

mons pubis

urethra

labia minora

labia majora

internal os

posterior
fornix

rectum

cul—de—sac
of Douglas

external os

cervical canal

anus

vagina

Fig. 20-10. Female
reproductive organs
as seen in sagittal
section.

shortening of the elastic fibers is a large factor in the retraction of the uterus after delivery.

Benign tumors, consisting largely of smooth muscle cells, may develop in the myometrium. These tumors are called *leiomyomas* of the uterus or, more commonly, "fibroids."

The endometrium is a special mucous membrane that lines the uterus. It is composed of 2 chief layers: a thick, superficial or *functional* layer, and a thin, deep or *basilar* layer. The functional layer changes greatly during the menstrual cycle and is lost almost completely during menstruation. The basilar layer is not lost during the menstrual flow and remains to regenerate a new functional layer when menstruation ceases.

Blood and Nerve Supply. Blood is supplied to the uterus by way of branches of the internal iliac and ovarian arteries (Fig. 13-15). After forming a plexus, the veins empty into the tributaries of the internal iliac and the ovarian veins. The blood supply of the superficial or functional layer is separate from that of the basilar layer of the endometrium; the former is by way of "spiral" or coiled arteries.

The uterus is supplied with fibers from both divisions of the autonomic nervous system. Visceral afferent fibers transmit impulses to the CNS.

The initial functions of the uterus are to retain, and to sustain, the new individual during the first 40 weeks of growth and development. The final function of the uterus is to expel the fetus and the placenta ("afterbirth") at the end of pregnancy.

The Menstrual Cycle

In a nonpregnant woman, the superficial layer of the uterine mucosa undergoes cyclic changes that are referred to as *menstrual cycles*. These changes are closely related to changes in the ovaries and involve a complex interplay between pituitary and ovarian hormones. Menstrual cycles recur from puberty to menopause, at intervals of 25 to 35 days, except when pregnancy and lactation intervene. A typical cycle can be described in terms of 3 broad phases: menstrual, follicular, and luteal.

The Menstrual Phase. The periodic discharge of bloody fluid from the uterine cavity is known as *menstruation*, or the *menses*. This discharge is associated with the shedding of the superficial layer of the endometrium; it consists of epithelial cells, mucus, tissue fluid and about 25 to 65 ml. of blood. Usually this blood is liquid, but if the rate of flow is excessive, clots may appear. Menstrual blood probably fails to clot because it first clotted in the interstitial spaces and was liquefied by fibrinolysins before escaping from the uterus.

Although menstruation actually is the terminal event of each cycle, it is the time most easily fixed by any woman; thus, in clinical practice, the first day of the menstrual flow is said to be the first day of the menstrual cycle. This flow may last from 1 to 8 days, but the average duration is 4 to 6 days. It is associated with a progressive degeneration of the superficial layer of the endometrium, which is accompanied by patchy areas of bleeding. Fortunately, only one small area at a time is involved; if all areas of the endometrium broke down simultaneously there would be severe hemorrhage.

As patches of bleeding develop, pieces of the superficial endometrium become detached. The uterine glands release their accumulated secretions and then collapse. The large collection of tissue fluid that was present also is lost in the menstrual flow. This process spreads gradually until the entire superficial layer of epithelium has disintegrated. The endometrium now is very thin because only the basilar layer of epithelium remains; the latter has a separate blood supply and is left intact throughout the menstrual period.

Ovarian activity during the menstrual phase involves the beginning growth and development of several primary follicles. However, under the influence of pituitary FSH, usually only one follicle is selected for ultimate maturation.

Follicular or Preovulatory Phase. This phase is associated with a rapidly growing ovarian follicle and the production of estrogen. These activities depend on a mixture of 2 pituitary gonadotrophins: FSH and LH. Early in the phase, FSH is the predominating hormone, but it seems that neither FSH nor LH acting alone can cause the production of estrogen.

For approximately 7 to 10 days, or from the 4th to 13th day of a 28 day cycle, there is a reorganization and proliferation of endometrial cells in response to the stimulating effect of estrogen. Even before the menstrual flow ceases, repair begins in those areas that first underwent destruction. Cells in the basilar layer undergo mitosis and aid in the regeneration of a new superficial layer; the covering epithelium is regenerated first, and then the superficial layer grows until it becomes at least 3 times as thick as the basilar layer; for this reason, the term *proliferative phase* also may be used in reference to this phase of the menstrual cycle.

As the ovarian follicle continues its growth and secretory activity, the rising estrogen tide causes a sharp shift in the FSH-LH mixture. As FSH secretion is inhibited, LH secretion is greatly increased and ovulation occurs. The follicular phase thus blends into the luteal phase.

Luteal or Postovulatory Phase. Following ovulation, LH stimulates the development of a corpus luteum and the secretion of progesterone. A considerable quantity of estrogen also is produced by the luteal cells, but progesterone is primarily responsible for the final preparation of the endometrium to receive a fertilized ovum.

This phase of the cycle also is called the *secretory phase* inasmuch as the lumens of the endometrial glands become filled with an abundance of secretions. The superficial endometrium becomes highly vascular, succulent, and rich in

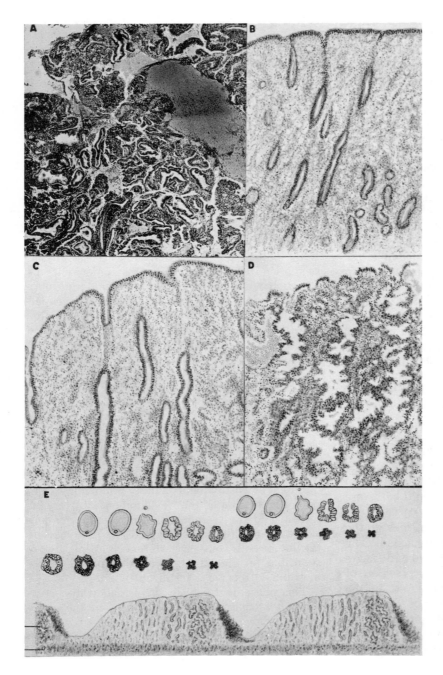

Fig. 20-11. Sections through the human endometrium at various stages of the menstrual cycle. (A) Menstrual phase; (B) proliferative phase; (C) at time of ovulation; (D) premenstrual phase. In (E) the changes in the thickness of the mucosa are shown; it is thickest just before the onset of menstruation and thinnest just as it ceases. Two complete sets of changes in the ovary are shown; one is regressing and the other developing simultaneously. (After Schroeder)

glycogen. Thickening of the superficial layer also involves an increase in the amount of tissue fluid (edema). These changes are maximal about one week after ovulation, corresponding to the expected time of arrival of a fertilized ovum.

If fertilization does not occur, the rising progesterone and estrogen tide serves to inhibit the secretion of LH. As a result, the corpus luteum begins to degenerate, estrogen and progesterone levels decline, and menstruation occurs as the superficial layer of the endometrium is deprived of its hormonal stimulation. On the other hand, if a fertilized ovum is implanted in the uterus, the corpus luteum continues to secrete progesterone for about 3 months. This is possible because of a hormone (chorionic gonadotrophin) produced by the developing embryonic tissues; this hormone is very similar to LH and serves to maintain the corpus luteum until the embryonic tissues are capable of producing progesterone and estrogen on their own.

The premenstrual phase, or late luteal phase, occupies the two or three days immediately preceding menstruation and corresponds to the degeneration of the corpus luteum. At this time there is an infiltration of polymorphonuclear leukocytes and degeneration of the connective tissue stroma of the superficial endometrium begins. Important vascular changes also occur just before the onset of the menstrual flow. Arteries that supply the basilar part of the endometrium are not affected by the decreasing supply of estrogen and progesterone, but the special coiled arteries that supply the superficial layer become markedly constricted. As a result, the overlying endometrium is deprived of blood and has an extremely pale appearance. The vasoconstrictive process apparently damages the arteriolar and capillary walls, because when the coiled arteries eventually dilate blood escapes through the walls and accumulates in pools beneath the endometrial surface. This blood soon breaks through the degenerating endometrial stroma, and the menstrual flow begins again. The appearance of the endometrium at various times in the menstrual cycle is shown in Figure 20-11.

Summary. *The menstrual phase* is associated with the shedding of the superficial layer of the endometrium. This has been referred to as a "cleaning of the domicile when the expected tenant failed to arrive."

The follicular or preovulatory phase is associated with the reorganization and proliferation of the endometrium following menstruation. Estrogen is essential for this early development of the uterine mucosa, and it is produced by a rapidly growing ovarian follicle under the influence of a mixture of FSH and LH. However, FSH is the predominating hormone. Eventually the rising estrogen tide inhibits the secretion of FSH and increases the secretion of LH, thus promoting ovulation.

The luteal or postovulatory phase is associated with the formation of a corpus luteum and the production of progesterone and estrogen under the influence of LH. Progesterone is primarily responsible for the final build-up of the endometrium preparing to receive a fertilized ovum. The rising progesterone and estrogen tide "shuts off" the secretion of LH and the corpus luteum degenerates. If the oocyte has not been fertilized, the menstrual flow begins again as the hormone level falls. However, if a fertilized ovum is implanted in the uterus, the corpus luteum is maintained by a hormone secreted by the developing embryonic tissue.

Thus, ovarian hormones are responsible for the cyclic changes in the uterine mucosa and for those changes that are essential to the maintenance and the development of the embryo, particularly in the early period of pregnancy. The ovaries, in turn, are controlled by the pituitary gonadotrophins.

Although estrogen initiates the changes that prepare the uterine mucosa for reception of the fertilized ovum, it is progesterone that is responsible for the final changes in the uterus and for maintaining the pregnancy. In other words, as one author says, "estrogen sets the stage for gestation and then calls forth progesterone for indispensable aid in getting the product of gestation embedded and maintained."

The uterine mucosa is prepared periodically for pregnancy. If fertilization does not occur, there is withdrawal of hormone support and a decrease in blood supply to the functional layer of the mucosa, with sloughing and menstrual flow.

The changes in the uterine mucosa, in relation to the events in the ovaries and the anterior lobe of the pituitary gland, are shown in the chart below.

Puberty and the Menarche

Extensive growth and development of ovarian follicles does not occur until the onset of *puberty* at 10 to 14 years of age. At this time, the secondary sexual characteristics begin to develop. The breasts, uterus and vagina start to mature; the pubic and axillary hair begin to grow, and there is a general "rounding" of the female body contour as fat is deposited.

Puberty terminates at *menarche,* the onset of the first menstrual period; the average age at menarche is 13 to 15 years, but it may range from 10 to 18 years. In general, the early cycles are irregular and many of them may be anovulatory (i.e., follicles may fail to rupture).

Puberty is initiated by a marked increase in the secretion of pituitary gonadotrophins. However, no one yet knows precisely what "triggers" pituitary activity. There is some evidence that the pineal gland (p. 553) acts as a "biological clock" in this respect, but the mechanism has not been determined.

CORRELATION OF HORMONAL ACTIVITIES WITH OVARIAN AND UTERINE CHANGES

Phase	Menstrual	Follicular	Ovulation	Luteal	Premenstrual
DAYS	1 2 3 4 5 6 7	8 9 10 11 12 13 14	15 16 17	18 19 20 21 22 23 24 25	26 27 28 1 2
OVARY	Degenerating corpus luteum; Beginning follicular development	Growth and maturation of follicle	Ovulation	Active corpus luteum	Degenerating corpus luteum
ESTROGEN PRODUCTION	Low	Increasing	High	Declining, then a secondary rise	Decreasing
PROGESTERONE PRODUCTION	None	None	Low	Increasing	Decreasing
FSH PRODUCTION	Increasing	High, then declining	Low	Low	Increasing
LH PRODUCTION	Low	Low, then increasing	High	High	Decreasing
ENDOMETRIUM	Degeneration and shedding of superficial layer. Coiled arteries dilate, then constrict again	Reorganization and proliferation of superficial layer	Continued growth	Active secretion and glandular dilatation; highly vascular; edematous	Vasoconstriction of coiled arteries; beginning degeneration

The Climacteric and Menopause

Between 45 and 50 years of age, a woman may expect to enter the period known as "change of life." The critical aspect of this period is the gradual failure of the ovaries to respond to pituitary gonadotrophin stimulation. *Climacteric* is a broad term that covers the entire period of gradual ovarian failure, and its highest point is the complete cessation of menstruation, or the *menopause.* Senile ovaries no longer produce ova or secrete hormones, and the period of possible childbearing is over. There is atrophy of the ovaries, uterine tubes, uterus, vagina, external genitalia and the breasts. During the early years of the menopause there may be various subjective symptoms such as hot flashes and outbursts of sweating due to instability of the vasomotor system. There may be headache, vague muscular pains and, occasionally, emotional instability.

The vagina

The vagina is a collapsible, musculomembranous tube, about 3½ inches long, lying between the bladder and the urethra, anteriorly, and the rectum, posteriorly. As shown in Figure 20-10, it extends downward and forward from the uterus to the external opening in the vestibule.

The upper end of the vagina is attached to the cervix a short distance above the projecting cervical lips, thus forming recessed areas. The deep recess behind the vaginal end of the cervix is called the *posterior fornix,* while the smaller recesses in front and at the sides are called the *anterior* and the *lateral fornices.* At the lower end of the vagina there is a thin fold of mucous membrane called the *hymen;* this fold shows great variation in shape, but usually it forms a circular border around the external vaginal orifice as shown in Figure 20-12. Occasionally the hymen may completely cover the vaginal opening (imperforate hymen), and surgery is required to permit the escape of the menstrual flow.

The wall of the vagina is composed of smooth muscle and fibroelastic connective tissue, lined with mucous membrane, which is thrown into transverse folds called *rugae.* The epithelium of the mucous membrane is stratified squamous, nonkeratinizing in type.

The vagina serves as the excretory duct of the uterus and provides a sheath for the penis for sperm deposition during sexual intercourse.

The Papanicolaou test ("Pap" smear) is of considerable clinical importance in the early diagnosis of carcinoma of the uterus. This simple, painless test involves the microscopic examination of cells taken from the posterior fornix of the vagina and from the cervix of the uterus; since malignant or cancerous cells have a characteristic appearance, they may be detected very early in the course of the disease and long before symptoms appear.

The external genitalia

The external genital organs (vulva) of the female are illustrated in Figure 20-12.

The **mons pubis,** or *mons veneris,* is the rounded pad of fat in front of the pubic symphysis. It is covered by dense skin and, at puberty, becomes covered with hair.

The **labia majora** are 2 prominent longitudinal folds of skin and underlying fat that extend backward from the mons pubis toward the anus. The skin of the labia majora contains numerous hair follicles, sweat glands and sebaceous glands.

The **labia minora** are 2 small folds of skin that are situated between the labia majora. Anteriorly, the folds meet to form the *prepuce,* a small hood of skin that partially covers the clitoris; the folds then extend backward on either side of the urethral and the vaginal orifices, following much the same course as the labia majora. There are no hair follicles or sweat glands in the labia minora.

The **clitoris** is a small structure that is composed of erectile tissue, corresponding in structure and in origin with the penis in the male. It lies under cover of the prepuce as described previously.

The **vestibule** is the cleft between the labia minora and behind the clitoris. The vagina and the urethra open into this area. The external opening of the urethra is located about 1 inch

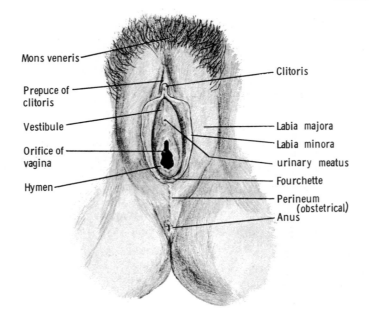

Fig. 20-12. External genitalia of female.

behind the clitoris and immediately in front of the vaginal orifice. The *greater vestibular glands* (Bartholin's glands) are situated in the floor of the vestibule, one on either side of the vaginal orifice. These glands secrete a mucoid lubricating fluid, and each drains into a duct that empties into the space between the hymen and the labium minus of its own side.

The **obstetric perineum** (perineal body) is the area between the vagina, anteriorly, and the anal canal, posteriorly. It is composed of a mass of muscular and fibrous tissue. To avoid tearing and undue stretching of these tissues during childbirth, an incision, called *episiotomy*, may be made in the perineum prior to delivery of the infant. The term *anatomic perineum* refers to the area between the pubis, anteriorly, the tip of the coccyx, posteriorly, and the thighs, laterally.

Blood and Nerve Supply. The blood supply of the external genitalia is from branches of the internal iliac arteries, and the venous blood eventually drains into the internal iliac veins.

The nerve supply is derived from both divisions of the autonomic system; vasodilator fibers are distributed to the blood vessels of the erectile tissue. The external genitalia are richly supplied with afferent fibers that transmit impulses to the CNS.

The mammary glands

The mammary glands, or breasts, are functionally related to the reproductive system since they secrete milk for nourishment of the young, but, structurally, they are related to the skin. Lying on the ventral surface of the thorax, each breast extends from the 2nd to the 6th rib, and from the sternum to the anterior border of the axilla of its own side. The size is variable, but each is hemispherical in shape. The posterior surface of the breast is concave as it is molded over the chest wall, primarily in contact with the fascia of the pectoralis major muscle.

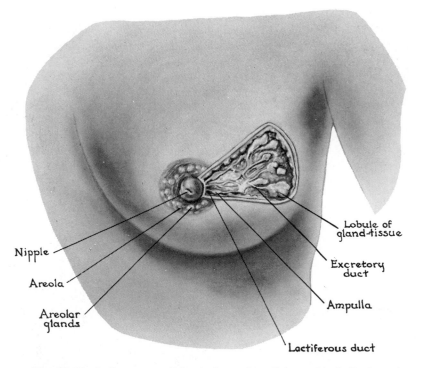

Fig. 20-13. Left mammary gland; drawn from living subject. Ducts and glandular tissue drawn from dissection.

Structure. The breast is composed of 15 to 20 lobes, each having its own individual excretory or *lactiferous duct*. Each lobe consists of lobules of glandular tissue supported by a connective tissue framework that contains a variable amount of adipose tissue. The lobules are drained by intralobular ducts that empty into the main lactiferous ducts.

On the ventral surface of each breast, slightly below center, there is a cylindrical projection or *nipple*. In its rounded tip are 15 to 20 perforations, the openings of the lactiferous ducts. The nipple is surrounded by a pigmented area called the *areola*, which becomes dark brown during pregnancy. The structure of the breast is shown in Figure 20-13.

Blood and Nerve Supply. Blood is supplied to the mammary glands by way of the internal mammary arteries and is drained into the corresponding veins. Lymphatic vessels drain into the axillary lymph nodes, a fact of considerable clinical importance in carcinoma of the breast. The nerves are derived from branches of the 4th, the 5th and the 6th thoracic spinal nerves.

Changes in the breasts during pregnancy and lactation are described on page 597.

SEQUENCE OF EVENTS IN REPRODUCTION

The process of reproduction really begins with the development and the maturation of germ cells of the parents, then progresses through ovu-

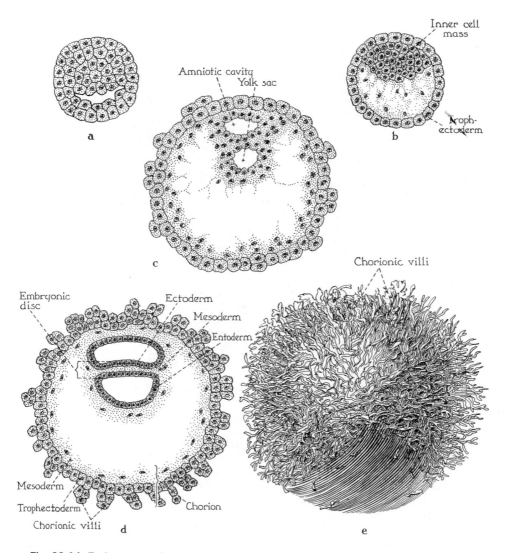

Fig. 20-14. Early stages of development. (a and b) The cells are separated into a peripheral layer and an inner cell mass. The peripheral layer is called the trophoblast or trophectoderm; the entire structure is called a blastocyst or blastodermic vesicle. (c) The formation of the amniotic cavity and yolk sac is indicated. (d) The location of the embryonic disk and the three germ layers are shown, together with the beginning of the chorionic villi. (e) The external appearance of the developing mass is shown; the chorionic villi are abundant. (Greisheimer, Esther M.: Physiology and Anatomy, ed. 8, Philadelphia, Lippincott)

lation, fertilization, implantation, development of the ovum through the embryonic and the fetal phases and, eventually, birth (parturition) or delivery of the new individual from the uterus to the external world.

The maturation of parental germ cells and the process of ovulation were described earlier in this chapter. Let us now consider the processes of fertilization, implantation, and the development of a new individual during the intrauterine period of life. For more details on these subjects one should consult a standard textbook on embryology.

Fertilization

Fertilization consists of the penetration of a secondary oocyte by a spermatozoon. Although millions of spermatozoa are deposited in the vagina, only one effects fertilization; the others ultimately disintegrate. Fertilization usually takes place in the distal third of the uterine tube.

Union of the oocyte and spermatozoon restores the diploid number of chromosomes (46) and determines the sex of the offspring, as well as all of its other hereditary complements. Because the oocyte always has an "X" sex chromosome, it is the spermatozoon (which may carry an "X" or a "Y" chromosome) that ultimately determines the sex of the offspring. If an "X" chromosome-bearing spermatozoon unites with the oocyte, the resulting offspring will be a female (XX). On the other hand, the union of an oocyte and a "Y" chromosome-bearing spermatozoon will result in a male (XY).

Implantation

The fertilized ovum (zygote) begins immediately to divide by ordinary mitosis, and passes rapidly through a two-celled, four-celled, eight-celled stage, and so on, until a solid mulberry-like ball of cells (morula) is formed. The developing mass is moved along through the uterine tube and reaches the cavity of the uterus about 3 to 4 days after fertilization. A gradual accumulation of fluid within the morula results in the formation of a cavity, and the dividing cells now differentiate into an outer layer or "shell" (the *trophoblast*) and an inner compact mass of cells that is destined to become the embryo (Fig. 20-14). This fluid-filled ball of cells, called a *blastocyst*, adheres to the surface of the endometrium and is ready to implant. That portion of the endometrium to which the blastocyst adheres, and in which it will implant, is called the *decidua basalis*.

The cells in the outer layer (trophoblast) secrete proteolytic enzymes that digest the adjacent endometrial cells and literally "eat a hole" in the uterine lining. The blastocyst nestles in this hole and buries itself as shown in Figure 20-15; the superficial wound is closed by a fibrin clot and by a portion of endometrium, the *decidua capsularis*, that is reflected over it. The remainder of the endometrium is referred to as the *decidua parietalis*.

Development of the Placenta and Membranes

Following implantation the trophoblast proliferates rapidly, and little fingerlike cords of cells, called villi, invade the surrounding decidua; the resulting disintegrating, liquefying, mucosal components serve as food for the embryo during this early stage of development. As the decidual invasion proceeds, maternal blood vessels are tapped, and a complicated labyrinth of blood-filled lakes or sinuses forms in the decidua basalis; this comprises the maternal portion of the placenta.

Meanwhile embryonic blood vessels are developing in the trophoblast, and, as soon as it is vascularized, this structure becomes the *chorion*. Another fetal membrane, the *amnion*, develops around the growing embryo, which is connected with the chorion by the body stalk, as shown in Figure 20-16. The villi in this region enlarge to form the *chorion frondosum* which, in turn, forms the fetal portion of the placenta. Villi on other parts of the chorion cease to grow and undergo almost complete degeneration. Thus denuded of villi, the greater part of the chorion presents a smooth surface and is called the *chorion laeve*. The body stalk ultimately becomes the umbilical

Fig. 20-15. Various stages in the process of implantation; the relation of the uterine muscosa to the blastodermic vesicle during implantation is shown. s, Decidua basalis; v, decidua parietalis; c, decidua capsularis; and o, the blastodermic vesicle, or blastocyst. (Greisheimer, Esther M.: Physiology and Anatomy, ed. 8, Philadelphia, Lippincott)

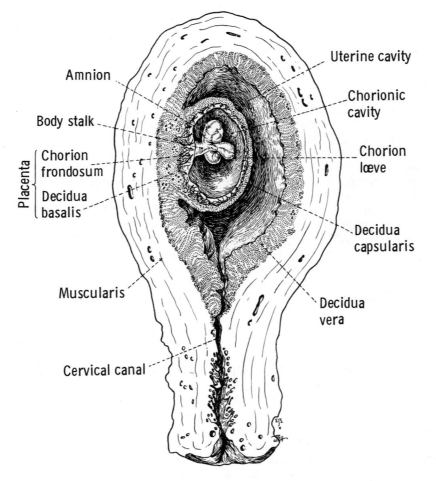

Fig. 20-16. Pregnant uterus, shown in sagittal section. The embryo is about 1 month of age. (Modified from Bumm)

Fig. 20-17. Diagram of placental circulation. Note that maternal and fetal circulations are completely separate. (Greisheimer, Esther M.: Physiology and Anatomy, ed. 8, Philadelphia, Lippincott)

cord of the fetus; two umbilical arteries and one umbilical vein convey fetal blood to and from the placenta.

In summary, the placenta consists of maternal and fetal portions: the decidua basalis and the chorion frondosum, respectively (Fig. 20-16). Each part has its own separate circulation, and there is no communication between the two (Fig. 20-17). The uterine arteries convey blood to the maternal lakes or sinuses, and the uterine veins carry blood away. Fetal circulation is illustrated in Figure 13-27 and described on page 377.

The functions of the placenta. This highly vascular organ serves as the respiratory, nutritive and excretory organ of the fetus. Oxygen and nutrients, provided by the mother, diffuse from the maternal blood sinuses through the walls of the villi into the fetal blood stream. At the same time, waste products produced by the fetus diffuse in the opposite direction—i.e., from the fetal blood stream into the maternal sinuses—and ultimately are eliminated by the mother.

The Intra-uterine Period

The intra-uterine or *prenatal period* lasts about 40 weeks, or 10 lunar months (28 days each). It may be subdivided into the period of the ovum, the period of the embryo, and the period of the fetus.

Period of the Ovum. The duration of this period is from 0 (the moment of fertilization) to 2 weeks. Implantation occurs on the 6th or 7th day, and primitive villi are formed after implantation.

Period of the Embryo. This period extends from the beginning of the 3rd week to the end of the 8th week (2nd lunar month). The chorionic villi are well developed, both fetal and maternal blood vessels are functioning, and a true placental circulation is established. During this time the rudiments of all the adult main organs are evolved.

Period of the Fetus. The duration of this period is from the beginning of the 9th week to birth, at the end of the 40th week. Few, if any, new major structures are formed, and the development that takes place during this period consists of the growth and maturation of existing structures. The fetus is distinguishable as human at the beginning of this period, and by the end of the 16th week (fourth lunar month) the external genitalia definitely reveal the sex.

By the end of the 24th week (sixth lunar month), the fetus weighs about 600 Gm. The skin is wrinkled, and the first fat deposits are made beneath it. By the end of the 32nd week (eighth lunar month), the skin still is red and wrinkled. However, the fetus weighs about 1,700 Gm., cries weakly and moves its extremities quite energetically. A fetus born at this time may survive, with proper care. By the 36th week, the average weight

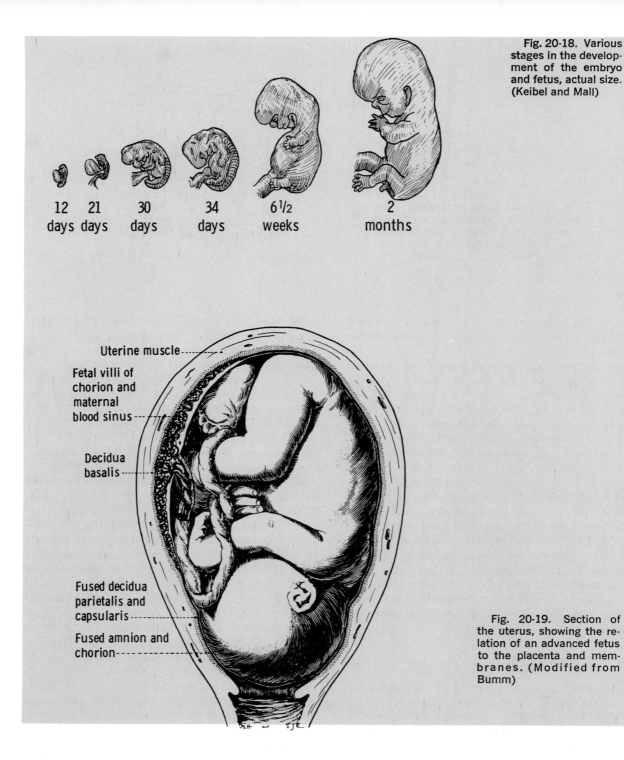

Fig. 20-18. Various stages in the development of the embryo and fetus, actual size. (Keibel and Mall)

12 days   21 days   30 days   34 days   6½ weeks   2 months

Uterine muscle

Fetal villi of chorion and maternal blood sinus

Decidua basalis

Fused decidua parietalis and capsularis

Fused amnion and chorion

Fig. 20-19. Section of the uterus, showing the relation of an advanced fetus to the placenta and membranes. (Modified from Bumm)

594

Esophagus

Heart

Liver

Stomach

Colon

Placenta

Symphysis pubis

Bladder

Vagina

Rectum

Fig. 20-20. Fetus in uterus at term. Sagittal section, showing head engaged about the beginning of labor.

is about 2,500 Gm., and the fetus has a very good chance of survival if born at this time.

Pregnancy reaches full term at the end of the 40th week (tenth lunar month). At this time the fetus is fully developed and has the characteristic features of the newborn infant. Various stages in the development of the embryo and the fetus are shown in Figures 20-18, 20-19 and 20-20.

Maternal Changes

We now return to the mother in whose uterus the above activities have been taking place. From the beginning of pregnancy the uterus enlarges to keep pace with the growth of the fetus. By the end of the 16th week the fundus of the uterus is about halfway between the symphysis pubis and the umbilicus. By the end of the 24th week the fundus has reached the level of the umbilicus. At the end of the 36th week the fundus has risen to the level of the xiphoid process of the sternum. But at this time the fetus settles into the pelvis, and the fundus falls a little below the xiphoid process during the last 4 weeks of pregnancy.

Throughout the entire 40 weeks of pregnancy the mother carries, protects, and nourishes the new life until it is ready for extra-uterine existence. By the 20th week she can feel "life" as the fetus moves in her uterus. The fetal heart sounds also can be heard at this time if a stethoscope is placed over the mother's abdominal wall.

During the intra-uterine period, the mother provides oxygen and eliminates carbon dioxide for the fetus. In addition, she furnishes food, water and inorganic salts; inasmuch as developing bones and teeth require large quantities of calcium, the mother must pay particular attention to this item in her diet. The elimination of fetal nitrogenous waste products places an extra load on the mother's kidneys; thus, frequent urine analyses and blood pressure determinations are advised during pregnancy to detect any signs of kidney failure or toxicity.

Acute toxemia of pregnancy is characterized by hypertension, edema and proteinuria. A very severe form of toxemia, referred to as *eclampsia,* is characterized by convulsions; it is one of the most dangerous complications of pregnancy. Hos-pitalization, bed rest and sedation are essential in the care of mothers with this condition. Termination of the pregnancy may be necessary to save the mother's life.

Labor or parturition

At the end of pregnancy, about 40 weeks after the last menstrual period, the uterus begins to undergo rhythmic contractions that ultimately lead to the birth of the infant. The sequence of events involved in this process is referred to as labor or parturition.

The **first stage** of labor consists of *dilatation* of the cervix. With each uterine contraction the amniotic sac of fluid that surrounds the fetus is forced into the cervical canal where it acts as a wedge to dilate the canal. In a typical delivery the amniotic sac ruptures just at the close of this stage, and the fluid escapes.

When the dilatation of the cervical canal is completed, the **second stage** of labor begins. This refers to the *delivery of the infant,* normally head first, through the cervical canal and vagina. It is at the time of the delivery of the head that tears may occur in the pelvic floor. Many obstetricians perform an episiotomy (p. 588) to prevent spontaneous tears; this incision is repaired before the mother leaves the delivery room.

The **third stage** of labor consists of the *delivery of the placenta,* or afterbirth. After this the uterus rapidly decreases in size (involution) primarily due to the contraction of smooth muscle fibers of the myometrium. This tends to close the open spaces of the endometrium or denuded walls of the uterus and prevent bleeding. A fatal hemorrhage can occur if the uterine muscle relaxes at this time.

Cesarean Section. If the diameters of the mother's pelvis are so small that spontaneous delivery seems to be impossible, or if the fetus is in distress, delivery is accomplished by cesarean section. This consists in removing the fetus by the abdominal route. An incision is made through the abdominal wall and through the uterine wall to accomplish delivery of the fetus.

Abnormalities of the Fetus. Some of the abnormalities that may occur due to disturbances in development of the embryo or the fetus are: hare-lip, cleft palate, web-hand, web-foot, incomplete formation of the diaphragm so that the pleural and the abdominal cavities are connected, patent foramen ovale, patent ductus arteriosus, spina bifida and amputation of a part of a limb. Textbooks of embryology or anatomy should be consulted for information about such anomalies.

Lactation

Estrogens produce growth of the duct system of the mammary glands, and progesterone stimulates development of the secretory tissue. The mammary glands reach their final stage of development at the end of pregnancy. The lactogenic or luteotrophic hormone of the anterior lobe of the pituitary gland stimulates the production of milk in the mammary glands that have been prepared by estrogen and progesterone. The mammary glands secrete milk for the nourishment of the newborn infant. The process is called *lactation.*

Changes begin to take place in the mammary glands as soon as the developing zygote (fertilized ovum) is implanted in the uterus. During the first half of pregnancy the epithelium of the lobes increases rapidly, and secretory portions are formed. During the latter half of pregnancy the cells begin to produce a secretion that is called *colostrum.* This is the fluid that is obtained from the breasts before the secretion of true milk begins. It may be expressed from the breasts immediately after delivery and is ingested by the newborn during the first 2 days of postnatal life.

For the maintenance of secretion, removal of milk is absolutely essential. If milk is not removed (e.g., breast feeding) the swelling of the breasts eventually disappears, milk ceases to be produced, and the mammary glands undergo involution. Under normal conditions, the production of milk continues for 6 to 9 months after the infant is born.

Extra-uterine Life

Following parturition, the extra-uterine or post-natal existence begins. This may be subdivided into various periods or phases.

The neonatal period, or period of the newborn, extends from the moment of birth to the end of the 4th week (28th day of extra-uterine life).

The period of infancy extends from the beginning of the 5th week to the end of the first year.

The period of childhood extends from the beginning of the second year to puberty.

The period of adolescence extends from puberty to the late 'teens in girls and to the early twenties in boys.

The period of maturity extends from the end of the adolescent period to old age or senility.

SUMMARY

1. Male
   A. Testes
      a. Located in scrotum; descend through inguinal canal
      b. Lobules contain seminiferous tubules; spermatogenesis; directly influenced by FSH, indirectly by ICSH; 22 regular, x or y sex chromosomes
      c. Interstitial tissue secretes testosterone; essential for maintenance of sex characteristics and functional system
   B. Duct system
      a. Epididymis: receives sperm from testes
      b. Ductus deferens (vas): from epididymis to ejaculatory ducts behind bladder; travels in spermatic cord with blood and lymph vessels and nerves
      c. Ejaculatory duct: formed by union of ductus deferens and duct from seminal vesicle on same side; empties into prostatic urethra
   C. Accessory structures
      a. Seminal vesicles: secrete alkaline substance that aids motility of sperm
      b. Prostate gland: surrounds proximal part of urethra; muscular tissue aids in ejaculation; glandular tissue secretes alkaline substance that aids motility of sperm
      c. Bulbo-urethral glands (Cowper's): open into urethra; alkaline secretion neutralizes acidity of urethra

d. Penis: external genital organ; composed of erectile tissue; distal end (glans) covered by prepuce; tissue spaces become turgid when distended with blood (erection), controlled by sacral autonomics

e. Semen: consists of sperm and secretions from accessory glands; ejected into vagina by muscular contractions; average 100 million sperm per cc.; average ejaculate 2 to 4 cc.; only one sperm can fertilize ovum

2. Female

A. Ovaries

a. Located lateral to uterus, attached to posterior surface of broad ligament, inferior to tubes

b. Ovarian follicles formed in cortex; usually only one follicle and oocyte mature each month; 22 regular, only x sex chromosome; FSH; estrogen; mature follicle bulges on surface of ovary

c. Ovulation: LH; release of oocyte from follicle; occurs every 28 to 30 days from puberty to menopause except during pregnancy

d. Corpus luteum ("yellow body") forms at site of ovulation; cells secrete progesterone and estrogen; if oocyte fertilized, corpus luteum persists for about 3 months; if not fertilized, corpus luteum degenerates; controlled by LH and LTH from pituitary

B. Uterine tubes

a. Lie in upper part of broad ligament; lateral end in intimate contact with ovary; fimbriae at distal end

b. Receive oocyte from follicle; place where fertilization occurs when sperm present; oocyte moved by peristalsis and ciliated cells; if fertilization does not occur oocyte disintegrates

C. Uterus

a. Hollow muscular organ in pelvis between bladder and rectum; upper portion called body; lower portion called cervix projects into vagina

b. Supported by muscles of pelvic floor and by ligaments: broad, cardinal, round and uterosacral

c. Posterior fold of peritoneum forms cul-de-sac or pouch of Douglas; myometrium consists of smooth muscle; endometrium is special mucosal lining composed of functional and basilar layers; functional layer lost during menstruation, regenerated by basilar layer

D. The menstrual cycle

a. Menstrual phase: flow lasts 1 to 5 days; superficial or functional layer of endometrium is lost

b. Follicular or preovulatory phase: regeneration of superficial layer; follicle grows rapidly during this phase, secretes estrogen essential for preliminary build-up of lining; ovulation occurs at the end of this phase

c. Luteal phase: progesterone from corpus luteum promotes final buildup of endometrium which becomes thick and engorged with fluid; if oocyte not fertilized, corpus luteum begins to degenerate, and menstrual flow begins again

d. Correlation of hormonal activities: see chart on p. 586

E. Puberty and menarche

a. Puberty: secondary sex characteristics develop; reproductive organs mature

b. Menarche: onset of first menstrual period; end of puberty

F. Climacteric and menopause

a. Climacteric: period of gradual ovarian failure; atrophy of reproductive organs

b. Menopause: complete cessation of menstruation; highlight of climacteric

G. Vagina

a. Collapsible, musculomembranous tube; between bladder and urethra in front and rectum behind; extends from uterus to vestibule; recesses around vaginal end of cervix called fornices; excretory duct of uterus

b. Hymen is circular border of mucosa around external vaginal opening.
H. External genitalia: mons pubis, labia majora, labia minora, clitoris, vestibule, perineum
I. Mammary glands
   a. Located on ventral thorax, 2nd to 6th rib, sternum to axilla, overlying pectoralis major muscle
   b. Composed of lobes and lobules of glandular tissue with adipose tissue in framework of connective tissue
   c. Intralobular ducts drain into main lactiferous ducts; milk provides the nourishment for the young
   d. Ducts open onto surface of nipple which is surrounded by pigmented skin called areola
3. Sequence of events in reproduction
   A. Maturation of germ cells
   B. Ovulation
   C. Fertilization: penetration of oocyte by sperm
   D. Implantation: embedding of blastocyst in decidua basalis
   E. Development of placenta and membranes
      a. Maternal portion: decidua basalis
      b. Fetal portion: chorion frondosum
      c. Fetal membranes: chorion and amnion
   F. Intra-uterine period lasts 40 weeks: period of the ovum; period of the embryo; period of the fetus
   G. Maternal changes: enlarging uterus to keep pace with fetus; "life" felt and fetal heart sounds heard by 20th week; extra load placed on mother to provide nutrients and remove wastes
   H. Labor or parturition
      a. First stage: dilatation of cervix
      b. Second stage: delivery of newborn
      c. Third stage: delivery of placenta
   I. Lactation
      a. Estrogens stimulate growth of duct system; progesterone stimulates the secretory tissue
      b. Mammary glands fully developed at end of pregnancy; LTH or lactogenic hormone of pituitary stimulates milk production or lactation
      c. Colostrum is secretion that precedes true milk
      d. Removal of milk essential for continued production
   J. Extra-uterine life: neonatal period, period of infancy, childhood, adolescence, maturity

PRACTICAL APPLICATIONS AND QUESTIONS

(Encircle the letter of the *best* answer to each of the following questions.)

Mrs. J. B. suspecting that she was pregnant, visited her obstetrician to confirm the diagnosis.

1. One of the first questions that the physician asked was one to determine the ovulation period. Which of the following statements regarding ovulation time is true?
   a. In a 28-day cycle, ovulation usually occurs 14 days after the onset of menstruation
   b. Ovulation is the rupture of a corpus luteum with the release of the ovum
   c. Ovulation is the shedding of the uterine mucosa in preparation for a fertilized ovum
   d. Ovulation occurs immediately before the onset of menstruation

2. After the history was taken and the physical examination completed, the doctor told Mrs. J. B. that she was 3 months pregnant. Mrs. J. B. asked many questions concerning her pregnancy. The doctor explained that some of the symptoms that she was experiencing were due to the rapid enlargement of the uterus. Concerning the uterus she learned that
   a. it is located anterior to the urinary bladder at the level of the symphysis pubis
   b. the expanded upper portion is called the cervix
   c. the increase in size is due, in part, to an increase in the size and the number of cells

600 THE REPRODUCTIVE SYSTEM

d. it is the structure concerned with the production of female germ cells and hormones

3. Mrs. J. B. was thrilled to think that much of herself and her husband would be transferred to the new individual. The structures of the germ cells concerned with heredity are

    a. zygotes

    b. chromosomes

    c. gametes

    d. centrosomes

4. Mrs. J. B. was told that the new individual at 3 months gestation now had the rudiments of all the main organs. This period from 3 months on is known as the

    a. period of the ovum

    b. period of the embryo

    c. period of the fetus

    d. neonatal period

5. Mr. J. B. also was happy about the coming event. In the process of fertilization the male germ cell unites with the ovum of the female. The mature male germ cell is called the

    a. gonad

    b. testes

    c. spermatozoon

    d. polar body

6. During the process of maturation, the chromosomes are reduced to one half the original number. By union of the male and the female germ cells, the characteristic number of chromosomes is obtained. This number is

    a. 23

    b. 46

    c. 96

    d. 13

7. The male germ cell is motile. The motility of the germ cell is enhanced by secretions from the

    a. scrotum

    b. seminal vesicles

    c. testes

    d. epididymis

Bibliography

PHYSIOLOGY

Best, C. H., and Taylor, N. B.: The Physiological Basis of Medical Practice. ed. 8, Baltimore, Williams & Wilkins, 1966.

Berne, R. M., and Levy, M. N.: Cardiovascular Physiology. St. Louis, C. V. Mosby, 1967.

Brooks, S. M.: Basic Facts of Body Water and Ions. New York, Springer, 1960.

Comroe, J. C.: Physiology of Respiration. Chicago, Year Book Medical Publishers, 1965.

Garb, S.: Laboratory Tests in Common Use. ed. 4, New York, Springer, 1966.

Goodale, R. H.: Clinical Interpretation of Laboratory Tests. ed. 5, Philadelphia, F. A. Davis, 1964.

Guyton, A. C.: Textbook of Medical Physiology. ed. 3, Philadelphia, W. B. Saunders, 1966.

Jellinck, P. H.: Biochemistry, An Introduction. New York, Holt, Rinehart & Winston, 1963.

Jensen, J. T.: Introduction to Medical Physics. Philadelphia, Lippincott, 1960.

Ruch, T. C., and Patton, H. D. (eds.): Physiology and Biophysics. ed. 19, Philadelphia, W. B. Saunders, 1965.

Sackheim, G. I.: Practical Physics for Nurses. ed. 2, Philadelphia, W. B. Saunders, 1962.

Snively, W. D.: Sea Within. Philadelphia, Lippincott, 1960.

Tepperman, J.: Metabolic and Endocrine Physiology. ed. 2, New York, Year Book Medical Publishers, 1968.

ANATOMY

Arey, L. B.: Developmental Anatomy. ed. 7, Philadelphia, W. B. Saunders, 1965.

Crosby, E. C., Humphrey, T., and Lauer, E. W.: Correlative Anatomy of the Nervous System. New York, Macmillan, 1962.

Goss, C. M. (ed.): Gray's Anatomy of the Human Body. ed. 28, Philadelphia, Lea & Febiger, 1966.

Ham, A. W.: Histology. ed. 5, Philadelphia, Lippincott, 1965.

Ranson, S. W., and Clark, S. L.: Anatomy of the Nervous System. ed. 10, Philadelphia, W. B. Saunders, 1959.

Romanes, G. J. (ed.): Cunningham's Textbook of Anatomy. ed. 10, New York, Oxford Univ. Press, 1964.

Truex, R. C., and Carpenter, M. B.: Strong and Elwyn's Human Neuroanatomy. ed. 5, Baltimore, Williams & Wilkins, 1964.

Williams, P. L., and Wendell-Smith, C. P.: Basic Human Embryology. Philadelphia, Lippincott, 1966.

PATHOLOGY

Anderson, W. A. D.: Pathology. ed. 5, St. Louis, C. V. Mosby, 1966.

Peery, T. M., and Miller, F. N.: Pathology. Boston, Little, Brown & Co., 1961.

CLINICAL SPECIALTIES

Danowski, T. S.: Clinical Endocrinology. vol. 1. Baltimore, Williams & Wilkins, 1962.

Eastman, N. J., and Hellman, L. M.: William's Obstetrics. ed. 13, New York, Appleton-Century-Crofts, 1966.

Harrison, T. R., et al (eds.): Principles of Internal Medicine. ed. 5, New York, McGraw-Hill, 1966.

Israel, S. L.: Diagnosis and Treatment of Menstrual Disorders and Sterility. ed. 5, New York, Hoeber Medical Division, Harper & Row, 1967.

Nelson, W. E.: Textbook of Pediatrics. ed. 8, Philadelphia, W. B. Saunders, 1964.

JOURNALS AND MAGAZINES

American Journal of Anatomy
American Journal of Physiology
American Journal of Nursing
Federation Proceedings
Journal of the American Medical Association
Journal of Applied Physiology
Medical Science
Medical World News
Scientific American

DICTIONARY

Dorland's Illustrated Medical Dictionary. ed. 24, Philadelphia, W. B. Saunders, 1965.

Glossary

Abdomen (ab-do′men). The part of the body extending from the diaphragm above to the pelvis below.

Abortion (ab-or′shun). The emptying of the uterus prior to the time of fetal viability.

Acapnia (ah-kap′ne-ah). A marked diminution in the amount of carbon dioxide in the blood.

Acetone bodies. Aceto-acetic acid, beta-hydroxybutyric acid and acetone; found in blood and urine in increased amounts whenever too much fat in proportion to carbohydrate is being oxidized. Also called *ketone bodies.*

Achlorhydria (ah-klor-hid′re-ah). The absence of hydrochloric acid in the gastric juice.

Acidosis (as-id-o′sis). Diminution in the reserve supply of fixed bases (especially sodium) in the blood.

Acuity (ak-u′it-e). Sharpness or clearness, especially of vision.

Adaptation (a-dap-ta′shun). Adjustment to a stimulus; also used to denote changes in the retina on exposure to different intensities of light; retina may be light-adapted or dark-adapted.

Adhesion (ad-he′zyun). Abnormal union of two surfaces as a result of inflammation; adhesions may form after an abdominal operation.

Adolescence (ad-o-les′ens). Period between puberty and adult life.

Adventitia (ad-ven-tish′e-ah). The outermost covering of a structure that does not form an integral part of it.

Albuminuria, orthostatic (al″bu-min-u′re-ah, or-tho-stat′ik). Postural albuminuria; albuminuria that disappears when the individual lies down for a time.

Alkali reserve. The total amount of alkaline salts (especially sodium bicarbonate) in the plasma and the corpuscles that is utilizable in maintaining the normal alkalinity of the blood. Also called *alkaline reserve.*

Alkalosis (al″kah-lo′sis). Increased bicarbonate content of the blood. It may be the result of ingesting large amounts of sodium bicarbonate, prolonged vomiting with loss of hydrochloric acid or hyperventilation.

Alveolus (al-ve′ol-us). A small cell or cavity; an air cell, one of the terminal dilatations of the bronchioles in the lungs; an acinus or terminal lobule of a compound gland (numerous branching ducts); a tooth socket.

Ameboid movement (ah-me′boid moov′ment). Movement of a cell by extending from its surface processes of protoplasm (pseudopodia) toward which the rest of the cell flows.

Amenorrhea (am-en-or-e′ah). The absence of the menses.

Amorphous (a-mor′fus). Without definite shape or visible differentiation in structure; not crystalline.

Ampulla (am-pul′ah). A saccular dilatation of a canal.

Amyl nitrite (am′il ni′trīt). A volatile organic compound, which, when inhaled, produces dilatation of the blood vessels; it is used in attacks of angina pectoris.

Analgesia (an-al-je′ze-ah). Loss of sensitivity to pain.

Anaphylactic (an-af-il-ak′tik). Increasing the susceptibility to an infection or to the action of any foreign protein introduced into the body following a primary infection or previous introduction of the same protein; decreasing immunity.

Anastomose (an-as′to-mōz). To open one into the other; used in connection with blood vessels, lymphatics and nerves.

Anesthesia (an-es-the′ze-ah). Loss of sensation.

Aneurysm (an′ur-rizm). A sac formed by the dilatation of the walls of an artery and filled with blood.

Anisocytosis (an-i-so-si-to′sis). A lack of uniformity in the size of red blood corpuscles.

Ankylosis (ang-kil-o'sis). Abnormal immobility and consolidation of a joint due to bony union.

Anoxia (an-ox'e-ah). A diminished supply of oxygen to the body tissues.

Antibody (an'te-bod-e). A specific substance produced by and in an animal or person as a reaction to the presence of an antigen. Antibodies react as agglutinins, lysins, precipitins, etc., with specific or related antigens; they are associated with certain globulin fractions of the plasma proteins.

Antigen (an'te-jen). Any substance which, when introduced into the blood or the tissues, incites the formation of antibodies or reacts with them.

Antrum (an'trum). A cavity or chamber, especially one within a bone, such as a sinus; the pyloric end of the stomach.

Aperture (ap'er-chur). An opening or orifice.

Aphasia (ah-fa'ze-ah). A loss of the faculty of language in any of its forms.

Apoplexy (ap'o-plek-se). A sudden loss of consciousness, followed by paralysis due to cerebral hemorrhage, or blocking of an artery of the brain by an embolus or a thrombus.

Aqueduct (ak'wē-dukt). A canal for the conduction of a liquid; the cerebral aqueduct of Sylvius connects the 3rd and the 4th ventricles of the brain.

Areola (ar-e'o-lah). Any minute space in a tissue; the pigmented ring around the nipple.

Articulate (ar-tic'u-late). To join together so as to permit motion between parts; enunciation in words and sentences. Divided into joints.

Ascites (as-i'tez). An accumulation of serous fluid within the peritoneal cavity.

Asphyxia (as-fiks'e-ah). Unconsciousness due to interference with the oxygenation of the blood.

Astereognosis (ah-ste"re-og-no'sis). Loss of power to recognize the form of an object by touch.

Asthenia (as-the'ne-ah). Weakness.

Asthma (az'mah). A disease characterized by recurrent attacks of dyspnea, wheezing and cough, due to spasmodic contraction of the bronchioles.

Ataxia (ah-taks'e-ah). A loss of the power of muscular coordination.

Atresia (ah-tre'ze-ah). Congenital absence or pathologic closure of a normal opening or passage; involution of ovarian follicles.

Atrophy (at'ro-fe). A wasting or diminution in the size of a part of the entire body.

Atropine (at'ro-pin). An alkaloid obtained from atropa belladonna; it inhibits the action of the parasympathetic division of the autonomic system.

Auricle (aw'rik-l). The pinna or flap of the ear; a small pouch forming the upper portion of each atrium.

Auscultation (aws-kul-ta'shun). The act of listening for sounds within the body; employed as a diagnostic method.

Azygos (az'ig-os). An unpaired anatomic structure; the azygos vein arises from the right ascending lumbar vein and empties into the superior vena cava.

Bolus (bo'lus). A rounded mass of soft consistency.

Bronchiectasis (brong-ke-ek'tas-is). Dilatation of the bronchi or of a bronchus. It is characterized by offensive breath, spasms of coughing and expectoration of mucopurulent material.

Buffer (buff'er). Any substance that tends to lessen the change in hydrogen ion concentration (reaction) which otherwise would be produced by adding acids or bases.

Bursa (bur'sah). A closed sac lined with synovial membrane containing fluid, found over an exposed and prominent part or where a tendon plays over a bone.

Caffeine (kaf'e-in). An alkaloid obtained from the dried leaves of tea or the dried beans of coffee; employed in cardiac disorders.

Calculus (kal'ku-lus). A stone formed in any portion of the body, such as a gallstone.

Calorie (kal'or-e). A unit of heat. A *small calorie* (cal.) is the standard unit and is the amount of heat required to raise 1 Gm. of water from 15° to 16° C. The *large calorie* (Cal.) is used in metabolism and is the amount of heat required to raise 1 Kg. of water from 15° to 16° C.

Canaliculus (kan-al-ik'u-lus). A small canal or channel; in bone, minute channels connect with each lacuna.

Cancer (kan'ser). A malignant neoplasm (tumor or new growth).

Carcinoma (kar-sin-o'mah). A malignant tumor or cancer; a new growth made up of epithelial cells, tending to infiltrate and give rise to metastases.

Caries (ka're-ez). Molecular decay or death of a bone in which it becomes softened, discolored and porous. Dental caries, decay of teeth.

Cast (kast). A mold of a tubular structure, such as a bronchial tube or a renal tubule, formed by a plastic exudate.

Castration (kas-tra′shun). Removal of testes or ovaries.

Cataract (kat′ah-rakt). A loss of transparency of the crystalline lens of the eye or of its capsule.

Celiac (se′le-ak). Relating to the abdominal cavity.

Centimeter (sen′tim-e-ter). The hundredth part of a meter; practically, 2/5 in.

Centriole (sen′tri-ol). Organelle within the centrosome or cell center.

Cerumen (se-ru′men). Ear wax.

Cervix (ser′viks). The neck; any necklike structure; especially the lower cylindrical portion of the uterus.

Cesarean section (se-za′re-an sek′shun). Extraction of the fetus by means of an incision through the abdominal wall and the uterus.

Chalazion (ka-la′ze-on). A small tumor of the eyelid; formed by the distention of a meibomian gland with secretion.

Cheilosis (ki-lo′sis). A condition characterized by lesions on the lips and at the angles of the mouth.

Chemotherapy (kem″o-ther′a-py). The treatment of disease by administering chemicals that affect the causative organism unfavorably, but do not produce serious toxic effects in the patient.

Chiasma (kigh-az′muh). A crossing; specifically, the crossing of the optic nerve fibers from the medial halves of the retinae.

Choana (ko-a′nah). Posterior naris; the opening into the nasopharynx of the nasal fossa on either side.

Chromidial (kro-mid′e-al) **substance.** Pertaining to granules of extranuclear chromatin seen in the cytoplasm of a cell.

Chromosome (kro′mo-sōm). A body of chromatin in the cell nucleus that splits longitudinally as the cell divides, one half going to the nucleus of each of the daughter cells; the chromosomes transmit the hereditary characters.

Chyle (kīl). The milky fluid taken up by the lacteals from the food in the intestine after digestion. It consists of lymph and emulsified fat; it passes into the veins by the thoracic duct.

Chyme (kīm). The semifluid mass of partly digested food passed from the stomach into the duodenum.

Ciliary (sil′e-ar-re). Relating to (1) any hairlike process, (2) the eyelashes, (3) certain of the structures of the eyeball.

Cocaine (ko-kān). An alkaloid from coca leaves; it is a local anesthetic, narcotic and mydriatic.

Collateral (kol-at′er-al). Accompanying; running by the side of; not direct; secondary or accessory; a small side branch of an axon.

Colloid (kol′oid). A state of subdivision of matter in which the individual particles are of submicroscopic size and consist either of large molecules, such as proteins, or aggregates of smaller molecules; the particles are not large enough to settle out under the influence of gravity. The dimensions are between 1 and 100 millimicrons.

Colostomy (ko-los′to-me). Establishment of an artificial anus by an opening into the colon.

Colostrum (ko-los′trum). The first milk secreted at the termination of pregnancy; it contains more lactalbumin and lactoprotein than the later milk.

Coma (ko′mah). A state of profound unconsciousness from which one cannot be roused.

Congenital (kon-jen′it-al). Born with a person; existing at or before birth.

Contralateral (kon″trah-lat′er-al). Situated on or pertaining to the opposite side.

Costal (cos′tal). Pertaining to a rib.

Crystalloid (kris′tal-oid). A body that, in solution, can pass through an animal membrane, as distinguished from a colloid that has not this property.

Curare (koo-rah′re). A highly toxic extract that paralyzes muscle; it acts on the motor endplates.

Cutaneous (ku-ta′ne-us). Pertaining to the skin.

Cyanosis (si-an-o′sis). A dark, purplish coloration of the skin and the mucous membrane, due to deficient oxygenation of the blood.

Cystoscopy (sis-tos′ko-pe). The inspection of the interior of the bladder.

Dentition (den-tish′un). Clinically, eruption of the teeth; morphologically the number, shape and arrangement of the teeth.

Diapedesis (di″ah-pe-de′sis). The passage of blood or of leukocytes through the unruptured walls of the blood vessels.

Diastole (di-as′to-le). The rhythmic period of relaxation and dilatation of the heart, during which it fills with blood.

Digitalis (dij-it-a′lis). The dried leaves of purple foxglove; it is used in the treatment of certain cardiac disorders.

Diopter (di-op′ter). The unit of refracting power of a lens; noting a lens whose principal focus is at a distance of 1 M.

Diploid (dip′loid). Having 2 sets of chromosomes, as normally found in the somatic cells of higher organisms.

Diurnal (di-er′nal). Daily.

Ectopic (ek-top′ik). Out of the normal place.

Edema (e-de′mah). An abnormal accumulation of clear, watery fluid in the lymph spaces of the tissues.

Effusion (ef-u′zhun). The escape of fluid from the blood vessels or the lymphatics into the tissues or a cavity.

Electrolyte (e-lek′tro-lite). Any substance that, in solution, conducts an electric current.

Electron microscope (e-lek′tron). Makes use of electrons emitted from a cathode. The lenses are magnetic fields, the strength of which can be varied by the amount of current passed through coils of wire which excite the magnetic fields. The resolving power is greatly increased; the magnification may be as great as 200,000 times in an electronmicrograph.

Embolism (em′bol-izm). Obstruction or occlusion of a vessel by a transported clot, a mass of bacteria or other foreign material.

Emphysema (em-fis-e′mah). Dilatation of the pulmonary air vesicles, usually through atrophy of the septa between the alveoli.

Empyema (em-pi-e′mah). The presence of pus in any cavity; when used without qualification, an accumulation of pus in the pleural cavity.

Endoplasmic reticulum (en′do-plas-mic re-tik′u-lum). Complicated system of internal membranes within cytoplasm of cell; ribosomes attached to inner surface.

Enuresis (en-u-re′sis). Involuntary passage of urine after the age of 3 years.

Epistaxis (ep-e-staks′is). Nosebleed; hemorrhage from the nose.

Erectile (e-rek′til). Denoting a vascular tissue, found in the nasal cavities, the penis and elsewhere, which, when filled with blood, becomes swollen and more or less rigid.

Evagination (e-vaj-in-a′shun). A protrusion of some part or organ.

Exophthalmos (ex-of-thal′mus). A protrusion or prominence of the eyeball.

Extravasation (ex-trav-as-a′shun). The act of escaping from a vessel into the tissues, said of blood, lymph or serum.

Extrinsic (ex-trin′sik). Originating outside of the part where found or upon which it acts.

Fasciculation (fa-sick″yoo-lay′shun). Localized contraction of muscle fibers or an incoordinated contraction of skeletal muscle in which the fibers of one motor unit contract.

Fimbria (fim′bre-ah). Any fringelike structure; especially the fringelike end of the uterine tube.

Fistula (fis′tu-lah). A pathologic or abnormal passage leading from an abscess cavity or a hollow organ to the surface or from one organ to another.

Flaccid (flak′sid). Relaxed, flabby, soft.

Flatus (flā′tus). Gas or air in the stomach or the intestine; commonly used to denote passage of gas by rectum.

Fovea (fo′ve-ah). A cup-shaped depression or pit.

Fundus (fun′dus). The bottom of a sac or hollow organ; that farthest removed from the opening.

Ganglion (gang′le-on). An aggregation of nerve cells within the brain, along the course of a sensory nerve, in one of the organs of special sense or in the autonomic system.

Gangrene (gan′grēne). A form of necrosis combined with putrefaction; death of the tissue.

Gel (jel). A colloidal system comprising a solid and a liquid phase that exists as a solid or semisolid mass; a jelly or solid or semisolid phase.

Gene (jēn). An ultimate, ultramicroscopic, biologic unit of heredity; selfreproducing; located in a definite position on a particular chromosome; a modifier of development.

Hematuria (hem-at-u′re-ah). The presence of blood in the urine.

Hemiplegia (hem-e-ple′je-ah). Paralysis of one side of the body.

Hemorrhoids (hem′or-oidz). Piles, a varicose dilatation of a vein of the superior or inferior hemorrhoidal plexus, causing painful swelling at the anus.

Hemostasis (hēm-o-sta′sis). The arrest of bleeding; the checking of the flow of blood through any part of a vessel.

Heredity (he-red′it-e). The transmission of qualities from parent to offspring.

Hilus (hi′lus). A depression or pit at that part of an organ where the vessels and nerves enter or leave.

Homeostasis (ho-mē-o-sta′sis). A tendency to uniformity or stability in the normal body states of the organism (Cannon).

Homologous (ho-mol′o-gus). Corresponding; having similar relations.

Hordeolum (hor-de′o-lum). A sty, an inflammation of a sebaceous gland of the eyelid.

Hyaluronidase (hy″a-lu-ron′i-dase). An enzyme causing breakdown of hyaluronic acid in protective polysaccharide barriers, promoting invasion of cells and tissues by the invading agent; it is a spreading factor.

Hyperplasia (hi″per-plā′ze-ah). The abnormal multiplication or increase in the number of normal cells in normal arrangement in a tissue.

Hypertrophy (hi-per′tro-fe). The morbid enlargement or overgrowth of an organ or part due to an increase in size of its constituent cells.

Hypophysis cerebri (hi-pof′e-sis ser′e-bri). Epithelial body of dual origin, located at base of brain in the sella turcica; pituitary.

Inflammation (in-flam-a′shun). A morbid series of reactions produced in the tissues by an irritant; it is marked by an afflux of blood with exudation of plasma and leukocytes.

Infundibulum (in-fun-dib′u-lum). A funnel-shaped structure or passage.

Inguinal (in′guin-al). Relating to the region between the abdomen and the thigh (groin).

Intravascular (in-trah-vas′ku-lar). Within the blood vessels or the lymphatics.

Intussusception (in″tus-sus-sep′shun). The infolding of one segment of the intestine within another segment.

Invagination (in-vaj-in-a′shun). The pushing of the wall of a cavity into the cavity.

Involution (in-vo-lu′shun). The return of an enlarged organ to normal size; retrograde changes.

Ipsilateral (ip″si-lat′er-al). Situated on or pertaining to the same side; homolateral.

Isotope (i′so-tōp). An element which has the same atomic number as another but a different atomic weight. Radioactive isotopes usually refer to elements rendered radioactive by artificial means. Radioactive isotopes of C, N, P, Na, K, Cl, I and some other elements, incorporated in the molecules of compounds, are introduced into the body in order to study various processes, such as intermediary metabolism.

Ketosis (ke-to′sis). The condition marked by excessive production of ketone bodies in the body.

Kilogram (kil′o-gram). 1,000 grams; about 2.2 pounds avoirdupois.

Kinesthetic (kin-es-thet′ik). Pertaining to muscle sense or to the sense by which muscular movement, weight, position, etc., are perceived.

Lecithin (les′i-thin). A monoaminomonophosphatide found in animal tissues especially nerve tissue, semen, egg yolk, and in smaller amount in bile and blood.

Leukemia (lu-ke′me-ah). A disease of the blood marked by persistent leukocytosis, associated with changes in the spleen and the bone marrow or in the lymphatic nodes.

Loin. The lateral (side) and posterior (back) part of the body, between the false ribs (thorax) and the top of the pelvis.

Lumen (lu′men). The space in the interior of a tubular structure such as an artery or the intestine.

Macula (mak′u-lah). A spot.

Malaise (ma-laz′). A feeling of general discomfort or uneasiness, an out-of-sorts feeling, often the first indication of an infection.

Meatus (me-a′tus). A passage or channel, especially the external opening of a canal.

Menopause (men′o-pawz). Termination of the menstrual cycles.

Metabolism (me-tab′o-lism). The sum of the chemical changes whereby the function of nutrition is effected; it consists of anabolism or the constructive and assimilative changes and catabolism or the destructive and retrograde changes.

Meter (me′ter). A measure of length; 100 cm.; the equivalent of 39.371 in.

Microgram (mi′kro-gram). One one-millionth of a gram, or 1/1,000 of a milligram.

Micron (mi′kron). One one-millionth of a meter or 1/1,000 of a millimeter; 1/25,400 of an inch.

Millimeter (mil′im-e-ter). 1/1,000 of a meter; about 1/25 of an inch.

Mitochondria (mit″o-kon′dre-ah). Organelles noted in differential staining of the cytoplasm of cells; contain enzymes that make possible the reactions whereby energy is liberated from food and stored temporarily in the chemical bonds of ATP.

Morphine (mor′fin). The chief narcotic principle of opium; used as a hypnotic and analgesic.

Mucus (mu′kus). The viscid watery secretion of the mucous glands; it consists of water, mucin, epithelial cells, leukocytes and inorganic salts.

Narcosis (nar-co′sis). Stupor or unconsciousness produced by some narcotic drug.

Necrosis (ne-kro′sis). Local death of tissue.

Nissl granule (nis′el). Chromophil granule constituting

one of the stainable substances of the cytoplasm of a nerve cell.

Nystagmus (nis-tag″mus). Rhythmic oscillation of the eyeballs, either horizontal, rotary or vertical.

Orifice (or′if-is). Any aperture or opening.

Ostium (os′te-um). A small opening, especially one of entrance into a hollow organ or canal.

Oxidation (oks-id-a′shun). The combining of food and oxygen in the tissues; chemically, the increase in valence of an element.

Oximeter (ox-im′e-ter). An instrument for measuring the oxygen saturation of hemoglobin in the circulating blood; it consists of an ear piece, a control box and a galvanometer.

Pacchionian bodies (pak-ke-o′ne-an). Small projections of the arachnoid tissue, chiefly into the venous sinuses of the dura mater.

Palpitation (pal-pit-a′shun). Forcible pulsation of the heart perceptible to the individual.

Paralysis (par-al′is-is). A loss of power of voluntary movement in a muscle through injury or disease of its nerve supply.

Parenchyma (par-eng′ki-mah). The essential elements of an organ; the functional elements of an organ, as distinguished from its framework, or stroma.

Parturition (par″tu-rish′un). The act of giving birth to young.

Pectoral (pek′to-ral). Pertaining to the breast or the chest.

Perimeter (per-im′et-er). An instrument delimiting the field of vision.

Perineum (per-e-ne′um). The portion of the body included in the outlet of the pelvis, extending from the pubic arch to the coccyx and between the ischial tuberosities.

pH. The symbol commonly used in expressing hydrogen ion concentration. It signifies the logarithm of the reciprocal of the hydrogen ion concentration expressed as a power of 10.

Phlebothrombosis (flebo″-throm-bos′is). Thrombosis of a vein without inflammation of its walls.

Physiotherapy (fiz″e-o-ther′ap-e). The use of natural forces, such as heat, light, air, water and exercise, in the treatment of disease.

Pilocarpine (pi-lo-kar′pin). An alkaloid that stimulates the parasympathetic division of the autonomic nervous system.

Plexus (plex′us). A network or tangle of interweaving nerves, veins or lymphatic vessels.

Potential (po-ten′shal). Possible, but not actual; capable of doing or being, though not yet doing or being.

Pressor (pres′or). Exciting vasoconstrictor activity, producing increased blood pressure; denoting afferent nerves that when stimulated, excite the vasoconstrictor center.

Prolapse (pro′laps). The falling down of an organ or other part, such as the uterus.

Proliferation (pro-lif″er-a′shun). The reproduction or multiplication of similar forms, especially of cells.

Psychosomatic (si″ko-so-mat′ik). Pertaining to the mind-body relationship; having bodily symptoms of a psychic, emotional or mental origin.

Pterygoid (ter′e-goid). Shaped like a wing.

Puberty (pu′ber-te). The age at which the reproductive organs become functionally operative.

Pus (pus). A fluid product of inflammation consisting of a liquid containing leukocytes and the débris of dead cells.

Rachitic (ra-kit′ik). Relating to or affected by rickets.

Ramus (ra′mus). A branch; one of the primary divisions of a nerve or a blood vessel; a part of an irregularly shaped bone that forms an angle with the main body.

Receptor (re-sep′tor). Nerve ending that receives a stimulus.

Reflection (re-flek′shun). The throwing back of a ray of light from a surface that it does not penetrate.

Refraction (re-frak′shun). The bending of a ray of light as it passes from one medium into another of different density.

Regurgitation (re-gur-gi-ta′shun). The flowing backward of blood through incompletely closed heart valves; the return of small amounts of food from the stomach.

Reticular (re-tik′u-lar). Netlike.

Retinaculum (ret″i-nak′u-lum). A special fascial thickening which holds back an organ or part; helps to retain an organ or tissue in its place.

Retroversion (re-tro-ver′shun). The tipping of an entire organ backward; turning backward without flexion or bending of the organ, as of the uterus.

Rh antigen or factor. An agglutinogen or antigen first found in the erythrocytes of the rhesus monkey, hence the Rh. Normally it is present in 85 per cent of white people; Rh positive and Rh negative are terms denoting the presence or absence, respectively, of this antigen. It can cause antibody formation only in Rh-negative persons or animals.

Ribosomes (rye′bo-somes). Organelles which appear as dots lining the endoplasmic reticulum; they are the protein factories of cells.

Sella turcica (sel′ah tur′sik-ah). A saddlelike depression on the upper surface of the sphenoid bone, in which the hypophysis lies.

Serotonin (sere″o-toe′nin). A compound (5-hydroxytryptamine) found in the blood stream; it has vasoconstrictive properties. It is possible that serotonin is concerned with some of the functions of the central nervous system.

Sinus (si′nus). A channel for the passage of blood; a hollow in a bone or other tissue; antrum; one of the cavities connecting with the nose; a suppurating cavity.

Sinusoid (si′nus-oid). A blood space in certain organs, as the spleen and the liver.

Spasm (spazm). An involuntary, convulsive, muscular contraction.

Spermatogenesis (sper″mat-o-jen′es-is). The process of formation and development of the spermatozoa.

Sphincter (sfingk′ter). A circular muscle that serves, when in a state of normal contraction, to close one of the orifices of the body.

Squamous (skwa′mus). Scalelike.

Sterility (ster-il′it-e). Infertility, lack of progeny, unproductiveness.

Stricture (strik′tur). A circumscribed narrowing of a tubular structure.

Stroma (stro-mah). The tissue that forms the ground substance, framework or matrix of an organ, as distinguished from that constituting its functional element, or parenchyma.

Susceptibility (sus-sep-tib-il′it-e). The characteristic that makes one liable to infection by disease.

Syncytium (sin-sit′e-um). A multinucleate mass of protoplasm produced by the merging of cells.

Syndrome (sin′drohm). A group of symptoms and signs, which, when considered together, characterize a disease or lesion.

Synovial (sin-o′ve-al). Of, or pertaining to, or secreting synovia; synovia is the viscid fluid of a joint or similar cavity.

Syringomyelia (sir-in″go-mi-e′le-ah). The existence of abnormal cavities filled with fluid in the substance of the spinal cord.

Systole (sis′to-le). The contraction of the heart muscle.

Tactile (tak′til). Pertaining to the sense of touch.

Tetanus (tet′an-us). Lockjaw; an acute infectious disease in which there is more or less persistent tonic spasm of some of the voluntary muscles; the first sign is stiffness of the jaw.

Tetany (tet′an-e). Intermittent tonic muscular contractions of the extremities.

Thrombophlebitis (throm″boe-fle-bye′tis). The condition in which inflammation of the vein wall has preceded the formation of a thrombus or intravascular clot.

Thrombosis (throm-boe′sis). The formation of a clot within a vessel during life.

Thrombus (throm′bus). A clot of blood formed within the heart or the blood vessels, due usually to slowing of the circulation of the blood or to alteration of the blood itself or the vessel walls.

Tinnitus (tin′i-tus). A ringing or singing sound in the ears.

Trabecula (tra-bek′u-lah). A septum that extends from an envelope into the enclosed substance, forming an essential part of the stroma of the organ.

Trigone (tri′gon). Denoting a triangular area, especially of the interior of the bladder between the opening of the ureters and the orifice of the urethra.

Ulcer (ul′ser). An open sore other than a wound; a loss of substance on a cutaneous or mucous surface causing necrosis of the tissue.

Umbilicus (um-bil-i′kus). The navel; the cicatrix (scar) that marks the site of attachment of the umbilical cord.

Urticaria (er-tik-a′re-ah). Nettle-rash; hives; elevated, itching, white patches.

Varicocele (var′ik-o-sēl). Enlargement of the veins of the spermatic cord.

Varicose veins (var′ik-ōs). Unnaturally swollen and tortuous veins.

Vertigo (ver′tig-o). Dizziness, giddiness.

Vesicle (ves′ik-l). A small bladder or sac containing liquid.

Vestibular (ves-tib′u-lar). Pertaining to a vestibule; such as the inner ear, larynx, mouth, nose, vagina.

Viscosity (vis-kos′it-e). A condition of more or less adhesion of the molecules of a fluid to each other so that it flows with difficulty.

Volvulus (vol′vu-lus). A twisting of the intestine, causing obstruction.

COMBINING FORMS AND PREFIXES

These forms, with a prefix or a suffix, or both, are those most commonly used in making medical words. G indicates those from the Greek; L, those from the Latin. Properly Greek forms should be used only with Greek prefixes and suffixes; Latin, with Latin. Often a vowel, usually a, i or o, is needed for euphony.

A- or **Ab-** (L) *away, lack of:* abnormal, departing from normal.

A- or **An-** (G) *from, without:* asepsis, without infection.

Acr- (G) *an extremity:* acrodermatitis, a dermatitis of the limbs.

Ad- (L) *to, toward, near:* adrenal, near the kidney.

Aden- (G) *gland:* adenitis, inflammation of a gland.

Alg- (G) *pain:* neuralgia, pain extending along nerves.

Ambi- (L) *both:* ambidextrous, referring to both hands.

Ante- (L) *before:* antenatal, occurring or having been formed before birth.

Anti- (G) *against:* antiseptic, against or preventing sepsis.

Arth- (G) *joint:* arthritis, inflammation of a joint.

Auto- (G) *self:* auto-intoxication, poisoning by toxin generated in the body.

Bi- or **Bin-** (L) *two:* binocular, pertaining to both eyes.

Bio- (G) *life:* biopsy, inspection of living organism (or tissue).

Blast- (G) *bud, a growing thing in early stages:* blastocyte, beginning cell not yet differentiated.

Bleph- (G) *eyelids:* blepharitis, inflammation of an eyelid.

Brachi- (G) *arm:* brachialis, muscle for flexing forearm.

Brachy- (G) *short:* brachydactylia, abnormal shortness of fingers and toes.

Brady- (G) *slow:* bradycardia, abnormal slowness of heartbeat.

Bronch- (G) *windpipe:* bronchiectasis, dilation of bronchial tubes.

Bucca- (L) *cheek:* buccally, toward the cheek.

Carcin- (G) *cancer:* carcinogenic, producing cancer.

Cardi- (G) *heart:* cardialgia, pain in the heart.

Cephal- (G) *head:* encephalitis, inflammation of brain.

Cheil- (G) *lip:* cheilitis, inflammation of the lip.

Chole- (G) *bile:* cholecyst, the gallbladder.

Chondr- (G) *cartilage:* chondrectomy, removal of a cartilage.

Circum- (L) *around:* circumocular, around the eyes.

Cleid- (G) *clavicle:* cleidocostal, pertaining to clavicle and ribs.

Colp- (G) *vagina:* colporrhagia, vaginal hemorrhage.

Contra- (L) *against, opposed:* contraindication, indication opposing usually indicated treatment.

Cost- (L) *rib:* intercostal, between the ribs.

Counter- (L) *against:* counterirritation, an irritation to relieve some other irritation (e.g., a liniment).

Crani- (L) *skull:* craniotomy, surgical opening in skull.

Crypt- (G) *hidden:* cryptogenic, of hidden or unknown origin.

Cut- (L) *skin:* subcutaneous, under the skin.

Cyst- (G) *sac or bladder:* cystitis, inflammation of the bladder.

Cyto- (G) *cell:* cytology, scientific study of cells, a device for counting and measuring cells.

Dacro (G) *tear:* dacrocyst, the lacrimal sac.

Derm- or **Dermat-** (G) *skin:* dermatoid, skinlike.

Di- (L) *two:* diphasic, occurring in two stages or phases.

Dis- (L) *apart:* disarticulation, taking joint apart.

Dys- (G) *pain or difficulty:* dyspepsia, impairment of digestion.

Ecto- (G) *outside:* ectoretina, outermost layer of retina.

Em- or **En-** (G) *in:* encapsulated, enclosed in a capsule.

Encephal- (G) *brain:* encephalitis, inflammation of brain.

End- (G) *within:* endothelium, layer of cells lining heart, blood and lymph vessels.

Entero- (G) *intestine:* enteroptosis, falling of intestine.

Epi- (G) *above or upon:* epidermis, outermost layer of skin.

Erythro- (G) *red:* erythrocyte, red blood cell.

Eu- (G) *well:* euphoria, well feeling, feeling of good health.

Ex- or **E-** (L) *out:* excretion, material thrown out of the body or the organ.

Exo- (G) *outside:* exocrine, excreting outwardly (opposite of endocrine).

Extra- (G) *outside:* extramural, situated or occurring outside a wall.

Febri- (L) *fever:* febrile, feverish.

Galacto- (G) *milk:* galactose, a milk-sugar.

Gastr- (G) *stomach:* gastrectomy, excision of the stomach.

Gloss- (G) *tongue:* glossectomy, surgical removal of tongue.

Glyco- (G) *sugar:* glycosuria, sugar in the urine.

Gynec- (G) *woman:* gynecology, science of diseases pertaining to women.

Hem- or **Hemat-** (G) *blood:* hemopoiesis, forming blood.

Hemi- (G) *half:* heminephrectomy, excision of half the kidney.

Hepat- (G) *liver:* hepatitis, inflammation of the liver.

Hetero- (G) *other* (opposite of homo): heterotransplant, using skin from a member of another species.

Hist- (G) *tissue:* histology, science of minute structure and function of tissues.

Homo- (G) *same:* homotransplant, skin grafting by using skin from a member of the same species.

Hydr- (G) *water:* hydrocephalus, abnormal accumulation of fluid in cranium.

Hyper- (G) *above, excess of:* hyperglycemia, excess of sugar in blood.

Hypo- (G) *under, deficiency of:* hypoglycemia, deficiency of sugar in blood.

Hyster- (G) *uterus:* hysterectomy, excision of uterus.

Idio- (G) *self, or separate:* idiopathic, a disease self-originated (of unknown cause).

Im- or **In-** (L) *in:* infiltration, accumulation in tissue of abnormal substances.

Im- or **In-** (L) *not:* immature, not mature.

Infra- (L) *below:* infra-orbital, below the orbit.

Inter- (L) *between:* intermuscular, between the muscles.

Intra- (L) *within:* intramuscular, within the muscle.

Kerat- (G) *horn, cornea:* keratitis, inflammation of cornea.

Lact- (L) *milk:* lactation, secretion of milk.

Leuk- (G) *white:* leukocyte, white cell.

Macro- (G) *large:* macroblast, abnormally large red cell.

Mast- (G) *breast:* mastectomy, excision of the breast.

Meg- or **Megal-** (G) *great:* megacolon, abnormally large colon.

Ment- (L) *mind:* dementia, deterioration of the mind.

Mer- (G) *part:* merotomy, division into segments.

Mesa- (G) *middle:* mesaortitis, inflammation of middle coat of the aorta.

Meta- (G) *beyond, over, change:* metastasis, change in seat of a disease.

Micro- (G) *small:* microplasia, dwarfism.

My- (G) *muscle:* myoma, tumor made of muscular elements.

Myc- (G) *fungi:* mycology, science and study of fungi.

Necro- (G) *corpse, dead:* necrosis, death of cells adjoining living tissue.

Neo- (G) *new:* neoplasm, any new growth or formation.

Neph- (G) *kidney:* nephrectomy, surgical excision of kidney.

Neuro- (G) *nerve:* neuron, nerve cell.

Odont- (G) *tooth:* odontology, dentistry.

Olig- (G) *little:* oligemia, deficiency in volume of blood.

Oo- (G) *egg:* oocyte, original cell of egg.

Oophor- (G) *ovary:* oophorectomy, removal of an ovary.

Ophthalm- (G) *eye:* ophthalmometer, an instrument for measuring the eye.

Ortho- (G) *straight, normal:* orthograde, walk straight (upright).

Oss- (L) *bone:* osseous, bony.

Oste- (G) *bone:* osteitis, inflammation of a bone.

Ot- (G) *ear:* otorrhea, discharge from ear.

Para- (G) *irregular, around, wrong:* paradenitis, inflammation of tissue in the neighborhood of a gland.

Path- (G) *disease:* pathology, science of disease.

Ped-[1] (G) *children:* pediatrician, child specialist.

Ped-[2] (L) *feet:* pedograph, imprint of the foot.

  [1] Ped—from Greek *pais*, child.

  [2] Ped—from Latin *pes*, foot.

Per- (L) *through, excessively:* percutaneous, through the skin.

Peri- (G) *around, immediately around* (in contradistinction to para): periapical, surrounding apex of root of tooth.

Phil- (G) *love:* hemophilic, fond of blood (as bacteria that grow well in presence of hemoglobin).

Phleb- (G) *vein:* phlebotomy, opening of vein for bloodletting.

Phob- (G) *fear:* hydrophobic, reluctant to associate with water.

Pneum- or **Pneumon-** (G) *lung* (pneum-air): pneumococcus, organism causing lobar pneumonia.

Polio- (G) *gray:* poliomyelitis, inflammation of gray substance of spinal cord.

Poly- (G) *many:* polyarthritis, inflammation of several joints.

Post- (L) *after:* postpartum, after delivery.

Pre- (L) *before:* prenatal, occurring before birth.

Pro- (L and G) *before:* prognosis, forecast as to result of disease.

Proct- (G) *rectum:* proctectomy, surgical removal of rectum.

Pseudo- (G) *false:* pseudoangina, false angina.

Psych- (G) *soul or mind:* psychiatry, treatment of mental disorders.

Py- (G) *pus:* pyorrhea, discharge of pus.

Pyel- (G) *pelvis:* pyelitis, inflammation of pelvis of kidney.

Rach- (G) *spine:* rachicentesis, puncture into vertebral canal.

Ren- (L) *kidney:* adrenal, near the kidney.

Retro- (L) *backward:* retroversion, turned backward (usually, of uterus).

Rhin- (G) *nose:* rhinology, knowledge concerning noses.

Salping- (G) *a tube:* salpingitis, inflammation of tube.

Semi- (L) *half:* semicoma, mild coma.

Septic- (L and G) *poison:* septicemia, poisoned condition of blood.

Somat- (G) *body:* psychosomatic, having bodily symptoms of mental origin.

Sta- (G) *make stand:* stasis, stoppage of flow of fluid.

Sten- (G) *narrow:* stenosis, narrowing of duct or canal.

Sub- (L) *under:* subdiaphragmatic, under the diaphragm.

Super- (L) *above, excessively:* superacute, excessively acute.

Supra- (L) *above, upon:* suprarenal, above or upon the kidney.

Sym- or **Syn-** (G) *with, together:* symphysis, a growing together.

Tachy- (G) *fast:* tachycardia, fast-beating heart.

Tens- (L) *stretch:* extensor, a muscle extending or stretching a limb.

Therm- (G) *heat:* diathermy, therapeutic production of heat in tissues.

Tox- or **Toxic-** (G) *poison:* toxemia, poisoned condition of blood.

Trache- (G) *trachea:* tracheitis, inflammation of the trachea.

Trans- (L) *across:* transplant, transfer tissue from one place to another.

Tri- (L and G) *three:* trigastric, having three bellies (muscle).

Trich- (G) *hair:* trichosis, any disease of the hair.

Uni- (L) *one:* unilateral, affecting one side.

Vas- (L) *vessel:* vasoconstrictor, nerve or drug that narrows blood vessel.

Zoo- (G) *animal:* zooblast, an animal cell.

SUFFIXES

-algia (G) *pain:* cardialgia, pain in the heart.

-asis or **-osis** (G) *affected with:* leukocytosis, excess number of leukocytes.

-asthenia (G) *weakness:* neurasthenia, nervous weakness.

-blast (G) *germ:* myeloblast, bone-marrow cell.

-cele (G) *tumor, hernia:* enterocele, any hernia of intestine.

-cid (L) *cut, kill:* germicidal, destructive to germs.

-clysis (G) *injection:* hypodermoclysis, injection under the skin.

-coccus (G) *round bacterium:* pneumococcus, bacteria of pneumonia.

-cyte (G) *cell:* leukocyte, white cell.

-ectasis (G) *dilation, stretching:* angiectasis, dilatation of a blood vessel.

-ectomy (G) *excision:* adenectomy, excision of adenoids.

-emia (G) *blood:* glycemia, sugar in blood.

-esthesia (G) *(noun) relating to sensation:* anesthesia, absence of feeling.

-ferent (L) *bear, carry:* efferent, carry out to periphery.

-genic (G) *producing:* pyogenic, producing pus.

-iatrics (G) *pertaining to a physician or the practice of healing* (medicine): pediatrics, science of medicine for children.

-itis (G) *inflammation:* tonsillitis, inflammation of tonsils.

-logy (G) *science of:* pathology, science of disease.

-lysis (G) *losing, flowing, dissolution:* autolysis, dissolution of tissue cells.

-malacia (G) *softening:* osteomalacia, softening of bone.

-oma (G) *tumor:* myoma, tumor made up of muscle elements.

-osis (**-asis**) (G) *being affected with:* atherosis, arteriosclerosis.

-(o)stomy (G) *creation of an opening:* gastrostomy, creation of an artificial gastric fistula.

-(o)tomy (G) *cutting into:* laparotomy, surgical incision into abdomen.

-pathy (G) *disease:* myopathy, disease of a muscle.

-penia (G) *lack of:* leukopenia, lack of white blood cells.

-pexy (G) *to fix:* proctopexy, fixation of rectum by suture.

-phagia (G) *eating:* polyphagia, excessive eating.

-phasia (G) *speech:* aphasia, loss of power of speech.

-phobia (G) *fear:* hydrophobia, fear of water.

-plasty (G) *molding:* gastroplasty, molding or re-forming stomach.

-poiesis (G) *making, forming:* hematopoiesis, forming blood.

-pnea (G) *air or breathing:* dyspnea, difficult breathing.

-ptosis (G) *falling:* enteroptosis, falling of intestine.

-rhythmia (G) *rhythm:* arrhythmia, variation from normal rhythm of heart.

-rrhagia (G) *flowing or bursting forth:* otorrhagia, hemorrhage from ear.

-rrhaphy (G) *suture of:* enterorrhaphy, act of sewing up gap in intestine.

-rrhea (G) *discharge:* otorrhea, discharge from ear.

-sthen (**ia**) (**ic**) (G) *pertaining to strength:* asthenia, loss of strength.

-taxia or **-taxis** (G) *order, arrangement of:* ataxia, failure of muscular coordination.

-trophia or **-trophy** (G) *nourishment:* atrophy, wasting, or diminution.

-uria (G) *to do with urine:* polyuria, excessive secretion of urine.

INDEX

Index

$\frac{6}{10}$

Thurs. crash notes resp.
~~my~~ notes resp.
~~read senses~~ ✗
~~dis & physiology~~

FRi: ~~crash notes senses~~
~~read my notes~~

Sat. Kidneys
Reproduction

Sunday - review + sociology